Psychological Problems
in Mental Deficiency

Under the Editorship of
GARDNER MURPHY

PSYCHOLOGICAL PROBLEMS IN MENTAL DEFICIENCY

THIRD EDITION

SEYMOUR B. SARASON

PART TWO BY SEYMOUR B. SARASON AND THOMAS GLADWIN

Harper & Brothers, Publishers, New York

To

My Mother and Father

CONTENTS

PREFACE TO THE FIRST EDITION

THE FIELD of mental deficiency has received relatively little attention from psychologists and psychiatrists. Perusal of standard texts in
psychiatry and abnormal psychology reveals that mental deficiency is
usually accorded a single (and small) chapter in which a critical evaluation of psychological theories, procedures, and results is distinguished
by its absence. It is small wonder that psychological work with the
mentally deficient has been considered as uninteresting and unfruitful. It is probably superfluous to state that this book is evidence of
my own belief that the psychological problems in mental deficiency
are as intriguing, puzzling, and pressing as those found in any other
clinical group. I hope that in this book I have succeeded in demonstrating that the psychological problems in mental deficiency present
a challenge to the theoretician as well as to the clinician. I might add
that I also hope that the reader will be impressed by how little we
know about some important problems in this area and how pressing
is the need for systematic research.

It is a pleasure to express my indebtedness to the following: to Dr.
Frederick J. Gaudet who introduced me to the field of psychology in
general and mental deficiency in particular and who has been a constant source of encouragement to me in my work; to Mr. E. N. Roselle,
Superintendent of the Southbury Training School, who made it possible for me to have the time and facilities to do research while I was
working in that institution; to Dr. Herman Yannet who helped in
countless ways to sharpen my thinking about the mentally deficient;
to Dr. Joseph Epstein who critically read and helped revise Chapter
3; to Dr. John Dollard who read the first two chapters and made many
helpful suggestions; to Dr. Donal Dunphy who read Chapters 5, 7,
and 8 and made helpful comments; to Dr. Muzafer Sherif with whom
I had many stimulating discussions about some of the problems raised
in Chapters 4 and 6; to the staff of the Sterling Medical Library whose

ix

ever-helpful efforts in securing whatever books I needed made life a
lot easier for me; to Miss Irma Janoff, Miss Patricia Pittluck, and Dr.
Harry Yamaguchi for help in reading proof; and to Mrs. Susan R.
Henry for her most accurate typing of the various drafts of this book.
I wish also to thank Dr. Carl I. Hovland for providing me with the
necessary secretarial help and for his ever-encouraging attitude. My
greatest indebtedness is to my wife, Esther Sarason, who has been
an invaluable partner in research and whose clinical acumen has been
invaluable in stating and clarifying the problems raised in this book.
Cases 1 and 2 in Chapter 4 were contributed by her, and Chapter 9
was based on her critical review of the literature.

SEYMOUR B. SARASON

September, 1949

PREFACE TO THE SECOND EDITION

ALTHOUGH I was gratified by the response to the publication of this book,
I soon became uneasy about the fact that I, like so many others, had
failed to give sufficient attention to the psychological aspects of the
parental problem. This I have tried to remedy by the addition of three
chapters. I want to thank my students in summer courses at the University of Michigan and the Michigan State Normal College for the
many helpful discussions I had with them about the parental problem
and for encouraging me to write the three additional chapters.

November 1, 1952
New Haven

SEYMOUR B. SARASON

PREFACE TO THE THIRD EDITION

THIS THIRD edition contains the entire monograph, *Psychological and Cultural Factors in Mental Subnormality,* which Dr. Thomas Gladwin, an anthropologist, and I prepared for the National Association for Retarded Children. This monograph was initially published as a Genetic Psychology Monograph (February, 1958), and we are grateful for the permission given by Dr. Carl Murchison of the Journal Press to reprint it in the third edition of *Psychological Problems in Mental Deficiency.*

In preparing the monograph, which is in large part a review of research literature, Dr. Gladwin and I attempted to avoid lengthy discussions of problems and problem areas previously covered by other writers. Consequently, there is little overlap between the contents of the monograph and the rest of the present book. While parts of the monograph represent elaborations of problems raised earlier in the book, most of it is concerned with research not even mentioned elsewhere in the book.

When the first edition of this book was published in 1949 I was aware of the importance of cultural factors, but I was even more aware that I could not do justice to them. When Dr. Gladwin agreed to join me in preparing the report for the NARC, I was relieved because I knew him to be equal to the task—a task, I might add, that no one in anthropology or sociology had attempted despite its obvious importance to these fields.

It would have been desirable if in this third edition the monograph and book could really have been integrated. There were several reasons why this could not have been done. First, having devoted the past two years to preparing the monograph, neither Dr. Gladwin nor I could generate the slightest bit of enthusiasm for the job of writing an integrated text. Second, aside from our lack of enthusiasm neither of us would have had sufficient time in the next few years to devote to such work. Third, although an integrated text is desirable, we did not think that the present form of publication placed an undue burden on the reader, particularly since in terms of content and orientation the monograph clearly supplements, rather than conflicts with, the book.

Working on the NARC report was a humbling experience for me because I became embarrassingly aware of some very important problems that had been discussed either sparingly or not at all in *Psychological Problems in Mental Deficiency*. But more important to me than any one of these problems was my increasing awareness of the general significance of the field of mental subnormality. I can best indicate what I mean by the following statement which I made at a meeting sponsored by the NARC on the occasion of the publication of the monograph:

What kinds of answers would most people, be they professional or not, give to the following questions: Why is it important that we attempt to understand the psychology of mentally subnormal individuals and the cultural ramifications of their conditions? Why should we expend time, money, and effort in attempting to improve their level of functioning when many of them would still be dependent on others for their survival? On the basis of my own public opinion poll conducted over the years I have concluded that the most frequent answers would all be variants of this: these individuals are what they are through no fault of their own and it is our obligation to do as much for them as we can. The "obligation" which is felt is usually justified on ethical or religious grounds. In the literature of the NARC, in legislation which is passed, and in the professional literature—in each instance the underlying justification for action is a felt need *to help* the subnormal individual. Speaking for myself, I have long subscribed to such a justification and I am quite sure that this is true for everyone here today. But—and this is an important "but"—I have come to the conclusion that the emphasis on this justification has unwittingly contributed to the continued *scientific* neglect of the field at the same time as it has contributed to a heightened public awareness of the need for doing more than we have for the mentally handicapped individuals.

Let me elaborate on this point by asking a question: Why is it that the research-oriented psychologist, anthropologist, sociologist and psychiatrist rarely concern themselves in their research with the mentally subnormal individual? I am sure that these types of researchers are in favor of helping the mentally handicapped individual, except, of course, that most of them have neither the interest nor the competence to do so. I would like to place emphasis on their *lack of interest* because I am talking of the research-oriented person from whom we do not expect practical service but rather the discovery of relationships which illuminate the nature of man, discoveries which we are finding in this age of space and the atom turn out to be the most practical of all. We do not expect these researchers to help us in the day-to-day management of our patients but we do expect that they will be devoting their research time to problems in the field. Unfortunately, there are pitifully few who are doing so. It is my thesis that this state of affairs is due to our failure—that is, the failure of those of us who have been in the· field—to recognize that research with the mentally subnormal individual is important not only because of what we may find out about him but, equally important, *what we discover about ourselves and our society.* In other words, we who have been in the field have put our case in terms of how we can help the afflicted individual and not in terms of how he can help us in better understanding ourselves and our society. We have, so to speak, seen only half the significance of this field, and the part we have ignored involves those problems which excite the research interest of those in the fields I have already mentioned. I may be putting it infelicitously, but I think I can communicate what I am thinking when I say that the research anthropologist, or psychologist, or sociologist, or psychiatrist needs the mentally subnormal individual in order better to understand the nature of man and culture—not only man in American culture but man in the myriad cultures in which he is found. We are offering these researchers a gold mine which we in our lack of vision and they in their lack of appropriate training have left unmined.

This, then, is the conclusion to which I have belatedly come as a result of the research survey which Dr. Gladwin and I carried out for the NARC. It is, in fact, one of the central themes of our monograph. If our posing of the problem in our report engenders in some researchers the attitude that they *have* to concern themselves with the problems of mental subnormality we will be more than satisfied.

SEYMOUR B. SARASON

October, 1958

PART ONE

Chapter 1

CRITERIA OF MENTAL DEFICIENCY[1]

CRITERION OF THE I.Q.

THE term mental deficiency has been applied to people who are by no means homogeneous in behavior, intellectual level or efficiency, physical characteristics, socio-economic status, cultural background, and development. Characterizing the mental defective as a distinct group is not an easy task because different investigators employ different operations and criteria in making a diagnosis. For example, there are psychologists, educators, and physicians who label any individual as mentally defective who scores less than an I.Q. of 70 on an intelligence test. The unquestioning faith that is put on the diagnostic meaningfulness of the I.Q. is seen in the not infrequent case where a child with an I.Q. of 68 or 69 is committed to an institution while the one with an I.Q. of 71 or 72 is not. The assumption seems to be that any slight difference in test score between two individuals is a reflection of some kind of a "real" difference in their past, present or future status. The child with an I.Q. of 68 or 69 is automatically labeled mentally defective and then takes on *in the thinking of the clinician* all the characteristics that have been associated with the label. In other words, the child takes on the characteristics of the class or category of mentally defective individuals not because these characteristics were observed but because he has been labeled. This seems to be a case of subordinating observation to language instead of language to observation. Doll has pointed out the inadequacies of the I.Q. approach (73):

"The use of any single I.Q. discounts the important multiple aspects of mental measurements, the disparity of results from different systems of psychometric measurement, the probable error of any single measurement of intelligence, the distinction between brightness and level, the overlap in

[1] Throughout this book the terms mental deficiency and feeble-mindedness will be used synonymously. In the British literature the term mental deficiency is usually used as a substitute for feeble-mindedness in the generic sense, the word feeble-minded being applied by British workers to what American workers call the moron.

1

intelligence between high-grade feeble-mindedness and low-grade normality. It employs an illogical and unvalidated statistical concept without safeguarding the welfare of the individual, his family or society. It further ignores the clinical varieties and the etiological origins. It stops short at an arbitrary statistical gate-post and does not concern itself with the many ramifications of the conditions which if adequately explored would reveal the absurdity of its point of view."

It cannot be emphasized too strongly that a low I.Q. score does not enable one to state in what ways a particular individual is different from others with an identical score, what his differential reactions are to a variety of situations, his attitudes toward himself and others, what effects he will produce on what kinds of people in what kinds of situations, and the relation of the foregoing not only to the presence or absence of central nervous system impairment but to the familial-cultural background in which he developed as well. It is extremely simple, although logically naïve, to "explain" a defective child's behavior on the basis of his low I.Q.—as if there were in the child a force varying inversely with the I.Q., "causing" him to behave as he does. For example, it is not unusual for people who know that a particular child has a low I.Q. to say in regard to a "stupid" act of his: "What can you expect from someone as low as that? If he had more brains he wouldn't have done it." It does not seem to occur to these people to ask why *this* child and not others with identical I.Q. scores behaved in the particular way, why *this* situation and not others elicited the "stupid" response, and why when superior children behave in the same way (running away, committing a crime, killing animals, etc.) the fact of their superior intelligence is not blamed for their behavior.

It follows from the previous discussion that subdividing the defective group according to I.Q. score—i.e., idiots, I.Q. 0–25; imbeciles, I.Q. 25–50; morons, I.Q. 50–70—increases the number of labels, however convenient they may be, without increasing our knowledge. Labeling an individual an imbecile does not tell us any more about him than when it is known that he has an I.Q. of 30, and knowledge of his I.Q. raises many more questions than it answers. The lack of relationship that may exist between intelligence test score and ability to learn can be seen in Gardner's study (95) of idiots and imbeciles, the latter being divided into a high and a low group according to mental age. Each subject was presented with several learning situations. In the first situation the child had to learn to get a food reward from one of three boxes covered with a black cloth. In subsequent situations the size and position of the black cloth which indicated the correct box were varied. In the final situation subjects found food in the box without a cloth, whereas black cloths were over the empty boxes. Gardner found that the performance of the low imbecile group (M.A. between 20 and 29 months) was almost as good as that of the high imbecile group (M.A. between 30 and 49 months), "indicating that mental test results do not tap some latent abilities."

TREDGOLD'S CRITERIA

Dependence on the I.Q. as the sole criterion of mental deficiency seems to have been largely an American phenomenon. In England, since the Mental Deficiency Act of 1913 and its subsequent revisions, the criterion of social adequacy has been emphasized. This emphasis is reflected in the definition of Tredgold (*301*, p. 4), who defines *amentia* as ". . . a state of incomplete mental development of such a kind and degree that the individual is incapable of adapting himself to the normal environment of his fellows in such a way as to maintain existence independently of supervision, control, or external support."

Tredgold's justification for his definition is seen in his statement (*301*, p. 4): "I think . . . we may say that the fundamental purpose of mind is that of enabling the individual so to adapt his conduct to the requirements of the normal environment of his race as to maintain an independent existence; that if he possesses this capacity he must be regarded as normal; but that if he lacks this essential mental attribute, he must be regarded as abnormal and mentally defective."

That the criterion of social adequacy is given far more weight by Tredgold than that of intellectual level is seen by his reference to cases with I.Q.'s between 90 and 100 who are considered mentally defective, and cases with I.Q.'s "considerably less than 70" who are not considered defective. One may indeed wonder how much agreement there would be between a representative sampling of American and English clinicians (1) if they were asked to pick out mental defectives from an unselected sample of a population, and (2) if each group had to check on the diagnoses already made by the other group. Tredgold (*301*, p. 29) implies that the amount of disagreement would probably be considerable.

Although Tredgold's criteria involve the study of more meaningful aspects of behavior than is true of the I.Q. approach, they cannot be considered to be free of ambiguities and value judgments. For example, on what kinds of operations and facts does one determine "a state of incomplete mental development"? Since Tredgold cites cases of mental deficiency whose responses in a test situation give them an average rating, it would follow that being able to function as well as one's fellows in response to a wide variety of test situations is unrelated to or is an unimportant *aspect* of an individual's development. It would seem that whatever conceptual processes are necessary for the solution of intelligence test problems are not to be considered in any way as forms of adaptation. In other words, being able to meet, like one's fellows, culturally determined standards of correctness in a test situation is not to be considered a form of adaptation.

Tredgold's assumption about the lack of relation between intelligence test results and social adaptation becomes more understandable when one bears in mind that to him the purpose of testing is to emerge with a number or an I.Q.—an attitude not restricted to English workers. Tredgold seems unaware that the testing situation is a social situation in which the observed relationships between the nature of the stimulus situation (the test item) and the overt and inferred behavior of the individual are as important as the correctness of the response. The individual's conception of, attitude toward, and response to the examiner, as well as his attitude toward himself, cannot be considered atypical of his responses to many nontesting situations. There is evidence to indicate that behavior in the testing situation is explainable by the psychological principles found applicable to other situations. Fries' observations (92), based on a longitudinal study beginning in infancy, reveal the similarity of response pattern between testing and nontesting situations. Studies by Hutt (144), Lantz (172), and McHugh (201) have indicated that the adequacy of an individual's responses to tasks in the test situation may be influenced by pretest experiences of success and failure, the order in which test items are presented, and familiarity with the examiner and the test situation. In other words, the verbalized and unstated (self-verbalized) responses of the individual in the test situation are learned responses in the sense that they have been engendered and maintained as a result of previous interpersonal experiences. In the case of Tredgold's so-called defectives who achieved an average intelligence rating but "who have proved quite incapable of fending for themselves in the community," the question to be answered is: What are the differences between the testing and social situations, as interpreted *by the individual* as well as by the observer, which call forth different responses, and how may they be related to previous interpersonal and learning experiences? To explain social behavior by the presence or absence of adaptability, and behavior in the test situation by another principle of behavior, is unjustified both in theory and in fact.

It seems clear that for Tredgold the criterion of mental deficiency is the inability to adapt to the "normal" environment of one's "fellows." Such a criterion, by its ambiguity, involves setting up additional criteria of a "normal environment," criteria which Tredgold does not present. To make the problem concrete, Goddard's study of the Kallikak family can be used as a basis for evaluating Tredgold's definition. Goddard's description of the two families stemming from a common paternal ancestor bears repetition:

"When Martin Sr., of the good family, was a boy of fifteen, his father died, leaving him without parental care or oversight. Just before attaining his majority, the young man joined one of the numerous military companies that were formed to protect the country at the beginning of the Revolution. At one of the taverns frequented by the militia he met a feeble-minded girl by whom he became the father of a feeble-minded son. This child was given, by its mother, the name of the father in full, and thus has been handed down to posterity the father's name and the mother's mental capacity. This illegitimate boy was Martin Kallikak Jr., ... and from him have come four hundred and eighty descendants. One hundred and forty-three of these, we have conclusive proof, were or are feeble-minded, while only forty-six have been found normal. The rest are unknown or doubtful.

"Among these four hundred and eighty descendants, thirty-six have been illegitimate.

"There have been thirty-three sexually immoral persons, mostly prostitutes.

"There have been twenty-four confirmed alcoholics.

"There have been three epileptics.

"Eighty-two died in infancy.

"Three were criminal.

"Eight kept houses of ill fame.

"These people have married into other families, generally of about the same type, so that we now have on record and charted eleven hundred and forty-six individuals.

"Of this large group, we have discovered that two hundred and sixty-two were feeble-minded, while one hundred and ninety-seven are considered normal, the remaining five hundred and eighty-one being still undetermined. ('Undetermined,' as here employed, often means not that we knew nothing about the person, but that we could not decide. They are people we can scarcely recognize as normal; frequently they are not what we could call good members of society. But it is very difficult to decide without more facts whether the condition that we find or learn about, as in the case of older generations, is or was really one of true feeble-mindedness.)" [2]

"Martin Sr., on leaving the Revolutionary Army, straightened up and married a respectable girl of good family, and through that union has come another line of descendants of radically different character. These now number four hundred and ninety-six in direct descent. All of them are normal people. Three men only have been found among them who were somewhat degenerate, but they were not defective. Two of these were alcoholic, and the other sexually loose.

"All of the legitimate children of Martin Sr. married into the best families in their state, the descendants of colonial governors, signers of the Declaration of Independence, soldiers and even the founders of a great university. Indeed, in this family and its collateral branches, we find nothing but good representative citizenship. There are doctors, lawyers, judges, educators, traders, landholders, in short, respectable citizens, men and women prominent in every phase of social life." [3]

The first question that might be raised about these families is whose environment shall be considered as normal and on what basis? If being able to progress in school, stay within the law, have sexual relations only with one's lawful mate, attend church, and be economically independent are to be considered "normal," then an alarming number of people, of whom the "bad" Kallikaks would be an insignificant number, are abnormal. Included in this group of abnormal people would be not only the so-called mental defective but the mentally ill (the psychotics), and that large group of neurotic or maladjusted individuals who without psychiatric supervision or control could not maintain an independent existence in whatever is considered their normal environment. Since most of these people cannot be considered to be suffering from incomplete

---

[2] H. H. Goddard. *The Kallikak family.* Macmillan, 1912, p. 18. Reprinted with permission of Henry H. Goddard.

[3] *Ibid.*, p. 29.

mental development—a fact of which Tredgold is cognizant—"abnormal" behavior cannot be used as a differentiating criterion of mental deficiency. It seems safe to state that there is no social behavior or characteristic peculiar to the defective person which is not found in many of the obviously nondefective ones. There may be a wide variety of conditions which make for a particular kind of social behavior so that the fact that the behavior is noted does not allow one automatically to ascribe it to this or that set of conditions.

The problem of what to consider the normal environment of an individual, in order to evaluate his adaptation to it, is further complicated when one attempts to determine what Tredgold means by the normal environment *of his fellows.*" In the case of the Kallikaks, tending as they did to be geographically close to each other,[4] the "fellows" of their environment were other Kallikaks; and from Goddard's descriptions many of them were able to maintain existence in *their* environment independent of supervision, control, or external support. That the niceties of life were absent from their environment and that their work habits and practices were not above reproach goes without saying, but the fact remains that they existed. Following Tredgold's biological orientation, one might be tempted to argue that individuals who could live through and maintain an existence in such an appalling environment as Goddard describes are biologically a hardy group.

In summary, Tredgold's criteria cannot be considered as diagnostically helpful because (1) they are stated in a way which may mean different things to different people; (2) Tredgold eschews the I.Q. because it does not differentiate defectives from nondefectives and hence he is left with independent social adaptation as the *only* criterion of the completeness of mental development; (3) there is no reason to believe that this criterion differentiates defectives from nondefectives any better than an I.Q.; (4) the concept of a "normal" environment is very vague and seems to be based on arbitrary standards of value and morality, neglecting the relationship between behavior and cultural variations; (5) being able to meet as adequately as one's fellows the requirements of the testing situation is considered as unrelated to the problem of mental development.

---

[4] It is not unusual to find circumscribed geographical areas within which a "tribe" of related defectives can be found. More often than not these "pockets," as Tredgold calls them (*301*, p. 63), are found in country areas.

A more general criticism of Tredgold's approach is that he does not present a theory of behavior development from which deductions may be made and tested so that one may determine how much weight to attach to what factors in understanding an individual's development. Without such a theory one is at a loss to determine how life situations are likely to be decisive in eliciting certain kinds of responses, why one and not another aspect of a situation can elicit one and not another kind of response, why one aspect of a situation elicits one kind of response in one individual (or group) and another kind in a second individual (or group). Unless one assumes that it is decided at birth in what situations a child will be fearful, what kinds of people he will like, what foods he will eat, with what children he will prefer to play, etc., the relation between his changing capacities and reaction patterns on the one hand, and life experiences on the other hand, must be studied. For example, Tredgold refers in passing to cases with I.Q.'s considerably less than 70 whom he does not consider mentally defective. Leaving aside the problem of labeling, he does not seem to consider it necessary to determine whether the social adequacy of these cases can be related to the presence or absence of certain life conditions in certain stages of their development; that is, why they behave as they do in contrast to the great majority of their fellows with identical intelligence quotients. Tredgold leaves untouched the problem of the nature and source of individual variation within a group selected on any social or intellectual criterion.

DOLL'S INCLUSIVE CRITERIA

Not all American workers have been uncritical adherents of the intelligence quotient as the sole criterion of mental deficiency (61, 83). Foremost among this group has been Doll, whose inclusive concept of mental deficiency is given in the following quotation (70):

"If we look to the substantial work in this field prior to the recent abuses of mental tests in the diagnosis of mental deficiency, we observe that six criteria by statement or implication have been generally considered essential to an adequate definition and concept. These are (1) social incompetence, (2) due to mental subnormality, (3) which has been developmentally arrested, (4) which obtains at maturity, (5) is of constitutional origin, and (6) is essentially incurable."

Doll's justification for the inclusion of the fourth criterion ("obtains at maturity") reveals a more critical approach to the problem of diagnosis than is the case with Tredgold. Doll is acutely aware of how misleading overall test scores can be, especially during infancy and childhood; how little is known about the relation in some children between extreme increases and decreases in rate of intellectual development on the one hand, and life experiences on the other; and how important it is to consider unfavorable situational conditions as a factor in social insufficiency. The puzzling nature of the sources of intraindividual variations and their bearing on the validity of diagnostic criteria are illustrated in Doll's comments (73) on Muench's follow-up study (212) of a group of children who in early adolescence had been considered feeble-minded by Adams and Doll on the basis of multiple criteria and clinical diagnoses.

"Yet the four of these ten individuals who could be traced and were seen 18 years later by George Muench appeared to be not feeble-minded. This result did not, we think, prove Muench's conclusion that some feeble-minded individuals can and do make suitable social adjustment, but rather that Adams and Doll could and did make unsuitable clinical diagnoses! . . . Was their change in status due to the fact that they were not committed to institutions but living in a normal society? On the contrary, Muench was unable to relate the changes to any specific therapy or regimen. It seems to us that Muench's data reveal delayed growth changes, and such a conclusion would be in accord with institutional experience. The present problem is to improve clinical diagnostic procedures so as to permit the prediction of such changes. We believe that the study of motor aptitude, mental pattern, and etiology will materially advance such a possibility."

One might question whether the concept of delayed growth changes has explanatory value or is largely a verbal restatement of the fact that test scores changed. The fact that the changes cannot be related to a specific therapy or an externally imposed regimen does not contraindicate the possibility that the systematic variation of the conditions of observation (the stimulus conditions), in addition to a more detailed knowledge of the nature and effect of previous life experiences and conditions of learning, may have thrown different light on the response tendencies of the individual. Why some people show these "delayed changes" and others do not is still a crucial problem.

It comes as somewhat of a surprise that Doll believes the present attack on some of these puzzling developmental changes should be toward better prediction as a result of the further study of "motor aptitude, mental pattern, and etiology. . . ." Although the problem of prediction by refining the measurement of what he calls "unitary traits" is of importance, one might ask whether it would not be more fruitful to focus attention first on those situations in which these traits become part of an individual's response repertoire, and on how variations in these situations affect the expression and strength of these traits. When these kinds of situational factors and learning principles can be understood, the clinician is in a better position to utilize a person's performance as a basis for testable hypotheses not only about previous experiences but about reactions to future ones as well. For example, some individuals (defective and otherwise) are more adequate with a verbally presented problem requiring an oral response than with a problem requiring the manipulation and organization of test materials. Before attributing such differences to differences in the inherent strength of mental factors, we should first note that not all children experience the same degree of success or failure, reward or punishment, in their initial efforts at purposive motor activity. Is it unreasonable to assume that continued experience of failure or punishment in such an activity *may* lead to its avoidance or to the experience of anxiety or helplessness when this activity is required? Levy (*181*) has pointed out how maternal overprotection can rob a child of experiences in neuromuscular performance which may result in awkwardness and incoördination in many situations. Ribble (*249*) has maintained that poor motor coördination can in some cases be related to the mother's attitude toward and her handling of the infant. In some cases where such speech difficulties as stuttering develop, Johnson (*150*) has demonstrated that the parents' unjustified fear that speech was not developing normally in their child *preceded* the appearance of the difficulty; that is, the difficulty appeared *after* the parents made their own diagnosis.

The importance of determining *the conditions of previous learning,* the way in which behavior was acquired, increases the complexity of the psychologist's job. It is not sufficient to know that a child is inadequate in a certain kind of stimulus task. One must also determine how the child views himself in regard to the task, what feelings are engendered by its presentation, and under what conditions adequacy might be attained. However, without knowledge of the conditions which might have produced the particular inadequacy obtained by research or from the case at hand, the psychologist's conclusions have only limited significance.

In an attempt to make the evaluation of the criterion of social incompetence more explicit, consistent, and valid, Doll has developed the Vineland Social Maturity Scale which provides evidence of motor, social, and linguistic aspects of development in terms of norms available for infancy through adulthood (68, 69). In contrast to the Binet, the Vineland Social Maturity Scale does not require direct examination of the subject but may be administered by interviewing someone who is well acquainted with the subject's everyday activities. The scale attempts to determine what a person *does* rather than what he *can* do. For example, on the 12 to 15 year level the individual's performance in the following activities is ascertained:

Plays difficult games.
Exercises complete care of dress.
Buys own clothing accessories.
Engages in adolescent group activities.
Performs responsible routine chores.

One of the chief merits of the Social Maturity Scale is that when included in a test battery it focuses the clinician's attention on the everyday activities of the individual and enables him to obtain a more comprehensive picture of the subject's functioning than if only the standard tests of intelligence had been administered. Too often the psychologist unjustifiably assumes that the level on which an individual functions on an intelligence test is representative of his functioning in all other situations. Defining social competence by a social quotient or social age is, however, open to the same objections as defining intellectual status by a test score. Although the Social Maturity Scale allows one to describe the nature of an individual's social activities, it does not allow one to determine the concomitant motivational factors in his social behavior or the social-cultural background in which they were acquired. In other words, because an individual obtains a low Binet and social I.Q., one cannot conclude that the condition responsible for such functioning is of constitutional origin, is essentially incurable, and will obtain at maturity.

Doll's awareness of this problem is indicated by his insistence that the diagnosis of mental deficiency should not be made until all six criteria have been fulfilled. In this connection Doll (74) has maintained that a distinction must be made between feeble-mindedness and intellectual retardation; in the latter there is intellectual inadequacy with the likelihood of ultimate social competence, whereas essential incurability is the hallmark of the former. The intellectually retarded can attain independent social-economic sufficiency, but the feeble-minded presumably cannot. According to Doll, intellectual retardation is a *pro tem* classification, while the diagnosis of feeble-mindedness or mental deficiency is not. However, since a diagnosis of mental deficiency includes a prediction of future status, it would appear that it should also be considered a temporary statement of conditions in the sense that confirmation depends on status at maturity. As long as a fair amount of error is involved in predicting status at maturity, the diagnosis of mental deficiency might best be considered in many cases as *pro tem*. Another reason for such caution concerns the consequences of a diagnosis of mental deficiency for the child. Once he is classified as mentally deficient he is treated as such, and the psychotherapeutic procedures which have been found effective with normals are not attempted with him—even though there is evidence that such cases respond to and benefit from such procedures (Chapter 10). It is not an academic question to ask what might happen if all cases classified as mentally deficient on the moron level were deliberately considered as nondefective and then over an extended period of time were given the benefit of the therapeutic procedures which have been found most effective with normal individuals. It would follow, of course, that in such a study the investigator should be able to make whatever environmental changes he deemed necessary. From data presented in subsequent chapters of this book, one might expect that the results of such a study would necessitate changes in the original diagnosis in more than just a few cases.

From the above considerations it can be seen that the validity of a diagnosis, no matter how inclusive and explicit the criteria, is a function of the sensitivity of the procedures employed and the status (at the time of diagnosis) of scientific knowledge about the way in which behavioral patterns are acquired and change. The present-day status of the psychological sciences does not allow one to consider predictions about future status and amenability to environmental change as other than tentative and subject to much error. The fact that an individual's status at maturity is different than what had been predicted earlier and that the behavioral change cannot be related "to any specific therapy or regimen" may be an indication of two things: (1) that our theoretical conceptions about behavioral development may be inadequate in that they do not take into account certain significant variables, thus preventing the investigator from asking "the right questions"; (2) that the diagnostic procedures employed may not give a complete or valid picture of the variables they purport to measure, significant though these variables may be. In Muench's study, for example, the follow-up procedures were concerned with intelligence test level, marriage history, court record, education, vocational and economic adjustment, neighborhood, etc. It does not appear that these kinds of data should be expected to explain behavioral changes. The complete absence of "personal" data does not allow one to conclude that motivational and interpersonal factors were unrelated to the changes in functioning which Muench obtained. When one attributes Muench's findings to "delayed growth changes," it would seem unjustifiable to assume that the data necessary for accepting or rejecting alternative hypotheses (motivational and situational factors, etc.) have been obtained. It might also be pointed out that when one assumes the presence of delayed growth changes which at present cannot be predicted, he is implying that mental deficiency must in some cases be viewed as a *pro tem* classification.

It should be noted at this point that the reliability and validity of a diagnosis of mental deficiency increase as the intellectual level of the individual decreases. In the case of idiots, imbeciles, and some morons the intellectual and social incompetency is usually found in the presence of demonstrable central nervous system impairment which rules out the possibility of any significant change in future status. The etiology of the impairment may be obscure, but the fact that there is impairment allows one to make some fairly definite predictions. As will be seen in the next chapter, this diagnostically happy situation does not obtain with many defectives in the moron and borderline classifications where the evidence for the constitutional origin of the condition is inconclusive or presumptive.

The failure of many investigators to adhere to a set of comprehensive criteria of mental deficiency, such as those given by Doll, makes it extremely difficult to determine either to what extent many published studies are comparable or the degree to which one might generalize from the findings of any particular study. The problem may be illustrated by discussing Schmidt's recent study (*264*) entitled "Changes in Personal, Social, and Intellectual Behavior of Children Originally Classified as Feebleminded." The subjects in her study were 322 boys and girls between the ages of 12 and 14 years who on the basis of intelligence tests had been placed in special centers of a large city school system. Of the five school centers three (A, B, C) were experimental in the sense that a special, individualized, intensive educational program was utilized in the classes; in the remaining two centers (D, E) the usual techniques were employed. Table I presents the intelligence quotients

TABLE 1.   The Range, Mean, and Sigma of the I.Q.'s for Each of Schmidt's Groups at Beginning of Study (*264*, p. 9)

Group	N	Range	Mean	Sigma
A	110	27–69	49.58	10.4
B	91	35–69	53.47	8.6
C	53	27–69	55.6	10.2
D	31	55–69	61.3	2.3
E	37	50–69	62.5	2.1

for the groups at the beginning of the study. The aims of the special educational program were:

"The purpose of the development of the experimental educational program was to provide school experiences which would help meet the needs of the participating boys and girls while in school, and prepare them for competent social adjustment in post-school years. To achieve these two broad general aims, the instructional program of the 3 experimental centers was directed toward these specific goals: (1) development of desirable personal behavior; (2) improvement of fundamental academic skills; (3) development of the manipulative arts; (4) improvement of work and study habits; (5) learning of occupational and related vocational information; and (6) pre-employment experience." (*264*, p. 40.)

The school program covered a three-year period and a follow-up study extended over a postschool period of five years. At 18-month intervals each child was administered various tests among which were the Stanford-Binet (L), Bernreuter Personality Inventory, and the Vineland

Social Maturity Scale. Table 2 shows the average score obtained on two of the tests by the experimental groups at (1) the beginning of the study, (2) the close of the school period, and (3) the end of the follow-up period. In contrast to the striking changes found in the experimental

TABLE 2. Mean Scores Obtained by Schmidt's Three Experimental Groups (1) at the Beginning of the Study, (2) at the Close of the School Period, and (3) at the Close of the Post-School Period (264, p. 87)

Group	Stanford-Binet			Vineland		
	1	2	3	1	2	3
A	50.5	71.6	89.3	60.3	87.4	107.2
B	54.4	72.0	83.8	59.1	94.1	84.8
C	47.7	76.2	83.0	64.7	89.3	83.8
Total	52.1	71.6	89.3	59.4	91.8	107.2

groups the control cases, who were given the Binet five years after the beginning of the study, showed a decrease in I.Q. At the beginning the average I.Q. of the controls was 60 and after five years it was 56.4. In comparing the two groups Schmidt stated:

". . . the Experimental group moved out of the classification of 'feeble-mindedness,' almost into the 'dull' classification. At that point, 11 of the group were already testing in the normal range, 1 in the high normal, be-tween 100 and 110. Only 1 person tested below an I.Q. of 60. Comparison with original tests indicated that, by this 5 years after original enrollment, 40.6% had already shown gains of 30 or more I.Q. points. There were no evidences of loss in any case at this point in the study; only 3 individuals showed gains of less than 10 points.

"On the other hand, the Control group was marked by decrease in I.Q., with only 4 of the total 68 showing gain, and such gain not greater than 4 points. Most of the I.Q. losses were slight, but there were individual losses as great as 20 and 22 points. The mean change over the period for the Con-trol group was a loss of 3.6 points, as compared with the 25.2 points gain shown by the Experimental group.

"The Binet retest test data here presented appears to substantiate the quality of experiential activities recounted for the Experimental group . . . and also to help explain the difference in quality and extent of these experi-ences over those of the Control group." (264, p. 90.)

On the basis of the standardized measures which she employed, in addition to the academic, vocational, and social activities of the experimental groups, Schmidt concluded that the average adjustment of these cases at the end of the study was equal to that of the average adult.

One of the first questions which might be asked about Schmidt's study is why the cases were classified as feeble-minded. Can one assume that these children are similar to those classified as feeble-minded by other investigators? In his evaluation of Schmidt's study Kirk (*166*) pointed out that the cases which she studied "are usually of the educable type who can become self-supporting" and are not considered feeble-minded. It might also be asked whether any similarity between the cases studied by Schmidt and others is due merely to common possession of a diagnostic label or to fundamental behavioral and constitutional characteristics. The problem could be put in the following way: When Schmidt uses the word feeble-minded does she refer to the same set of diagnostic criteria and investigative procedures as, for example, Doll does? It will be seen that the answer must be in the negative. According to the data Schmidt presents, the cases she studied showed indications of intellectual inadequacy and social incompetence as measured by the Binet and Vineland Social Maturity Scale (see Table 2). One might say that presumptive evidence for meeting two of Doll's criteria was present. As regards the other criteria Schmidt presents no data at all. Was the presumed feeble-mindedness of her cases due to a constitutional insufficiency existing at birth or shortly thereafter? Was there evidence for assuming that familial-cultural factors were *not* related to the intellectual and social incompetency?[5] Was there reason for assuming at the beginning of the study that the condition of these children was incurable? Were there objective grounds for believing that at maturity the level of functioning would have shown no change from that at the beginning of the study? Since the data necessary for an adequate answer to these questions are not given, one may conclude that by calling her groups feeble-minded Schmidt was referring to the fact that they made low scores on tests of intelligence and social maturity. By feeble-minded Schmidt does not seem to mean a condition that is

[5] That familial cultural factors were probably related to the intellectual and cultural status of her subjects can be seen in Schmidt's statement (*264*, p. 38) that "cultural patterns in the home and community were definitely inferior. . . . In addition to . . . material lacks, the great majority of the homes were badly riddled by internal emotional conflicts as well."

essentially incurable, will obtain at maturity, and is of constitutional origin. It can be seen that the tendency for investigators to utilize different criteria for mental deficiency can only serve to make comparisons between studies hazardous and to limit the generalizations which one might make from any particular study.

One may wonder whether the controversy that has arisen about the significance of Schmidt's results is not partially due to different conceptions about the nature of mental deficiency. If one accepts incurability as a criterion of mental deficiency, he will naturally be surprised at Schmidt's findings and tend to question their validity. In raising such a question it would seem that one is creating a pseudoproblem because he would unjustifiably assume that when Schmidt uses the word feeble-minded she is also employing the criterion of incurability. *The investigator who uses incurability as a criterion does not mean the same thing by feeble-mindedness as does Schmidt.* Although one might criticize Schmidt's conception of the nature of mental deficiency as being narrow and misleading, in addition to limiting the degree to which he might generalize from her findings, he cannot conclude that her findings are invalid.[6] The significance of Schmidt's results must be found in terms of *her* conception of feeble-mindedness, narrow and unacceptable though it may be considered by others. However, even when the results are judged according to her criteria, their significance can still be considered equivocal because the composition of her groups is uncertain. At one point (*264*, p. 8) Schmidt indicated that her groups were not necessarily representative of all "feeble minded" adolescents "since there remains always the possibility that variables of physical handicap or

---

[6] Kirk (*166*) raised some questions about the authenticity of Schmidt's data. He could not obtain her original data and the inconsistencies he noted were based on statistics from the Board of Education of the city in which the study was made and on test data secured for a small portion of her classes. He noted the following: (1) The I.Q. distribution of Schmidt's classes was markedly different from that for special classes as a whole in the city, suggestive of some kind of selective factor; (2) according to class records the range of I.Q.'s in Schmidt's classes did not correspond to her published data; (3) she did not explain how her children, who initially read at first-grade level, could have been given the Bernreuter Personality Inventory, which requires a high level of reading comprehension; (4) there were errors of statistical tabulations in the published report. In her rejoinder Schmidt (*265*) maintained that the Board of Education statistics which Kirk employed were so internally inconsistent as to be worthless as a basis of criticism. She did not make a point-for-point refutation of Kirk's evaluation. It would seem that until all of Schmidt's data are made available for complete rechecking, Kirk's criticisms (and their implications) cannot be considered as having been conclusively demonstrated to be without foundation.

emotional aberration may produce a state of pseudo-feeblemindedness not recognized by an examining psychologist." Schmidt does not estimate how many of her cases may have been pseudofeeble-minded and one is forced to question the homogeneity of her groups. Had more comprehensive criteria of mental deficiency been used, Schmidt's attention might have been more sharply focused on those familial-cultural and developmental factors which allow for determining pseudofeeblemindedness. It should be noted that her criteria of mental deficiency do not allow her to describe the composition of her groups at all precisely. In duplicating her study one could not be sure that "similar" cases were being obtained.

THE CULTURAL FACTOR

Before concluding this chapter mention should be made of a problem which is of importance in a discussion of the criteria of mental deficiency. This problem is concerned with the relation between cultural factors and test scores. One might more correctly say that the problem is the failure of the investigator to relate his test findings and behavioral observations to the individual's cultural background. For example, comparing an individual's behavior to social norms, on the basis of which social competency is evaluated, raises the following questions: How did psychological and cultural factors interact to produce this individual's behavior, and how representative is this constellation of the group on which the norms were based? One might approach this problem by asking still another question: Why hesitate to evaluate an African native child by the norms of the Stanford-Binet or the Vineland Social Maturity Scale? Psychologists and anthropologists would answer that the environmental stimuli (conditions, practices, attitudes, etc.) to which the African child learns to respond are so different from those of our culture that one is not justified in evaluating his behavior in situations to which he has never been exposed. The fact that the Alorese people of the South Pacific include the eating of rats in their diet cannot be judged by our own culturally determined attitudes. In both cases the reactions to the sight of the rat call forth learned patterns of response, the difference in reaction being a cultural one. Although most people would agree that it would be unsound to evaluate the African or the Alorese by the cultural practices of Americans, the fact is often overlooked that Americans (or other western groups) differ so widely among themselves that it seems more correct to speak of American cultures instead of *an* American culture. There are behavioral differences between people who live in the country and those who live in the city, between those in one geographic region and those in another, between those with some education and those with a good deal of it, between those of one religion and those of another, etc.[7] Although these differences are not as extreme as those found between primitive and western cultures, the fact that there are wide cultural variations within a large national or political unit would seem to make it necessary to study the relation between behavior and these variations in cultural practices. In the case of a Kallikak child, for example, it is clear that the practices, attitudes, and people to which he was exposed were quite different from what many other non-Kallikak children experienced. A Kallikak mother did not rear her child the way non-Kallikak mothers did. How and why the Kallikak mother rewarded and punished her child, and for what behavior, would not be characteristic of the non-Kallikak mother. In other words, the "culture" of the Kallikak child was different from that of other children and to evaluate the social behavior of the former by the norms of the latter may be quantifying the difference but not explaining it. That cultural differences may be related to, although not necessarily caused by, intellectual differences points up the importance of determining the relation between behavior and cultural constellation. A study of such relationships raises the question as to what cultural practices are psychologically relevant in the sense that variations in these practices produce behavioral variations.

The untenable nature of psychological test interpretations which are not related to the cultural background of the group being studied can be seen in Rau's study (245), the object of which was "to discover to what extent there was feeblemindedness among the children in the country schools of chosen districts of a county in Devon, England, where there was reported to have been a great deal of inter-marriage due to isolation." Psychological tests were given to the children and on

---

[7] Kinsey, Pomeroy, and Martin's study (165), *Sexual behavior in the human male,* is an excellent example of how variations in the expression of a particular area of behavior are related to variations in such cultural factors as educational level, occupational status, rural-urban background, religious group, degree of religious adherence, and geographic origin. There is reason to believe that intellectual and social functioning is also influenced by these factors. How these factors impinge upon and become psychologcially relevant for the developing individual remains a problem for research.

the basis of their scores Rau concluded that more than half of the children were mentally deficient. The following description of one of the villages she visited serves as a basis for evaluating the meaningfulness of her conclusions.

"As the size of the families ran from four to ten, the struggle to get along was rather extreme in some cases. There were busses several times a day to the nearest town, and although the inhabitants would have to walk only a mile each way in order to catch a bus, the headmistress said that very few ever went, and those few went only to the cinema, and did not mix with the town people. While talking to a village wood chopper, working on the squire's land, it was found that he had never left that part of the country because he was afraid of wild animals! This is just an example to show the extreme ignorance of these isolated people about the outside world. That man earnestly believed that there were wild animals in all other parts of the country that would hurt him. He willingly admitted that he could not 'get on' here, as there were no opportunities, but he was afraid to leave.

"The children in the school had never seen a railway station until they were taken by the present headmistress about two and a half years before. At present they very seldom went away, and some had never left the village. If they are taught anything about history or current events, all the subjects have to be in some way related to their present lives, or it makes no impression, for it is so very far removed. The whole atmosphere of the village was friendly, although a bit gossipy, and the people mixed among themselves quite well.

"As far as the school was concerned, the work being done was rather doubtful, for, although the headmistress was very sincere in her attempts, and seemed to honestly believe that her methods were correct, anyone who has ever seen dull children taught in a special school would soon see that much was left undone. One could hardly blame this on the teacher, as she had received training solely for normal children, and although she was very definitely interested in the children's mental state, she considered them hopeless. Her main complaint was of their very bad memories and lack of concentrating power. In the first place, she was not a woman of very steady nerves, and the situation had become rather acute by the time the visit was made. Her children were yelled at too much, and they were so continually being punished that it had ceased to mean anything to them. The school room was in a constant stir, both with the children talking and the teacher yelling at them, which is hardly an appropriate atmosphere for learning. As was said before, the blame cannot be placed upon the teacher, for unless she has been especially trained or adaptable to that sort of work, it can easily be seen that the situation was not an easy one. The fact that she had lost her husband a few months before and was only sleeping every other night when she took sleeping powders probably made a very great difference in her behavior, and it is hardly fair to judge her teaching from one visit.

"Most of the children had to walk up a hill a mile long to come to school, and, as nearly all went home to lunch, they made the climb twice every day. This was rather hard on some of the very young children, though they did not seem to mind, even if they did get tired. The school hours were from 9:30 to 12:30; 1:45 to 4:30, with two short play periods. There were two rooms, one for infants, and one for all the other standards together. For this reason there was a great amount of individual work done, as class work with so many different ages was impossible. The teacher stayed with the older children entirely, and the infants were taught by a supplementary teacher, who was a distant member of the first family mentioned, although she seemed very capable and interested."

In light of such conditions several questions can be raised: How helpful or psychologically revealing is it to compare the test scores of these children to norms derived from testing children of a rather different cultural background?[8] If one attributes the condition of the children who were "mentally deficient" to intermarriage and isolation, how does he explain the cases whose scores were on the average level or above it? Were defective and nondefective children found in the same families? Can one assume that child-rearing practices among the village families were the same? Were the children who received low test scores also inadequate in meeting the demands made upon them *by their own culture?* It would seem that one is justified in concluding that the data necessary for understanding the nature and source of these children's psychological functioning are not contained in test scores or in superficial descriptions of community organization.

The importance of cultural factors may be seen in the studies by

[8] The relation between test scores and cultural background is often overlooked. In this connection it is interesting to note the attitude of Binet and Simon as reflected in the following statement made by them in 1908 (*39*, p. 267): "In the word, retardation is a term relative to a number of circumstances which must be taken into account in order to judge each particular case. We can make the boundary between moronity and the normal state more definite by considering a special category of subjects. We wish to speak of defective adults whom we have had occasion to observe in the Parisian hospitals who were subjects for custodial care. This forms a special category for many reasons: first on account of nationality and race, it is a question as to whether they are Parisians or persons living in the regions of Paris; second, on account of social conditions; all belong to the laboring class. *The limit that we place for them would not be correct for any others; we express complete reserve for the application of it which one would wish to make for subjects of different environments.*" (Italics mine.)

Warner and Lunt (*309*), Davis, Gardner, and Gardner (*64*), and Warner, Havighurst, and Loeb (*310*) on the relation between social class and behavioral patterns. These studies demonstrate how different the cultural pattern of one social class in a community may be from another in the same locale. The child born and reared as a member of a particular social class experiences or is exposed to different influences than is the child of another social class. Unless the factor of social class is taken into account, any attempt to understand the acquisition of behavioral patterns, their intellectual or social aspects, will be superficial and misleading.

The importance of cultural factors has also been shown in anthropological investigations (*34, 79, 158, 206, 207, 322*). These studies have underlined the importance, among other things, of variations in child-training practices and family constellations as sources of variation in behavior. Differences in child-training practices have been found important for understanding differences not only between cultures, but within a culture as well. DuBois' study (*79*) of the Alorese culture illustrated this point very clearly. The Alorese mother, who was required to work in the fields, could take care of her child only before she went to the fields and after she returned. As a result the child did not have the supporting influence of the mother during his most formative period. As Kardiner pointed out (*159*): "Tensions from hunger, the need for support, for emotional response, were therefore greatly neglected, and the child was left in the care of older siblings, relatives, or other persons. The consistency of the disciplines was therefore destroyed; the image of the parent as a persistent and solicitous helper in case of need was not built up. The ego was feeble in development and filled with anxiety. The patterns of aggression remained amorphous." The failure of Alorese parents to react to their children in a consistent, sympathetic, and satisfying manner was evident not alone during the infancy period.

"Parents have no scruples about appropriating anything a child may have, or about treating it carelessly at the same time that they admit the child's ownership of the property. This is in marked contrast to the rigidly scrupulous attitudes of some other nonliterate peoples such as certain American Indian tribes. Repeatedly I gave children small gifts, ranging from candy to a tin container, only to see these gifts in the hands of an adult a few minutes later, while the child stood by without source of redress. One of the major difficulties in using free-play techniques was that adults could not be kept from joining the children and appropriating the toys. As young people begin producing or acquiring property of greater value in adult eyes, this situation becomes more acute. . . . A quarrel between two boys over a bow illustrates several aspects of this situation.

"Padalang, a boy of about fourteen, gave his bow to an uncle, who promised to mend it for him. When it was mended, the uncle handed the bow to his son instead of returning it to his nephew. The son in turn loaned it to a playmate, who broke it beyond repair. When the nephew discovered what had happened he went to the house of the boy who had broken the bow and seized his bow in compensation—a thoroughly adult procedure. The two boys came to blows and soon both were bellowing with rage and pain. Adults took a hand in separating them and suggested various compromises, which the enraged boys both stubbornly refused to accept. Adult relatives became sufficiently excited to begin snatching the bow from each other's hands. At this point two neutral observers rushed in, seized the bow, and broke it into pieces.

"Fantan the Interpreter, who was one of the two neutral observers, commented afterward that they would not have dared to break the bow in this fashion if two adults had been quarreling, but instead everyone would have taken sides and tried to settle matters by compromise. Trivial as this incident is, it illustrates not only the helplessness of children in protecting their own property, but also the peculiar harshness toward growing children that manifests itself repeatedly in teasing, ridiculing, frightening, and beating, as well as in a certain contemptuous highhandedness where their property interests are concerned. . . .

"In addition to corporal punishment, teasing, ridicule, and deception are widely used, not only in disciplining children but also as favorite forms of amusement, especially among young men. I have seen youths in their late teens and early twenties send boys on fool's errands and deceive them with false promises of rewards for services, and then guffaw with laughter when the crestfallen child returned. Fantan the Interpreter one day called to an eight-year-old girl whom we passed on the trail, saying he had just left some honey at her house and she had better hurry home for it. Actually, we had taken some ripe breadfruit to her house but it had been eaten up before we left. On another occasion, a man of about twenty-eight sent a twelve-year-old boy to fetch a bunch of bananas he said he had left at the foot of the village. In return he promised the boy six of them. The boy raced gleefully to the indicated spot but returned saying he had not found them. He was sent off again, and when he returned the second time he realized that he had been deceived. A group of six or seven grown men were sitting about watching the procedure and laughing heartily, to the boy's evident shame and anger."[9]

With such childhood experiences it is not surprising to find that stinginess about food and strong mutual distrust of each other were characteristic of the Alorese. They constantly haggled over money and power. But the accumulation of wealth was accompanied by the fear that the envy of others would be aroused. The giving of a feast was the technique employed by the wealthy individual to satisfy the oral needs of the envious as well as to reduce his own anxiety about their aggressive feelings toward him. However, there were individual differences among the members of this society. These were revealed in the eight biographies which Du Bois was able to obtain. "Each of these eight people had an individual character, but nevertheless all had certain features in common, not because they followed certain conventions in common but because the deeper fabric of their personalities was molded on similar lines. Furthermore, the points at which the individuals differed in character structure could be clearly tracked down to variations in the influences at work during the period of growth. Where parental care was good, specific variations in character appeared" (159).

Although the relation between child-training practices and behavioral pattern has received increasing attention in recent years, the relation of the former to intellectual functioning has not received the attention which it seems to merit. In a later chapter an attempt will be made to state the possible importance of cultural factors for some of the problems in mental deficiency.

---

[9] C. DuBois. *The people of Alor.* University of Minnesota Press, 1944, p. 63. By permission of the publisher.

Chapter 2

PROBLEMS IN CLASSIFICATION

In the present chapter some of the ways in which mental defectives have been classified will be discussed. As was pointed out in the preceding chapter, the term mental deficiency is applied to a group of individuals among whom the heterogeneity of symptoms is very marked. One of the purposes of a classificatory schema is to group cases in such a way that the differences between groupings are greater than the differences within groupings. In short, the aim is to produce homogeneous groups. The question, of course, is, homogeneous for what variables? One could group mental defectives according to sex, for example, and have perfectly homogeneous groups. However, if one were interested either in the origins of the mental deficiency or in the social-psychological-educational consequences of the condition, classification according to sex would not be particularly helpful. If professional journals in the field of mental deficiency can be used as a guide, the primary interest of some researchers, mostly physicians, is in determining the etiological factors (i.e., germinal defects, metabolic and glandular disorders, birth injury, infection, etc.) which produce mental deficiency. Other researchers, primarily psychologists, have been interested in the behavioral consequences of mental deficiency, some workers being cognizant of and controlling for etiological differences while others overlook them. The differences of interest among researchers are reflected in differences in the classificatory schemes they employ. However, as psychological procedures have become more refined and their validity more firmly established, they have been increasingly utilized as a research tool in the study of etiological factors. Later on in this chapter it will be seen that for a large segment of the mentally defective population (the garden-variety defective) the psychological approach may be most important in establishing the role of certain etiological factors. Before taking up various classifications it seems advisable to devote some attention to the distinction between etiology and diagnosis.

Diagnosis refers to the procedure whereby one attempts to correlate observations and measurements so that predictions about the course of a presenting condition may be made and appropriate therapeutic measures taken. The significance given to what is observed depends primarily on the clinician's previous experience with a wide variety of conditions and his knowledge of the systematic findings of others. For example, the fact that an individual has a high fever is not a particularly helpful finding because it may be the result of a wide variety of conditions. If in addition to the high fever the individual has a rapid pulse, sore throat, vomiting or chills, the physician is able to narrow down the range of possible conditions which might explain the presenting symptoms. At this point therapeutic measures might be started, but the course of the condition cannot be definitely predicted because the presenting symptoms could appear in widely differing conditions. If shortly after the onset of the above symptoms the individual's tongue has become red at the tip and edges and its papillae red and swollen, and a scarlet-red eruption has appeared on the individual's body, the constellation of symptoms makes the diagnosis of scarlet fever the most likely among remaining possibilities and predictions about future status a less hazardous procedure. It is obvious that the diagnostic procedure is not a mere recording of isolated symptoms; it involves a detailed noting and weighting of symptoms according to the constellation in which they appear, an acute awareness of the overlapping of symptoms among a wide variety of conditions, and the need to subject one's conclusion to the test of subsequent events.

Etiology, in contrast to diagnosis, refers to the study of the origin of a condition, that is, an attempt to describe the antecedent factor or factors without which the condition would not occur. It is apparent that a condition can be diagnosed without knowledge of the etiological factors. In the case of scarlet fever, for example, the condition was described or diagnosed for many years before the particular streptococcus responsible for it was isolated. The common cold and cancer are a few of the many conditions which can be diagnosed without knowledge of the etiological factors. The importance of the study of etiological factors is that their isolation allows for a more direct attack on the problem of therapy and prevention.

TREDGOLD'S CLASSIFICATION

In the following pages Tredgold's etiological classification will be discussed first not only because of historical priority but because of its continued use by most workers with only minor variations. Following Tredgold's classification the more general, psychologically oriented, diagnostic groupings will be discussed.

According to Tredgold, cases of mental deficiency can be divided, in regard to their causation, into four groups:

1. Amentia or mental deficiency due to inheritance. In these cases the defect is considered to be of "germinal, intrinsic or endogenous" origin. Tredgold has labeled this group the *primary* amentias.
2. Amentia or mental deficiency due to environment. In these cases the defect is of extrinsic or exogenous origin. Tredgold has labeled this group the *secondary* amentias.
3. Amentia or mental deficiency due to both inheritance and environment.
4. Amentia or mental deficiency without discoverable cause.

It should be noted that the terms primary and secondary amentia *each* refer to conditions in which the constellation of symptoms, the behavior and physical manifestations, are by no means similar. As will be seen later, among the primary amentias will be found individuals with gross cortical defect, no observable cortical defect, severe metabolic disfunction, no metabolic disturbance, intellectual functioning on the idiot level, and intellectual functioning on the moron and borderline levels. These conditions are grouped together because of some assumed defective characteristic in the genes contributed by either or both parents, the defective characteristic being the antecedent factor without which the condition would not have arisen. The defective characteristic is presumably not the same in the different conditions. Since knowledge of gene structure in human beings is extremely meager and is not derived from direct observation, statements about the mechanisms of heredity are largely based on animal and plant experimentation. Despite these obstacles, there is abundant evidence that certain human physical characteristics (skin color, eye color, etc.) can best be explained by the mechanisms of heredity experimentally studied in plants and lower animals. Such explanations are given weight *because there are no other testable assumptions which can explain the available facts or make as accurate predictions.* Where alternative explanations are available and can be experimentally attacked, attributing a condition to a germinal disposition can be regarded only as a tentative conclusion. This is especially true where the condition being studied is distinguished not by observable or measurable physical characteristics, justifying the drawing of a parallel with animal studies, but by a response or behavioral pattern which has been learned in a particular cultural setting. A child born of Chinese parents in China will "inherit" certain physical characteristics similar to those of the child born of Chinese parents in America; however, the response or behavior patterns of these children will be different although the same psychological principles of behavior are operative in both cases. To attribute behavioral similarity between parent and child to some kind of germinal disposition is to assume that the cultural milieu in which the behavior was and is elicited, the relation between response and stimulating situation, is of secondary importance. Such an approach overlooks the fact that *behavior does not exist in the genes* and cannot be "explained" by them. That physical or constitutional factors are important in behavioral expression is not the same as saying that they are the "cause" of the behavior.

Explanations which attribute behavioral similarity between parent and child to mechanisms of inheritance seem to be a device that is used whenever data necessary for an explanation according to psychological principles are not available. If all of a man's children should have as ungovernable a temper as he has, some people might look upon this datum as an indication of the potency of inheritance (*301*, p. 255). These same people would probably not advance such an explanation if this man and his children shared a violent dislike for baked beans. The following statement of Tredgold regarding the role of inheritance in mental deficiency bears close scrutiny (*301*, p. 27):

"The presence of an hereditary, and therefore germinal, disposition is shown by the occurrence in the family of a marked and exceptional amount of mental abnormality. This abnormality, however, is not always of the same kind, and it occurs in two, possibly three, different forms. In the first the mental abnormality in the family is of precisely the same kind as that in the patient, the best known example being amaurotic family idiocy. In the second, the family abnormality is chiefly in the form of intellectual dulness, but other forms of mental disorders also occur, and it may be that there is no essential difference between this and the next group. In the third, the inheritance takes the form of a variety of mental abnormalities; thus one member may have been insane, another psychoneurotic, another epileptic, another a dement, and perhaps another a dullard or a defective. In my experience, the majority of cases of primary amentia come from families of this latter kind, and which are characterized by an exceptional proneness to different forms of mental abnormality."

It would seem justifiable to conclude from Tredgold's remarks that any and all behavioral deviations may be considered inherited if there is any indication of "neuropathic ancestry" and even if widely differing deviations occur in the same family. If one member of the family has delusions of persecution, another obsessive fears of dying, and another is intellectually retarded or defective, this extreme diversity of behavior can be explained by merely assuming that gene changes have taken place. Why the gene changes in one offspring should result in schizophrenia instead of some other mental disorder, why another offspring should be psychoneurotic instead of epileptic, and why still another should be intellectually dull instead of a manic-depressive psychotic are questions about individual variation for which Tredgold has no answer except to postulate unobservable and unmeasurable gene changes. It is somewhat paradoxical that Tredgold's reliance on gene changes as the etiological factor does not allow him a greater range of accurate predictability, as one would expect, but instead makes prediction practically impossible. A theory which explains the facts but cannot predict them is not particularly helpful.

Tredgold's contention of a genetic relationship between mental disorder, such as schizophrenia, and mental deficiency is not supported by the facts. Kallmann, Barrera, Hoch, and Kelley (156) have studied the frequency of mental deficiency in the blood relatives (siblings, children, grandchildren, nephews, and nieces) of an unselected group of schizophrenic hospital patients among whom were 218 twin pairs with schizophrenia in at least one member. Monozygotic or identical and dizygotic or fraternal twin pairs were used. Data on the incidence of schizophrenia and mental deficiency in the families of a group of normal and retarded children were also available. As the authors point out (*156*), in order to confirm the assumption of a genetic relationship between schizophrenia and mental deficiency one would expect that:

1. There should be an increase in the frequency of mental deficiency among the blood-relatives of schizophrenic persons, and this increase should be proportional to the degree of consanguinity, showing the highest values in the group of the monozygotic co-twins of schizophrenic twin patients.
2. The incidence of schizophrenia should be increased in the offspring of feeble-minded parents as well as in those individuals who have a mentally defective parent in addition to a schizophrenic one, as compared with the schizophrenic rates for the children of normal average parents and for the descendants of matings between one schizophrenic and one normal parent, respectively.

The statistical results did not in any way confirm the above suppositions and the authors concluded that their findings were "obviously in contradiction" to a theory which postulates a genetic relationship between a mental disorder such as schizophrenia and mental deficiency.

Although Tredgold's conception of genetic transmission cannot be accepted *in toto,* there is general agreement that certain kinds of mental deficiency have a genetic origin. For classificatory purposes these can be divided into (1) those conditions, like amaurotic idiocy and phenylpyruvic oligophrenia, in which there is a fairly definite and consistent constellation of physical-anatomical-metabolic symptoms, and (2) those cases, like the Kallikaks, in which physical symptomatology is largely absent and intellectual and social incompetency are the outstanding characteristics. In the former, as will be seen later, the frequency of appearance of the condition in the immediate family and ancestry, together with the striking similarity of physical symptoms, can best be explained by the presence of a recessive or dominant gene; in the latter, the similarity of inadequacies between parent and offspring is thought to be best explained by a lack of potentiality for normal development which presumably has its origin in a not normally differentiated set of genes. In most of the cases where the condition is characterized by a fairly clear-cut constellation of physical symptoms, the intellectual deficiency is very severe, usually falling in the idiot and imbecile classifications, whereas in the case of the Kallikak or "garden-variety" type, the individual usually falls in the moron or borderline classifications.

It should be noted at this point that in cases with a well-defined constellation of physical symptoms there is no correlation between the occurrence of the condition and such factors as cultural setting, economic status, psychological factors involved in parent-child relationships, life experiences, and prenatal or postnatal injury. There is no available alternative explanation which covers the facts as well as one which assumes the presence of a recessive or dominant gene. Not only does it explain the facts but it states the conditions under which the unique constellation of symptoms will occur again. With the garden-variety type of mental deficiency, however, the picture is not as clear-cut. Starting with the fact that one or both parents of these cases has been judged intellectually and socially incompetent, it is apparent that such cases will usually be found in a cultural setting different from whatever is considered the norm, in the most physically impoverished surroundings, and experiencing a parent-child relationship which again is different from whatever is considered most conducive for the optimal development of a child. The descriptions of Goddard (*104, 105*), Town (*299*), and others bring this out clearly.

Skodak's Study of Foster Children

The relationship that exists in garden-variety deficiency between intellectual and social incompetency on the one hand, and a variety of psychological-economic-cultural factors on the other, raises the which-came-first question: What is the etiological factor or factors? Skodak's study (*273*) of the intellectual growth of children in foster homes might well serve as a basis for a discussion of this question. In her group of 154 children, 140 of whom were illegitimate, who had been placed in foster homes *before six months of age,* Skodak found 16 children whose true mother had been adjudged feeble-minded (*273*).

"Since the development of children whose parentage is known to be defective but who have nevertheless been placed in foster homes of average or above average status furnishes the greatest possible contrast between true-family background and environmental opportunity, the group of children whose background was known to be the poorest in the entire group was selected for special study. Sixteen children were available whose mothers ranged from 50 to 74 in I.Q. and had in addition been diagnosed as definitely feeble-minded on the basis of other criteria. The mean I.Q. of these mothers was 66.4, their mean education 7.6 grades. The mean education of the true fathers of the children was ninth grade and their mean occupational classification 6.3, or equivalent to very slightly skilled laborers. The social histories of the true families were strikingly poor, with many near relatives in state and local institutions, long records of family dependency, and other characteristics associated with familial inferiority."

Van Steenberg's descriptions (281, p. 361) of the true mothers and the conditions in which they lived, descriptions which are based on a follow-up field study, in addition to Skodak's own statements, suggest that most, if not all, of these feeble-minded women would be classified as the "garden-variety" defective in Tredgold's classification of primary amentia. Van Steenberg's descriptions are strikingly similar to Goddard's portrayal of the Kallikaks.

When the 16 children of defective mothers were examined at approximately 2½ years of age, they had an average I.Q. of 116; when they were retested at approximately 5 years of age their average I.Q. was 108. The decrease in I.Q. from first to second test is undoubtedly due in large part to the well-known unreliability of test scores obtained with young children; that is, knowledge of a 2-year-old child's I.Q. does not allow one to predict too accurately what his quotient will be when he is 5 years old. However, knowledge of a 5-year-old's score enables one to predict much more accurately what his standing is likely to be when he is 10. Although Skodak's group is admittedly small, should future study of these children continue to show the same results, a reorientation of thinking regarding the etiology of garden-variety mental deficiency will be in order.[1] Skodak's findings were foreshadowed in Goddard's Kallikak study done in 1914. He noted four cases who had been removed from the Kallikak culture when they were children and had been reared with "good" families (104, p. 61). In two cases both parents were defective and in two cases one parent was defective and the other normal. There was no indication that any of the four were feeble-minded, a statement which could not be made of any of the other siblings. Goddard also notes two other Kallikaks who were removed from their environment at an undetermined age; one of these he has

[1] In a personal communication Skodak kindly supplied the writer with the test scores of these children when they were 7 and 13 years of age. At 7 the average I.Q. was 96 and at 13 it was 104.

labeled feeble-minded and the other undetermined (*104*, p. 62). In both these cases the data presented are inadequate for anything but a hazardous conclusion. The criteria which Goddard used to diagnose mental deficiency are very vaguely stated and the field data only sketchily presented. If two clinicians personally observing the same individual can arrive at different conclusions or diagnoses, the amount of error involved in the interpretation of a field worker's observations, based sometimes on secondary and tertiary sources, must be considerable. Goddard's diagnostic labels have an unknown degree of reliability and validity which imposes a serious limitation on his conclusions. Before making any further generalizations on the basis of the work of Skodak and other investigators, Woodworth's (*326*) criticisms of Skodak's study should be discussed.

Three major criticisms of Skodak's interpretation of her findings on the above group of sixteen children have been advanced by Woodworth. The first is (*326*, p. 64) : "The sample is certainly selected—selected, that is, by the placement officials who must not place a child known to be feeble-minded and who would scarcely place a child of a feeble-minded mother until they were reasonably sure the child was normal. How many children of feeble-minded mothers were *not* placed we are not told, and consequently we have no basis for computing the expectancy of low, medium and high intelligence in children of defective parents." This is a valid criticism which should act as a caution against overgeneralization. In any future study of a similar group it would be necessary to know not only which children of defective mothers were *not* placed but, equally important, the procedures, psychological and medical, on the basis of which the decision not to place such children was made. If there were children who were not considered "normal" for placement, how was the decision or diagnosis arrived at? As was stated previously, psychological tests or developmental scales are not very reliable with infants, so if some children were not placed because of test scores the error of selection might well be lessened by an unknown degree. Another mitigating factor that must be taken into consideration in evaluating the possible size of the selective error is that if Skodak had a large, unselected group of feeble-minded mothers a small percentage would be expected to have children with central nervous system impairment which would prevent normal development. If intellectually normal mothers give birth to such children, there is no reason why defective mothers would not be expected to do so as well. The observation (73) that children of the Kallikak or garden-variety type of mental deficiency tend to show apparently normal development in the early years of life makes one question again how many of the children *not selected* for placement within the first half-year of life had some kind of physical or motor disability not necessarily related to the fact that the mothers were mentally defective. This statement is based on the assumption that the defective mothers were largely of the Kallikak type.

The above discussion should not be interpreted as a denial of Woodworth's criticism but rather as a statement of the complicating factors that enter into the evaluation of a study such as Skodak's.

Woodworth's second criticism is that feeble-minded mothers cannot be treated as homogeneous from the standpoint of etiology. "In particular, a mother whose defect is due to injury received at her own birth should be considered separately. In any such case, there is no reason at all for expecting poor heredity in the offspring." This is another source of error which must be taken into account in designing a study in this area. However, as has been pointed out in the previous discussion, there is reasonable ground for assuming that the majority of defective mothers in Skodak's study were garden-variety rather than brain-damaged or "secondary amentia" cases.

The third criticism by Woodworth is that "the own mothers of these 16 children, according to their education and I.Q.'s, belong rather in the borderline than in the definitely feeble-minded group." This criticism is based on the fact that the I.Q. of the mothers ranged from 50–74 and that their mean education was 7.6 grades. Regarding the surprisingly high level of school attainment of these defective mothers, Stoddard (281, p. 363) has effectively demonstrated (1) that the grade placement of a child is by no means a good indication that he is doing the work of that grade, (2) that in many schools children are promoted from grade to grade because of chronological age and not because of achievement, (3) that the average I.Q. of the children in a grade in one region may be very different than is found in the same grade in another region. To those who have had contact with school systems these facts will come as no surprise. To utilize the fact that some mothers had I.Q.'s as high as 74 as contraindicating a diagnosis of mental deficiency is to assume that the I.Q. is the sole and sufficient criterion of mental deficiency. The fallacy of this assumption has been pointed out in the preceding chapter and need not be discussed further. That the diagnosis of mental deficiency in Skodak's study was made on the basis of multiple criteria is apparent from the quotation on page 32.

On the basis of his critical evaluation of Skodak's study as well as the comprehensive investigation of foster children by Freeman, Holzinger, and Mitchell (90), Woodworth concluded: "Both these investigations prove that *some* children of mentally defective parents develop normal intelligence when reared in good homes. . . . Before placement policies are radically relaxed it would be well to let investigators progress some distance farther in exploring the genetic and environmental factors in feeblemindedness." With this conclusion one can but agree. Discussion in this area has been clouded by an either-or, black-and-white attitude regarding the importance of heredity and environment. Posing the problem in terms of an heredity-environment dichotomy, which is more apparent than real, overlooks our lack of scientific knowledge about the relationship between acquired behavior and the conditions of learning. The problem might better be stated as follows: Under what social-cultural conditions containing what psychologically relevant variables does a child of defective parents acquire his behavioral pattern? How do these conditions and variables differ from the case of the child of whatever is considered normal parents? Under what conditions does the child of defective parents acquire normal behavioral patterns? Under what conditions does the child of normal parents acquire behavioral patterns similar to those of the garden-variety defective? Posing the problem in this way emphasizes that the problem of the etiological factors in garden-variety deficiency is part and parcel of the broader problem of individual variations in behavior.

Regarding future research in this area, it would seem necessary for investigators to develop procedures which will allow one to relate statements of group differences or variation within a group to specifiable differences in conditions of learning. For example, in the Freeman, Holzinger, and Mitchell study the following was found (90, p. 165):

"The mean intelligence quotient of the 120 children who had at least one mentally defective parent was 92.9. The most significant fact to be noted, however, is that the children who remained with their own parents until they were at least 5 years of age had a mean intelligence quotient of 87.2, as compared with an average of 95.1 for those who were removed before that age. Of the entire 120 children, only 4 (3.3 per cent) had an intelligence rating below 70.

"The second group consists of 26 cases in which both parents were definitely reported as being mentally defective. The mean intelligence quotient for these children is 81.2, which is considerably lower than that found when only one parent was defective. The contrast between early and late removal is again shown by the means of 86.0 and 78.1 respectively. The average age of commitment for these children was 5 years, 10 months, while that for the entire (foster-home) group was only 3 years, 6 months. Moreover, the homes in which they were placed . . . were much poorer than those of the group as a whole. . . . It is thus evident that these children were placed in quite poor homes and at a relatively late age. Under more favorable conditions, they might be expected to make an even better showing."

When these findings are considered together with the fact that the average intelligence quotient of foster children was significantly lower than that of the foster parents' *own* children, the importance of parent-child relationships in the early years becomes apparent. However, the term parent-child relationships refers to an area of knowledge where observational procedures are relatively crude and indirect, theoretical approaches widely divergent, and experimental studies difficult to carry out. For example, what is to be considered a "good home" or a "good parent"? In the Freeman, Holzinger, and Mitchell study, homes were rated on the basis of material environment, occupation of foster father and mother, "social activity," and "evidence of culture." Knowledge of these factors does not enable one to state the conditions in which the own children of foster parents acquired their behavioral patterns. What were the infant-rearing practices of the true mothers and foster parents? What differences existed in these practices between a "good parent" and a defective one? To what extent are the intellectual variations among the foster children as well as among own children due to variations in parent-child relationships? If differences in intellectual level or functioning are to some degree related to infant-rearing or childhood-training practices, it would seem to be equally as important to determine how much of the intellectual variation *within* a group is due to variations in these practices as it is to determine the sources of variation *between* groups.[2]

[2] More often than not the researcher stops his analysis after obtaining differences between the groups he is studying. The explanation advanced for the group differences usually does not account for the deviant cases in each group, the exceptions which do not prove the

The term *secondary amentia* is applied by Tredgold to those cases in which adverse "environmental" factors operating before, during, or after birth are responsible for the condition of mental deficiency. By environmental Tredgold refers to those internally or externally produced conditions which result in irreparable central nervous system defect. Encephalitis, German measles, x-ray irradiation, iso-immunization (Rh factor), and birth trauma are some of the environmental nonhereditary causes of mental deficiency. It should be kept in mind that Tredgold uses the term environmental in a restricted sense which may at first be confusing to the psychologically oriented reader who uses the term to refer to any stimulus having physical and/or psychological relevance that impinges upon the individual. Tredgold restricts the term to those constellations of stimuli which result in an irreversible brain damage. When in the preceding section it was stated that environmental conditions may have a causal relationship to garden-variety deficiency (primary amentia), the term environmental was used in its broader sense.

Lewis' Subcultural-Pathological Dichotomy

In contrast to Tredgold's etiological classification, Lewis (*186*) has proposed dividing the mental deficiencies into two main types: the subcultural and the pathological. Under the pathological type Lewis groups all those cases "whose condition is invariably associated with and in most cases due to some definite organic lesion or abnormality." The pathological type includes all cases of secondary amentia in addition to those primary amentias where the physical constitution is markedly different from that of the normal. The pathological type, because of the intervention of alien factors, represents a variety of *abnormal* variation from the mass of normal persons. In contrast to this group

---

rule. Gill (*102*) has stated the problem clearly: "Let us suppose a research begins with the hypothesis that brain abnormality as detected by the electroencephalogram is correlated with a certain type of overaggressive behavior disorder in children. A group of such children is studied and the per cent of abnormal EEG's is higher than in the normal population; but some of the normals have abnormal EEG's and some of the behavior problems have normal EEG's. The next most productive type of research would be, we believe, an intensive study of these anomalous cases in the hope of more sharply defining the variables. Instead of that, the researcher will more likely turn to the study of the EEG in yet another motley group, motley of necessity because of the confused state of our nosology. The result is that empirical study is piled on empirical study without progressive delineation and clarification of variables."

Lewis describes the subcultural type as a form of *normal* variation: "The subcultural . . . includes those cases of mental defect in which no such alien factor is found. The deficiency is only an extreme of normal variation of mental endowments. There is no definite cleavage between this group and the mass of normal persons. The higher grades of subcultural deficiency merge gradually into the lower grades of dullness or of temperamental instability. There seems to be a close biological kinship between the subcultural defective and the main body of normal persons—a kinship which cannot be attributed to the pathological defective."

It is clear that the subcultural defective is the garden-variety, Kallikak type of Tredgold's primary amentia. Although Lewis leans to the belief that subcultural deficiency is inherited, he maintains that unfavorable environmental (used broadly) factors may in some cases account for the condition.

It should be noted that Lewis' dichotomy is descriptive rather than etiological. He accepts Tredgold's etiological classification but feels that it tends to obscure the social problem which the subcultural defective presents. Lewis feels that classifying the garden-variety (subcultural type) defective with other forms of primary amentia does not emphasize that the subcultural type, by far the largest of all the defective groups, is a pressing social problem which demands remedial measures different from those applicable to the pathological type. As Lewis himself has said, his dichotomy does not add to our knowledge of the etiology of mental deficiency or sharpen available diagnostic procedures, but is intended to present forcibly the importance of the problem of the subcultural defective.

It is not clear from Lewis' discussion why the garden-variety defective was given the label *subcultural*. He does state that the subcultural type is almost always found in conditions characterized by "pauperism, slumdom and their concomitants," and that under the increasing competitive nature of modern society "there is a definite tendency for these groups to be precipitated out of the general life of the community." It would seem that Lewis considers the culture of these defectives to be not as good as or on a lower level than that of the rest of society. Although one might question the scientific value of comparing cultures in terms of goodness or badness, the important point that Lewis seems to be making is that the culture of these defectives is *different* from that of other groups. It is not surprising that Lewis, interested as he was in the problem of social control, should have emphasized the almost perfect correlation between certain cultural conditions and the appearance of garden-variety or subcultural deficiency. Although almost two decades have passed since Lewis presented his views, there has been relatively little research on the problem of the relationship between cultural conditions and intellectual functioning. By cultural conditions is meant not only physical surroundings and economic status but, more broadly, the ways in which the behavior of people in the culture impinge upon and mold the behavioral patterns of succeeding generations. There is no reason for believing that the anthropological procedures which have proved so fruitful in understanding primitive cultures would be inapplicable or less fruitful in studying the culture of the garden-variety (subcultural) defective.

STRAUSS' ENDOGENOUS-EXOGENOUS TYPOLOGY

Through the work of Strauss and his colleagues of the Wayne County Training School, the endogenous-exogenous typology has been widely used by research workers. The endogenous label refers to the garden-variety, Kallikak type of primary amentia, and is also synonymous with Lewis' subcultural type. The exogenous or brain-injured type is defined by Strauss as follows (*285*, p. 4): "A brain-injured (exogenous) child is a child who before, during, or after birth has received an injury to or suffered an infection of the brain. As a result of such organic impairment, defects of the neuro-motor system may be present or absent; such a child may show disturbances in perception, thinking, and emotional behavior, either separately or in combination."

The exogenous label as used by Strauss is *not* applied to those primary and secondary amentias where there are gross or major neurological symptoms associated with obvious motor disfunctioning.[3] It is applied only to those cases, estimated by Strauss to be approximately 15 to 20 percent of all defectives, where there are minor neurological symptoms associated with no obvious motor disfunctioning. The condition is diagnosed by Strauss when there is a history of encephalitis, meningitis, premature birth, prenatal or postnatal trauma, or very difficult labor.

---

[3] The term exogenous is not used in this way by all workers. Doll (*71*) and Heath (*133, 134*) include *all* defectives with the exception of the garden-variety type in the exogenous category.

In addition, those cases who have a negative history of brain injury but who upon neurological and psychological examinations show the "syndrome of exogeneity" are also included in the category. If a child's social and test behavior and the results of the neurological examination point to the presence of a brain lesion, he is included in the exogenous category. It should be noted that if neurological symptoms are absent but the child's behavior in social and test situations possesses certain characteristics to be described below, he is labeled as exogenous. Exogenous cases almost always have parents and siblings of normal intelligence, although Strauss recognizes the "mixed" type in which a child with defective parents and siblings, presumably endogenous, shows exogenous symptoms. The intelligence quotients of this group range from approximately 50 to 90.

Strauss has described the characteristics of the brain-injured or exogenous child in the spheres of perception, thinking, and social behavior. The characteristics which Strauss has found to differentiate the exogenous from the endogenous child in each of these spheres will be described briefly.[4]

1. *Perceptual.* In a task requiring the individual to reproduce a design from a model, as in the marble board test described by Werner and Strauss (*317*), the reproductions of the exogenous child are marked by a discontinuous and incoherent pattern. The child does not seem to follow the model, his attention seems to skip from one part of it to another, and the finished product appears disorganized. Strauss (*285*, p. 35) has said that "one or two incoherent placements on the marble board cannot be regarded as significant, but two or more incoherent moves on more than two patterns give strong indication of a disturbed visuomotor perception, particularly if the subject shows the same kind of disturbance in the execution of his drawings." The endogenous child shows a more systematic procedure, follows the pattern of the model, and the correctness of the performance increases with growth or mental age. In other studies involving the perception of figure-ground relationships Werner and Strauss (*319*) have demonstrated that the exogenous child paid attention to aspects of the perceptual stimulus (i.e., a figure embedded in a structured background) which were

---

[4] Psychological studies of the endogenous and exogenous groups are more fully described in Chapter 5.

not used by a group of normal and endogenous children. Another characteristic noted by Werner (*315*) in the exogenous child is perseveration: the persistent continuation of an activity once begun.

2. *Thinking.* In a study of conceptual activity in the exogenous and endogenous groups Strauss and Werner (*286*), using a sorting test procedure, demonstrated that the exogenous child is especially prone to group objects in a way that is uncommon, far-fetched, and peculiar. In other words, objects were put in relation to each other on the basis of an unessential detail.

3. *Behavior.* By means of a behavior rating scale, Strauss and Kephart (*284*) had institution teachers and cottage parents rate a group of defective children with whom they were well acquainted. The raters were not aware that part of the group was endogenous and the other exogenous. The results indicated that the exogenous group was reliably differentiated from the others on such items as being "erratic, uncoordinated, uncontrolled, uninhibited, and socially unaccepted."

In the course of his study of exogenous children Strauss was struck, on the one hand, by the behavioral dissimilarity between them and the endogenous group and, on the other hand, by their similarity to adults who had suffered some form of brain injury. In particular Strauss was influenced by the work of Goldstein (*114*) with brain-injured soldiers. The comparison of the exogenous defectives with brain-injured adults raises several questions. In the case of the brain-injured adult described by Goldstein neurological symptoms seem to have been unmistakably present and in many cases motor disfunctioning was conspicuous. In other words, the neurological criteria for diagnosing brain injury seem to have been met. In the exogenous group, however, Strauss states that "defects of the neuro-motor system" may be present or *absent*. Since neurological procedures have usually been relied upon to give data on the basis of which brain injury has been diagnosed, one might ask how Strauss determines brain injury when there is no indication of neurological defect. To diagnose brain injury in the absence of neurological signs is to assume that "exogenous" behavior, in test and nontest situations, arises only when there is a brain lesion. In those exogenous cases where there are only minor neurological symptoms one might also ask (1) with what frequency these minor signs would appear in a group of clearly normal people, and (2) how reliable is the neurological examination in the sense that a group of neurologists examining the same patient will come to similar conclusions. Is the neurological examination of patients with minor neurological disturbance as reliable as it is with those with major disturbance? Because Strauss' work has given rise to a good deal of psychological and educational research, further discussion of these problems will be found in the next chapter which will be devoted to a more detailed presentation and evaluation of some of the procedures, neurological and psychological, by which brain injury is diagnosed.

Chapter 3

PROBLEMS IN THE DIAGNOSIS OF BRAIN INJURY

SINCE the turn of the present century tremendous strides have been made toward understanding the relation between behavior and brain functioning. Animal experimentation, surgical refinements, improvements and innovations in recording apparatus, and the intensive study of human subjects suffering from conditions similar to those experimentally produced in the laboratory animal have all helped to contribute to the progress that has been made. The study of the soldier and civilian who have suffered a brain injury has been especially helpful in showing how changes in behavior may be related to the demonstrable lesion. In light of the fact that previous to the brain injury these people functioned in an adequate fashion, the manifest behavioral changes can be logically related to the altered condition of the brain. The study of these cases with different degrees of injury located in various areas of the cerebrum as determined by x-ray and surgical procedures has sharpened the neurological criteria of what constitutes abnormal functioning of the brain. Since these criteria of pathology were present in brain-injured and not in clinically normal individuals, their presence must be considered indicative of brain injury even though direct observation of the injury may not be possible. The value of these neurological criteria is that not only do they indicate cerebral disfunction but their presence in many cases enables one to localize the area of brain injury.

It should be noted at this point, however, that a demonstrable brain lesion does not necessarily mean that the intellectual functioning of the individual has been impaired. Whether or not intellectual impairment follows a brain injury depends on the area of the brain affected. If the lesion is in the cerebral cortex (see Figs. 1 and 2), which in man is larger and more differentiated than in any other animal, intellectual impairment or "deficit" is a definite possibility although even here not an inevitable consequence. If the lesion is restricted to the subcortical areas (corpus striatum, thalamus, and hypothalamus), intellectual impairment is not likely. Below will be presented the major divisions of

43

the cerebrum with brief statements of how injury affects functioning. The reader who wishes a comprehensive treatment of the central nervous system is referred to the work of Fulton (*93*), Grinker (*124*) and Wechsler (*312*).

The major divisions of the cerebral hemispheres include the frontal, temporal, parietal, and occipital lobes. Deep within the hemispheres, in

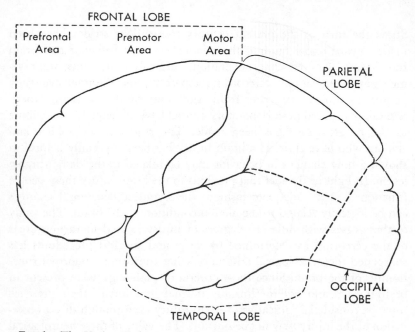

Fig. 1.   The Various Lobes on the Lateral Surface of the Left Cerebral Hemisphere.

the interbrain, lie the basal ganglia. It is of interest that the names of the lobes are arbitrarily derived from the overlying cranial bones and therefore lack any measure of specificity in regard to intrinsic neuroanatomical and physiological boundaries. The function of the brain is the product of equilibrated actions of the entire nervous mechanism and is manifested as a summation of the activities of the component parts. Current investigation constantly expands our knowledge of the neural mechanisms and has contributed much to the understanding of the pathways connecting portions of one lobe with another. Areas united in this manner have been shown to possess similar physiological capacities and others are known to influence and qualify responses, thereby making it mandatory to view the brain as a mechanism in which the diverse portions participate in the performance of specific actions. The destruction of one area, while resulting in a disturbance in function, may in time be compensated for by intact structures which

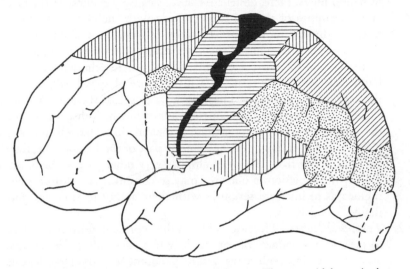

Fig. 2. The Motor Fields of the Cerebral Cortex. The pyramidal area is shown in black; the extrapyramidal areas are shaded; the eye fields are stippled. (From Roy R. Grinker's *Neurology*, 3rd edition. Courtesy of Charles C Thomas, Publisher, Springfield, Illinois.)

are capable of taking over the function of the area destroyed or otherwise altered. In this manner, a margin of safety is provided for preserving the physiological mechanism.

The functional capacities of the major divisions of the cerebral hemispheres are summarized in the following paragraphs.

1. *Frontal Lobes.* The most forward portions, or the prefrontal areas, are concerned with whatever is subsumed under normal intellectual and social behavior. Irritative or destructive lesions involving these areas, especially when bilateral, may result in restlessness (hyperactivity), memory deficits, inordinate difficulty in conceptual think-

ing, distractibility, inappropriate boasting, euphoria, hostility, and uncontrolled emotional expression. Lesions of these areas in children lead to much more grave disorders of behavior and arrest of mental development than do similar lesions in adults.

The more posterior portions of the frontal lobe are concerned with voluntary motor activity and give rise to the pyramidal system of neural fibers. Here, destructive lesions cause weakness of the face and extremities of the contralateral side with inability to perform fine, coördinated movements. Irritative lesions cause convulsive activity. Destructive lesions of the lower aspect of the posterior portion of the frontal lobe in the dominant hemisphere (the left in right-handed persons) may result in a disturbance of speech confined to the expressive sphere; not knowing how to speak, the patient is incapable of performing the coöperative movements indispensable for the production of speech. Although mental disturbances are most prone to occur in lesions of the anterior part of the frontal lobe, they may also result from lesions of almost every other part of the brain. An expanding lesion in one area may so compress and distort other regions as to interfere seriously with their ability to function normally.

2. *Temporal Lobes.* Hearing is bilaterally represented in this region, so permanent deafness of cortical origin occurs only in destructive lesions involving both areas, a rare phenomenon. Irritative lesions may cause auditory hallucinations. The olfactory divisions of the temporal lobes are located in the inferior and medial portions. Again, bilateral destructive lesions are necessary to interfere with the sense of smell. Irritative lesions may produce hallucinations of taste and smell frequently accompanied by peculiar dreamlike states. Visual hallucinations consisting of formed images have also been caused by irritative phenomena. A speech disturbance in the receptive sphere follows destruction of the sensory speech center in the superior temporal region of the dominant hemisphere. While able to speak, the patient does not understand the significance of words, his mother tongue sounding foreign to him. Visual disturbances can also occur in lesions of the temporal lobes. These consist of scotomata: defects in the field of vision confined to the side opposite the lesion.

3. *Parietal Lobes.* This region is primarily concerned with the inter-

pretation of sensation. Included in the modalities represented are the awareness of spatial relations, the appreciation of position and discriminatory sense, and the evaluation of size, shape, weight, and texture. While the more gross qualities of touch, pain, and temperature reside in the thalamus, the evaluation of differences in the intensity and the quality of such stimuli requires an intact parietal cortex. Destructive lesions result in deficiencies in the appreciation of the stimuli mentioned, and irritative lesions may produce subjective sensory seizures over the contralateral half of the body. A sensory type of speech disturbance may be caused by a lesion in the dominant parietal lobe where the center for the comprehension of the printed word is located.

4. *Occipital Lobes.* In this region is located the cortical representation of vision, the end point of the retinal projections to the cerebral cortex. Irritative lesions produce unformed visual images; destructive processes cause defects in the contralateral half of the visual field. Bilateral destruction of the occipital lobes causes cortical blindness.

5. *Basal Ganglia.* This includes the thalamus, the hypothalamus, and the corpus striatum. These component portions of the interbrain are situated deep within the central and basal portions of the hemispheres. The thalamus acts as a relay station in the transmission of impulses from the hypothalamus to the higher cortical centers. Portions of the thalamus are sensory in nature and are concerned with the gross appreciation of pain, temperature, and touch. Vital autonomic centers within the hypothalamus regulate heat production, sleep, water balance, carbohydrate metabolism, sweat secretion, pupillary action, bladder and intestinal activity. The hypothalamus also contains the coördinating center for emotional expression. Through its connections with the posterior lobe of the pituitary gland the activity of both structures is integrated. The manifestations of disease are reflected in disorders of metabolism and water balance, pathological sleep, abnormal sexual development, and disturbances of growth.

Lesions of the thalamus cause sensory disturbances in the modalities mentioned. Spontaneous pains of thalamic origin may be referred to areas of skin rendered anesthetic by a thalamic disorder. There may also be an overreaction to sensory stimuli and a loss of certain psychic reflexes characterized by a loss of emotional expression at times seen in lesions of the hypothalamus.

The corpus striatum exercises a tonus inhibitory effect on the skeletal musculature. Lesions involving this region give rise to muscular rigidity, known as extrapyramidal rigidity in contrast to the spasticity found in lesions of the premotor cortex of the frontal lobe. Striatal lesions may also be manifested by paucity of movements, rigidity of facial expression, absence of associated arm movements in walking, and a rhythmic tremor of the head and hands. Choreic and athetoid disturbances are also ascribed to lesions of the striatum. Little is known of the pathways through which the basal ganglia influence peripheral mechanisms. Unfortunately, a great deal of the function ascribed to these structures is hypothetical and it is only during the past decade that neuroanatomists and neurophysiologists have begun to explore these physiological mechanisms with some degree of accuracy. The subject, therefore, remains highly controversial.

This brief review would be incomplete without a short note concerning the functions of the cerebellum. This structure controls dynamic and static coördination of voluntary movements. Disturbances in function result in ataxia as seen in the staggering, swaggering gait and grossly incoördinate movements of the extremities and trunk. Because of the marked decrease in tonus, the limbs may be placed in bizarre positions. Since lesions of the cerebellum may injure the vestibular pathways, dizziness may be a prominent symptom of cerebellar disease. Abnormal eye movement (nystagmus) may also accompany such lesions.

It will be seen that not all areas of the cerebral cortex are equally essential for whatever is meant by normal intellectual functioning. For example, injury to the occipital lobes may cause severe visual disability without any impairment of learning capacity being present. That such a disability may, however, have disturbing behavioral repercussions is well described by Cobb (50, p. 553):

"Lesions of the brain may affect personality in a direct and primary way, or secondarily by complex psychological reactions such as fear and discouragement. A person may have a hemianopsia from a lesion of the occipital areas and never notice the visual defect. After a neurological examination has brought this blind area to his attention, he may become preoccupied with his defect and become anxious, afraid to cross the street and restricted in social relations. In this case the lesion itself did not cause a psychological effect, because it was a lesion of the lowest cortical level of integration. Fear, aroused by discovering the trouble, did cause psychological reactions of the highest levels. A more obvious example is the varied responses of old people to hemiplegic 'strokes' from thrombotic lesions of the motor cortex. This common neurological disorder is borne by some with courage and equanimity. Others are thrown into a deep depression. The variability of reaction is rarely a question of the type or location of the lesion, but an expression of the whole life experience of the person who gets the stroke."

Gross damage to the motor areas or motor pathways, as in some cases of cerebral hemorrhage or bullet wounds, may result in extensive paralysis of the body without any deterioration in intellectual adequacy. Disturbances in the olfactory area or extrapyramidal system are also unlikely to result in intellectual impairment. However, should the lesion be of a radiating or diffuse nature, as in cases of tumor, infection, or inflammation, intellectual impairment may become apparent as other cortical areas become involved. Injury to the parietotemporal areas or the frontal lobes is likely to be accompanied by marked changes in intellectual functioning, although cases to the contrary have been reported in the literature. The following quotation from Hebb concerns a patient who had one-half of her cerebral cortex removed (135):

"The examination (with the old Stanford-Binet) was begun with Year XVI, test 3, 'differences between abstract words.' The test was solved 'very readily' and the examiner shifted to Year XVIII. A score of 46 with one vocabulary list was made. 'She was able to report one out of the series of eight digits forward, and one of the seven reversed. Her summaries for both of the (memory) passages in test 4 were judged satisfactory. Her solution of test 6 was correct in (b).'

"This was the third time the test had been given the patient (others before complete hemi-decortication), but more than a year had elapsed since the second examination, and it seems impossible to explain such a performance by practice effect, in the presence of any serious, generalized loss. The repetition of digits, forward and backward, should alone be enough to show that for some things the patient's abilities were above the average for the general population. It is clear, of course, that these data do not mean that other abilities were unaffected. . . . The significant fact here is the objective evidence supporting the clinical opinion that the patient's abilities were in some respects well retained; and the fact that even if other test abilities were impaired the patient still had average or above-average ability in the kind of task which is the core of the Binet test. Such things as comprehension of words, differentiation of abstract terms, memory for complex verbal material and solution of reasoning problems, are the kind of task which is most successful in differentiating various levels of intellectual development in normal subjects."

Hebb describes other cases where there was bilateral removal of large masses of the cortex without the generalized intellectual impairment that one would expect, although some impairment was observed in psychological tests. Such findings emphasize, as Cobb has pointed out, that no two brains are the same and that similar degrees of injury to comparable areas may have different consequences in different individuals. In one individual a lesion may result in little or no intellectual impairment while in another marked disability may become apparent. The results of frontal lobotomies and lobectomies in psychotic patients demonstrate that similar surgical procedures in comparable areas do not produce uniform changes in behavior.[1] In general, the evidence from studies of frontal lobe injuries in man indicates that some kind of intellectual impairment is likely but the nature and degree of impairment in the individual case are unpredictable.

One of the most practical results of these studies is that the diagnostic validity of clinical or indirect procedures, as in the neurological examination where direct observation of the brain is not possible, has been considerably increased. Since the phenomena described are found in the presence of organic brain disease, the fact that they obtain in a given case makes the tentative assumption of brain injury justifiable in patients in whom direct observation of the brain is not possible. Similarly, the evaluation of behavioral symptoms has also been sharpened. However, since the statement about the validity of a criterion should also contain something about its limitations, it should be remembered that the presence of isolated neurological signs does not necessarily mean that any inadequate functioning need be expected or, perhaps more important, that any observed peculiar behavior is *ipso facto* the result of the presumed brain abnormality. This is especially true where the peculiar behavior can be shown in individuals with no neurological criteria of brain injury. For example, in frontal lobe injuries one of the

---

[1] In frontal lobotomy the connections between the frontal cortical areas and subcortical centers are severed; in frontal lobectomy the frontal areas are removed.

most frequently noted characteristics is the inability of the patient to perform adequately on tests involving concept formation. The diagnostic value of such behavior must be tempered by the fact that similar behavior has been noted in schizophrenics and has been observed even in some neurotic individuals, in both instances neurological criteria of brain injury being completely absent. Similarly, in most cases of frontal lobe or other cortical injury electroencephalographic (brain-wave) recordings have been of an abnormal nature. The fact that in a given case of suspected brain injury the brain-wave recording is the only abnormal sign must be cautiously evaluated because 13 percent of a clinically normal population has been found to have abnormal records (101). If the abnormal electrical activity is focused in a particular cortical area, all other areas being normal, the possibility of brain injury receives added confirmation because such foci are less frequently found in clinically normal people. Even with this added confirmation the possibility still exists that the individual's presenting symptoms and abnormal brain-wave record are not necessarily related. Available evidence seems to warrant the conclusion that no single neurological or psychological procedure or "sign" is sufficiently pathognomonic of intellectual impairment due to brain injury as to be used as the sole criterion. Diagnoses based on multiple signs probably have a higher degree of validity, although even here data are lacking about the number of times the diagnosis is wrong. The tendency is to remember and report the times when the "signs" worked, and to forget when they did not.

To be diagnostically discriminating for brain injury, a neurological or behavioral symptom or constellation of symptoms must be found only in individuals with a demonstrable injury and not in any other condition. In order to establish the diagnostic values of these symptoms, large-scale neurological and psychological studies of unselected samples of the population are necessary. Such studies are lacking for many neurological and psychological criteria. Since the clinician tends to see selected cases, he cannot be sure how many of the symptoms he considers diagnostic or "suggestive" of brain injury he would also find in the general population. This would seem to be especially true where the more outstanding symptoms (confusion, aphasia, intellectual deterioration, marked incoördination, etc.) are absent and only "minor" signs (altered reflexes, abnormal brain waves, "peculiar" behavior, intellectual inefficiency, etc.) are present.

Knowledge about pathological brain function in the human has come largely from the study of individuals whose development had been normal until alien factors produced brain alteration. *These cases should not, of course, be confused with the mentally defective case whose development has been retarded since birth.* Many cases of mental deficiency, especially those in the idiot and imbecile classifications, show marked physical and intellectual impairment which at autopsy have been shown to be related to diffuse brain damage. The presence of major neurological symptoms and marked intellectual incompetence, in addition to a history of retarded development since birth, is sufficient ground for assuming that irreversible brain damage has occurred. These cases, which will be described in later chapters, do not present any particular diagnostic problem, although the etiology of the condition may be unknown. In these cases one can validly classify the individual as mentally defective and describe the nature and extent of the pathological brain condition.

Strauss' Brain-Injured Child

In the preceding chapter Strauss' endogenous-exogenous typology was discussed. It will be remembered that the endogenous type is identical with the garden-variety defective and Lewis' subcultural type. The exogenous type refers only to those cases where *minimal* brain injury is said to exist. According to Strauss, the following four criteria constitute the basis for a diagnosis of minor brain injury (*285*, p. 112):

"1. A history shows evidence of injury to the brain by trauma or inflammatory processes before, during, or shortly after birth.
 2. Slight neurological signs are present which indicate a brain lesion.
 3. When the psychological disturbance is of such severity that a measurable retardation of intellectual growth can be observed, the immediate family history indicates that the child comes from a normal family stock and that he is, in general, the only one of the siblings so afflicted.
 4. When no mental retardation exists, the presence of psychological disturbances can be discovered by the use of . . . qualitative tests for perceptual and conceptual disturbances."

In regard to the first criterion one might ask what the main sources of the case-history material are. On the justifiable assumption that parents were the chief source of material, the question arises as to how much reliance can be put on case-history data supplied by them? For example, the fact that a mother reports that labor was extremely difficult does not allow one to assume that the child was in any way affected. What appears as a routine delivery to the attending obstetrician may be to a mother the most hellish of experiences. Read (247) has well described how the anticipatory fear reactions of the expectant mother plus the impersonal atmosphere of the delivery room can engender severe and incapacitating "psychological" pain which may prolong labor without necessarily injuring the child. What a mother considers to have been a difficult experience for her need not have been physiologically stressful or frustrating to the newborn. In the absence of confirmatory evidence a mother's report about the experience of labor and its effect on her child cannot be considered reliable.

In recent years research workers (171, 267) have pointed out how before, during, and immediately after birth the child is subject to the danger of asphyxiation. In some cases the prolonged loss of oxygen seems to have produced brain damage which resulted in mental deficiency, in other cases brain damage produced physical handicap without intellectual impairment, and in other cases there was no untoward influence at all. Consequently, when one is considering an individual whose neurological examination is negative but whose case history notes the fact that he was a "blue baby," one is not justified in using such a datum as a basis for a diagnosis of brain injury.[2] Even if the individual's behavior seems to be characteristic of the brain-injured child, conclusive evidence for a brain lesion is far from present. In order for behavioral characteristics to be diagnostically discriminating it would have to be shown that the behavioral characteristics of exogenous children are not found in endogenous ones. The result of the psychological studies by Strauss and his colleagues invariably show some overlap between the two types.

The following case reported by Strauss may serve as an illustration for some of these points:

"Case I. J. de T. y. T., son of a wealthy Spanish family. Father a prominent attorney, mother educated according to the standards of the upper social class. Parents 31 and 17 years old respectively at the time of marriage.

[2] Ford (85, p. 17) pointed out: "The 'blue' asphyxia is of little significance, and it has been estimated that this occurs to some extent in 90 per cent of all new-born babies."

An only child. Pregnancy and delivery were both normal but the child was blue (a sign of asphyxia) at birth and the usual procedures were applied. He walked and talked somewhat later than usual and had no serious childhood diseases. He was an extremely disobedient and obstinate child with destructive tendencies, very easily excited. He seemed to be fearless. Not accepted by other children because of his constant teasing and tormenting. Cared for by a personal nurse. When 6 years old, he was entered in a private school but could not be admitted to a class with other children. Two teachers were employed for him alone since one teacher refused to stand it without relief for the entire day.

"At 8 years and 6 months of age he was admitted to our clinic. He had a second grade school achievement; psychometric testing was impossible because of extreme restlessness and distractibility. He was always 'on the move,' exploring everything in the house, particularly technical equipment, electric switches, door bells, elevators, etc. Asked questions incessantly, like a machine gun. Very affectionate with all the persons in the house. When taken to bed, he did not sleep until midnight but asked another question every five minutes. On the days following his admission he was still very restless and disinhibited but meticulous and pedantic in the arrangement of his belongings and everything handled by him at the table or in the classroom. Play in the garden consisted in trying to destroy flowers or bushes but without ill-humor or anger. Always smiling and good-humored. At dinner time he ate enormous quantities of food and drank a glass of water or milk with one gulp. In church he was very distractible, wishing to give money to all the collection boxes. After two weeks in the clinic he was more adjusted but still very distractible. He was discharged after one and one half years with an intelligence quotient within the normal range and admitted to a private school. Then attended class with children of his age and in an examination proved to be ninth in placement among forty children." [3]

The absence of any neurological data in this report would indicate that it was noncontributory so far as brain injury was concerned. The fact that the child was a blue baby may or may not indicate brain injury. In light of the absence of neurological signs very little weight can be given to the birth history. It is not clear what is meant by walking and talking "somewhat later than usual" because that is not an uncommon finding in the histories of a group of clinically normal children. Insofar as neurological signs and developmental data are concerned, there is

[3] A. A. Strauss and L. E. Lehtinen. *Psychopathology and education of the brain-injured child*. Grune & Stratton, 1947, p. 2. All quotations from this book are used by permission of the publisher.

little evidence to suggest the presence of a brain injury. There is reason to believe that study of an unselected sample of the population would reveal individuals whose intellectual and social adjustment was adequate but in whose histories events "suggestive" of brain injury would also be found. In the case reported by Strauss the behavior of the boy was considered typical of the brain-injured child. However, Strauss does not present the detailed data necessary for the testing of alternative hypotheses. As was pointed out before, Strauss has not demonstrated (1) that the behavioral characteristics of brain-injured children appear in no other group, (2) to what extent each exogenous child possesses the significant characteristics, and (3) to what extent nonexogenous children possess these characteristics. For example, in his comparison of brain-injured and behavior-problem children on certain behavioral characteristics Strauss (285, p. 93) found an overlap between the groups on 50 percent of the variables. It would seem that where neurological and developmental signs are largely negative in regard to brain injury, basing the diagnosis on behavioral characteristics is not likely to be very reliable.

Parental reports about their children's early illnesses also cannot be considered as highly reliable. Strauss (285, p. 2) presents a case where the only unusual statement about the child's early years was that he "nearly died from whooping cough at 3 months of age." This statement was presumably included to indicate that the high fever associated with such a condition might have caused some brain destruction. However, one might ask whether the quoted statement reflects parental interpretation or a physician's written report. What is a serious condition to a parent, causing countless sleepless nights, may not be so considered by the physician. If all the mothers of children who had whooping cough at a very early age were interviewed, statements similar to the one Strauss reports would probably be obtained in cases where no question of brain injury exists. It seems unjustified to ascribe a presumptive brain injury to an inflammatory condition such as whooping-cough encephalitis in the absence of any other confirmatory evidence.

In regard to the second criterion, the appearance of slight neurological signs, it should be noted that the presence of these signs is indicative of pyramidal and extrapyramidal disfunctioning. These signs are not indicative of brain injury to cortical areas concerned with intellectual activity. When these signs are found and mental deficiency is present, it does not necessarily follow that the lesions responsible for the pyramidal and extrapyramidal signs are related to the cause of the mental deficiency. In order for these slight neurological signs to be diagnostically discriminating it would have to be shown that they occur only when there is also further injury to those brain areas responsible for intellectual activity. If these signs were found in defective as well as nondefective cases, in garden-variety deficiency as well as in other types, in socially adequate as well as in inadequate cases, then the presence of these signs would not be diagnostically helpful. Such a large-scale neurological study is lacking. However, Strauss (283) did compare a group of exogenous and endogenous defectives as to the incidence of neurological signs. Of 21 exogenous cases 16 (76 percent) showed pyramidal and extrapyramidal neurological signs, and of 82 endogenous cases 32 (39 percent) showed similar signs. Since both groups showed signs of brain damage by indirect neurological procedures whose validity and reliability are unknown, Strauss' conclusion that some garden-variety defectives fall into a "mixed-type" category must be questioned. It would seem that one is equally justified in concluding from the same findings that the neurological criteria employed by Strauss are not diagnostically discriminating.

The following quotation from Strauss reveals his reasons for not relying on electroencephalography in ascertaining brain injury (285, p. 112):

"The electro-encephalogram is usually indicative of brain lesion in these children; its use as a diagnostic instrument is limited, however, since it quite often reveals similar pathological findings in children with behavior disorders who, on the basis of history and examination, do not belong in the group of brain-injured children. The same technic may even show deviations in otherwise perfectly normal children. The electro-encephalogram is, therefore, an aid in diagnosis when other symptoms make the picture, 'brain injury,' probable, but it does not assist in the selection if other indications are missing."

This quotation has been presented because the arguments advanced by Strauss against the diagnostic value of brain-wave recordings seem to summarize those that have been advanced here against his own criteria for brain injury. The last sentence of the quotation is especially interesting in light of Strauss' own statement (285, p. 112) that the first three of his four criteria (see p. 52) are not uncommonly negative in his exogenous group. This means that the diagnosis of brain injury is sometimes made only on the basis of the patient's performance on tests of perceptual and conceptual disturbance (criterion 4).[4] However, since these tests have been validated against neurological and case-history findings, if the latter are not very discriminating for brain injury the psychological tests cannot be expected to be more so. In other words, if the validity of the criteria to which a test is compared is not high, if the criteria do not indicate what they purport to indicate, the validity of the test will be low. In summary, Strauss' procedures for the diagnosis of the exogenous child can be criticized because (1) no conclusive evidence has been presented which would prove that the behavior and intellectual activity of these children are in all cases attributable to a brain injury; (2) the presence of pyramidal and extrapyramidal signs of brain injury does not necessarily mean that any concomitant intellectual retardation and/or behavioral peculiarity is related to the injury; (3) the criteria of brain injury employed by Strauss have not been shown to be characteristic of the exogenous alone or even of all exogenous cases; (4) diagnosing brain injury on the basis of psychological test results assumes a degree of validity for these tests which does not seem warranted; (5) the fact that exogenous cases seem to behave like some brain-injured adults cannot be considered proof that brain injury underlies "exogenous" functioning. From the above considerations one seems justified in concluding that the behavioral peculiarities which Strauss observed in his exogenous cases have not been conclusively shown to be a result of minimal brain injury. That alternative explanations are possible can be seen in the following statement by Strauss (285, p. 77):

"It should not be overlooked, however, that there is an unavoidable personal equation resulting from the scientific training and the theoretical preference of the clinician. If he prefers the psychoanalytical theory or the theory of behaviorism, if he stresses environmental factors or factors of heredity, or if he adheres to neurophysiological theories or to psychological ones, his evaluation of motivational factors will be colored by these preferences. For the sake of clarity we wish to state that we shall follow in this discussion a

---

[4] Cases in which the first three criteria are absent (especially the third) would presumably be those with no measurable intellectual retardation. It should be noted, however, that even in the group with defective quotients Strauss (283) includes some cases who show no positive neurological signs. These cases have presumably been diagnosed on the basis of test performance or case-history material. The possible sources of error in such a procedure have been discussed above.

neurological viewpoint, being aware that other interpretations are just as possible but that we consider this factor the outstanding one in understanding our methods of treatment and reeducation of the brain-injured child."

Whether Strauss' neurological bias gives a more valid picture than a psychological one cannot be determined by available data. Chidester and Menninger (47) presented the case of a presumably defective boy with signs of minimal brain injury whose exogenous-like behavior was psychoanalytically interpreted and treated.[5] Their purely psychological approach produced a marked change in the boy's intellectual and social levels of functioning.

Strauss' typology has given rise to psychological studies, especially those by Werner, which are ingenious and stimulating. The criticisms which have been advanced here are directed not at these studies but rather at the interpretation of results. It would be a decided contribution to the field if it could be demonstrated by other than indirect evidence that in each exogenous child there is a brain injury which is in some way or other related to his behavior. It would also have to be shown that "exogenous" behavior is not found in the absence of such a presumptive brain injury.

Before concluding this chapter it should be emphasized again that among many mental defectives, especially on the lower rungs of the intelligence scale, the presence of major neurological signs, marked physical handicap, and intellectual incompetence—all present since birth —makes the diagnosis of diffuse brain injury a valid one. In many of these cases direct procedures have demonstrated the nature of the pathological brain condition. The exogenous child, by the very absence of major neurological symptoms or marked intellectual retardation, presents a much more difficult diagnostic-etiologic problem.

[5] This case is more fully discussed in Chapter 10.

Chapter 4

PROBLEMS IN TEST INTERPRETATION

In the preceding chapters the point has been stressed that mentally defective individuals differ widely among themselves on many variables. One of the reasons why this variability has been obscured is the manner in which psychological tests have been employed. In the present chapter some of the problems which arise in the interpretation of test results will be discussed. It will be seen that to many of these problems there are no satisfactory answers and that the necessary experimental research is yet to be done. It will also be seen that some of these problems are not peculiar to work with the mentally deficient but arise whenever the clinical psychologist endeavors to understand an individual in the test situation.

For many years after the introduction of the 1916 Binet and other standardized tests, the aim of the psychological examination was to emerge with a number—the ubiquitous I.Q. If two individuals obtained the same quotient or mental age, they were considered to have the same degree of intelligence, although their everyday functioning and behavioral patterns conveyed differences between them which overshadowed any similarity in test rating. The assumption of similar functioning for individuals with similar test scores has resulted in many surprises as well as in practical difficulties.

Gerald was 38 years old when he was seen in the outpatient clinic. He was a tall, toothless, Andy-Gumpish, pleasant fellow whose parents were now considering commitment to an institution for defectives. His retardation had been noticed from infancy and he had been brought up in a sheltered, overprotected home environment. He had gone to grade school for only a few years and was withdrawn because of a complete lack of progress. Gerald was given the 1937 Stanford-Binet (L) on which he obtained a mental age of 6 years and 4 months with an I.Q. of 42. On reading tests his achievement was on the second-grade level. During the subsequent interview with his parents they stated that although Gerald never learned any reading while in school, they had given him enough individual attention so that he enjoyed reading the newspaper. This statement the psychologist took to mean that Gerald liked to look at the newspaper, an activity which some ever-hopeful parents of defective children interpret as a sign of latent intellectual activity. However, the parents insisted that their son could read the newspaper and answer questions about what he read. At a later date Gerald was given a newspaper to read and although his comprehension was not as good as his parents had said, he did comprehend at a level which was well above the second grade. His reading fluency was also well above that level.

The psychologist's surprise at this boy's reading performance stemmed from the assumption that an individual of this mental and chronological age, like others of similar age and level, could not read at all well, let alone comprehend what he read. In effect what the psychologist was doing was placing this individual in a class or category of cases where reading proficiency was not to be expected. It should be realized that recharacterizing this case as "unusual" does not, of course, explain how he learned to perform as he did. The intriguing question is what were the differences between the stimulus conditions which produced a somewhat adequate learning reaction and those which did not? This case has been presented at this point only to emphasize that a test score may not be revealing of an individual's learned pattern or behavior. A test score does not tell one what a person does; this can be determined only by detailed observations before and during testing from which clues might be obtained about the relation between present performance and previous conditions of learning.

When a child in an institution for defectives is at the point where he is ready for vocational training, it is the practice to apprentice him to one of the employees: painter, carpenter, baker, seamstress, housekeeper, etc. The attempt is made to place a child in a job to which his intellectual capacities seem adequate. However, more often than not the intelligence test ratings of the children in any one vocational situation vary considerably. It is by no means an uncommon occurrence to find that the child with lower test rating performs much more adequately than the one with a higher rating. Since each vocational supervisor likes to have the "smartest" children in his production unit, he will sometimes rebel against taking one with a relatively low test score only to admit later that the child was one of the best he ever had. It is when job placements within the institution are made on the basis of test scores that the value of psychological tests is justifiably held suspect by other employees.

Another factor which has vitiated the value of many psychological studies in this field has been the failure to take account of the different etiological factors. Getting the average I.Q., academic achievement, or behavioral adjustment of a group of defectives, without taking account of the different etiological factors, makes the unwarranted assumption that differences in etiology are not related to the variables being studied. The absurdity of such an approach can perhaps be illustrated by turning momentarily to the field of the mental illnesses or the psychoses. If one were to determine by psychological procedures the average I.Q. or the degree of maladjustment in a psychotic population, one would immediately be asked about the composition of the group. How many were schizophrenics or how many of what kinds of schizophrenia were included? How many were manic-depressives, paretics, seniles, or involutional melancholics? The reason for these questions is the knowledge that not all psychotic conditions have the same generalized effect on functioning, the same tendency to result in intellectual deterioration, to occur with equal frequency among men and women, or to have the same physiological concomitants. The "average" psychotic like the average citizen is distinguished by his infrequent occurrence. It will be seen from the above that results of psychological studies which have treated defectives without regard to differences in etiology must be critically evaluated. In this connection attention may now be turned to the Binet scales (1916 and 1937), the most frequently used tests of intelligence in the psychological examination of defectives. In an attempt to sharpen the diagnostic value of the Binet, investigators (*173, 199, 246, 294, 306*) have compared the performance of defectives and normals of comparable mental age. For example, in the most recent study along these lines Thompson and Magaret (*294*) compared 441 defectives with 1326 normals on Form L of the 1937 Binet. The groups were arranged so that defectives of any given mental age could be compared to a normal group of similar level. In Table 3 are found the Binet items on which defectives did significantly better than the normals, and vice versa. Of the 73 Binet items which Thompson and Magaret were able to subject to statistical analysis, 43 failed to differentiate between the two groups. In

TABLE 3.   Items on Stanford-Binet Scale, Form L, Which Differentiate Defectives from Normals with a P of .01 or Less (294)[1]

Items on Which Defectives Surpass Normals

Location	Name	Ages
III, 1	Stringing beads	3
III, 5	Drawing a circle	3
V, 2	Folding a triangle	4–5
V, 4	Drawing a square	4–6
VI, 1	Vocabulary	5–6
VI, 2	Bead chain	4–7
VII, 1	Picture absurdities I	5–7
VIII, 2[a]	Wet Fall	6–7
VIII, 5	Comprehension IV	6–9
X, 2	Picture absurdities II	7–10
XI, 1	Memory for designs	8–10
XIII, 4	Problems of fact	8–10

Items on Which Normals Surpass Defectives

Location	Name	Ages
II ½, A	Identification by name	3
III, 6	3 digits forward	3–4
III ½, 5	Identification by use	3–4
IV, A	Sentence memory I	4–5
IV ½, 2	4 digits forward	4–6
VI, 5	Picture comparison	5–8
VII, 3	Drawing a diamond	6–9
VII, 5	Opposite analogies I	6–10
VII, 6	5 digits forward	6–10
VIII, 2[a]	Wet Fall	8–10
VIII, 4	Similarities and differences	7–10
VIII, 6	Sentence memory III	6–10
IX, 4	Rhymes	8–10
IX, 6	4 digits reversed	7–10
X, 4	Reasons I	8–10
X, 6	6 digits forward	8–10
XII, 2	Verbal absurdities II	9–10
XII, 6	Minkus completion	9–10
XIV, 5	Directions I	9–10

[a] This one item is easier for mental defectives of mental ages six and seven than for six- and seven-year-old normals. It is easier for normal eight-, nine-, and ten-year-olds than for mental defectives of eight-, nine-, and ten-year mental ages. It is the only item examined which shows significant differences in opposite directions at different mental age levels.

[1] Used by permission of the American Psychological Association, Inc.

light of the previous discussion it will be seen that the composition of Thompson and Magaret's defective group is unknown. One wants to know how many of the different diagnostic etiologic groups would be found among their defectives and whether the differences listed in Table 3 would still obtain if the normals were compared to each of the etiological groups. The importance of diagnostic-etiologic factors can be seen when one considers the interpretations which have been made of the results obtained in the Binet studies cited above. Three main interpretations have been made.

THE INFLUENCE OF "PAST EXPERIENCE"

Binet items which are easier for defectives than for normals depend more heavily upon past experience for a successful solution. The assumption underlying this statement is that since the defectives are chronologically older than the normals with whom they have been equated for mental age, differences between them are a function of "experience." Conversely, Binet items which are more difficult for defectives depend less upon past experience. Thompson and Magaret have effectively demonstrated the untenability of this interpretation. They had two experienced Binet examiners independently rate all Binet items for their dependence on past experience. They found on the basis of their ratings that "those items which are easy for defectives are slightly less dependent upon experience than those which are more difficult for them." The interpretation according to past experience has been and still is in vogue among clinicians. Aside from the ambiguity of the phrase "past experience," clinicians seem to have been unaware that the past experiences, psychological and otherwise, of the garden-variety defective are probably not the same as those of the child whose deficiency may be the result of prenatal or postnatal pathological processes, or of the defective child in whom epilepsy may be a primary or secondary factor. To assume similarity in experience for these groups is as unrevealing as if one were to maintain that the past experiences of schizophrenics, manic-depressives, and senile psychotics were similar. It should also be noted that the interpretation of a given defective's performance in terms of a characterization applied to a large group is usually based not on observations of *that* defective but on a process of pigeonholing.

THE CONCEPT OF RIGIDITY

Kounin (*168*) has proposed an explanation of the differences between defectives and normals of similar mental age in terms of the concept of rigidity. Rigidity, which Kounin assumes to increase with chronological age, refers to the degree of functional relationship between "neighboring regions" of a person's psychological structure. According to Kounin, the defective and the normal child of similar mental age have the same number of neighboring psychological regions, but in the former the rigidity of the boundaries between regions is much greater. This difference in rigidity would account for the defective's difficulty in relating things together as in sorting tests.

In his experiments Kounin used a younger and an older feeble-minded group in addition to young normals, all three groups being of similar mental age and thus presumably having the same number of neighboring mental regions or the same degree of differentiation. In one of the experiments each subject was asked to draw cats "until he became satiated and wanted to draw no more. After having become satiated with the drawing of cats, he was asked if he wanted to draw bugs. After having become satiated with drawing bugs, he was asked if he desired to draw turtles. Finally, after having become satiated with drawing turtles, he was asked whether or not he felt like drawing rabbits." In order to test his assumption that the older the individual "the less will the satiation of one need co-satiate neighboring needs," Kounin computed the percentage of co-satiation:

$$\frac{\text{Satiation time on cats} - \text{satiation time on bugs (or turtles, rabbits)}}{\text{Satiation time on cats}} \times 100$$

Co-satiation was highest with young normal children and lowest with old feeble-minded subjects. Since co-satiation was assumed to be a reflection of the degree of communication between neighboring mental or psychological regions, it was concluded that the young normals were least rigid and the old feeble-minded most rigid. Kounin's studies were an outgrowth of earlier studies by Lewin (*184*), who, using normal and feeble-minded subjects, asked each child to draw moon faces until a point of satiation had been reached, after which they were told to draw whatever they wished. The normal children continued to draw freely for a greater length of time than the feeble-minded, although the latter had drawn moon faces for a longer period of time than the former. Lewin concluded that the feeble-minded had difficulty in shifting from one activity to another in the same psychological region.

In his critique of Kounin's structural concept of rigidity Werner (*316*) pointed out that whereas Kounin concluded that shifting easily from one (satiated) activity to a similar one was a sign of rigidity, Lewin concluded that the failure to shift from one satiated activity to another of the same region was a sign of rigidity.

"Both authors seem to neglect the dynamic relation of a certain task to the particular mental make-up of the subject. In the light of this relationship the seeming contradiction between the results of the two experiments disappears. Any monotonous task, such as drawing moon faces or cats for a considerable time, is usually disagreeable to a normal child because it interferes with his desire for free and spontaneous activity. He welcomes the opportunity to shift to spontaneous drawing. As a rule feeble-minded children are not opposed to monotonous work; they rather like it. Everybody familiar with feeble-minded children has noticed the stereotypy even of their free activity. Many of these children never get tired of drawing the same objects, such as an aeroplane, or a cowboy, or a car. Because of these differences of the attitude of normal and feeble-minded children toward monotonous work, definite conclusions as to structural rigidity cannot be drawn from satiation experiments. Since feeble-minded children possess a considerable tolerance to monotonous work it is probably easy to persuade them to draw bugs after cats, and turtles after bugs. A feeble-minded child changes easily to a similar drawing and continues with it, probably not because the two activities are rigidly set one against the other but because he welcomes small changes within an otherwise stereotyped activity. That this behavior cannot be accounted for by a low degree of co-satiation between cat-drawing and bug-drawing is shown by the fact that a greater objective difference between the drawing activities may have opposite effect. If the feeble-minded child is requested to draw freely after having been satiated with a stereotyped drawing he may, as Lewin has shown, continue only for a very short while. Though Kounin's and Lewin's results seem contradictory, actually Kounin demonstrated only once more what Lewin had already shown, and that is: feeble-minded, compared with normal persons, display a higher degree of functional rigidity, viz., a greater perseverance in pursuing a monotonous task." (*316*)

In his reply to Werner's critique Kounin (*169*) pointed out that (1) comparison of his study to Lewin's was not warranted because the latter did not control for mental age but rather equated his groups for chronological age, and the assumption that rigidity increases with chronological age could not therefore be tested; (2) Werner's criticisms did not explain the marked differences in behavior between the younger and older feeble-minded group but Kounin's hypothesis that rigidity is a function of chronological age did explain them; (3) Werner's statement that feeble-minded children like monotonous work more than normal children was a descriptive or phenotypical statement that was "hardly an explanation." Goldstein (*115*) has also taken exception to Kounin's conception of rigidity. He maintained that "rigidity occurs when an organism is unable to come to terms with its environment in an 'adequate' way. It is a means of protection against 'catastrophic conditions.' Rigidity is one type of reaction to a situation to which the individual is inadequate. Distractibility [jumping from one idea or task to another] and other types of reactions may also result from catastrophic conditions." From Kounin's approach distractibility appears to be unrelated to rigidity, whereas from Goldstein's point of view they are intimately related in the sense that they are reactions to a task which is beyond the individual's capabilities. In reference to the drawing of animals in Kounin's study, Goldstein contended that "the individual has not the *Einstellung* [mental set] for single objects where the one has nothing to do with the other one, but for drawing; and in this *Einstellung* the difference between drawing one object or four objects is not significant. He tries to do his best, that is, to do the whole job; and this . . . [because] he has a great tendency to fulfill the task as well and as quickly as possible within his capacities." However, should the task be beyond the child's mental capacities, distractibility may appear. "If we do not know the special approach [of the individual] toward an event, we can never decide how it was experienced. And only knowledge in regard to this point may lead us to avoid totally wrong interpretations about similarity, tasks, and the like." It is important to note that basic to Werner's and Goldstein's criticisms is that *interpretation of behavior must take into account the relation between the nature of the stimulus task and the capacity, mental set, or attitude of the individual.* Werner and Goldstein do not question Kounin's *results* but they do question whether the concept of rigidity as defined by Kounin is as helpful for understanding behavior as knowledge about the relation between mental set and the nature of the stimulus task.

When one views Kounin's hypotheses from a clinical approach, several objections may be raised. Kounin's assumption that a normal and a defective child of similar mental age have the same number of neighboring mental regions or "the same degree of differentiation" does not seem to be tenable. Sarason and Sarason (260) have shown that even within one etiological grouping, the garden-variety defective, similarity of Binet mental age may be the result of a very different pattern of successes and failures which is associated with differences in behavioral pattern and intellectual efficiency. It should be noted in passing that Kounin's groups were institutionalized cases and cannot be considered representative of defectives in general. In the next chapter it will be seen that institutionalized and noninstitutionalized defectives of similar mental age differ markedly on many variables. In addition, no control seems to have been exercised as to the length of institutionalization. The child who has been institutionalized for ten years cannot be considered as similar to one who has been institutionalized for one or two years, even though they may have the same mental age. Kounin's older defective group may well have been institutionalized much longer than the younger group and their increased rigidity be due to that variable rather than to age *per se*. These considerations suggest that rigidity may not be a simple function of chronological age.

Thompson and Magaret attempted to determine the degree to which Binet items were dependent on rigidity. "All items . . . were rated on a six point scale in such a way that an item receiving a high rigidity rating would be more difficult for a 'rigid' person to perform than would be an item receiving a low rating." The raters were thoroughly familiar with Kounin's theoretical position and had no knowledge of which items had been easier or harder for the defectives. Surprisingly the mean rating for the items which were easier for the defectives was not different than for those which proved difficult for them. Thompson and Magaret concluded: "When the hypothesis of rigidity is examined in this fashion, it is clear that the differentiating items in the present study are not adequately explained by the hypothesis."

McNemar's General First Factor

On the basis of their findings Thompson and Magaret favored the hypothesis that the items which were more difficult for defectives *than for normals* were heavily loaded with the general first factor isolated by McNemar (204) in his statistical analysis of the Stanford-Binet scale. What psychological functions or phenomena are to be indicated by this statistically isolated factor is difficult to say. "Brightness" and "general intelligence" are two of the labels which have been attached to the factor. Thompson and Magaret do not make any assumption about the nature of the factor in concluding "that at least in the present case a statistically isolated factor bears an important relationship to a clinically significant behavior variable." In light of the previous discussions one may assume that the "clinically significant behavior variable," mental deficiency, is itself composed of unknown etiological variables which when controlled may produce different results. Doll's study (76) of birth-injured defectives is relevant at this point. In order to determine which tests of the 1916 Binet were particularly easy or difficult for birth-injured feeble-minded children, Doll compared their performance not only to that of a group of normals but to that of a group of presumably garden-variety defectives as well. Three comparisons were possible: birth-injured with normals, birth-injured with garden-variety defectives, and garden-variety defectives with normals. In this way Doll could determine whether the difference between the birth-injured and the normals on a given item was related to the fact that the former were defective or to the fact of their birth injury. Although the number of cases was small, Doll's analysis showed that many Binet items were not of equal difficulty for his two defective groups. Therefore, to compare defectives as a group to normals, which has been so frequently done, obscures test differences related to etiological factors. Much of the psychological work stimulated by Strauss' endogenous-exogenous typology also emphasizes how two defective groups, equated for both chronological and mental age, show different patterns of success and failure on the items of the Binet and other tests. Although some questions were raised in Chapters 2 and 3 about the composition of Strauss' exogenous group, the results of these investigations clearly demonstrate that defectives cannot be treated as a homogeneous group for comparative purposes. In attempting to evaluate further the differences in test performance obtained between normals and defectives, it may be profitable to return to the findings of Thompson and Magaret in Table 3. It will be noted that of the twelve items on which defectives surpass normals, eight require a response to a visual stimulus and that six of these eight do not require any oral response. Of the twenty items on which normals surpass defectives, all but two require an oral response to a verbal stimulus. It would seem that defectives do poorly in a face-to-face interview type of stimulus situation. When the school-like nature of these situations is considered in light of the defectives' unpleasant school and interpersonal experiences, one may wonder to what extent emotional factors interfere with intellectual efficiency. In support of this possibility is the fact that eight of the twenty items on which normals surpassed defectives involved memory. It has been demonstrated (*185, 244*) that performance on memory items is adversely affected by fear and anxiety reactions and therefore cannot be relied upon as a valid indication of intellectual capacity.[2]

Variables in the Test Situation

In the preceding paragraphs psychological studies comparing defective and normal groups were evaluated. A point to be noted in regard to these studies is that they were concerned almost exclusively with whether a test item was passed or failed and not with the psychological determinants involved. The observed and inferred behavior of the individual, the relation between the stimulus situation and the subsequent response, were not the objects of study. If one is to go beyond the pass-fail criterion, it would seem important to determine the variables in the test situation which may influence an individual's functioning. Unfortunately, there has been relatively little research in this area. What research has been done suggests that when the testing situation is viewed as another learning situation, important clues about the origin and nature of an individual's behavior may be obtained.

It is commonplace but necessary to state that the testing situation is a form of interpersonal relationship. The behavior of the subject in the testing situation cannot be considered as unique in contrast to his behavior in previous life situations. The child entering the testing situation brings with him (1) attitudes toward the functions of the examination and the purposes of the examiner, (2) attitudes toward himself in relation to his conception of the situation, (3) anticipations

---

[2] The cases presented on pages 83, 91, 104, and 308 are clinical examples of how attitudinal and situational factors may affect performance. Zimmerman, Burgemeister, and Putnam's study (*338*) on the effect of glutamic acid on test functioning also indicated that memory items are sensitive to attitudinal factors. Lantz's study (*172*) of the effects of a previous experience of success and failure on test functioning also suggests that performance on memory items is affected by emotional factors.

of adequacy or inadequacy, (4) fantasies about the consequences of success or failure in terms of approval-disapproval or reward-punishment, and (5) response tendencies or mechanisms which serve to reduce the effects of anxiety and to protect him from the exposure of his inadequacies. What the individual experiences upon entering the testing situation enables the examiner to determine the relation between stimulus conditions and behavioral responses not only in the present situation but in past ones as well. It is the function of the psychologist to determine what features of the testing situation have stimulated the overt or inferred responses of the individual. It cannot be emphasized too strongly that whatever the child experiences upon entering the testing situation is related to certain aspects of *that* situation. The response of a child entering the testing situation is usually not the same as when he enters a candy store; the difference in response is in part a function of the nature of the stimulating situation.

From the above considerations it can be seen why the determination of what a child experiences upon entering the testing situation provides data for making deductions about previous conditions of learning. If the child's present reactions can be described, then one has some clue as to how these reactions may have been related to and possibly influenced past performance. The point to be emphasized is the importance of determining what features of the present stimulus situation are associated with the observed or inferred behavioral responses.

It should not be thought that the testing situation begins when the first test item is administered. For example, it is the practice of many psychologists to have the first contact with a child outside of the testing room, preferably in the presence of the mother. The facial expression of the child upon meeting the examiner, the ease and speed with which he reacts to the proffered handshake, the degree and nature of his verbalization, his dependence on the mother, the mother's attitude toward the child and the examination, the manner in which the child enters the testing room—these and similar observations can be very revealing of the psychological factors influencing the child's interpretation of and behavioral reaction to the situation.

Up to this point the discussion has centered around the psychological factors at work when the child enters the testing situation. How these factors will be related, the manner in which they reach expression, and their effect on intellectual adequacy during the course of the examination have been shown to be a function of several variables. Hutt (144) has demonstrated that the order of presentation of Binet items significantly influences the adequacy of performance for certain kinds of cases. According to the standard instructions given by Terman and Merrill (292), once the basal age of the child has been ascertained the examination is carried up the scale until an age level has been found in which all the tests are failed. They state further that the tests at each level should be given in the order followed in the booklet. It was Hutt's hypothesis that this standard procedure "offers the subject a succession of tasks of constantly increasing difficulty and therefore requires him to be able to tolerate the increasing frustrations inherent in such a situation. Such a procedure is likely to result in decreased motivation in proportion to the subjects degree of maladjustment." Hutt describes an "adaptive" testing procedure with the Binet in which if the subject fails an item he is given an easier one and if he passes an item he may be given a more difficult one. Hutt also recommends beginning with an item that does not require "considerable concentration, rapid response, or prolonged and involved verbal directions." The standard and adaptive procedures were alternately used with cases referred to an educational clinic. Results indicated that (1) the adaptive procedure did not affect the norms of the test; that (2) in those cases which were rated as very well adjusted there was no difference in test score between those "standardly" tested and those "adaptively" tested; but that (3) in cases who were rated as very poorly adjusted those who were adaptively tested did significantly better than those standardly tested. These results suggest that passing or failing an item is not a simple function of any single factor or group of factors that would be subsumed under the label of intelligence. Equally as important to consider are the attitudes that a person brings to the situation, the way in which they influence his interpretation of the situation, and the way in which the nature of the situation influences the attitudes.

McHugh (201) gave the 1937 Binet (L and M) to a group of children who were about to be entered into kindergarten. Forty-five children were tested on Form L and 46 on Form M. After approximately two months, during which the children attended school for an average of 30 three-hour sessions, each child was retested on the form alternate to that of his initial test. It was found that in the two-month period the children made a mean gain of 5.84 months and 6.07 I.Q. points.

The differences between test and retest were statistically significant. One form of analysis made by McHugh was to divide the Binet items into those which can be successfully passed through some manual or manipulative behavior and without the use of oral speech, and those which cannot be successfully passed without the use of oral speech. This analysis indicated "that with approximately equal opportunity to improve in both manual and speech items from first to second test and over the same age levels of the test this group of 91 children showed 11.2% improvement in speech items as compared with 4.7% manual items" (201, p. 21). The children who made the largest I.Q. gains also made the largest improvement in speech items. McHugh's conclusion was that inexperience in talking to teachers, shyness in a new situation, and fear of the examiner, who was a strange person, were some of the factors inhibiting oral speech behavior during the first test. The testing situation was one which these children had not experienced before and for which they had no specifically learned responses. As one would expect, they refused more speech than manual items—being asked to manipulate materials was by no means as novel as to respond orally to "strange" questions. As was concluded from Hutt's study, McHugh's findings emphasize how passing or failing a test item is in part a function of the mutual influences of previous experiences and the nature of the present stimulus situation.

In a preceding paragraph the psychological factors that may be present when a child enters the testing situation were discussed. It follows, of course, that the role of these factors during the formal examination will be in part a function of the nature of the stimulating task—the test items. The child who has experienced failure and ridicule in classroom recitations, who views himself as inadequate and inferior, whose verbal responses to questions have been associated with anticipations of disapproval or punishment—such a child will probably react with heightened apprehension and anticipations of failure if he is immediately presented with test items which demand an oral response to a verbally presented problem. To such a child the test situation is similar to the face-to-face interview kind of situation in which he has learned to feel inadequate. His failure with such test items is not fully explained by a word like "inability" or a phrase like "lack of capacity." The nature of the stimulus task, the demands it makes on the child, and his previous experiences in similar situations are all factors that must be taken into account if one is interested in more than merely noting whether an item was passed or failed.

One of the items on the eight-year level in the Binet, the Wet Fall, requires the child to answer questions based on a passage read to him by the examiner. The child is also given a copy of the passage which is taken from him when the examiner is finished reading. To the child who cannot read or has a severe reading disability the passage that he is given to look at may stimulate such preoccupation with his inadequacy that he is not listening to the examiner. Consequently, when he is asked questions about the passage he may be unable to respond. A similar reaction may obtain when a child is shown the imposing Binet vocabulary list. To explain such failure by "inability" is obviously neglecting important psychological factors. To say that the child "failed" the item is also not telling the whole story. The nature of the stimulus task must be considered in evaluating the adequacy of response.

THE PROBLEM OF SELF-VERBALIZATION

That characterizing test performance on a pass-fail or adequate-inadequate basis may obscure the psychological phenomena leading up to the response can also be seen in the superficial distinction that is usually drawn between verbal and performance tests. The results of these tests are sometimes interpreted as if the psychological processes stimulated by them are mutually exclusive. Although the objective nature of the stimulus tasks in verbal and performance tests are very different, in the former the task being administered and responded to by oral speech and in the latter oral speech usually being absent, introspective analysis suggests that in both kinds of test situations self-verbalization may be present. In other words, even though oral speech may not be required for a successful solution to a performance task, in many cases the solution is mediated by a process of "talking to yourself." For example, on the nine-year level in the Binet the subject is shown a card with two designs and he is allowed to look at it for ten seconds, after which he is asked to reproduce them from memory. Although oral speech is not required of the subject, he is verbalizing to himself relationships, attaching verbal symbols to the stimulus figures, which after the card is removed may act as cues for reproducing the figures. In a Binet item like paper cutting on the nine-year level, the subject's final response also seems to be preceded by a process of self-verbalization. A performance scale like the Arthur (17) seems to engender similar processes.

Robert was a 20-year-old boy who had been institutionalized since the age of 13. His Binet mental age was 6 years and 8 months with an intelligence quotient of 44. On the Kohs block designs, using the Arthur instructions and scoring, Robert received credit for 11 of the 17 designs. He successfully finished two other designs but did not receive credit because he exceeded the time limits. For his Binet mental age his Kohs performance is extraordinary. The degree of conceptualization necessary for the solution of these designs would hardly be expected from one with his mental age. In doing the designs Robert occasionally and spontaneously verbalized aloud his procedure: "Here you need one that's all red, and here you need one that's part red. That's not right, you need this kind, etc." In effect this boy was able to verbalize a procedure, to utilize verbal symbols in attacking the problem. His motor responses were apparently mediated by self-verbalization.

John, who was an honor student in a third-year college course in testing, was asked to be the subject in a classroom demonstration of the Kohs block designs. To the surprise of everyone John had inordinate difficulty with the designs and could only complete the first eight designs. An introspective report revealed that John had been very anxious and tense because he anticipated doing poorly in front of his teacher and classmates; that the colored designs "had absolutely no meaning for him" and that he didn't know how to proceed; and that his mind was a "blank." It seemed clear from John's report that nonintellectual factors prevented him from formulating (verbalizing) a procedure.

Gellerman (97) made some very interesting observations on the role of verbalization in the solution of form discrimination problems. He was interested in the discrimination of *form per se* and the influence of background upon the discrimination of form. His apparatus consisted of "two small boxes with hinged lids . . . mounted 3 feet apart on a platform. The box lids could be locked shut. Food could be introduced underneath each of the boxes by means of a food carriage which ran on a track immediately beneath the box platform. The experimenter sat behind a one-way vision screen about 12 feet from the boxes. . . . The starting-point for the subject was a chair located beside the experimenter's screen and directly before the box-apparatus. The subject's task was to go from this point to the box-apparatus and open one of the two boxes, thereby securing food. . . . The actual forms which the subjects were required to discriminate were various combinations of cardboard placed behind two windows of the form-presentation frame." Gellerman used as subjects two *two-year-old children*.[3] "At no time were any of the subjects given any verbal instructions in connection with the principal problem of the investigation, i.e., the response to form." In the first part of the experiment a white triangle on a black background was shown on one side of the apparatus, and on the other side of the apparatus a black area.

"Nancy learned the correct response at once; that is, her first 20 responses all were correct. In connection with this immediate adaptation to the problem, the verbal behavior of this subject is of interest. On her first trial Nancy paused briefly and viewed the form-presentation-frame windows one of which now contained the triangle. . . . Then she traced the general outline of the two upper sides of the triangle with her right forefinger and said, 'That's an A.' This performance was followed almost immediately by her opening the nearby (correct) box and taking food. For several trials she continued tracing the outline of the figure with her finger (either with her finger in the air or against the glass). Then gradually she stopped to view the stimuli from greater distances. By the tenth trial she did not leave the starting-chair until she had looked back and forth from one stimulus window to the other. Several times such expressions as 'Over der' occurred as she left the starting-chair and went directly to the correct box. Jimmy took 220 trials to meet the criterion of learning. After running about 160 trials, during most of which he had a position habit to the left, he showed signs of reacting to the triangle. His solution of the problem appeared comparatively suddenly. It was accompanied by a formulation which included the verbal response, 'Dis one,' and the tracing of the triangle as described above with Nancy" (97).

In another part of the experiment two stars were presented as figures. "The positive star [rewarded by food] was placed with one point directly up and the negative star was placed with one point directly down. Thus the negative figure was rotated in effect 36 degrees from the position of the positive figure."

"Jimmy did not learn this discrimination in 50 trials. Nancy missed just half the 30 trials she was given in her first day's work on this test. Near the end of this series of trials she almost refused to work. Her talk about the

[3] Gellerman also used young chimpanzees, but the comparative aspects of the results will not be discussed.

problem was profuse, but she did not solve it. During the last few trials she began to cry and to stamp her feet following erroneous responses. She finished this series of trials evidently as far from a solution of the problem as she had been before starting the test. The manner in which she formulated and solved this 'star' problem was observed quite accidentally by the writer. Following her supper on the day in which the 30 trials described above took place, Nancy crawled into my lap while I was reading the evening newspaper. This behavior was habitual for Nancy. After a few minutes my reading was suddenly interrupted by Nancy's exclamation, 'Oh, look, Daddy, look, look, look.' This statement was accompanied by pointing to an advertisement in the paper. I looked at the general place indicated by her pointing, but failed to observe anything unusual. Then Nancy remarked, 'Look, Daddy, that one's up side down.' . . . At the top of the advertisement was a row of eight stars, *one of which was actually up side down in relation to the other seven*. It was the type of printer's error which adults commonly overlook. For this particular child on this particular occasion it proved a most noteworthy occurrence. I drew the incident to a close by putting the newspaper away without comment. Next day in the experimental situation Nancy walked up to the forms and looked from star to star. Then she said, 'That one's up side down,' quickly turned to the other side, and made the correct response to the positive (point-up) star. Thereafter her responses in this test were 100% correct. This incident gives a clear-cut picture of the verbal solution of a problem of form discrimination" (97).

If self-verbalization may mediate the final response in a performance task, the following questions arise: (1) Why are some individuals able to formulate an adequate procedure, indicating good conceptual thinking, in a performance type of stimulus task and not in the verbal-Binet type, and vice versa? (2) Why may talking over a problem *to yourself and in your own words* result in a more or less adequate solution than when one is required to respond orally *to someone else?* (3) What is the relation of these factors to previous experiences or conditions of learning? It is frequently asserted that mental defectives do better on performance than on verbal tests. It has been maintained that this discrepancy is due to the defective's inability to handle verbal symbols or concepts. Although such an explanation seems valid as a broad generalization, it does not satisfactorily explain why the self-verbalized formulations of some defectives suggest a higher level of functioning than their oral verbalizations. Although it is undoubtedly easier to obtain and evaluate the spoken responses of an individual, the "silent" processes associated with the response appear equally as important in understanding the genesis of his performance.

In the preceding sections the point was stressed that in order to understand the test functioning of mental defectives the etiological differences among them must be controlled. The second point that was stressed concerns the complex and subtle psychological factors which operate in the test situation. On this second point there has been relatively little research, not only with defectives but with nondefective groups as well. There has been little research recognition of the fact that the testing situation, involving as it does an interpersonal relationship, cannot be considered in terms of pass or fail or total scores if the aim is to determine what psychological factors affected an individual's responses. An attempt has been made in this chapter to indicate how the psychological predispositions of the individual and the nature of the stimulating conditions determine his overt and covert responses. Recognition of these factors makes the testing situation the object of study not only for clinical psychologists but for all psychologists who are interested in how behavior influences and is influenced by a variety of stimulus conditions. If the psychologist working with animals had been interested merely in whether his subject could traverse a maze or reach a criterion of success in a certain length of time, many of the facts about the learning processes—its principles and conditions—would never have been discovered. By starting with a clearly formulated set of assumptions which identified what was thought to be the relevant variables, and then setting up the appropriate conditions to test these assumptions, it was possible to describe the *processes* which led to the final response. Not only were the assumed relevant variables subjected to the test of experimentation, but new variables were identified which became the object of further research. In contrast to this situation, the clinical psychologist seems to have neglected the study of the psychological processes of his subject in focusing attention on the evaluation and quantification of his final response.

In the following pages the psychological examination of cases of the kind frequently seen by clinical psychologists is reported. It is hoped that these reports will make concrete some of the points discussed previously.

CASE 1
(Medical Diagnosis: Cerebral Palsy[4])

Background Material

Helen was brought to the Outpatient Clinic of the Training School to be tested in order to determine eligibility for commitment. Since birth the left side of her body has been paralyzed. Up until 1943 Helen had been living with her parents and when both of them died during that year she went to live with her brother. The brother indicated that Helen had been overprotected all her life and had not been given an opportunity to learn tasks which were within her reach and from which she could derive satisfaction. The brother, who is single, stated that Helen is alone most of the day and has become increasingly unstable. He would like to commit her until she is trained to do things which will give her a feeling of independence. Helen's family, who appear affluent, are very attached to her and look upon commitment as a means of her obtaining feelings and habits of independence which will make her happier when she returns to live with them permanently. A report of a previous electroencepholographic examination was supplied by the brother; the record "indicates a mild degree of diffuse cerebral damage more on the right than on the left and with a definite focal attenuation in the right parietal region. There is no indication of an expanding lesion." Aside from the fact that she had attended school only for several years and that private tutoring had not been successful, no other data were available at the time of the examination.

Psychological Report (1/23/45) (C.A. 35–8)

General Observations

Helen, who was very neatly dressed, is a dark-haired and dark-complexioned woman with dark circles under her eyes. Her left hand appeared stiff, with some of the fingers clenched and the others extended rigidly. She seemed unable to engage in any activity which involved the coördination of both hands, and usually prearranged the fingers of her left hand in a position to enable them to be of some aid. She was able to move her left arm quite well, although not as freely as her right one. Helen held a pencil clumsily and could not write easily. Hand tremors were observed. She was able to print letters with long bold strokes. Her left foot was stiff and dragged a bit.

Helen was very fearful during testing and frequently rubbed her eyes

[4] Cerebral palsy (see Chapter 7) may be defined as a motor defect existing at or shortly after birth and associated with pathologic abnormalities of the brain.

and exclaimed excitedly, "I'm too nervous to talk. Look how I'm shaking." Although she became more relaxed as testing progressed, she was prone to anticipate and become upset by failure. It seemed that she was fearful of having her inadequacies exposed and tried to cover for them by giving vague, general answers which could be applicable to most any question. Helen had great difficulty in comprehending directions; how much of this difficulty was due to a mental defect and how much to the anxiety aroused by her feelings of inadequacy is difficult to estimate. In conversational speech, as well as in response to the vocabulary list, this girl's enunciation and use of words were excellent and in marked contrast to her overall test inadequacy. When responding to questions about her activities and family relationships, the coherence, fluency, and "insightfulness" of her replies were atypical for mental defectives. Helen's verbalized feelings of inadequacy usually were followed by statements about her strong desire to learn to do something useful so that she would not be dependent upon her brothers and sisters. It seemed clear, however, that her need for achievement was not as strong as the fear of failure or the tendency to avoid any situation because of the anticipation of inadequacy. Her tendency to self-derogation is so strong that any achievement on her part would be viewed by her as insignificant and consequently be no source of encouragement.

Tests	Results	
Terman-Merrill (L)	M.A. 8–8	I.Q. 58
Wechsler-Bellevue (Verbal Scale)		I.Q. 71
Rorschach	See text	

Discussion

Terman-Merrill (L). Basal was established at 5 years with final successes at the average adult level. Within this range all items requiring the definition of words were successfully passed. At the average adult level her sole success was in giving differences between abstract words. In contrast to these successes it should be noted that all items involving the presentation of a visual stimulus (picture absurdities, drawing a diamond, memory for designs, etc.) were failed. Although she seemed to recognize the inadequacy of her diamonds, she could not improve her performance. That her failure on the diamonds is possibly due to a defect in visual perception rather than in the motor sphere is indicated by the following: When she was asked to read a word she was usually unable to do so, but if she spelled aloud the letters of the word she was then usually able to read the word correctly. It was as if she was able to respond to auditory cues more adequately than to visual ones. Also, when she had finished a word, she was likely to go to a word on the line above or below from where she had started. She was not aware of her inability to focus on successive words in a line. In this connection it should be noted that on the fourth picture absurdity at year 7 Helen stated that "a girl is smoking a pipe"—a most unusual faulty perception. Helen was completely unable to adopt a critical attitude toward any kind of absurdity problem. Although fearfulness and anticipation of failure may have affected her efficiency, the discrepancy between her unusual verbal facility and her severe inadequacy with problems involving a sustained conceptual process or a response to a visual stimulus suggests that nonemotional factors are playing a decisive role. Her performance is similar to that found in some mental defectives with a known brain injury. It may well be that her emotional behavior is a learned response to inadequacies due to a brain injury.

Rorschach. Of the 10 responses Helen gave, 6 were whole responses largely of the vague, undifferentiated, irrational variety. Her responses usually started with a content which fitted part of the blot, but her uncritical elaborations resulted in an irrational concept. When she was questioned about a response she tended to become confused and flustered and when asked to trace her response she would outline the blot in a very unprecise manner. At times the examiner felt that the area responded to in the performance was not always the one that she used in the inquiry. For example, during the performance on Card II it seemed that Helen was using the top center small detail as "a steeple," but in the inquiry she said that the two red details were the steeple. In describing a response Helen did not seem aware of the necessity of relating the different parts she was enumerating; the fact that she had labeled her response seemed sufficient explanation for the various parts she enumerated. In describing her approach as uncritical it should not be thought that she responded quickly or impulsively. Her reaction times were extremely long and she constantly voiced feelings of indecision and uncertainty. It seemed as if these feelings were in some way a recognition of her inadequacy in the situation rather than the cause of it. The only times Helen was able to incorporate in her responses any of the objective characteristics of the blots were on the last three cards: giving a flower to Card VIII, a tree to Card IX, and another flower to Card X. In each of these responses form was secondary to color and the whole card was responded to in a diffuse, undifferentiated fashion. All other responses were pure form. One might deduce from Helen's performance—her responses as well as her behavior—that her intellectual defect and the attitudes connected with it would make any learning situation, intellectual or social, one that she would rather avoid than enter. When a situation requires Helen to respond when she feels inadequate, she is likely to do so in an irrational, inadequate manner. In light of the observation on the Binet concerning Helen's severe perceptual defect, it is not surprising that her performance on the

Rorschach is of the kind that has been described. It may well be that in situations which do not involve responding to visual cues Helen's adjustive capacity is not as inadequate as her Rorschach would indicate. An indication of this would be the relatively appropriate and coherent nature of her conversational speech noted in a previous section.

Conclusions

To interpret the intelligence quotients earned on the tests according to usual psychometric classifications would be to neglect important aspects of Helen's behavior. Though technically the intelligence quotients suggest mental deficiency, her vocabulary, verbal expression, and social reasoning as revealed in conversation hardly resemble that commonly associated with a mentally deficient person. It might be said that her facility with and correct use of language would not be expected to be acquired by the ordinary defective. That her mental functioning is uneven is evident. This irregularity is probably due in large part to brain pathology on the one hand, and, on the other, to emotional instability. How much of her social incompetence is due to the brain defect and how much to overprotection is difficult to estimate. The present problem is to decide whether commitment to the Training School is warranted. The brother indicated that he desired commitment so that his sister might learn to do certain things which would eventually give her a feeling of independence and an opportunity to improve in reading. He indicated that he was not interested in custodial care but would take Helen out when she could more or less get along on her own. Until about two years ago Helen lived with her parents and was apparently not trained to engage in activities for self-occupation. Now that her parents are dead and Helen lives with her brother, she is left alone a large part of the time, and as a result has become more unstable. To expect institutionalization to reduce anxiety and instill independence in a girl who has been overprotected all her life seems a hardly possible task. It would even be difficult with someone who does not possess Helen's handicap. To compensate for the privations that the girl has experienced all her life by being so handicapped would take a very large amount of individual attention to effect even a small change. To expect a woman whose only security has been the affection of her family to become more stable in surroundings where this feature does not exist is to remove the very thing which can aid her. In terms of the brother's purposes, institutionalization is not feasible.

It was felt that learning some tasks was essential for Helen's well-being and a plan which could utilize community resources was recommended. It was suggested that she be enrolled in the training program of the Workshop of the Society for Crippled Children in her city. When it was suggested that this possibility for training should be tried before commitment, the brother said that this still would not solve the problem of Helen's being left alone most of the time. The possibility of a companion was discussed and the brother indicated that the family had tried to get one but those who applied for the job were unsatisfactory. This examiner favors the training at the Workshop if Helen can be placed in a foster home or if a similar living arrangement can be made. Commitment is recommended only as a last resort.

Subsequent History

Helen was enrolled in the Workshop. It was the opinion of the staff that she could be taught to go to and from home, increase her use of her left hand, and learn to do tasks which would occupy her when she was alone. Although she gained considerably in self-confidence as a result of the Workshop program, she was unable to go from her home to the Workshop without completely losing her direction. Since it was not possible to get a companion for her and she was still alone a good part of the time, the Workshop recommended that she be admitted to the Training School. This recommendation was carried out. Because of this girl's experience of overprotection and the traumatic shock of her separation from her family, it was arranged that she be seen each day by the psychologist on a psychotherapeutic basis. An initial problem was Helen's inability to go from her cottage to the psychologist's office, a distance somewhat less than a quarter of a mile, without getting lost. At first she refused to go, saying that she would get lost. On the first few trips she was accompanied by the psychologist, who attempted to point out cues that Helen might use as a bearing. Being accompanied by the psychologist reduced Helen's apprehension, increased her desire to come to the office, and made it easier for her to attempt the trip herself. The first couple of times she came alone she was told that the psychologist would be watching from her office in order to see where Helen might make a mistake and to make sure that she did not get lost. After a few trials Helen was able to come to the office without any difficulty. She was also able to go to other parts of the institution without any difficulty in orientation. For the first few weeks the interviews were largely taken up with Helen's attitudes toward the other girls in her cottage. She was surprised at how rough they were and the coarse language they used, and she was afraid that they might not like her and would pick on her. Her adjustment to the other girls was complicated by their jealousy of the fine clothes she had and the attention and affection which her family demonstrated. She constantly reiterated that the girls "are not my type." The chief functions of the interviews seemed to be to give Helen an opportunity to unburden her feelings, to feel that despite her separation from her family there was someone who was interested *in her,* and to anticipate and reduce the apprehension which would arise with each new situation. The fact that her family visited her frequently also prevented any strong feelings of rejection.

Helen was enrolled in the occupational therapy and continuation school programs. Because of her intense desire to read and in light of her severe visual defect, special reading techniques were employed. A gadget was devised which Helen could manipulate and which allowed only one line at a time to be exposed, thus preventing her tendency to wander all over the page. She was also instructed to spell each word to herself, then to spell it aloud, and then to attempt to pronounce it. She was aided at all times by the continuation-school teacher, who began with words which Helen already knew. Within a period of two years Helen was able to read and comprehend on about the fifth-grade level, although for optimal results it was necessary for the teacher to observe her directly because even with the mechanical aid there was a noticeable tendency for her visual gaze to shift unexpectedly to other parts of the page. Helen, who had never been able to write before, was also taught to write a legible and coherent letter.[5]

CASE 2

(Tentative Medical Diagnosis upon Admission: Garden-Variety Deficiency)

Background Material

Harold, born in 1928, was illegitimate. Little is known of his infancy except that his mother's home was "very dirty, poorly furnished, and meals served very irregularly." His mother was born in 1897 and was committed to a county home at the age of six years. When she was eleven she was committed to a girl's reformatory. After her release she married and had five children; her extramarital affairs ultimately resulted in divorce, before and after which she lived with Harold's father until he died in 1930. The father, who was born in 1872, was supposed to be of low mentality and had been married twice before he lived with Harold's mother. After the father's death, the mother went to live with another man. In 1930 she was committed to the state farm at which time she was found to have syphilis and gonorrhea. On a psychological test she had an I.Q. of 78. After her release she married Harold's present stepfather; the course of this marriage has not been smooth because of her promiscuity.

In 1930, when his mother was sent to the state farm, Harold was placed

---

[5] The writer wishes to express his indebtedness to Miss Helen Kreitler for her painstaking efforts in teaching this girl to read and write.

in a children's home where he was described as nervous, high-strung, frail, and appearing much younger than his years. In 1932 he was placed in a foster home where he seemed to make a satisfactory adjustment until an older brother was also placed there. It is reported that Harold was better liked than his brother, who was always picking on him. The friction between the brothers forced the foster mother to request their removal. In 1935 they were placed in another foster home where the same difficulties appeared. In 1939 Harold was placed in another foster home from which he ran away to his mother on five different occasions. Nocturnal enuresis and masturbation, which had been noted from an early age, persisted. "The foster mother continued to see that he had no liquids after supper. . . . She promised him rewards if he showed improvement, scolded him, tried to embarrass him, all to no effect. On occasions when the bed was dry, he was happy and duly praised. Foster mother stated that he lies when questioned about his misbehavior. He has stolen money, food, and articles of little value from the foster home and neighbors. Foster mother has noticed him on some occasions talking to himself, or laughing or crying when he is alone, but he will not explain what he is thinking of. Sometimes he has been heard to say that he wishes his mother were dead. He gives away in trades his possessions for articles of lesser value. He becomes angry for no apparent reason and throws things around haphazardly." Although his real mother claimed to like and want him, the social worker felt that it was on a superficial and mercenary level. In 1943 Harold was placed back in the children's home.

At this time he was given in a city clinic a psychological test upon which the diagnosis of mental deficiency was made and commitment effected shortly after. The Stanford-Binet (L) was given and he earned a mental age of 9 years and 10 months and an I.Q. of 68. The psychological report notes that "the memory tests were somewhat inconsistent and he passed some of the memory tests after having failed similar tests at a lower level. The inability and unevenness in performance are often characteristic of organic cases." A marked reading disability was noted and it was felt that his maximum capacity was "somewhat higher than the figure of 68 obtained." The psychiatrist reported, "I feel that Harold's stealing of valueless articles is a good indication of a lack of affection in his life. I feel very pessimistic about the outcome of this boy if he is returned to his mother before he has habit training because some disappointment with his mother may lead him into criminality and prison. I recommend admission to the Training School. In the interim of waiting, if it could be possible I recommend tutoring along manual lines by a volunteer worker who would have enough patience with him and who would give him some attention, thereby satisfying somewhat the love starvation from which he is suffering."

Harold's school history reveals that he has always done poor work, repeated the first grade, and was three years in the fifth grade. He was not accepted by his playmates, partially due to an enuretic odor. He did not participate in group activities. Among neighborhood boys he seemed to be more tolerated than accepted. His behavior antagonized them to the point of rejection. He seemed to obtain greater satisfaction playing by himself.

Harold's behavior during his first few weeks at the Training School for defectives was marked by several attempts to run away—on one occasion he stole a bicycle in order to get to his destination quickly. When he was brought to the testing room, the examiner was advised to make sure an attendant was ready to prevent another runaway attempt. The boy's behavior and results of the tests administered were as follows:

Psychological Report (1/31/44) (C.A. 15-10)

General Observations

Harold is a quiet, gracious, red-headed boy of good height, with badly bitten fingernails. During testing he was very friendly and coöperative and his eagerness, which had a genuine flavor, tended to add a certain charm to his behavior. He was generally alert and his interest was manifested by a toned-down enthusiasm which was revealed by sparkling eyes and an occasional slight reddening of the face. These physical reactions were most apparent when he was praised for the solution of a problem. A strong need for affection and sympathetic attention seemed to be the roots of his excellent coöperation. Though Harold usually responded readily, reticence and caution nevertheless preceded or characterized his replies. Anxiousness for the results was not expressed during the examination, but some uneasiness was apparent. Prior to testing the boy mentioned that he was told that his leaving the institution depended on the tests. During the interview Harold's speech was good, but his verbal usages were not always correct.

Tests	Results	
Terman-Merrill (L)	M.A. 11-0	I.Q. 74
Arthur Point Scale	M.A. 14-11	I.Q. 100
Rorschach	See text	
Metropolitan Achievement		
Reading	Grade 3.9	Age equivalent 9-3
Vocabulary	Grade 3.3	Age equivalent 8-7
Arithmetic Fundamentals	Grade 3.9	Age equivalent 9-3
Language Usage	Grade 2.4	Age equivalent 7-7
Spelling	Grade 2.9	Age equivalent 8-2
Gray's Oral Reading	Grade 2.9	

Discussion

Terman-Merrill (L). Basal year was established at 7 with final successes at 14 years. There was a marked difference in adequacy of response between items involving a verbal response to an orally presented problem and items involving a response to a visually presented stimulus. On the former items Harold's performance was hesitant and variable in efficiency. He failed vocabulary at 8 years, rhymes at 9 years, finding reasons and word-naming at 10 years, verbal absurdities at 11 and 12 years, abstract words at 12 years, and all orally presented items at 14 years. Although vocabulary was established at the 6-year level, he was able to define enough abstract words at 11 years to receive credit for the item. On many of the vocabulary items Harold seemed to comprehend the meaning of the word but did not have the facility to express it. His spontaneous conversational speech seemed well above the 6-year level. In contrast to these failures Harold passed all orally presented memory items through the 12-year level. His unpredictability with orally presented items is best seen in his performance on verbal absurdities at 9 years; he passed the first two, failed the next two, and passed the last absurdity, which is very rarely passed by defectives. That orally presented problems or face-to-face situations engender variability in efficiency can be seen when one compares his present performance on memory items with his precommitment performance, which led the examiner at that time to hypothecate an "organic" involvement. It would seem that in a face-to-face situation requiring an oral response to an orally presented problem efficiency of performance becomes impaired.

On items involving a response to a visually presented stimulus which may or may not involve a verbal response, Harold's performance was efficient and adequate; he passed the drawing of a diamond at 7 years, paper cutting at 9 and 13 years, memory for designs at 9 and 11 years, picture absurdities at 10 and 14 years, and bead chain and plan of search at 13 years. The only visually presented problems which Harold failed involved reading: reading and report at 10 years, Minkus completion at 12 years, and dissected sentences at 13 years. In light of Harold's general mental level it does not seem justifiable to ascribe his severe reading disability solely to an intellectual defect. When one considers his preschool and school experiences and the attitudes of self-depreciation which they probably reinforced, his reduced efficiency in face-to-face situations becomes more understandable.

Arthur Point Scale. As might be expected from his Binet performance, Harold's score on this test, which does not require articulated verbal responses, was well within the average range. He worked quickly but reflectively with very little trial-and-error behavior. On the Porteus mazes he passed all mazes up to and including the twelfth year on the first trial, passed the 14-year maze on the second trial, failed average adult I, and passed average adult II on the second trial. On Healy P.C. I, seven of his nine placements obtained maximum scores. On his first encounter with the Knox Cubes Harold's range of performance is atypical for defectives: he passed the first seven items, failed the eighth, passed the ninth, failed the tenth and eleventh, and then passed the twelfth. In the writer's experience no defective has been able to pass the twelfth Knox Cube item. Harold's performance on the Kohs Block Designs was characterized, as on the Knox and verbal absurdities (IX) on the Binet, by failure on the easier items and success on the harder ones: he passed the first design, failed the next four, passed the next two, failed the next two, passed the next one, and failed the remainder. His relatively low score and variable functioning on the Kohs do not seem to be explained by mental retardation. It is not that he lacks the intellectual power for conceptual thinking, because his performance on many Binet and Arthur items strongly suggest that he is able to formulate and sustain the correct solution to a problem. Why he is consistently adequate on the Porteus mazes, which involve formulation and criticism of a procedure, and relatively inadequate on the Kohs is not explainable at this time.

In summary it should be emphasized that in a situation which does not involve a face-to-face relationship or verbal responsiveness Harold's performance is atypical for defectives. It would seem that when he can formulate a problem in his own way (his own words?), aided by the constant presence of a visual stimulus, Harold is likely to perform efficiently. If this conclusion is correct, it suggests that previous learning situations involving face-to-face situations have engendered behavioral patterns which have interfered with efficient functioning.

Achievement Tests. Harold's reading is characterized by omission of letters, careless additions, and substitutions. He is very unsure of himself, and his impulsiveness reduces his efficiency. The spottiness of his performance indicates that his comprehension of reading matter is well below the fourth grade. In arithmetic Harold is best on addition, is weaker in multiplication and subtraction, and is unable to divide. At present he simply does not possess the basic skills which would enable him to progress in arithmetic.

Rorschach. The most important conclusion derived from an analysis of Harold's 24 responses is that the preciseness with which the content of the responses fitted the area of the blot selected is atypical for defectives. None of his responses is irrational in the sense that there is a discrepancy between content and blot area. The following responses illustrate how well he was able to fit his imagery to the blot areas:

Card I

1. Two bears

1. (d-lateral side projection) As he was sitting up and smelling for honey (Q) how he has his nose stuck up in the air.

Card VII

1. Two girls holding up two baskets

1. (W) holding up baskets on heads (Q) I see their hands and feet.

Card IX

1. Two big mother bears and baby bears

1. (dr—orange without finger-like projections, and including area directly underneath the usual moose's head where orange fades into green) Mother bear is laying down in leaves (Q) don't see her feet because she is laying down (Q) I see her head and the back of her body—I just see the head of the baby bear. (Q) the mother bear is so fat here (pointing to area beneath moose's head) because it is so bulged up (Q) (leaves?) they always go in leaves and they are leaves because of the color—they are brown.

Of the 24 responses, two were human movement, fourteen were animal movement, five were form responses, two were texture responses with form primary (Fc), and one was a color-form (CF) response. The preponderance of movement responses indicates a personal or subjective responsiveness to the cards. The relative absence of color and shading emphasizes his lack of awareness of or responsiveness to the objective and obvious characteristics of the stimuli. He does not respond to the cards in an impersonal way, a characteristic which reduces the range of stimuli of which he is cognizant and to which he responds. If Harold's reactions to the cards are representative of his behavioral pattern, one would expect that his reactions to people and situations would be highly personal in the sense that he becomes more aware of his own needs, fears, and fantasies and less aware of the objective features or requirements of the stimulus situation. He becomes too preoccupied with himself to respond or adjust to the needs of other people. When a situation forces him to make a response, there is no indication that he can do so in a reflective or unimpulsive manner. One would expect him to respond either in a diffuse way or in a highly constricted manner. It is as if this boy has learned that responsiveness to others is less satisfying than solutions through fantasy. Another factor which would interfere with the satisfying social expression of his needs is his passivity. His responses do not contain the aggressive content that one would expect from a boy his age; the one response in which form was secondary (CF) was unaggressive in content. His responses were characterized by a passive-dependent quality to such an extent that one may assume that such needs are extremely strong and ungratified. Although one might expect that such emotional deprivation would result in aggressive behavior, there is little evidence in the record that this boy finds expression of aggression easy or gratifying. One would expect that the expression of aggression would be indirect rather than direct and impulsive rather than delayed—but rarely satisfying. One gets the picture of a boy whose basic needs have not been satisfied and who because of the lack of satisfying compensating activity is in a fairly constant state of tension and unhappiness.

Conclusions

Harold's test performance indicates that his intellectual capacity is not of a defective variety. In situations requiring little or no verbalization but involving self-verbalization and conceptualization, Harold's performance does not suggest mental defect. In face-to-face learning situations involving a sustained conceptual process Harold performs in a variable fashion, although even here there are indications that his capacity is higher than his functioning level. His severe reading disability which lowered his Binet score is not completely explained by his retardation because his reading level is well below what one would expect from his mental level. In light of his background it seems justified to assume that his preschool and school experiences reinforced attitudes toward himself and others which interfered with the learning of the academic skills. Although Harold is not mentally defective, his unfavorable family situation makes his discharge from the institution inadvisable at this time. His strong need for affection, which has already caused him to run away, must be satisfied if he is to become interested in and benefit from a training program. Unsympathetic disciplinary action or handling will make it difficult for this boy to unlearn his present maladjustive attitudes toward himself and others. He should attend the academic school and also begin a vocational program. Because an institutional setting probably cannot give him the necessary individualized treatment, an early return to the community should be considered.

Subsequent History

Since his commitment Harold has run away from the institution six times. He has invariably returned to either his own or the foster home. His very strong need for love and sympathy seems to have been one of the factors behind these runaways. It might be said that his longing to be with his mother, noted even before his commitment, has made it difficult for Harold to accept any of the institutional staff as a substitute. This has accentuated his feelings of loneliness and attitude of hostility toward the institution. His explanation for his initial runaway was simply that he wanted to see and be with his mother. It is not surprising that Harold is known as an "up and downer"; one day he appears content and does excellently on the job and the next day he may be sullen, moody, and useless as a worker. He gets angry quickly and is likely to fly off the handle. He has stolen various objects both in the institution and during his runaways. When he is caught doing something wrong he will hang his head in shame and grin sheepishly. Although he is a likable boy and has a hail-fellow-well-met manner, his moodiness, undependability, and impulsivity have made it difficult for him to establish enduring friendships. He is not a leader in his group but rather a follower. Harold has had many different training jobs in the institution but his inability to withstand frustration and to adjust to the requirements of the situation has made for short tenure on each job. An activity which he seems to enjoy is making wooden objects, using magazine sketches as models. He works alone and figures out the problem himself. On one of his vacations at home he obtained a job by himself. His supervisor reported that Harold was a good worker and had picked up the work very quickly during his first two days on the job. Harold had to be returned to the institution because his mother could not give him adequate supervision. In July, 1947, Harold was given the Wechsler-Bellevue Scale. He obtained a performance scale I.Q. of 105, a verbal scale I.Q. of 70, and a full scale I.Q. of 85.

After one of Harold's earlier runaways, during which he had a homosexual episode with an older man, it was arranged for him to come to the psychologist to talk things over. Although Harold had been always very friendly with the psychologist and appeared very eager "to talk over what bothered him and made him unhappy," in no interview was he able to verbalize spontaneously any personal feelings. When the interview was handled in a nondirective fashion, Harold usually sat with a sheepish grin on his face, his head slightly bent, completely unable or afraid to express himself. When a more directive approach was used, Harold would simply deny that anything bothered him or that he was unhappy. Despite the unproductiveness of the interview, Harold always chose to make more appointments. When the psychologist remarked about this discrepancy, the boy again could find nothing to say. After a couple of months the interviews were terminated by the psychologist when it became apparent that he could not establish other than a superficial relationship with Harold and that the latter could not terminate the relationship because the former might view it as an aggressive, rejecting act.

During the fourth year of his institutionalization Harold was given a job working with a middle-aged female employee who was able to show him a good deal of personal attention. It was a shipping-clerk type of job and he apparently liked it. The employee seemed to serve as a mother substitute to

Harold and the relationship appeared, as no other one had, to be emotionally satisfying to him. His misbehavior became infrequent to the point where he was considered for return to the community.

CASE 3
(Medical Diagnosis: Cerebral Palsy)

Background Material

John was born January 27, 1923, the third of six siblings. He was born a month prematurely several days after the mother returned from the hospital where she had pneumonia. Delivery occurred without the use of forceps and there was no suggestion of intracranial hemorrhage. At the age of eight months the boy was hospitalized for an abscess of the throat, and the mother was told at the time that he had a cerebral hemorrhage as a result of which his left arm and leg were paralyzed. There is no history of convulsions. He had no treatment after leaving the hospital until 1929, when he was again hospitalized for orthopedic work. In 1939 additional corrective surgery was attempted which necessitated four admissions to a hospital. As a result of these operations the boy was able to walk better, but it was still necessary for him to use crutches.

John started school at the age of six and left at 16 when he was in the seventh grade, although it is probable that his achievement was actually lower and that he was pushed from grade to grade. The boy always impressed people as being very lethargic and his slow manner of talking usually was interpreted as an indication of his mental retardation. He had practically no friends and showed little initiative in developing activities or interests. During one summer, however, he did become interested in mounting butterflies, but this interest soon disappeared. His most abiding interest has been in repairing clocks and it is reported that he has had surprising success in this endeavor. The family, aside from an overprotective mother, has shown little genuine interest in the boy. The two younger siblings' attitude toward him is one of tolerance and they have seldom if ever sacrificed their own pleasures for the sake of their brother. The three older siblings live away from the home. The father, who is incapacitated also because of a cerebral hemorrhage, is very dependent on the mother and never assumed much responsibility for his son's care. The family lives in a five room cottage in an isolated part of a small Connecticut town. There are no light or toilet facilities. The water supply is provided through a hand pump in the house. Their heat is furnished by two stoves which are fueled with wood and whatever coal they can pick up from the railroad tracks.

In 1941, John was given a psychological examination and obtained an I.Q. of 72. The psychologist stated that the boy's test results were barely above the high-grade defective level and that his capacity to profit by vocational training would be impaired by his physical handicap. On an aptitude test given to him in a state employment office in 1942, he did poorly on all sections of the test.

John was referred for testing to the outpatient clinic of the Southbury Training School as a possible case for commitment. The boy, his family, and the interested social agencies were all very eager for commitment.

The following is the psychological report.

Psychological Report (3/19/44) (C.A. 21)

General Observations

John is a crippled boy whose left arm and leg have little mobility, making crutches necessary. Even with crutches this boy can get around only in a very slow manner, especially going up and down stairs. However, it was never necessary to aid him in any way.

This boy seemed neatly dressed, although close inspection of his clothes showed them to be well worn and in the process of tearing. There was never any question of his coöperativeness but he rarely ventured a spontaneous opinion or statement unless the conversation was initiated by the examiner. John usually spoke in a soft almost inaudible tone and it seemed as if it were difficult for him to open his mouth any distance. It was frequently necessary, therefore, to urge him to speak louder and repeat what he had said, although such directions did not produce too clear, audible speech except for a few minutes. Only occasionally did John say anything which was revealing of himself or his activities. He did speak about the fact that he liked the movies a great deal and that it was his chief means of recreation; he expressed a dislike for war pictures because too many of them were being shown. He also mentioned his tinkering with clocks and said that he liked to try to repair them. The extent of his success in this line could not be accurately determined but he did seem to know what he was talking about. In general, it was the examiner's impression that this boy leads a narrow, monotonous existence in which his own imagination and thoughts have become substitutes for environmental stimuli. It would seem that the present environment is of little value in helping him utilize his potentialities intellectually or emotionally.

Tests	Results	
Terman-Merrill (L)	M.A. 12	I.Q. 80
Arthur Point Scale	M.A. 11–5	I.Q. 76
Rorschach	See text	

Discussion

Terman-Merrill. Basal was established at 9 years with successes through 14. On those items involving the abstraction of meaning in terms of form relationship, as in paper cutting and memory for designs, this boy succeeded on all levels (9, 11, and 13) where these tests are given. Reasoning on the basis of verbally presented problems was good and represented his upper level of successes: passing verbal absurdities at 9, 11, and 12 years, similarities at 11, problem of fact at 13, and the directions item at 14 years. At the 14-year level the picture absurdity was also passed. There was a noticeable tendency for poor functioning in items involving memory; such items were the only ones failed at 10 and 11 years, digits reversed one of the two items failed at 12, and word memory and bead chain two of the three items failed at 13 years. The reason for this memory picture may be the fact that John seemed to have a good deal of anxiety during this test and, as is sometimes found in such cases, a relatively poor memory reflected this state. This boy's vocabulary was well within his general range of functioning, vocabulary and definition of abstract words being established at 12 years. John's timidity and difficulty in speech, plus his limited background, are factors which probably have hindered verbalization. In general, this boy is not functioning in a defective manner and the quality of his work seems to indicate that the obtained results are a minimum.

Arthur Point Scale. The lower score obtained on this test must be understood in light of this boy's slowness in the manipulatory tasks which make up a good part of it. On the Seguin, Casuist, and Mare and Foal items, involving relatively gross manual dexterity, John's slowness and cautiousness depressed his scores somewhat. However, in a task involving abstraction in terms of form relationships, the Kohs Block Designs, he went well beyond his obtained mental level on the scale. He had little difficulty with the designs, and only failed to complete the last one. He worked carefully and seemed to enjoy the challenge which the increasing difficulty of the designs presented. On the Porteus Mazes he likewise showed efficient planning and foresight; and although he made errors, he rarely repeated the same one twice. The results of this test corroborate the conclusion reached from the Binet as to the nondefective nature of this boy's functioning.

Rorschach. John's responses to the ink-blots were all adequate in terms of form level and several were so well seen that they must be considered as being above average.

Card I

1. 2 eagles close together	1. This part is one wing of this bird and this is the head (Q) it looks like an eagle I'm making at home for a clock—in here is the clock and the two eagles are

standing on the clock—the part around here is the
wooden part of the clock (the clock and the wooden
frame are traced by John as two concentric circles in
the area usually seen as a "bell").

Card X

1. the white space
looks like a turtle

     1. (John was asked to trace the response which is
found in the inside white space in which a "wish
bone" is commonly seen.) These are four legs sticking
out of the shell—and this is the head (Q) I'd say he's
walking because that's the only time his legs are out—
he draws them in when he's not walking—the same
for the head.

From John's comments it seemed that he interpreted the instructions of
the test to mean that the whole card was to be used for a response. His initial
comment to Card I was, "It's hard to judge." In Card III he saw the usual
men and went on to say that he couldn't figure out what the red areas might
be. A similar whole approach was also evident in Card VIII. It is not surprising that 6 of his 12 responses were of the whole variety. It is important
to note that this whole approach did not interfere with his better judgment.
The whole responses he gave were of good form and where he could not
give such a response he was able to shift and respond to details. The
only time when John seemed unable to shift was in Card VI, to which he
said, "I can't get that one. I never saw one like that before." His rejection
of this card seemed due as much to his cautious, need-to-be-certain attitude
as to adherence to the whole approach. Whereas some individuals with the
whole approach might feel compelled to respond, John would not do so unless he was very sure that he could justify what he said. An indication of his
cautious approach is his long reaction time to the cards. On the basis of the
above observations it might be said that John is a very insecure person who
tends to respond only when he is sure of himself. These self-attitudes probably prevent him from responding spontaneously and his overcautiousness
might very well be interpreted by some as a lack of intellectual capacity.
This conclusion would hold especially for those situations in which adjustment to unfamiliar people and tasks is required and where he feels "on the
spot."

     As one might expect, the constellation of determinants in John's record
indicates a rather subjective and self-conscious type of responsiveness. This
conclusion is based on several considerations. First, in explaining his responses he would tend to relate them to his own experience. Second, John
responded only once to the physical properties (color and shading) of the
card; even though his attention was frequently drawn to the colored areas
either he stated that color was not an integral part of his response or he did

not use the colored areas at all. An example of how this boy does not respond to the more obvious characteristics of external stimuli is Card X, where his first response (the turtle) was to the white area. A third factor indicating John's personalized approach is his giving of two human movement responses (II and III). Fourth, he also gave several additional animal movement responses.

When his subjective (self-centered) way of responding is taken in conjunction with the already mentioned fear or reluctance to respond, one gets the picture of a boy who would have great difficulty in expressing personal feeling or in initiating an interpersonal relationship. This is the record of an individual who would avoid situations in which he would be expected to respond. He is an essentially constricted individual who has few ways of personal expression.

Conclusion

On the basis of the psychological findings it is felt .that a diagnosis of mental deficiency is not warranted. In light of his physical handicap as well as his unstimulating family environment, in addition to the geographic isolation of his home, the social dependence of this boy cannot be taken at face value. There is no indication that a brain injury is interfering with intellectual functioning.[6]

It is the examiner's impression that this boy has the capacity of being economically and socially self-sufficient. Because of his physical handicap he may need outside aid from time to time, but such dependence should not be attributed to intellectual incompetence. To·institutionalize this boy will result in reinforcing his dependency (and an unhealthy behavior pattern) and insuring that he will always be a custodial case. Community resources should be more effectively utilized before this boy is institutionalized for life.

Follow-Up Report

On the basis of the psychological report John was sent for several months to the New York Institute for Crippled and Disabled for physical reeducation work. Although he was taught how to get around with a cane instead of crutches, his anxiety about his physical inadequacy hindered him from gaining the confidence necessary for greater independence. At the present time he uses his cane sparingly. While at the Institute John participated in the war training program at New York University, where his performance in inspection work resulted in his promotion to machine shop training. When returned to Connecticut, a home was found for him and a job obtained involving the assembling of rather small pieces which contained an

[6] An electroencephalogram taken subsequent to the psychological examination was normal.

insecticide used by the armed forces. He has already been given one raise and he seems to be doing a very adequate job. In striking contrast to his former barren existence, John has made friends and seems to be more independent than ever before.

CASE 4[7]
(Diagnosis: Mental Deficiency, Unknown Etiology)

When Ned was born in 1940, he cried to such an extent that an x-ray of the lungs was taken. It was found that the baby had "a lack of oxygen" and he was in and out of an oxygen tent for six weeks. According to his mother, he sat alone at eight months, stood at sixteen months, walked at twenty-two months, talked a bit at five years, made complete sentences at six years, uses fingers and hands clumsily, and is still unable to tie his shoes. Ned was entered in school in 1945 and the following is the report of his kindergarten teacher:

"Ned entered kindergarten September, 1945. During the year I observed that Ned found it difficult to adapt himself to his new environment. Whenever he felt the other youngsters were treating him badly he would use physical force in order to gain his point. That is, Ned would scratch, kick, spit, put his hands around a youngster's neck as if to choke the child. Also he made marks on other children's drawing papers during work period.

"Ned also was retarded in his speech. He could not pronounce simple words, and the only medium he had for communicating with others was shaking his head and making funny sounds.

"Also he was not able to take care of his physical needs and often displayed this lack of control in the room.

"He was extremely lacking in motor control. Because of this, skipping and marching was a difficult task.

"I promoted him to Grade One in June, 1946. The following September he spent a month in Grade One and on the request of the first grade teacher returned to the kindergarten. He improved slightly physically and mentally during the second year in the kindergarten.

"However, by June, 1947, he could not do kindergarten work as well as the slowest kindergarten child. Nevertheless I promoted him to Grade One on condition.

"During the course of his second year I recommended that Ned be tested by the State. In the spring of the year he was tested and the exam-

---

[7] The writer is indebted to Mr. Frank Auld for contributing this case.

iner told me he would recommend that Ned stay home a year and then spend another year in the kindergarten. I, also, feel this would be good for Ned."

Ned was tested (Stanford-Binet, 1937 L) in 1947 at which time he received an M.A. of 4–2 and an I.Q. of 65. The psychological examiner recommended that Ned be excluded from school for one year.

In 1948 Ned was reëntered in school. During that year, on the recommendation of the school, he was brought by his mother to the Pediatric Clinic of the New Haven Hospital for an evaluation. An x-ray of the skull was taken and the results were considered "indeterminate." There was a suggestion of premature ossification of the coronal sutures, but it was "impossible to tell whether or not sutures are closed."

It was the pediatrician's impression that Ned was mentally deficient and a psychological examination was recommended. The pediatrician also observed that Ned's mother "was too ambitious for him." The family history was noncontributory for an etiological diagnosis.

Psychological Examination (8/15/48) (C.A. 7–11)

General Observations

Ned is small for his age. He has green eyes and blond hair, is slender of build and pale in complexion. He came to the clinic neatly dressed. Ned seems very immature socially: he came into the office dragging a pull-toy behind him; he did not know how to take his coat off and hang it up; in the bathroom he did not turn the water on and off for himself but expected the examiner to do it for him; his language was childish; and he asked several times (more than most children of his age) whether his mother would come for him. Ned expects other people to do things for him—even things he could do for himself. For example, in the bathroom he did not manage the faucet for himself, and in the examining room he asked the examiner to untie a belt on a doll for him—later he untied it without help.

Ned seemed a little distractible during the tests. His attention shifted to objects in various parts of the room; at one time he heard a fire engine and immediately ran to the window; later, he heard a baby cry and, turning his head toward the sound, exclaimed, "Somebody cry!" Although one reason for these shifts in attention seems to be an inability to refrain from attending to new external stimuli (distractibility), another reason is his desire to divert the examiner from continuing the test. When a task became too hard for him, Ned might ask a question about something in the room or suggest another task he would rather do—for example, "I want to make lines over there" (on the easel).

His speech was very childish. He spoke poorly—softly and unclearly. His words were poorly formed: for example, "tock" for "clock," "spoo" for "spoon," "loo" for "blue." He used baby words: "choo choo" instead of "train" or "engine." He formed sentences with difficulty. In short, his verbalizations are characteristic of the average 3.5-year-old child. He has certain habits of orderliness that seem related to his desire to conform to his mother's wishes. He has learned a few habits of putting things in their place. For example, he said he wanted to put the furniture back into the doll house before his mother came back; he wanted to close the door, which was ajar; he wanted to put building blocks back into the bag they came from. That Ned is very dependent on his mother is evidenced by the following: (1) When the two came into the office, he stayed close by her side, saying hardly a word. (2) He was quite concerned during the examination that she return.

Apparently his mother is much concerned that Ned "do well." She came with him to the examining room and stayed until the examiner explained that it was not customary for parents to stay. As she left she admonished Ned, "Now be a good boy and do what the doctor says." After the tests were over, the examiner remarked to the mother that Ned was nicely mannered ("You have a nice boy . . .") and she replied, "Yes—I think he's shown a great improvement in the last year or two . . . I hope he'll make out all right."

Tests	Results	
Revised Stanford Binet (L)	M.A. 5–4	I.Q. 67
Arthur Point Scale	M.A. 5–7	I.Q. 71

Discussion

Revised Stanford-Binet Intelligence Test (L). Ned earned a mental age of 5 years 4 months on the Binet, which yields an I.Q. of 67. This lies at the boundary between borderline intelligence and mental defect. It is likely, however, that his I.Q. on future examinations will be somewhat lower because the tests from the six-year level on up become increasingly more dependent on conceptual thinking and verbalization, activities which are markedly defective in this boy. For example, Ned failed all items on the seven-year level so completely that it is unlikely that on reëxamination in a year he will be able to show a sufficient increase in mental age to maintain an I.Q. of 67. If his I.Q. should decrease, it will obviously be due not to any deterioration process but to the fact that his intellectual inadequacy will become more apparent.

He is most facile at tasks that do *not* require "immediate memory" (paying attention to language) or verbalization at a conceptual level. Conversely, he does most poorly in tasks requiring conceptual thinking. He can count up to four with difficulty; he does the six-year number concepts test barely satisfactorily. These accomplishments are likely the result of special training by his mother and do not indicate understanding of number concepts. There is no indication on this test that Ned's intellectual capacity is above the defective range.

Arthur Point Scale. Ned's best performances on the scale were on the Seguin Form Board, the Mare and Foal test, and the Picture Completion test, all of which he passed at the six-year level. These tests have in common the fact that they are activities in which conceptualization or self-verbalization of a procedure is not important.

Ned gave up rather easily on the Two-Figure Form Board, filling only one hole because he failed to fit the remaining pieces into the second hole on the first attempt. Similarly, he accepted inferior solutions for the Picture Completion test and did not persevere to find better pieces. One should not think, however, that with more perseverance he would do greatly better on the scale; the chief cause of his failure on the scale is lack of ability.

Summary and Conclusions

The results of the two intelligence tests given indicate that Ned is probably not capable of school work in regular classes. Intellectually he is at present at the boundary between borderline intelligence and mental defect. It is probable that his mental age will increase slightly in years to come, but that the increase will be so slow that his I.Q. will stay the same or decline. In estimating his future mental capacity we must keep in mind his present inability to do conceptual thinking. This deficiency will likely be a serious limitation to further increases in M.A. score on the Binet.

Socially, Ned is quite immature. His intellectual and social limitations suggest that he needs special instruction. If he is given special instruction, he may be able in time to learn to read simple materials and to do a few sums. In the examiner's opinion, it is probable that his academic progress will not go beyond these accomplishments. He can probably learn to take care of his everyday needs (dress himself, wash, avoid common dangers) and to do some useful work that is not intellectually too taxing, i.e., work that is routinized and requires no judgment.

Taken together with the facts in the medical history and his obvious social immaturity, the psychological results and observations seem to warrant a diagnosis of mental deficiency. The combination of facts indicate a true developmental retardation rather than an "environmental" one.

The examiner feels that Ned's mother should not be permitted to harbor false hopes that her son can be "trained out of" his backwardness. The extent of his limitations must be explained to her. She should understand that he will probably never be capable of ordinary school work, or of ordinary work requiring flexibility and judgment. She should be encouraged to let Ned do just as much for himself as he can, however. There are a few evidences that she does a little too much for him, and that there are some tasks of which he is capable that he has not learned to do for lack of opportunity.

It is recommended that psychological examinations be given at yearly intervals in order to evaluate Ned's progress. If his mother's attitude toward him is not changed and individual academic instruction is not given, there is no reason to expect that this boy will show any "improvement."

Chapter 5

GARDEN-VARIETY MENTAL DEFICIENCY

In Chapters 1 and 2 mention was made of the garden-variety or sub-cultural defective. The diagnosis in these cases is made when intelligence test results indicate "defective or inferior intelligence in one or both parents and in practically all of the siblings, and on the failure to find any evidence in either the history or physical examination suggesting [nonhereditary] factors. . . . Mental status is practically invariably in the moron classification" (331). These criteria, as stated, are in practice open to several sources of error. First, more often than not it is impossible to give a battery of psychological tests to the parents of these children in order to evaluate their intellectual functioning. Consequently the clinician must depend on "impressions" or a written report by a social worker for data to satisfy the criterion of defective or inferior parental intelligence. That such procedures do not have a satisfactory degree of validity is precisely one of the reasons why psychological testing gained the support that it did. Although the impressions of the clinician may agree in some cases with the subsequent results of testing—and these are cases he tends to remember—there is no scientific evidence to indicate that such subjective procedures are reliable or valid. That the data necessary for fulfilling the criteria of garden-variety deficiency are in practice usually not available can be seen in Table 4. The table includes all the cases that had been committed to an institution during a six-month period and for whom a diagnosis of garden-variety deficiency had been made. It seems clear that the evaluation of parental and sibling intelligence is largely made on the basis of reports from secondary and tertiary sources.

Another source of error in using the criteria of garden-variety deficiency is the sole dependence on test scores for a diagnosis. Halperin (127) gave the Penrose-Raven Progressive Matrices Test to the parents and siblings of 318 institutionalized defectives. In 143 cases of aclinical amentia, presumably the garden-variety type, approximately

101

TABLE 4. Available Test Data on Patient and Family in 20 Unselected
Cases of Garden-Variety Deficiency

Case	Precommitment Tests (Patient)	Mother Tested	Father Tested	No. of Siblings	No. of Siblings Tested
1	Binet	No	No	8	2
2	Binet	No	No	4	0
3	Binet	No	No	9	5
4	Binet	Yes, data not available	Father unknown	0	0
5	Gesell Scale	No	No	8	5
6	Binet, Otis Ferguson, Healy P.C. I	Yes	No	1	0
7	Wechsler-Bellevue	No	No	2	0
8	Binet, Otis, Ferguson, Healy	No	No	5	3
9	Binet, Otis, Ferguson, Healy	Yes	No	7	6
10	Binet	No	Father unknown	3	0
11	Binet	Yes	No	1	1
12	Binet	Yes	No	1	1
13	Tested—data not in history	No	No	4	0
14	Wechsler-Bellevue, Goodenough, Woodsworth-Cady	No	No	5	0
15	Binet, Ferguson	No	No	4	2
16	Binet	No	No	2	0
17	Binet	No	No	2	0
18	Binet	No	No	3	0
19	Wechsler-Bellevue, Goodenough, Woodworth-Cady	No	No	5	0
20	Binet	No	No	2	0

38 percent of the mothers were defective, 54 percent were inferior, and 8 percent were normal. Of the fathers, approximately 25 percent were defective, 64 percent inferior, and 12 percent normal. Although these results confirm the assumption that the parents of patients diagnosed as garden-variety defectives tend themselves to have defective or inferior test ratings, it should be noted that the result of a single test is considered sufficient for an evaluation of mental functioning. Whether the parents with defective or inferior test scores were socially adequate,

economically self-sufficient, and independent of external supervision was a factor that was not considered. Labeling an individual as defective on the basis of a low test score seems to rest on the assumption that whatever abilities are necessary for independent social or vocational day-to-day functioning are unrelated to whatever abilities the test is supposed to measure. If this assumption is *not* made, then the level of intellectual activity indicated by an individual's job performance or social competence must be given at least as much weight as his test score. If the level of activity in the job and test situations is not the same, there is no logical reason for giving more weight to one or the other situation. The problem of the examiner is to determine how differences in adequacy of response may be related to differences in stimulus conditions. For example, it is a common occurrence for some college students with very high test ratings to do poorly in mathematics, whereas others at a similar level find such courses a snap. In the case of the former it is not unusual to find that their anticipatory reactions of anxiety and inadequacy toward the subject matter, unduly reinforced by their initial failures, prevent them from learning those procedures which make for adequate comprehension. In such cases mathematics performance and test rating *are both characteristic of the individual's functioning.* It is misleading to attach more weight to either of the two situations. What is important to determine is why the person is more adequate in one situation than in another. In the case of defectives one must likewise determine what factors make for a level of adequacy in one situation, e.g., a job, which is above or below the level indicated by the test situation.

Sarason (258) has presented the case of a girl whose efficiency and adequacy in the test and the job situation were markedly different. She had been institutionalized when she was 15 years of age. The diagnosis was garden-variety defective. Several years after her commitment she was assigned to the hospital laboratory to do the simplest of routine tasks. After one year she was able to perform the following tasks:

1. Sterilization and chemical cleansing of glassware used in bacteriology and quantitative chemistry.
2. Preparation of bacterial media, physiological and chemical solutions used in bacteriology, hematology, and qualitative chemistry.
3. Cleansing of volumetric, graduated, and hematological pipettes and special chemical filters.

4. Complete urinalysis, except for microscopic including qualitative and quantitative sugars, albumin, acetone tests, and specific gravity.
5. Streaking and plating of bacterial cultures with aseptic technique.
6. Assistance in quantitative blood and tissue chemistry as in total proteins, lipids, sodiums, and potassiums.
7. Staining of hematology and bacterial slides.
8. Taking stool cultures and finger blood tests alone.
9. Keeping daily record of work performed.
10. All blood typing (all work is, of course, checked by the head of the laboratory).

This girl was also receiving and responding to instruction in the use of the microscope. As a result of her performance, which was a surprise to the hospital staff, she was given a phychological examination. The results of the testing were:

Terman-Merrill (L)	M.A. 10–6	I.Q. 70
Arthur Point Scale	M.A. 10–11	I.Q. 73
Rorschach		
Achievement		
Reading	Grade 3.9	Age equivalent 9–3
Arithmetic	Grade 4.9	Age equivalent 10–4
Spelling	Grade 3.0	Age equivalent 8–3

"Before and during the examination this girl seemed very anxious and insecure. Although she had known the examiner for several years and had come to him for advice and help, she was tense, somewhat overly polite, and seemed as if she had decided to avoid at all costs doing or saying the 'wrong' things. It was as if she felt that much depended on how well she did on the tests. (It is a commonly expressed attitude among institutionalized children that if they do well on their 'brain' tests they might be placed back in the community at an early date.) The desire to do well, to impress and achieve, was very strong in this girl. Associated with these feelings was an equally strong anticipation of failure. Her desire to impress and achieve was so strong that even before directions for a task were completed she would nod her head knowingly, although it was evident that her anxiety about her ability to grasp directions prevented full comprehension. When she was given the memory-for-designs item on the Binet, she very quickly and inaccurately scribbled some designs which had no relationship to the originals. Questioning revealed that she thought she was to reproduce the designs as quickly as possible. When given another piece of paper and told that speed was not a factor, she did noticeably better.[1] In light of the influence which

[1] The card with the designs was not exposed a second time.

her attitudes exerted over comprehension of directions it is not surprising that she failed almost every item involving exact recall. On items involving a sustained oral response to a verbally presented problem, she had difficulty in expressing herself, stammered a great deal, became upset, and had to be encouraged often in order to calm her and obtain a clear response. For example, it was approximately six minutes before she was able to express clearly her thoughts concerning the second verbal absurdity at eleven years. On the Rorschach, where in contrast to the Binet she could formulate her responses in her own way and where tracings eliminated much questioning by the examiner, the accuracy of form of her responses was very good, even though she tended to respond to the whole card. She was not satisfied with the irregular features of the blots but attempted to improve upon them, and her embellishments definitely enhanced the form accuracy of her responses."

It seems reasonable to assume that the intellectual level and efficiency of this girl's job performance are above those revealed by her behavior in the test situation. To use either the job or the test situation as an indicator of her intellectual adequacy would, however, obscure the fact that her behavior in both situations is characteristic of her functioning. The question to be answered is: What were the differences between the two situations which may be related to the differences in response that they stimulated? The test situation was not unfamiliar to this girl. However, it may be assumed that her previous experiences in such a situation were not of a kind to arouse feelings of adequacy or self-confidence. The nature of the situation—its teacher-pupil, question-answer quality—was one in which she had experienced failure and one on which unpleasant consequences were based. As in the teacher-pupil relationship, this girl knew that she was being tested by a person whose opinions were important to her future. Another factor which would heighten the stressfulness of the situation was the inordinate strength of her desire to do well at the same time that she fearfully anticipated failure. In summary it may be said that this situation engendered feelings and attitudes toward the self, the test, and the examiner which interfered with efficient performance. In contrast to the above, this girl's learning process in the job situation was rather different. Her initial tasks upon coming to the job did not involve learning new responses. She felt happy about working in the laboratory, developed strong feelings of loyalty to her supervisor, and was rewarded by the personal interest shown her. Gradually she was given other responsibilities to which she responded adequately. The relationship between the girl and her supervisor was such that failures or mistakes or shortcomings of the former were not accompanied by ridicule, embarrassment, or withdrawal of interest by the latter. The girl's behavior was rewarded by feelings of achievement, responsibility, and recognition.

A question that might legitimately be asked about this case is the suitability of the diagnosis of mental deficiency on the basis of which she was committed to an institution. The answer depends in large measure on the criteria employed. If one goes according to test score, he might say that both at the time of commitment and on subsequent testing this girl possessed defective or inferior intelligence. To utilize the criterion of test score is legitimate as long as one is aware that labeling this girl as defective indicates little about her psychological functioning and development. However, since a diagnosis of mental deficiency is interpreted to mean that the intellectual and social inadequacy is due to some kind of defect that existed at or shortly after birth, the test score criterion may give misleading implications. In the present case, for example, home conditions had always been extremely unfavorable from a social, economic, and moral viewpoint. The mother was noted for her promiscuity and had at one time been committed to the state farm. There were ten children in the family and this girl received practically no supervision. According to the case history she was encouraged by her mother "to go out on the streets at night" and have sexual relations with older men. In light of this type of background it would be hazardous to assume with any degree of confidence that this girl's social and intellectual inadequacies were completely due to a lack of potentiality for normal development.

Another question that might be raised concerns the validity of this girl's having been placed in the garden-variety etiological grouping. Of her eight living siblings, one is reported to have an I.Q. of 71. There are no data on the other siblings, although there is no evidence from the case history that they would have obtained low test scores. The mother was reported as having an I.Q. of 56 and the father was at one time considered as "fairly intelligent but dissipated." Although some might maintain that these data are presumptive evidence for establishing an etiological diagnosis, one is justified in maintaining that in this case the difference between presumption and fact may be considerable.

Cases like the one just presented are not the rule among institution-alized, garden-variety defectives. The frequency of such cases in an institutional population is not high, probably because the program for such children is determined more by test score classification than by a conscious attempt to apply or to experiment with psychological prin-ciples of behavior. This statement should not be taken to mean that all institutionalized garden-variety defectives are capable of vocational suc-cess at a level above that indicated by test scores. What is meant is that the institutional setting seldom provides conditions of learning which are calculated to increase adequacy of response.

FOLLOW-UP STUDIES

The misleading nature of diagnoses based on test scores is further revealed by the studies (*14, 19, 81, 161*) which have followed into adult life children who had been diagnosed as mentally defective when in grade school. Although these studies did not take account of etiological factors, the description of the socio-economic-cultural background of these noninstitutionalized cases suggests that many were of the garden-variety type. It has been estimated that while the garden-variety defective makes up from 45 to 55 percent of all institutionalized de-fectives, they comprise about 65 to 75 percent of defectives in the community. It would be expected, therefore, that studies of community defectives would include some of the garden-variety type.[2] These studies showed that the academic achievement, economic self-sufficiency, and social adjustment of these groups were surprising in light of their original intellectual classification. In Baller's study (*19*) of 206 sup-posed defectives, all with I.Q.'s below 70 when in grade school, 33 completed eighth grade, 3 finished high school, and 1 entered college. In some who reached junior high school their curriculum had been of a special type. As to economic self sufficiency, 27 percent were wholly self-supporting, 57 percent were partially so, 8 percent were totally

[2] Many of the problems raised by Schmidt's study (Chapter 1) confront us again here. The reliance on a score from a single test, the absence of any developmental or neurological data, and the paucity of information about the intellectual and social competence of parents and siblings make the drawing of conclusions about the composition of the groups very hazardous. How many of these cases would not have been called defective if more data were available is unanswerable. Although the writer has stated that some of the cases were *probably* of the garden-variety type, it should be emphasized that this is a deduction and not a fact. These studies have been included here as much to point up methodological problems in diagnosis as to see what light may be shed on garden-variety deficiency.

dependent, and 8 percent were confined in institutions. Although Baller's defective group was far more dependent than his control group, it is surprising that as many did as well as they did in view of the fact that the study was made during a severe depression. As part of a similar follow-up study, Fairbank (81) attempted to locate 22 of the original group of 166 who had the lowest test ratings and had also been described as having "no prospect of becoming self-supporting adults." When approximately sixteen years later 17 of the 22 were located and re-studied, 8 of the men were self-supporting, 4 of the women had married economically adequate husbands, and 5 were dependent on family or community.

"One of the [I.Q. 58] boys in this group who showed many delinquent traits in 1914 and had a history of feeblemindedness, insanity, and immorality, spent four years in the first grade, and after six months in the second grade, spent the remaining three and a half years in the ungraded class. . . . At fourteen this boy got a work permit and for almost ten years has been working steadily and successfully with an insulator company as a responsible inspector. . . . He is very proud of the fact that once when he was home on sick leave for a few days, they sent for him to come back because his substitute had spoiled several hundred dollars' worth of material in his absence. He says, 'I was no good in school, but when I got married, I knew I'd got to dig out.' There has been no further delinquency, although infrequently he goes on a spree. He has learned to read the newspapers through having become interested in athletics, but can write only his name.

Hegge (136) has reported on the occupational status of 177 higher-grade defectives during the Second World War. The subjects in his study were parolees from the Wayne County Training School. Hegge divided his subjects into those with Binet I.Q.'s between 50 and 75 and those with quotients of 76 or more. Although the cases were not divided into etiological groupings, it may be assumed that since the garden-variety defective represents between 45 and 55 percent of an institutional population, many of Hegge's cases fell in that category. Hegge found that (1) his cases were not significantly dependent on family or friends for employment, (2) a large proportion worked above the unskilled level, (3) the majority held their jobs for three months or more, (4) the lower I.Q.'s compared well with the higher I.Q.'s on most of the variables studied, and (5) there was no relationship between I.Q. and wages. Regardless of the influence of a war economy on employability, these findings suggest that the level of intellectual activity reflected by job performance is not uncommonly above that indicated by test score.

One of the most recent follow-up studies of noninstitutionalized defectives is that by Kennedy (*161*) on 256 "morons" who when in grade school in a Connecticut town achieved I.Q.'s between 45 and 75 and had been diagnosed as defective. At the time of restudy the average age of the subjects was 24 5 years. Kennedy was able to obtain in the same community 129 nonmoron controls whose inclusion in the study "was considered to be essential because it was felt that an estimate of the social and economic adjustment of morons would be meaningful and valid only if their records were matched, in every particular, against those of nonmorons with approximately the same social and economic backgrounds and status. By this procedure all factors except the crucial variable of intelligence, as measured by I.Q. tests, would be held constant." The two groups were matched for age at starting school, chronological age, race, sex, country of birth, nationality, and father's occupation. Table 5 presents the distribution of original I.Q.'s.

TABLE 5. Distribution of I.Q.'s in the Moron Group of the Connecticut Follow-up Study (*161*)

I.Q. Level	Total		Males		Females	
	No.	%	No.	%	No.	%
	256	100.0	159	100.0	97	100.0
50	1	0.4				
51	1	0.4	1	0.6	1	1.0
52	4	1.6	1	0.6	3	3.0
53	3	1.2	1	0.6	2	2.0
54	4	1.6	2	1.2	2	2.0
55–59	30	11.7	16	10.1	14	14.5
60–64	54	21.1	34	21.4	20	20.7
65–69	77	30.1	48	30.3	29	30.0
70–75	75	29.2	51	32.1	24	24.8
Unknown	?	2.7	5	3.1	2	2.0

The following are some of the major results of this study:
1. *Level of Schooling.* Of the total moron group, 81.6 percent attended special class or terminated school training below the eighth grade; 8.2 percent attended high school; and one moron completed

high school. As one would expect, the level of schooling attained by the control group far exceeded that of the experimental group.

2. *Commitment to State Institutions.* More morons than nonmorons came from families in which a member had been in some kind of state institution (26.9 vs. 16.3%). Of the morons, 11.3 percent had been in some kind of state institution, in contrast to 3.1 percent of the nonmorons. There were twice as many commitments to correctional institutions among the families of the morons as among the nonmorons (56.5 vs. 28.6%). "A startling disclosure, however, is the fact that a much smaller proportion of the families of morons than nonmorons had records in state hospitals (mental) (34.8 vs. 57.1%) or in the Mansfield State Training School for the feeble-minded (1.4 vs. 9.5%)".

3. *Economic Status.* Slightly more morons than nonmorons were found to be wholly self-supporting (75.5 vs. 68.6%). More married and unmarried moron males were wholly self-supporting than the corresponding groupings among the nonmorons. "The differences, by any possible test, between morons and nonmorons with respect to self-support are actually so slight, and the patterns are so shifting, that the only possible conclusion is that both groups are in about the same status in this regard. Certainly the morons show no detectable signs of greater dependency upon others than do the matched nonmorons."

4. *Employment Level.* "Fewer morons than nonmorons, of both sexes, are employed in the three highest kinds of occupations: professional, semi-professional and managerial (1.2 vs. 10.4%). Many fewer morons than nonmorons are employed in clerical and sales work (3.7 vs. 25.6%). About twice as many morons as nonmorons are employed in domestic and personal services (6.1 vs. 3.2%), but approximately the same proportion are engaged in agricultural work (2.9 vs. 2.4%). Many more morons than nonmorons are in the laboring occupations (83.7 vs. 56.0%), but almost as many morons as nonmorons are skilled laborers (13.1 vs. 17.6%), although many more morons than nonmorons are semi-skilled (54.9 vs. 31.2%) and unskilled laborers (15.7 vs. 7.2%)." There was little difference in earning power between morons and nonmorons, especially among the males. There was also a slight tendency for morons to remain on a job longer than nonmorons.

5. *Work Performance.* Employers rated morons and nonmorons for

nine questions on a four-point rating scale ranging from generally unsatisfactory to highly satisfactory. The employers were asked to rate their moron or nonmoron employee on accuracy, speed, learning rate, judgment, learning ability, absenteeism, promptness, efficiency, and relations with other employees. In regard to accuracy, although the morons are "considerably more likely than nonmorons to drop to the lowest level of accuracy, they are almost as apt as the latter to rise to the highest possible plane." In regard to speed of work "morons fall below nonmorons in the topmost bracket of extreme speed; but they are also less numerous than nonmorons in the very lowest level, that of marked slowness." In learning rate the morons are rated as considerably slower than the nonmorons. On a noncomparative basis 9.1 percent of the morons were given the highest ratings and 35.5 percent received the next highest for rate of learning. In regard to learning ability (are they capable of performing a more skilled job?) the morons received more of the lower and fewer of the higher ratings than the nonmorons. "Despite their relatively inferior rating, this question nevertheless reveals the important fact that over half of the morons are said to be able to perform more skilled jobs with the help of additional training." On the remaining variables the morons tended to get lower ratings on reliability of judgment, absenteeism, tardiness, efficiency, and co-worker relations. In regard to highest ratings "there is not much difference between the proportions of morons and nonmorons who receive highest ratings on one or two points, but above this the morons fall rapidly behind. . . . It is noteworthy, however, that some morons reach the top on six, seven, and eight criteria, and two get top ratings on all nine counts."

6. *Family Background.* In contrast to the nonmorons more of the parental families of morons had homes broken by divorce or desertion; more of their families had records of commitment to state institutions; fewer of their fathers were engaged in jobs on the upper occupational levels; more of their families needed relief and by more than one agency; their families also received greater amounts of work relief; court records were more prevalent in parental families of morons; more of their fathers and siblings had such records. Considerably more of the parents of the morons were aliens.

In light of Kennedy's findings about differences in family background between her two groups one might question the validity of the statement that "all factors except the crucial variable of intelligence . . . would be held constant." To the extent that the parental families of morons showed signs of "being less well adjusted, more problematical, more disturbed, and economically less well off," the obtained differences between the groups cannot be explained solely by differences in intelligence test score. To the extent that unfavorable home background influences intellectual efficiency and personal-social adjustment, the obtained differences between the groups cannot be considered the sole function of the intelligence variable. It would seem more correct to describe Kennedy's research as a study of the differences between morons coming from a troubled background and nonmorons coming from a relatively less troubled one.

Kennedy's final summary follows (*161*, p. 97):

". . . Our study reveals that morons are socially adequate in that they are economically independent and self-supporting; and that they are not serious threateners of the safety of society, but are rather frequent breakers of conventional codes of behavior. Their inadequate academic background and their relatively poor records of work performance offer support for Doll's estimate that 'the individual feebleminded adult may approximate the norm in one respect or another of [the] requirements of social desirability under favorable circumstances or for a limited time or after long standing habituations' in these particular respects; but Doll's further statement that their 'social success is at best temporary, marginal and precarious,' if taken as a general and unqualified judgment is, on our evidence, overdrawn.[3] The morons we studied are, by and large, successful in their social adjustment within limitations, which are apparently imposed by their inferior mental capacities. Doll's remark . . . that 'they find some humble niche in society which they can fill without becoming such a social menace that society becomes gravely concerned about them' seems to fit the actual situation very well.

"Indeed, the present author feels strongly that most if not all morons are unjustly designated as 'feebleminded' in the literal sense. They may be subnormal in many respect, as compared to nonmorons, but in many others they do not even show subnormality."

As was pointed out in an earlier paragraph, one can question whether

---

[3] This statement rests on the questionable assumption that Kennedy and Doll mean the same thing by feeble-mindedness. Since Kennedy's cases had been diagnosed on the basis of a single test score, one cannot assume that similar diagnoses would have been made by Doll (see Chapter 1).

the limitations in the social adjustment of the moron can be wholly attributed to their "inferior mental capacities" as reflected in a test score. If one assumes that unfavorable home background can influence intellectual efficiency and personal-social adjustment, then the test scores of the morons may be considered representative of their *functioning* but not necessarily of their *capacity*. When one considers the work performance of the moron group not with reference to the nonmorons but in relation to the intellectual level indicated by their test scores, the discrepancy between functioning and capacity becomes clearer. For example, 18 percent of the morons were working in managerial, clerical-scales, and skilled occupations. It seems reasonable to assume that the intellectual processes necessary for learning these occupations are not completely different from those called for in the solution of intelligence test items. If this assumption has some validity, one may further assume that for some morons the level of intellectual activity reflected by their occupation is above that indicated by their test quotient. In regard to academic achievement the same discrepancy between achievement and test performance appears. However, these considerations should not obscure the fact that only a relatively small percentage of the morons seemed to show the test score-achievement discrepancy. To the psychologist the problem still remains one of understanding individual differences: Why did some morons make a conventional adjustment while others did not; why did some seem to achieve more than others; why did some morons achieve more and make a more conventional adjustment than some nonmorons; why is it that most morons make an adequate adjustment in the community while others require institutionalization? Perhaps future studies which are both culturally and psychologically oriented will supply some of the answers to the problems posed by individual variations in behavior. The kinds of material which future studies will have to obtain may be seen from the studies by Abel and Kinder (*1, 8, 163*) on the vocational and personal adjustment of institutionalized and noninstitutionalized subnormal girls. They showed that differences between groups were related to differences in the nature of family relationships. In a study of the vocational adjustment of noninstitutionalized subnormal girls Abel (*1*) found:

"The successful girls had a home in which they were not rejected psychologically. Often the fathers treated them severely, particularly in restricting their recreational opportunities. But almost every girl had a sympathetic mother. These mothers were often harassed by hard work both in their homes and in a factory, but nevertheless they genuinely loved their daughters and shared their lives with them. . . . Among the 17 girls who were failures, 14 came from severely unfavorable homes, homes in which they were rejected by the mother, driven and dominated too much by one or both parents, and from a situation where too much responsibility was thrown on their shoulders without any accompanying affection and guidance. Two of these girls became sex offenders, one ran away. One girl was institutionalized by her mother to get her out of the way. Another girl came from a home of much higher intelligence than her own, a home in which her intellectual limitations were not accepted. It is interesting that we had two girls in the successful group who had parents and siblings of considerably higher intelligence than themselves, but in these homes the mother in the one case, and the stepmother in the other, were understanding and showed genuine affection for the girls."

Observations such as these suggest that future studies which are both culturally and psychologically oriented will supply some of the answers to the problems posed by individual variations in behavior. Miller and Dollard (*209*, p. 1) have stated the problem clearly: "To understand thoroughly any item of human behavior—either in the social group or in the individual life—one must know the psychological principles involved in its learning and the social conditions under which this learning took place. It is not enough to know either principles or conditions of learning; in order to predict behavior both must be known."

PSYCHOLOGICAL STUDIES

In contrast to some other etiological groupings relatively little is known about the early development of the garden-variety or subcultural defective. Since these cases do not present any outstanding physical or neurological symptomatology, they are usually not seen in clinics until their deficiencies have become manifest in school difficulties or antisocial behavior. The development of the garden-variety defective from birth to the beginning of the school period represents a gap in our knowledge which future research will have to fill.

In regard to early diagnosis of mental deficiency the following statement by Gesell bears discussion (*99*, p. 124):

"... In some instances the retardation of the moron during infancy may be so mild as to escape attention. Lacking pronounced physical stigmata he may present a plausible picture. It is, of course, well known that even an adult moron sometimes passes for normal in the absence of an adequate diagnosis. An infant moron may be capable of adaptive eye movements, may stare with apparent attention, may smile. According to report, 'He is no trouble at all; he is a good baby.' Perhaps too good; there may be some disquietude because of the lack of vigor in his behavior, but it is optimistically assumed that as he grows older he will be different. The optimism is not warranted. A series of examinations will fail to show any trend toward improvement. It is a very exceptional case of mental deficiency which cannot be diagnosed in the first year of life."

Gesell's statement refers to morons in general without consideration of differences in etiology. Although he presents case studies to show the predictive value of his developmental scales, Gesell does not present systematic follow-up data which would allow one to determine whether his statement holds for all defectives regardless of etiology. In cases of mental deficiency accompanied by gross physical malformation an early diagnosis can be made with a fair degree of reliability and validity. In the absence of physical stigmata or neurological signs, as in the case of the garden-variety defective, the reliability and validity of an early diagnosis remain to be demonstrated. Systematic investigations (21, 118, 195) of the reliability and validity of intellectual ratings of infants by means of developmental scales bear out Doll's warning (71) that "the clinician should . . . be cautious regarding the prognosis of mental deficiency if the examination is made during the period of infancy or early childhood rather than after adolescence." In contrast to Gesell's statement is that of Doll (73): "... it appears that the familial [garden-variety] type of high grade mental deficiency shows a tendency toward delayed retardation which makes the early detection of these cases difficult by psychometric devices alone, especially those of the Binet-Simon variety." In view of Doll's experience that the retardation of the garden-variety defective may not be evident at the early years when the Binet is first applied, it may be questioned whether an infant developmental scale such as Gesell's will be more discriminatory. These conflicting views point up the necessity for research in this area.

Many of the psychological studies of the garden-variety defective have been in terms of comparing the endogenous (garden-variety) and exogenous (brain-injured) types. Because these groups have been studied in relation to each other, no attempt will be made here to consider them separately. The reader is referred to Chapters 2 and 3 for a discussion of the criteria for the diagnosis of brain injury. He should bear in mind that the exogenous or brain-injured includes only those cases with *minimal* brain damage, no obvious motor defect, and with intelligence quotients of 50 or above. The exogenous type does not include brain-injured cases with obvious motor defect, such as the cerebral palsied (Chapter 7). The endogenous-exogenous typology has been most fully developed and studied by Strauss, Werner, and others at the Wayne County Training School.

Strauss (*282*), using the Binet, Ferguson Form Board, Pintner-Patterson, and Arthur Point Scale, separated defectives whose performance age was one year or more below their Binet M.A. from those whose performance age was three years or more above their Binet M.A. In the group ($N = 30$) with performance age below mental age there were 19 exogenous and 5 endogenous cases. In the group with performance age above mental age ($N = 100$) there were 5 exogenous and 32 endogenous cases. From these same groups Werner and Strauss (*317*) selected 21 with high performance and 29 with low performance and compared them on the construction of patterns made with marbles on a mosaic board. The high-performance group made many less errors than the low-performance group. When cases were matched for Binet M.A. and I.Q., the differences in performance still remained. Among the low performance group 11 were diagnosed as exogenous and 10 as endogenous; the average Binet M.A., I.Q., and performance M.A. were similar, although the cases were not matched. An analysis of the mosaic board procedure showed that the endogenous (garden-variety) group attacked the task "globally" with uninterrupted, unidirectional lines, whereas the pattern of the exogenous group was incoherent and characterized by unrelated, discontinuous lines and moves. In the high-performance group the endogenous-exogenous differences occurred "to a certain extent."

In a subsequent study Werner and Strauss (*318*) played melodic patterns on the piano and the children were asked to sing them. "The endogenous group made errors strikingly similar to those of normal children of the same mental age. Normal as well as endogenous children, if confronted with a difficult pattern, will change it by making it simpler, less articulate, more homogeneous. . . . The melodic reproductions of the exogenous group contained errors rarely seen among normal and endogenous children. Their reproductions lacked melodic-harmonic synthesis or satisfactory endings, or were unrelated to the original pattern." In the same study Werner and Strauss constructed a

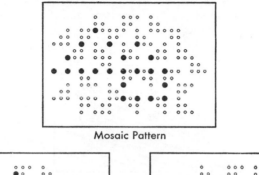

Mosaic Pattern

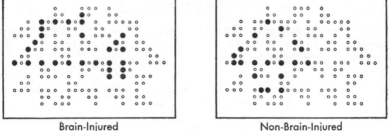

Brain-Injured   Non-Brain-Injured

Fig. 3. Performance of Brain-Injured and Non-Brain-Injured Cases on the Marble Board Test. (*318;* by permission of the American Association on Mental Deficiency.)

new marble board in order to study the role of background in figure-ground relationships. "Here the holes formed a definitely structured background. Against the strong influence of such a background the child had to construct five different figures, by copying each one successively from the examiner's board" (see Fig. 3). Werner and Strauss found that in the exogenous group the background interfered with the construction of the figure and resulted in a disorganized pattern. ". . . Interference of the background is actually one of the conditions for incoherent organization. The endogenous child, it is true, may also be confused by a strong background configuration, but his confusion is of a different kind. Whereas the exogenous type oscillates between figure- and background-configuration the endogenous child, due to his global trend, sticks to the figure. He may, however, form a crude figure which only vaguely resembles the original pattern. In brief, the errors of the endogenous type are due to the vagueness of his comprehension and construction of the marble figures; the errors of the exogenous type are due to a lack of differentiation between the marble figures and the background configuration." Werner and Strauss (*319*) studied further the figure-background relationships in the exogenous and endogenous types of tachistoscopic presentation of cards containing

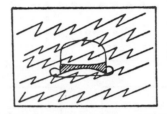

Fig. 4.   Test Card Used in the Study of Figure-Background Relations. (*319;* by permission of the *Journal of Abnormal and Social Psychology* and the American Psychological Association, Inc.)

black-and-white line drawings of objects embedded in homogeneous backgrounds: jagged or wavy lines, squares, crosses, etc., (see Fig. 4). The pictures were exposed for one-fifth of a second and the child was requested to tell what he saw. Each card was presented twice in succession. "Seventy-five and one-half percent of the reactions of the exogenous group were to the background alone, whereas only 13.9 percent of the reactions of the endogenous type refer to the background. There are surprisingly few pure object-reactions among the children of the exogenous group, viz., 11.7 percent as compared with 58.3 percent object-reactions of the endogenous type. An analysis of the scores for individual children reveals that of the 25 individuals of the endogenous group 19 show three or less background-reactions. On the other, 19 of the 25 individuals of the exogenous group show three or less object-reactions."

Further evidence of perceptual differences between the two groups is found in the studies by Werner and Thuma (*320, 321*) on flicker-frequency and apparent movement. In the case of flicker-frequency the critical fusion point was lower for the exogenous (brain-injured) at the three different brightness levels employed, the difference at the lower brightness levels being greater than at the higher. In the study of apparent movement a vertical and a horizontal line were presented in brief and alternating exposures. The exogenous group experienced the two lines as a single line in angular motion at a lower rate of succession than did the endogenous (garden-variety) group. In other words, the exogenous group tended to see two lines in succession and at rest at a time interval sufficient for apparent movement in the endogenous group. Werner and Thuma concluded that the reactions of the exogenous group "might be regarded as results of an impairment of the normal mechanism of integration and, following Goldstein, that the lesions may interfere with the interaction of regions of the nervous system in such a way as to lead to a relative isolation of neural events. Such an isolation might be supposed to result in a perseveration or prolonged after-effect of stimulation as a consequence of the reduction of the inhibitory action of the cortex on lower centers. The lower critical frequency for the brain-injured group may be explained on this hypothesis since a perseveration of the after-effects of the successive flashes might be expected to yield fusion at a lower rate of stimulation" (*321*).

Werner (*315*) also studied differences in rigidity between the exogenous and endogenous types. He defined rigidity "as lack of variability and adaptability" of response. Perseveration, the persistent repetition or continuation of an activity once begun, was the particular aspect of rigidity with which he was concerned. In the four experimental situations employed "reproduction of material, either visually or auditorily presented was a common feature of all four tasks. Depending on the particular test, the child reproduced either by drawing, by speaking, or by motor action." Since the results of the four experiments were similar, only the first experiment will be presented here.

"*Experiment I: Reproduction of Tone Rhythms.* Twelve rhythmic patterns were presented. By pressing a key, a tone of constant pitch and of any desired length could be produced on an oscillator. Each rhythm consisted of a number of these tones of very short and of long (one second's) duration.

The subject, blindfolded, was requested to listen to each rhythm carefully, and to reproduce it immediately by pressing the key. A preliminary practice series of six patterns preceded the main series."

Werner noted the total number of wrong patterns as well as the following special kinds of perseverative activity: "(a) *Simple perseveration* may be defined as a single repetition of an immediately preceding pattern; (b) *repetitive perseveration* is the repetition of a pattern occurring more than once within the series; *iterative (jumping), or delayed,* perseveration is a suddenly appearing repetition of a pattern which had been presented two or more trials earlier in the series." In Table 6 are presented the results of this experiment. Werner concluded that the rigidity of the endogenous (garden-variety) de-

TABLE 6.   Perseverations Occurring During Reproduction of
Tone Rhythms (*315*)

Group	Total Number of Wrong Patterns	Perseverations (Percentage of Number of Wrong Patterns)			
		Total	Repetitive	Delayed	Simple
Endogenous	221	10.9	2.3	1.4	7.2
Brain-Injured	293	31.4	18.0	8.9	4.5
ρ (Chi-Square)		$< .01$		$< .01$	

fective is "related predominantly to 'global' behavior, i.e., to perception or action organized as undifferentiated wholes." In contrast, the rigidity of the brain-injured is "probably the result of isolation of certain elements of a series. These isolated elements may become self-contained and detached from the continuity of the series to such an extent that they either may be repeated over and over again or 'jump' suddenly into the fore in spite of the incongruity of such behavior."

In evaluating the results of the above studies an initial question that might be raised concerns their diagnostic value to the clinician. In other words, to what extent can these findings be utilized in deciding whether a given case fits into the endogenous or exogenous group? A similar question concerns the degree of overlap between the two groups in the experimental situations. For example, in the study of melodic reproductions (see p. 116) 11 percent of the patterns of the endogenous group were incoherent, meaningless, and unrelated, in contrast to 61 percent in the exogenous group. Although the difference is statistically significant, it should be pointed out that the results are given in terms of *responses* and not of *individuals*. What would be important to know is how many endogenous cases gave such responses and how many of the exogenous cases gave few or many such responses.[4] Is the 61 percent of such responses the result of a few exogenous cases giving many such responses, or of all or most of the cases contributing equally? In other words, how many of the exogenous and endogenous cases gave the same number of such responses? In the study of the perception of figure-background relationships by tachistoscopic presentation (see p. 118) Werner and Strauss give some of their results in terms of individuals: ". . . Of the 25 individuals of the endogenous group 19 show three or less background-reactions. On the other hand, 19 of the 25 individuals of the exogenous group show three or less object-reactions." Although these results indicate that 6 cases (approximately 25 percent) in the endogenous group gave more than three background-reactions, it is not possible to state how many of the exogenous cases gave the same number of such responses. The degree of overlap for object-reactions is also not calculable. Without such data one does not know how many *non*brain-injured cases may be expected to give a response considered "characteristic" of brain injury. Werner's findings in his rigidity experiments may be similarly analyzed (see Table 6). Here again responses rather than individuals are treated in percentages and again one does not know the extent to which each case contributes to the total. For example, 18 percent of the wrong patterns of the exogenous (brain-injured) group were of the repetitive perseverative type. This 18 percent may be the result of a few cases who gave many such responses or of a large number of cases who gave few such responses. If the former is the case, it would suggest that a comparison on an individual basis might not give as significant a difference between the two groups.[5] Werner and Thuma's study of flicker-frequency (see p. 119) may be discussed from the standpoint of overlap between the

[4] It might also be pointed out that the reliability of judging melodic reproduction was not given.

[5] It might be pointed out that the use of chi-square is not justified in Table 6 because one of the assumptions underlying the use of this statistic is that each entry in a cell is independent of all other entries in the cell. In Table 6 an individual may be represented several times in a given cell, thus destroying the independence of each entry.

groups. At a brightness level of 30.0 millilamberts the average critical flicker-frequency of the exogenous group was 34.83 in contrast to 40.63 for the endogenous cases, a statistically significant difference. "There are only two children in the brain-injured group who reached the average of the control [endogenous] group and only two of the controls whose thresholds were as low or lower than the average of the children with brain injury" (321). Although this statement suggests a wide difference between the individuals in each group, it should be noted that 8 cases (40 percent) in the endogenous group had critical flicker-frequencies almost identical with those of cases in the exogenous group.[6]

It seems reasonable to conclude on the basis of available evidence that Werner, Strauss, and others have not demonstrated that exogenous *individuals* possess characteristics which are only rarely found in garden-variety *individuals*. It follows, therefore, that behavior in the test situations employed cannot be used with a high degree of certainty as a basis for diagnosis of brain injury in the absence of neurological evidence (see p. 57). Frazeur and Hoakley's study (88) is informative on this point. Unlike Werner and Strauss who used extreme groups (those whose performance age was one year or more below or three years or more above the Binet mental age), Frazeur and Hoakley matched 9 exogenous cases on a one-to-one basis with endogenous cases of similar age and Binet I.Q. They then compared the two groups on the Arthur Point Scale. Using the 1 percent level of confidence they found no statistically significant difference between the two groups either on performance quotient or on any of the 8 subtests. With the 5 percent level of confidence, only the Porteus Mazes distinguished between the two groups. The only other significant finding was in variability on the Mare and Foal test. Although their groups were small, the results confirm the expectation that the test patterns obtained on extreme groups by Werner and Strauss do not necessarily discriminate between exogenous and endogenous cases in general.[7]

Heath (133) studied differences in rail-walking performance between

---

[6] In comparing the two groups the writer dropped the single number to the right of the decimal point: critical flicker-frequencies of 38.8 and 38.5 were considered as 38, etc.

[7] Hoakley and Frazeur (140) also compared 18 matched cases on Binet performance. No significant differences were obtained except in the drawing of a diamond. "But this, in itself, cannot be used as a diagnostic tool since, of the fifteen pairs having this test, nine made equal scores." In regard to their study Hoakley and Frazeur stated: "We have presented it as a warning to psychologists to use diagnostic patterns with extreme caution until they are thoroughly authenticated, and even then to keep in mind that the case under consideration may be the exception to the rule."

endogenous and "exogenous" subjects. It must be kept in mind that he included in his exogenous category all cases other than the garden-variety (endogenous) type. He did not restrict the exogenous group to those who showed minimal motor defect and minor or no neurological signs. The test which Heath devised consisted of three wooden rails: the first was 9 feet long and 4 inches wide, the second was 9 feet long and 2 inches wide, and the third was 6 feet long and 1 inch wide. Each subject, with shoes removed, was asked to walk each rail "in such a way that the heel of the second foot (i.e., the foot completing the step) touched the toe of the first foot." Speed was not considered in scoring. Heath found that the exogenous group did significantly poorer than the endogenous cases in rail-walking performance and concluded that this type of test might ultimately be of help in determining etiology. However, since the criteria by which the two groups were *originally* classified are only sketchily given, one cannot determine the validity of Heath's division of his cases into brain-injured and nonbrain-injured groups. Until the rail-walking test is used with groups whose neurological status is unequivocal, enabling one to place each group on a continuum of neurological involvement, the diagnostic-etiologic value of the test must be questioned.

Bolles (*41*) made a study of the "qualitative differences in certain of the thinking processes of aments, dements, and normal children of approximately the same mental age." Her "primary aments" were presumably of the institutionalized, garden-variety type, and her dements were schizophrenics of the hebephrenic variety who had average intelligence before the onset of the psychosis. The aments and dements were comparable for chronological age, mental age, sex, institutionalization, and American birth. The normal group consisted of intellectually average boys with mental ages comparable to those of the two deviant groups. There were 10 cases in the normal and defective groups and 9 in the psychotic group. Each subject was observed in a variety of test situations: sorting tests (Holmgren wools, Weigl, object sorting), the Kohs Block test as revised by Goldstein, and the Feature-Profile test from the Pintner-Pattern Scale (see Table 7). Bolles found that there were four different ways in which objects were classified (*41*, p. 46):

1. *Identity.* The subject brings together only those objects which are exact sensory equivalents. If there are any discrepancies between them, the objects are not brought together.
2. *Partial Identity.* The subject brings objects together that are similar in

TABLE 7. Three of the Test Procedures Employed by Bolles in the Study of Aments, Dements, and Normals (After 41)

Holmgren Test	Weigl Form-Color Sorting Test	Object Sorting Test (A)
The wools of the Holmgren Test for color blindness were used in a revised manner. a. The subject was asked to select all that belonged with a particular sample. He was then asked why they belonged together. If the subject had selected a small number of skeins the experimenter picked up other samples of the same primary hue and asked if they might be included. The subject was then asked to select skeins belonging to each of the primary hues. b. Three skeins were placed in front of the subject. The experimenter pointed to the middle skein and asked with which of the other two skeins it belonged. Of the latter, one skein was the equivalent of the center skein in tint, and other was the same hue but of different tint and saturation. c. Two groups, each containing samples, were placed before the subject. One group consisted of different tints and saturations of the same hue, and the other of different hues of the same tint. The subject was asked which belonged together, or which were more alike. Explanations of the basis of choice were requested.	Twelve cardboard figures containing 3 forms (squares, triangles, circles) were put before the subject. Each form appeared in 4 colors: red, yellow, blue, and green. The subject was asked to "put those together that belonged together." After he had sorted the figures in one way he was asked why they belonged this way. Then he was told to put them together in another way, or in a different way. If the subject classified first on the basis of color and was unable to do so on the basis of form, the figures were turned upside down so that they were all a uniform white and he was asked to sort them. After this procedure, the figures were again turned back to the colored side and the original instructions repeated to see whether the subject could now shift from one point of view to another voluntarily and thus sort according to both attributes.	The test materials consisted of 38 figures that varied in 4 attributes: color, form, material and dimension. There were 3 colors, red, yellow, and blue; 2 types of material, wood and paper; 3 forms, rectangles and triangles of varying proportions, and semicircles; and 4 different thicknesses. The test materials were placed before the subject in random order and he was asked to put those together that he thought belonged together. After one type of sorting had been completed he was asked to do it in another way in order to see whether he was able to shift his attention from one aspect of the situation to another.

some ways. The similarity seems still to be on a sensory level. The objects seem to be equivalent in terms of some one sensory attribute.

3. *Co-functionality.* The subject brings the objects together because they seem to belong together in a concrete situation. The relationship between them seems to depend upon their being used together in a specific set of circumstances.

4. *Categorical Similarity.* The subject brings together objects that belong to the same general category. The objects are taken as representative of a class and not in terms of some specific attribute or function each possesses.

". . . These types constitute a series in which there are more and more discrepancies between the objects classed together. In order to see any basic similarity between objects in the 'categorical similarity' classification, it is necessary to overlook a wide range of variation. In the 'identity' type of classification there are no discrepancies between the objects. According to the definition of abstraction as the process of overlooking individual variation to grasp a basic similarity the series may be said to make up a series of 'levels of abstraction.' Grouping on the basis of 'identity' performance is the most concrete and on the basis of 'categorical similarity' the most abstract." In contrast to the normals, the aments and dements tended to respond concretely. They also were unable to shift voluntarily from one aspect of a situation to another. Table 8 summarizes the performance of the three groups on the Weigl Form-Color sorting test. It will be seen that the defectives tended to sort according to color and were unable "to drop" this criterion and utilize another (form). Bolles describes the performance of one of the aments who sorted first according to color: "When the figures were turned to the white side, and the subject was again asked to sort them, he proceeded in a slow laborious way as if the task was very difficult. He arranged them into four piles in which different forms were mixed up. When asked how he had done this, he said, 'Done with back up. For you to see if I had the same colors together.' The subject behaved as though controlled by the earlier attitude. He seemed to regard the figures as colored figures 'with the backs up' and so was not impressed by other similarities in the materials presented to him." Bolles points out that the chief difference between aments and normals was not in the type of classification employed but in the inability to shift from one type to another, a characteristic which Bolles

TABLE 8. Performance of Aments, Dements and Normals on the
Weigl Color-Form Sorting Test (41)

Type of Organization	Subjects		
	Dements	Aments	Children
Grouped according to two categories	3	1, 5	(all)
Grouped first for form	1, 2, 3, 5, 6, 7, 9	7	1, 2, 3, 4, 10
Grouped first for color	4	1, 2, 3, 4, 5, 6, 8, 9, 10	5, 6, 7, 8, 9
Stated basis of sorting (color).....	4	1, 2, 3, 4, 5, 6, 8, 9, 10	(all)
Stated basis of sorting (form).....	2, 9	0	(all)
Grouped for form only after white side given	4	4, 7, 8	0
Arrangement of figures in symmetrical design	1	3, 4, 5, 7, 8, 10	0
Arrangement of figures in terms of a specific situation	0	2, 3, 4, 8	0

noted was found in cases of cerebral lesions. *It is important to note that although Bolles and Strauss both used garden-variety defectives in their studies, the former is struck by the similarity of their performance to brain-injured cases and the latter emphasizes their dissimilarity to brain-injured cases.*

In comparing the garden-variety defectives with other groups a question that arises concerns their homogeneity on the variables being studied. If it should be found that the garden-variety group is not homogeneous in test functioning, it would seem important to control for this factor in comparative studies. In other words, in comparing schizophrenics with other psychotics an attempt is made to state the type of schizophrenic case being used (paranoid, hebephrenic, etc.), and the homogeneity of the garden-variety defective should similarly be studied.

Sarason and Sarason (260) selected 40 institutionalized garden-variety defectives on the following criteria: (1) the neurological examination was negative, (2) only those cases were chosen in which more than one child in the family was in the institution, (3) all members of a given family had to have a similar degree of mental defect. Each case was given the 1937 Binet (L), the Arthur Point Scale, the Rorschach, and an electroencephalogram. The cases were divided according to the Kohs-Binet relationship: Those ($N = 11$) whose mental age on the Kohs Block Designs was at least 18 months beyond the Binet M.A. were put in one group; those ($N = 16$) whose mental age on the Kohs was at least 18 months below the Binet were put into a second group; and the remainder were put in a third group. Only the first two groups were studied. There was no significant difference between them for average mental or chronological age. On the Binet the Kohs-below-Binet group did significantly poorer on the drawing of a diamond, memory for designs, and paper cutting. Table 9 shows the number of

TABLE 9. Number of Individuals Failing the Different Combinations of the Three Selected Binet Items (260)

Possible Combinations of Failure on Three Selected Binet Items	Kohs Below Binet	Kohs Above Binet
Failed diamond only	0	0
Failed diamond and memory for designs only	0	0
Failed diamond and paper cutting only	1	0
Failed diamond, memory for designs, and paper cutting	5	0
Failed memory for designs only	2	1
Failed memory for designs and paper cutting only	4	1
Failed paper cutting only	1	1
Failed none	3	8

individuals who failed any combination of the three Binet items. On the Rorschach the Kohs-above-Binet group made fewer responses, delineated them more precisely, rejected more cards, and gave less human movement responses. In Table 10 are presented the EEG data.

TABLE 10. Number of Individuals in Each Group Having a Given Kind of EEG Record (260)

Type of EEG Record	Kohs Above Binet	Kohs Below Binet
Very fast		
Moderately fast	1	2
Normal	9	6
Moderately slow		3
Very slow	1	4

In the Kohs-below-Binet group 60 percent of the cases had an abnormal EEG record, but only 18 percent of the Kohs-above-Binet group had such records, a statistically significant difference. When one considers the three Binet items (drawing a diamond, memory for designs, and paper cutting) on which the groups differed, it may be said that for a successful solution of each the individual is required to verbalize or to formulate to himself a mode of attack. The same may also be said for the Kohs Block Designs on which the two groups differed by the very nature of the method of analysis. Why the two groups differed in their adequacy with these tasks is difficult to say. Earlier studies by Bender (30), Goldstein (117), and Wechsler (311) have indicated that failure with this type of task is characteristic of the brain-injured case. Although the cases in Sarason and Sarason's study showed no neurological indication of brain damage, it is interesting that the group (Kohs-below-Binet) who did poorly on these tasks also had an unusually large incidence of abnormal brain-wave records. Added confirmation for the belief that some garden-variety defectives have brain malformations is seen in Benda's post-mortem study (28) of 20 such institutionalized cases in most of which he found developmental anomalies in the spinal cord and brain. Benda's findings should not be considered representative of all garden-variety defectives because his sample was small and selected and the results have not been confirmed by others. Mautner (196) reported findings similar to those of Benda, but very few of his small sample were of the familial or garden-variety type.

Much caution has to be exercised in evaluating the Sarason's findings. First, the number of cases in each of the two groups is small. Second, poor performance on the three Binet tasks and the Kohs designs was not always associated with an abnormal brain-wave record; it should be noted that two individuals in the Kohs-above-Binet group had abnormal brain waves. Third, it cannot be assumed that failure on the three Binet tasks and the Kohs designs is due only to the interfering effects of a brain injury. On the Kohs designs, for example, Sarason and Potter (259) found that in a group of nondefective behavior-problem children with no indication of brain damage a poor Kohs performance in relation to the Binet M.A. was much more frequent than one that was as good as or better than the Binet M.A. In this connection it is interesting to note that in the Sarason and Sarason study the group who did most poorly on the Kohs was far more socially maladjusted and vocationally inefficient than the group who did best on the Kohs. With these cautions in mind the following conclusions seem warranted:

1. Within the garden-variety grouping there are significant differences in test functioning or patterning which seem related to social and vocational adjustment; inordinate difficulty with tasks of a visuo-motor nature involving self-verbalization of a procedure is associated with adjustment difficulties.

2. There is evidence that *some* of the garden-variety defectives who show marked inadequacy in the visuo-motor sphere and also possess abnormal brain-wave records *may* have some form of brain injury. These cases represent a very small portion of this etiological grouping.

In relation to the first conclusion mention should be made of the fact that more than half of the Kohs-above-Binet group succeeded on at least 13 of the 17 Kohs designs, and two succeeded on all of them. Aside from the fact that a high Kohs score has been considered (*311*, p. 134) as contraindicating mental deficiency, these results raise the problem of explaining how these subjects were able to perform so well on a task on which the majority of defectives and many nondefectives do poorly. It was hypothecated in a preceding paragraph that an adequate Kohs performance requires a self-verbalized conceptual process. If this assumption has merit, it follows that for these cases the level of conceptual thinking is a function of the nature of the task. In the face-to-face Binet situation, where an oral response to a verbally presented problem is usually required, the quality of conceptual thinking of these cases was well below that indicated by their Kohs performance. These considerations raise the following questions for future research: (1) What kinds of verbalized or nonverbalized responses (anticipations, attitudes, emotional level) are elicited by one stimulus task (Kohs) which are not obtained by another (Binet)? (2) How are these differences in response related to previous learning experiences?

Findings similar to those of Sarason and Sarason have been obtained by Bijou (*36, 37, 38*), although the etiological grouping of his cases is not given. Bijou found "that mentally retarded boys having high Arthur Performance Quotients (PQ's) relative to Binet I.Q.'s also have high arithmetic attainment relative to reading achievement. Furthermore, boys showing such a test configuration receive above-average proficiency ratings in shop work (provided their Binet I.Q.'s are above 65), and are judged to be better adjusted than boys of comparable mental ages but having low PQ's. In contrast, boys with low PQ's split into two subgroups when relative accomplishment in reading and arithmetic is taken into account: half succeed well in arithmetic; half fail miserably in the subject. . . . These same boys are rated as below-average in shop work and are considered inferior in personal-social adjustment compared with their matched mates" (37). Bijou then selected 4 cases from each of his two extreme groups and studied their developmental histories. Those in the low P.Q. groups he found were frequently ill during childhood, indulged in delinquent activities, received frequent punishment, made fair progress in school, and had unsatisfactory interpersonal relationships. In the high P.Q. cases Bijou found evidences of problem behavior, lack of adjustment to the classroom situation particularly because of reading difficulties, inadequate personal-social habits, and no unusual incidence of illness. The finding that the high P.Q. group had developed unfavorable attitudes toward the reading and classroom situations sheds light on their relatively poor performance in the face-to-face, school-like Binet situation. A subsequent study by Wallin and Hultsch (307) of children referred to a public-school clinic primarily because of possible mental deficiency and secondarily because of behavior problems did not show the fairly clear-cut results obtained by Bijou. The differences in results may in part be due to the fact that Bijou used white male institutionalized cases, whereas Wallin and Hultsch used noninstitutionalized males and females, the majority of whom were colored; also, Bijou had more extensive data on which to evaluate behavior than did Wallin and Hultsch. It may well be that because the P.Q. and I.Q. may be derived from numerous combinations of successes and failures, they may not be relied upon to give consistent results. The fact that an individual obtains a relatively high P.Q. may obscure the fact that he did well on the subtests (i.e., Seguin, Casuist, and Mare and Foal) in which speed was primary, and did poorly on the subtests (Knox, Kohs, and Porteus) in which formulation of a procedure was important. In other words, although the P.Q. may be higher than the I.Q., the individual may have done most poorly on those subtests which require an intellectual process similar to that required in the Binet. If two individuals of similar mental and chronological ages had P.Q.'s higher than I.Q.'s, but one case did poorly on the Kohs and Porteus subtests and the other did well, one would probably not conclude that they had the same "performance ability." In Table 11 are presented the total Arthur point score, the point score for each subtest, and the P.Q. and Binet I.Q. of 15 garden-variety defectives selected at random from all such cases with Binet mental ages between 6–6 and 7–5. The most striking feature of the table is that almost invariably the P.Q. is higher than the I.Q., the average difference being 19 points. In addition, it is clear from the table that the high P.Q.'s are largely due to the fact that the speed tests are given as much weight in the final total score as the tests requiring a conceptual process, which is tantamount to giving the speed tests undue weight. The fact that the P.Q. is almost invariably higher than the Binet I.Q. is surprising but not unexpected. Kinder and Hamlin (164), using a discrepancy of 10 points between the Binet and Pintner-Patterson as a criterion, found only 9 percent of their cases with a higher Binet I.Q. and 33 percent with a higher P.Q. Patterson's analysis (229) of the Arthur Point Scale likewise showed a marked tendency for the P.Q. to be higher than the I.Q. She also found that the "puzzle and formboard types of test (Mare and Foal, Manikin and Feature Profile, Casuist and Seguin form boards) contributed more than the other subtests to the high initial scores." When readministrations of the scale were viewed as indicators of learning ability, Patterson (230) found that defective children who had a relatively high school achievement tended to gain more on readministration than those who had low achievement. The high and low achievement groups were matched in age, intelligence quotient, and institutional residence. It is interesting to note that there was no difference between the two groups in initial P.Q.

On the basis of the psychological studies discussed in this chapter, it seems warranted to conclude that there is no single test pattern which clearly differentiates garden-variety defectives from other groups. This conclusion is not surprising when one takes several factors into account. Garden-variety defectives are a heterogeneous group, differing among themselves in emotional stability, institutionalization, age at and length of institutionalization, family constellation, previous life experiences, physical attractiveness, urban or rural residence, etc. It

TABLE 11. Binet and Arthur Point Scale Results of 15 Garden-Variety Defectives with M.A. between 6-6 and 7-5

Case	Total Point Score	Knox	Seguin	Casuist	Feature-Profile	Mare and Foal	Healy	Porteus	Kohs·	P.Q.	Binet I.Q.
1	30.62	5.53	6.58	4.83	2.30	4.49	2.59	3.05	1.25	86	55
2	19.69	2.11	7.36	4.44	1.28	1.58	1.60	1.20	.12	69	59
3	21.84	.58	6.58	3.85	2.22	4.71	3.86	—1.08	—1.12	66	55
4	23.67	2.67	5.78	4.78	2.96	4.97	2.30	2.39	.12	68	54
5	36.84	1.55	5.78	3.83	4.53	5.74	6.65	6.73	2.03	84	49
6	10.62	2.11	5.78	2.35	1.28	.95	.43	—1.54	.12	50	50
7	22.65	2.11	5.78	3.04	1.28	5.74	2.19	2.39	.12	62	51
8	14.54	.58	2.91	3.62	2.63	2.88	1.22	.33	.37	52	49
9	37.87	1.06	9.70	6.06	4.04	6.01	3.96	5.79	1.25	84	50
10	35.50	2.67	4.48	5.36	3.94	6.01	5.35	5.79	1.90	75	43
11	39.44	2.67	8.92	4.05	3.70	5.23	5.53	5.17	4.17	84	47
12	36.10	.58	7.36	4.99	3.87	5.49	5.50	4.57	3.74	77	47
13	31.74	2.67	5.09	2.65	3.49	3.42	5.56	7.35	1.50	69	47
14	17.06	.10	5.78	2.92	3.85	3.56	1.27	—1.54	1.12	52	47
15	21.67	—1.34	6.58	2.51	4.29	4.27	3.79	1.20	.37	57	45

would have been surprising if studies which did not control for all or a majority of these variables should have found a "characteristic" test pattern. When one matches garden-variety and brain-injured individuals for M.A. and C.A., he cannot assume that they are also comparable on the variables noted above. To what extent the failure to obtain clear-cut test patterns is due to the fact that significant variables other than M.A. and C.A. have not been considered can be answered only by future research. It may also be that the tendency to view test performance from the standpoint of the pass-fail criterion rather than in terms of patterns and conditions of present and past learning has been a major factor making for the inconclusive findings.

Chapter 6

CULTURAL FACTORS IN THE ETIOLOGY OF
GARDEN-VARIETY DEFICIENCY

THE social and intellectual incompetency of the garden-variety defective has generally been assumed to be due to the limitations imposed by an inferior hereditary endowment. Despite the well-nigh perfect correlation between garden-variety deficiency and unfavorable social conditions the consensus among workers in the field is that cultural factors are relatively unimportant in the causation of the condition. Some evidence against this traditional opinion has already been presented in Chapter 2. In the present chapter research findings concerning the relation between infant-rearing practices and individual development will be discussed and their applicability to the present problem explored.

Implicit in all approaches to the study of the individual is the assumption that the period of infancy is of special importance in shaping the individual's behavioral pattern. Physical and emotional mothering (fondling, caressing, rocking, etc.), consistency of parental response, stimulation and reinforcement of the child's responsiveness to the environment, absence of prolonged physical and emotional frustrations with their attendant increase in bodily tension and unrest—these are some of the factors that are considered conducive for the learning of those attitudes toward self and others which make for efficient and productive use of the individual's capacities. The child whose hunger drive is satisfied "by the clock," whose bodily tensions and crying spells are not rewarded by the satisfying experience of physical contact with or attention from the parents, whose needs are sometimes responded to promptly and gently and at other times belatedly and gruffly, whose initial vocalizations and locomotions are not rewarded by parental enthusiasm and increased attention—the behavioral pattern of such a child is expected to contain attitudes toward self and others which interfere with full and efficient utilization of capacities. It is not at all clear how the infant's acquired responses to selected stimuli in his environment become integrated with his increasing awareness of himself as a person distinct from others. In the case of a child who is fondled only at certain times of the day and is the recipient of perfunctory and unemotional attention from his parents, there is little opportunity for natural responsiveness to be rewarded and by such reinforcement to be repeated. One would expect that in such a child the tendency to respond to others would become weak and, perhaps, the tendency to avoid the responsiveness of others would become strong. How such learned behavior affects a child's growing conception of himself and others is a process which is not at all clear at present, but that such a process occurs may be assumed. When parental behavior changes markedly after the child has become aware of himself as a person distinct from others, the effect of this change on the child's attitudes toward self and others is less difficult to understand. For example, when for the first year or so of his life he has learned to expect that his mother will gratify his needs, relieve his tensions, and encourage and support him in mastering new activities, an abrupt change in the relationship can affect his attitudes in several ways. As Kardiner (79, p. 12) has pointed out: "The result is first that the conception of the mother changes from good to bad. This means that certain expectations previously freely entertained must now be suppressed and compensatory activities invented. The failure of this latter must give rise to anger toward the mother, which must likewise be suppressed. Then follows an alteration of the child's conception of itself with respect to its mother, namely, the feeling of not being loved, a lowering of self-esteem, and either an increase in its independence or an accentuation of its dependence." The validity of this formulation is well illustrated in DuBois' study, *The people of Alor* (79). In a later section it will be seen that the acquisition of maladjustive behavioral patterns before the formation of attitudes toward self and others has crystallized seems to have a more insidious influence on development than when such patterns are acquired afterward.

Investigators are by no means agreed as to the effect of certain infant-training practices and experiences on later functioning. While some workers maintain that breast feeding is psychologically and physically more beneficial than bottle feeding, others point out that many infants who have been bottle-fed show no untoward effects. Still others maintain that the important variable is not the method of feeding but the accompanying attitudes of the mother toward her child. Some pediatricians strongly advocate that an infant be fed only at stated intervals, whereas others feel that following a schedule produces undue tensions in the child and ignores the importance of prompt gratification of his needs. In order to reduce the effects of oral frustration some pediatricians advocate feeding on an *ad lib* or *laissez-faire* basis. The data necessary for evaluating these and other contradictory contentions about specific child-training practices are not available. It may be anticipated, as Mowrer and Kluckhohn (*211*) and Dubois (*78*) have maintained, that a single child-training practice is rarely sufficient to explain the acquisition of a behavioral pattern. The significance of a child-training practice lies in the manner and motivation of the parent applying it, the effect on the child experiencing it, the degree to which the motivation and manner of the parent in regard to the practice is indicative of a more generalized attitude toward the child, and the degree to which the effects on the child are also experienced in other kinds of situations with the parent. Orlansky (*223*) concluded similarly on the basis of his critical review of the literature on infant care and personality: ". . . We are led to reject the thesis that specific nursing disciplines have a specific, invariant psychological impact upon the child. Instead, it appears that the effect of a particular discipline can be determined only from knowledge of the parental attitudes associated with it, the value which the culture places upon that discipline, the organic constitution of the infant, and the entire socio-cultural situation in which the individual is located. In short, it is contended that personality is not the resultant of instinctual infantile libidinal drives mechanically channelled by parental disciplines, but rather that it is a dynamic product of the interaction of a unique organism undergoing maturation and a unique physical and social environment."

That certain child-training practices and experiences during the first year of life have a deleterious effect on intellectual and emotional growth has been revealed by clinical and experimental studies. The prolonged absence of the mother or the effects of the lack of "mothering" seem to reduce the degree of the child's responsiveness or awareness of ongoing activities. Since the mother is the almost exclusive source of the child's external stimulation, it would be expected that his responsiveness would be a function of the degree of stimulation by her. In the absence of gratification, responsiveness is more likely to be extinguished than reinforced. The following illustrative case is taken from Ribble.

"Little Bob was born in the maternity hospital where the writer was making studies of infants at the time. He was a full-term child and weighed six pounds three ounces at birth. During the two weeks' stay in the hospital the baby was breast fed and there was no apparent difficulty with his body functions. The mother, a professional woman, had been reluctant about breast feeding because she wished to take up her work as soon as possible after the baby was born, but she yielded to the kindly encouragement of the hospital nurses, and the feeding was successful. Both mother and child were thriving when they left the hospital.

"On returning home the mother found that her husband had suddenly deserted her—the climax of an unhappy and maladjusted marriage relationship. She discovered soon after that her milk did not agree with the baby. As is frequently the case, the deep emotional reaction had affected her milk secretion. The infant refused the breast and began to vomit. Later he was taken to the hospital and the mother did not call to see him. At the end of a month she wrote that she had been seriously ill and asked the hospital to keep the child until further notice.

"In spite of careful medical attention and skillful feeding, this baby remained for two months at practically the same weight. He was in a crowded ward and received very little personal attention. The busy nurses had no time to take him up and work with him as a mother would, by changing his position and making him comfortable at frequent intervals. The habit of finger sucking developed, and gradually the child became what is known as a ruminator, his food coming up and going down with equal ease. At the age of two months he weighed five pounds. The baby at this time was transferred to a small children's hospital, with the idea that this institution might be able to give him more individual care. It became apparent that the mother had abandoned the child altogether.

"When seen by the writer, this baby actually looked like a seven months' foetus yet he had also a strange appearance of oldness. His arms and legs were wrinkled and wasted, his head large in proportion to the rest of the body, his chest round and flaring widely at the base over an enormous liver. His breathing was shallow, he was generally inactive, and his skin was cold and flabby. He took large quantities of milk but did not gain weight since most of it went through him with very little assimilation and with copious discharges of mucus from his intestines. The baby showed at this time the pallor which in our study we have found typical of infants who are not mothered, although careful examination of his blood did not indicate a serious degree of anemia. He was subject to severe sweating, particularly during sleep. A thorough study showed no indication of tuberculosis. The child's abdomen was large and protruding, but this proved to be due to lax intestinal muscles and consequent distention with gas and to a greatly enlarged and distended liver, which was actually in proportion to that of the foetus. There was no evidence of organic disease, but growth and development were definitely at a standstill, and it appeared that the child was gradually slipping backward to lower and lower levels of body economy and function.

"The routine treatment of this hospital for babies who are not gaining weight is to give them concentrated nursing care. They are held in the nurse's lap for feeding and allowed at least half an hour to take the bottle. From time to time their position in the crib is changed and when possible the nurse carries them about the ward for a few minutes before or after each feeding. This is the closest possible approach to mothering in a busy infants' ward. Medical treatment consists of frequent injections of salt solution under the skin to support the weakened circulation in the surface of the body.

"With this treatment the child began to improve slowly. As his physical condition became better, it was possible for our research group to introduce the services of a volunteer 'mother' who came to the hospital twice daily in order to give him some of the attention he so greatly needed. What she actually did was to hold him in her lap for a short period before his 10 A.M. and 6 P.M. feedings. She was told that he needed love more than he needed medicine, and she was instructed to stroke the child's head gently and speak or sing softly to him and walk him about. Her daily visits were gradually prolonged until she was spending an hour twice a day, giving the baby this artificial mothering. The result was good. The child remained in the hospital until he was five months of age, at which time he weighed nine pounds. All rumination and diarrhea had stopped, and he had become an alert baby with vigorous muscular activity. His motor coordinations were of course retarded. Although he held up his head well and looked about, focusing his eyes and smiling in response to his familiar nurses, he could not yet grasp his own bottle or turn himself over, as is customary at this age. The finger sucking continued, as is usually the case with babies who have suffered early privation.

"In accordance with the new hospital procedure, as soon as the child's life was no longer in danger, he was transferred to a good, supervised foster home in order that he might have still more individual attention. Under this regime, his development proceeded well and gradually he mastered such functions as sitting, creeping, and standing. His speech was slow in developing, however, and he did not walk until after the second year. The general health of this child is now excellent at the end of his third year; also his

'I.Q.' is high on standard tests, but his emotional life is deeply damaged. With any change in his routine or with a prolonged absence of the foster mother, he goes into a state which is quite similar to a depression. He becomes inactive, eats very little, becomes constipated and extremely pale. When his foster mother goes away, he usually reacts with a loss of body tone and alertness, rather than with a definite protest. His emotional relationship to the foster mother is receptive, like that of a young infant, but he makes little response to her mothering activities except to function better when she is there. He has little capacity to express affection, displays no initiative in seeking it, yet fails to thrive without it. This lack of response makes it difficult for the foster mother to show him the affection which he so deeply needs. Without the constant friendly explanations of the situation from the visiting nurse, she would probably have given up the care of the child."[1]

INSTITUTIONALLY REARED CHILDREN

The study of children whose early infancy was spent in an institutional setting provides data on the deleterious effects of the absence of frequent and consistent external stimulation of the child, what Ribble calls the lack of gratification of the infant's "stimulus hunger." Gesell has described how by the very nature of the institutional setup the infant is unable to receive attention and how in the course of the day different people with different attitudes handle the child. As Gesell (99, p. 321) points out, the institutional infant may be "propped up, possibly at regular intervals, and for predetermined periods; but not always at the psychological moments which are most favorable; nor with the endless variations and surprises which naturally enter into the flexible living of a domestic circle. The caretaker, having propped him for the sitting-up period, even places a toy at his disposal. But the propping is of necessity done in a somewhat hurried and impersonal manner, because the very same attention must be repeated for a sizeable number of babies. There can be no waiting for and adaptation to psychological moments. There is too much to be done. Nor is there much time for improvisation-play with the baby. . . . The institution tends to channelize the psychology of the baby by restricted and somewhat standardized impacts. It delimits the scope of the infant's behavior by paucity of impacts. This paucity has nothing less than an impoverishing effect."

[1] M. A. Ribble. *The rights of infants*. Columbia University Press, 1943. By permission of the publisher.

A systematic approach to the problem is represented by Goldfarb's studies (*107–113*) of children who spent their early infancy in an institution. In one of these studies 15 children who had been institutionalized at the average age of 4.5 months and transferred to foster homes at approximately 37 months were compared to 15 children who had experienced foster-home placement from early infancy. The occupational status of the mothers of the institutional children tended to be higher than that of the mothers of the foster-home group; both were equal in educational achievement. The foster homes to which the institutional children were subsequently sent seemed to have more favorable advantages for a child than the foster homes of the control group. When both groups were given psychological tests at 34 and 43 months of age, the institutional children received significantly lower test scores, showed immature speech development, and in general presented many more indications of maladjustive behavior. When similar studies were made with older age groups who also differed in regard to early institutional experience the incidence of feeble-mindedness was markedly greater in the institutional group. Their behavior was characterized by aimlessness, impulsivity, inability to achieve or maintain personal relationships and to respond to the needs of others or to express personal feeling. "Cold, isolated, depriving experience during the first months of life impedes the normal development of such mature qualities as personal security and independence, a deep, personal, reciprocating interest in others, appropriate inhibition, and a reflective, organizing mental approach to problems. The very absence of these qualities in deprived children has also made it very difficult to reach them on more than a casual basis or to affect significantly their adjustment subsequent to transfer from the institution. Treatment efforts, case work activity, and the best wishes of foster parents have been of limited consequence where the damage resulting from psychological privation first occurred at a very early age and was then exaggerated by a prolonged elaboration of the privation experience over several years" (*112*).

Skeels and Dye (*272*) studied the effects of differential stimulation on mentally retarded children. The origin of their study deserves retelling.

"Two children under a year and a half, in residence at the state orphanage, gave unmistakable evidence of marked mental retardation. Kuhlmann-Binet intelligence tests were given both children. C.D., thirteen months of age at time of examination, obtained an I.Q. of 46, and B.D., at sixteen months, scored an I.Q. of 35. Qualitative observations of the examiner substantiated a classification of imbecile level of mental retardation. In the case of B.D., the examiner felt that the child's actual level was perhaps slightly higher, but not to exceed ten points or an I.Q. level of 45. As check tests for further corroboration, the Iowa Tests for Young Children were used. Mental ages of approximately six and seven months respectively were obtained.

"Obviously a classification of feeble-mindedness would not be justified if based on results of intelligence tests alone, particularly at these young ages. However, behavioral reactions in conjunction with the examinations of the pediatrician, and observations by the superintendent of nurses relative to activity or lack of activity of these children in the nursery in contrast with other children, gave ample substantiation for a classification of marked mental retardation. C.D., at thirteen months, was making no attempts to stand, even with assistance. She could not pull herself to an upright position with the aid of crib or chair, nor did she display much manipulative activity with blocks or play materials. Spontaneous vocalization also was lacking. B.D., at sixteen months, was not vocalizing, was unable to walk with help and made relatively no responses to play materials in the nursery."

Both children were illegitimate and their mothers had been adjudged feeble-minded. The two children were transferred to the school for the feeble-minded.

"Six months after transfer, the psychologist visiting the wards of the institution was surprised to notice the apparently remarkable development of these children. Accordingly, they were re-examined on the Kuhlmann-Binet, C.D. obtained an I.Q. of 77 and B.D. an I.Q. of 87. Twelve months later they were tested again with I.Q.'s of 100 and 88, respectively. Tests were again given when the children were forty months and forty-three months of age, respectively, with I.Q.'s of 95 and 93.

"In the meantime, inquiries were made as to reasons for this unusual development. Their 'home' or ward environment was studied. It was observed that the attendants on the ward had taken a great fancy to the 'babies.' They were essentially the only pre-school children on the ward, other than a few hopeless bed patients with physiological defects. The attendants would take these two children with them on their days off, giving them car rides and taking them down town to the stores. Toys, picture books and play materials were purchased by these admiring adults. The older, brighter girls on the ward were also very much attached to the children and would play with them during most of the waking hours. Thus it can be seen that this environment turned out to be stimulating to these pre-school children of low initial mental level."

As a result of these observations retarded children in the orphanage were transferred to the institution for the feeble-minded. Thirteen children were transferred, the mean chronological age at transfer being 19.4 months, with a range from 7.1 to 35.9 months. The mean I.Q. was 64.3, with a range from 35 to 89. "That such retardation was real and observable was substantiated by the reports of the pediatrician and nurse in charge, indicating lack of development." The transferred cases were compared to a control group of 12 cases who had had intelligence tests before the age of two, were in continuous residence at the orphanage, and had not attended any kind of preschool. Social histories and psychometric data indicated that the parents of the children in both groups represented the lower educational and occupational levels. Of the five mothers in the experimental group on whom there were psychometric data, four had I.Q.'s below 70 and one had an I.Q. of 100. Of the nine mothers in the control group on whom psychometric data were available, seven had I.Q.'s below 70, one had an I.Q. of 79, and the other of 84.

When transferred to the school for mental defectives the experimental group was placed on wards with older and brighter girls. There were very few younger children on these wards aside from the experimental children.

"The attendants and the older girls became very fond of the child placed on the ward and took great pride in its achievement. In fact, there was considerable competition between wards to see which one would have their 'baby' walking or talking first. The girls would spend a great deal of time with the children, teaching them to walk, talk, play with toys and play materials, and in the training of habits.

"Most of the clothing for these children was made by the older girls. The girls were so fond of the children that they would actually spend their small earnings and allowances to buy them special foods, toys, picture books, and materials for clothing. Similarly attendants gave of their time, money, and affection, and during their free hours frequently took the children on excursions, car rides, and trips. In addition, it was the policy of the matron in charge of the girls' school division to single out certain of these children whom she felt were in need of special individualization and permit these children to spend a portion of time each day visiting her office. This furnished new experiences including being singled out and given special attention and affection, new play materials, additional language stimulation, and contacts with other office callers.

"An indication of the interest in these children was shown by the fact that a baby show was held for one of the Fourth of July celebrations. Each ward made a float upon which its 'baby' rode, dressed in costume. Prizes were awarded for the winning baby, most attractive costume, and best float.

"The spacious living rooms of the wards furnished ample room for indoor play and activity. Whenever weather permitted, the children spent some time each day on the playground, supervised by one or more of the older girls. In this situation, they had contacts with other children of similar ages. Outdoor play equipment included tricycles, swings, slides, sand box, etc."

In contrast to the experiences of the experimental group, the control group remained in an environment characterized by the relative absence of external stimulation and the lack of any enduring or consistent adult-child relationships.

"Up to the age of two years, the children were in the nursery of the hospital. This was limited to a rather small play room with additional dormitory rooms of two to five beds each. The children were cared for by two nurses with some additional assistance by one or two girls of ten to fifteen years of age. The children had good physical and medical care, but little can be said beyond this. Contacts with adults were largely limited to feeding, bathing, dressing, and toilet details. It can readily be seen that with the large number of children per adult, little time was available for anything aside from the routines of physical care. The girls who assisted the nurses accepted the work as a necessary evil and, in general, took little personal interest in the children as individuals. Few play materials were available and little attention was given to the teaching of play techniques. The children were seldom out of the nursery room except for short walks or short periods of time out of doors for fresh air."

In Table 12 are presented the developmental results for the experimental and control groups. Although each child was tested several times, only the results of the first and last tests are given. It can be seen from the table that while all the experimental children showed an increase in quotient, the mean change being +27.5 points, all but one of the control showed a decrease, the mean change being —26.2 points. The significance of these results seems clear: The child who is not consistently and satisfyingly stimulated by people in his environment,

TABLE 12. Mental Development of Individual Children in Experimental and Control Groups as Measured by Kuhlmann-Binet Intelligence Tests (272)

Experimental Group

Case No.	Before Transfer C.A. (Months)	I.Q.	C.A. at Transfer (Months)	Last Test C.A. (Months)	I.Q.	Length of Exp. Period (Months)	Change in I.Q.
1	7.0	89	7.1	12.8	113	5.7	+24
2	12.7	57	13.3	36.8	77	23.7	+20
3	12.7	85	13.3	25.2	107	11.9	+22
4	14.7	73	15.0	23.1	100	8.1	+27
5	13.4	46	15.2	40.0	95	24.8	+49
6	15.5	77	15.6	30.1	100	14.5	+23
7	16.6	65	17.1	27.5	104	10.4	+39
8	16.6	35	18.4	43.0	93	24.6	+58
9	21.8	61	22.0	34.3	80	12.3	+19
10	23.3	72	23.4	45.4	79	22.0	+ 7
11	25.7	75	27.4	51.0	82	23.6	+ 7
12	27.9	65	28.4	40.4	82	12.0	+17
13	30.0	36	35.9	89.0	81	52.1	+45

Control Group

Case No.	Test I C.A. (Months)	I.Q.	Last Test C.A. (Months)	I.Q.	Length of Exp. Period (Months)	Change in I.Q.
14	11.9	91	55.0	62	43.1	−29
15	13.0	92	38.3	56	25.3	−36
16	13.6	71	40.9	56	27.3	−15
17	13.8	96	53.2	54	39.4	−42
18	14.5	99	41.9	54	27.4	−45
19	15.2	87	44.5	67	29.3	−20
20	17.3	81	52.9	83	35.6	+ 2
21	17.5	103	50.3	60	32.8	−43
22	18.3	98	39.7	61	21.4	−37
23	20.2	89	48.4	71	28.2	−18
24	21.5	50	51.6	42	30.1	− 8
25	21.8	83	50.1	60	28.3	−23

whose responsiveness is neither encouraged nor rewarded, and who experiences these lacks during a period when language, motor patterns, and self-attitudes (dependent on language) are ordinarily acquired— such a child will tend to fail to develop normally according to developmental scales.

Woodworth's comments (326, p. 80) about the Skeels and Dye study are interesting: "The striking gains of some of the children are evidence, as much as anything, of the unreliability of infant intelligence tests, but the experiment at least showed that feeble-minded women are capable of providing adequate mental stimulation for babies of average intelligence; and this is probably not the first time that a feeble-minded nurse has done a good job, under general supervision, for a child of normal intelligence. The experiment can also serve to cast doubt on the belief sometimes held that a feeble-minded mother will so depress the I.Q. of her child in the first few years as to handicap him for life." It is very surprising that in his discussion of this study Woodworth does not mention the fact that a control group was used. If the unreliability of infant tests is to be used as an explanation of the gains of the experimental groups, why did not the control group also gain? If test unreliability is the important factor, one would expect that within each group there would be some who would gain and some who would lose in test score. The fact that all in the experimental group gained while all but one in the control group lost does not make the explanation in terms of test unreliability a very important or plausible one. Woodworth's statement about the mothering ability of feeble-minded girls seems based on a deëmphasis of the fact that in the Skeels and Dye study these girls were *institutionalized and very carefully supervised in a ward setup in which the introduction of a young child would give these girls an opportunity, perhaps their only institutional opportunity, to express and receive affection.* How these girls would rear children in the community without supervision cannot be determined by their institutional behavior. As will be pointed out later, the available evidence indicates that such girls do not rear children in what Woodworth would call an acceptable, mentally stimulating manner. Undoubtedly defective mothers differ in the child-rearing practices they employ, but the sources and effects of these differences have yet to be studied systematically. It does not seem justified to use the Skeels and Dye study as positive evidence for the "mothering ability" of defective mothers. Finally, it should also be noted that Woodworth failed to mention that in the Skeels and Dye study the institutional personnel were an important, stimulating factor in the children's environment (see p. 142).[2]

Spitz (279) was able to study directly the development of infants born in two rather different institutional settings. One was a nursery in a penal institution, most mothers being pregnant upon admission. "The background of these children provides for a markedly negative selection since the mothers are mostly delinquent minors as a result of social maladjustment or feeble-mindedness, or because they are psychically defective, psychopathic, or criminal." The other institution was a foundling home, the children being placed because of the mothers' inability to support them. There was a tendency for these mothers to be better socially adjusted and more "normal" than those of the nursery children. The outstanding difference between the two groups was in the kind and degree of relationship with the mother.

"In Foundling Home there is a head nurse and five assistant nurses for a total of forty-five babies. There nurses have the *entire* care of the children on their hands, except for babies so young that they are breast-fed. The latter are cared for to a certain extent by their own mothers or by wet-nurses; but after a few months they are removed to the single cubicles of the general ward, where they share with at least seven other children the ministrations of *one* nurse. It is obvious that the amount of care one nurse can give to an individual child when she has eight children to manage is small indeed. These nurses are unusually motherly, baby-loving women; but of course the babies of the Foundling Home nevertheless lack all human contact for most of the day.

"Nursery is run by a head nurse and her three assistants, whose duties do not include the care of the children, but consist mainly in teaching the children's mothers in child care, and in supervising them. The children are fed, nursed and cared for by their own mothers or, in those cases where the mother is separated from her child for any reason, by the mother of another child, or by a pregnant girl who in this way acquires the necessary experience for the care of her own future baby. Thus in nursery each child has

[2] The fact that the Skeels and Dye experimental group showed test-score increases after a period of residence in an institution for the mentally defective should not obscure the fact that the environment of the usual inmates in such institutions does not possess the stimulating features of that of the experimental group. In fact, Crissey (59) found that loss of I.Q. with continued institutional residence was more marked in institutions for defectives than in an orphanage and a juvenile home.

the full-time care of his own mother, or at least that of the substitute which the very able head nurse tries to change about until she finds someone who really likes the child."

Spitz points out that the nursery mothers, restricted as they were by penal confinement, lavished attention and affection on their infants, in constant competition among themselves as to who had the biggest, healthiest, and most intelligent baby. In fact, it was Spitz's observation that the amount of love given to these children amounted to over-protection and overindulgence. Each child was evaluated during the first and last third of the first year of life by the Hetzer and Wolf baby tests (*138*). On the first test the nursery infants obtained an average developmental quotient of 101.5 and the foundling group 124. On the second test toward the end of the first year the nursery infants obtained an average of 105 while the foundling group obtained an average quotient of 72. When two years later the foundling home was revisited, 21 of the original group were still available for study. Despite their increased chronological age, motor, speech, and intellectual develop-ment was markedly retarded. Even in height and weight these children were far below their age norms. Because children in the nursery gen-erally left at the end of a year, it was not possible to make a follow-up study. However, during the original study 29 nursery children left the institution after they were one year old; the age varied from 13 to 18 months. "This means that the *oldest* of them was *half-a-year younger* than the youngest child in our follow-up in Foundling Home, and *two-and-a-half years younger than the oldest.*" In spite of the wide age difference the nursery children surpassed the revisited foundlings in many areas of development.

An interesting finding of Spitz concerns the extreme susceptibility to illness and the high mortality rate among the foundling group:

"In spite of the fact that hygiene and precautions against contagion were impeccable, the children showed, from the third month on, extreme suscepti-bility to infection and illness of any kind. There was hardly a child in whose case history we did not find reference to otitis media, or morbili, or varicella, or eczema, or intestinal disease of one kind or another. . . . During my stay an epidemic of measles swept the institution, with staggeringly high mor-tality figures, notwithstanding liberal administration of convalescent serums and globulins, as well as excellent hygienic conditions. Of a total of 88 chil-dren up to the age of 2½, 23 died. It is striking to compare the mortality among the 45 children up to 1½ years, to that of the 43 children ranging from 1½ to 2½ years; usually the *incidence* of measles is low in the younger age group, but . . . in the younger group, 6 died, i.e., close to 40%. The significance of these figures becomes apparent when we realize that the mortality from measles during the first year of life in the community in question, outside the institution, was less than ½%."

In striking contrast was the finding that during the 3½ years the nursery children were studied not a single child died, and in the 14 years prior to the study only three deaths were recorded. "Intercurrent sickness was limited, on the whole, to seasonal colds, which in a moderate number developed into mild respiratory involvement; there was comparatively little intestinal disturbance; the most disturbing illness was eczema."

On the basis of the work of the above investigators and others (*18, 33, 46*), it may be concluded that the lack of satisfying physical contact, the absence or inconsistency of maternal stimulation, and the failure of the environment to reward the infant's responsiveness to people and objects have a pervasive and retarding effect on mental and physical development. In such an environment the child's awareness of, interest in, and satisfaction from people and objects acquire little drive or "need" strength, making the acquisition of intellectual and social skills, dependent as these are on interpersonal relationships, unrewarding and consequently unlikely to be acquired.

Garden-Variety Deficiency and Child-Rearing Practices

When in the light of these considerations one attempts to evaluate the infant-rearing practices to which the garden-variety defective is subjected, he is hindered by a lack of observational data. Although in recent years increasing attention (*62, 63*) has been paid to the relations among social class, child-rearing practices, and behavioral pattern, there have been no systematic studies in which intellectual status has been singled out for investigation. Consequently, one must depend primarily on clinical observations for the formulation of hypotheses. The absence of systematic data will necessitate extensive quotation from the observation of others if the reader is to get "the feel" of the cultural setting of the garden-variety defective.

The culture, physical and psychological, into which many garden-variety defectives are born may be gleaned from the following description of one of the Kallikak homes:

"On one of the coldest days in winter the field worker visited the street in a city slum where three sons of Joseph live. She had previously tested several of the children of these families in the public school and found them, in amiability of character and general mentality, strikingly like our own Deborah, lacking, however, her vitality. There was no fire in their eyes, but a languid dreamy look, which was partly due, no doubt, to unwholesome city environment. In one house she found the family group—six human beings, two cats, and two dogs—huddled in a small back room around a cook stove, the only fire in the house. In this room were accumulated all the paraphernalia of living. A boy of eleven, who had been tested in the school previously, was standing by the fire with a swollen face. He had been kept home on this account. In a rocking-chair, a little girl of twelve was holding a pale-faced, emaciated baby. In the corner two boys were openly exposing themselves. The mother was making her toilet by the aid of a comb and basin of water, set on the hearth of the stove; a pot and kettle were on top. The entrance of the field worker caused no commotion of any kind. The boy with the swollen face looked up and smiled, the mother smiled and went on with her toilet, the girl with the baby smiled, the boys in the corner paid no attention. A chair was finally cleared off and she sat down, while everybody smiled. She learned that the husband made a dollar a day and that the girl next older than the child of twelve was married and had a baby. Another younger girl was at school, the family having been at last able to provide her with shoes. The girl of twelve should have been at school, according to the law, but when one saw her face, one realized it made no difference. She was pretty, with olive complexion and dark, languid eyes, but there was no mind there. Stagnation was the word written in large characters over everything. Benumbed by this display of human degeneracy, the field worker went out into the icy street.

"A short distance farther on, she came to the home of another brother. The hideous picture that presented itself as the door opened to her knock was one never to be forgotten. In the first home, the type was no lower than moron. One felt that when winter was over and spring had come, the family would expand into a certain expression of life—but here, no such outlook was possible, for the woman at the head of this house was an imbecile. In one arm she held a frightful looking baby, while she had another by the hand. Vermin were visible all over her. In the room were a few chairs and a bed, the latter without any washable covering and filthy beyond description. There was no fire, and both mother and babies were thinly clad. They did not shiver, however, nor seem to mind. The oldest girl, a vulgar, repulsive creature of fifteen, came into the room and stood looking at the stranger. She had somehow managed to live. All the rest of the children, except the two that the mother was carrying, had died in infancy."[3]

McPherson's description (205) of defective families, published in 1937, indicates that Goddard's observations made at the beginning of the century are not "dated." The following are descriptions of the H————y and H————n families:

The H————y Family

"The father of this family was a laborer, very deaf. Accused by wife of having relations with daughter. He was said to be alcoholic. The mother, 48, admitted to Belchertown in 1932, with an I.Q. of .68. Attempts were made to improve her care of the family under the supervision of the S.P.C.C. for eleven years but she did not improve. She kept a filthy home, was sexually promiscuous, and had incestuous relations with son, who may be father of twins born in 1930. Her own husband requested her commitment to this institution following her arrest for neglect of home. This family has been known to welfare departments for years. Children of this family, Louise, Harry, and Ruby, were committed in 1930 to the Division of Child Guardianship. Louis, age 23, I.Q. .70. Was committed to Belchertown State School in 1934. In 1930, he was in court charged with incest with mother and sister, charge later changed to assault and battery. In court in 1933 for abuse of a female child, committed to County Jail and then to Belchertown. He escaped in 1934. Louise, 20, I.Q. .69. Was committed to Belchertown in 1934. She was in Juvenile Court as delinquent child, admitted having relations with father and brother. Had been in care of Social Service Division of Department of Mental Diseases where she was found to be childish and incompetent and she was returned to aunt who found her unmanageable and requested her removal. Harry, age 18, I.Q. .47. Sent to this school in 1930. He was suspected of imitating incestuous acts he had seen at home. Has defective speech. Ruby—no information. Earl, 14, I.Q. .52, speech defect. Admitted to State School in 1931. Margaret, 9 years old, in care of Division of Child Guardianship. Said to be very backward. Her paternity is denied by father of this family. Winifred, age 7, I.Q. .63. Admitted in 1933. It is suspected that her own brother is the father."

The H————n Family

"The father was said to be feeble-minded and lacking in responsibility. Never able to make a living for family. He was related through his mother

[3] From H. H. Goddard, *The Kallikak family*. Macmillan, 1912. By permission of Henry H. Goddard.

with two other families at the state school. The mother was suspected of being immoral with star boarder in the home, whom she permitted to have relations with daughters for the sake of money. The home was kept in terrible shape. Mother and children caked with dirt and covered with vermin. Younger children said to have sores where rats nibbled fingers and toes. The children, as we know them at this school, consisted of Henry, age 41, said to be simple. He married and his wife was said to be not much brighter. Mentally incapable of earning a living and providing a home for family. Robert, 48, said to be feeble-minded. Sexually abused his sister. Emma May, 36, I.Q. .55. Had been sexually abused by boarder in home. Was committed to Wrentham State School in 1915, transferred to this school in 1923. Hattie, 33. Was in the care of Children's Aid Association from 1915–1919. Placed in many foster homes but did not do well. She was sent to Lancaster as a stubborn child because of instruction of younger children in sex matters and experiences with boys. Was paroled and again returned. Released in 1924 and became pregnant. She was committed to this school in 1926 with an I.Q. of .85. Discharged as not feeble-minded but she has never gotten along well in the community. Married and deserted her husband for another man. She was diagnosed at the Psychopathic Hospital as a psychopathic personality without psychosis. Martha, 31, I.Q. .47. Admitted to this school in 1923. Sexually abused by brother. Rosie Ella, 28, said to be feeble-minded. Under guardianship of Children's Aid Association of Hampshire County. Laura Ellen, 26, I.Q. .76. Admitted to this school in 1923. Tried parole in 1937 but she did not adjust well and wanted to return. Alice, 25, I.Q. .49. Admitted to this school in 1923 and can do first and second grade school work. Lena May, 22, supposed to be the illegitimate child of a boarder in the parents' home. She has since died."

The following is a partial description of the "Nineveh" family reported by Bice in 1947:

"The father, whose date of birth is unknown, was the son of American-born parents of German extraction. He was a Protestant. At maturity he was estimated to be of borderline mentality, one report indicating a mental age of 10 years 6 months. The father informed a social case worker that he was a printer by trade; however, during the time he was known to social agencies he did not work as a printer. He was a junk dealer and reported earnings of as much as $100.00 a month. His conception of the occupation of a junk dealer may be reflected in the fact that he was at one time arrested for receiving stolen goods and was given a suspended sentence. Sentence was also suspended on another occasion when he was found guilty of abandoning his children. From 1936 to 1940 the family was on relief. One worker who investigated the case reported that the father saw no harm in permitting the children to roam the streets at any time they chose and he encouraged them to beg. When he died, a neighbor expressed the consensus in the community: 'It was sad, but it was a blessing to the county.'

"The mother was also the child of American-born parents; their ancestry was Irish. She was a Roman Catholic. She was married at the age of 15 and had not reached her 16th birthday when her first child was born. In the 29 years which followed, there were 19 additional children born of this union, 10 of whom died in infancy. A social case worker stated in her reports that the mother was 'careless' and 'gave the impression of being mentally defective.' At maturity her mental age was reported to be 8 years and 8 months. Harriet's mother considered herself a nervous person whose health had been ruined by worry over the health of her children.

"Charles, the oldest child, was found to have but little academic ability; the only activity in which he did well was drawing, a talent also possessed by some of his siblings. He, as well as all the other children who did not die in infancy, was committed to the care of the state board of children's guardians. Later he spent one year at a training school for the feeble-minded. He has been arrested on numerous occasions. He later married and, by the time he was 39 years of age he had seven children. During the war he sold soft drinks at a small stand in a shipyard. He had little interest in the education of his children. When the authorities insisted on school attendance, he said that the members of the family were so attached to each other that they could not bear to be separated long enough for the children to be in school.

"Doris, second child of the Ninevehs, married a man whose brother was in an institution for the feeble-minded. By the time she was 33 she had had five children, all of whom were wards of the state.

"Eric had a school record much like that of his siblings. Though crippled by poliomyelitis, he used to do acrobatic stunts and make chalk drawings on city sidewalks in order to solicit funds from onlookers. He was arrested twice for disorderly conduct. He was found at the age of 27 to have a mental age of 7 years 3 months, and was committed to a state institution for the feeble-minded.

"Frances entered public school at the age of six and left ten years later when she was in the sixth grade. Later, when the girl was in conflict with the law, her mother said: 'I don't know what has become of all the education the children had.' While she was attending school, Frances earned from three to four dollars a week selling matches, wax paper, and notions on the street.

"The first report of Frances' delinquency was made when she was 17 and was arrested for soliciting in a nearby city. Thereafter she continued to be known to social agencies as a prostitute. The records contain such entries as: 'girl is known prostitute'; 'was arrested in a disorderly house'; 'her earnings were three or four dollars a night.' Frances had two children, both of whom were given the same first and middle names. The father of the first child was a neighbor. The second child was born when Frances was 20. Her experiences had by that time been so varied and extensive that the child's paternity could not be established. Frances was committed to an institution for delinquent women. At that time she had syphilis and gonorrhea.

"At the age of 24, she was committed to a training school for the feeble-minded. Psychologists indicated that she had a mental age sufficiently high so that, if one were to judge on that basis alone, she might be considered a borderline case; however, her judgment was poor, her reasoning inferior, and her comprehension limited. Her total functioning was considered to be on a feeble-minded level."[4]

Town's study (299) of 141 defective families rounds out somewhat the above descriptions:

1. The mortality rate among such families is larger than that of the general population. One hundred and fifteen children in 56 families died in infancy or before 14 years of age, prompting Town to comment that "this great mortality is doubtless accounted for largely by the low mentality of the mothers which prevented the proper care of the children."

2. In 28 families marriages were broken by desertion, abandonment, separation, annulment, or divorce.

3. In 37 percent of the families housekeeping conditions were recorded as "flagrantly" bad. "Keeping a house in order, preparing regular meals and caring for a family of children is a task much too great for the feeble wits of the mothers of these families."

4. Malnutrition was found in 21 families.

5. Illegitimate maternity was found in 51 families. Incest occurred in 7 families, and prostitution in 14 families.

6. Reformatory, penitentiary, jail, or prison terms were recorded in 38 families.

7. In 20 families at least one child was removed from the custody of

---

[4] Harry V. Bice, "Mental deficiency, moron level." In Arthur Burton and Robert E. Harris (eds.), *Case histories in clinical and abnormal psychology*. Harper, 1947, pp. 383–385. Reprinted by permission of the author and the publisher, and through the courtesy of the North Jersey Training School, the New Jersey State Board of Child Welfare, and the State Home for Boys at Jamesburg.

the parents. "Each transfer of custody implies parental neglect serious enough to be classified by a court as constituting improper guardianship."

8. In 20 families habitual practice of physical violence toward other members of the household was noted.

Mickelson (208) has presented data on the defective parent which cast a somewhat different light on the problem. She studied 90 families in which one or both parents had been diagnosed as mentally defective; in 74 percent of the cases the wife had been so diagnosed, in 8 percent the husband, and in 17 percent both husband and wife. The families were divided on the basis of adequacy of care given to children: satisfactory, questionable, or unsatisfactory.

"Thirty-eight or 42 per cent of the families were rated as having given their children Satisfactory care; 29 or 32 per cent were rated as having given Questionable care; and 23 or 26 per cent were rated as having given Unsatisfactory care. Although necessarily subjective, this judgment was based in every instance on the absence or presence of social evidence which is customarily accepted as indicative of child neglect. For example, a rating of Satisfactory meant not only the absence of complaints from the community, but positive evidence that the children were kept clean, adequately fed, clothed and supervised, and regular in school attendance. A rating of Questionable indicated some inconsistency or inadequacy of care but not of sufficient degree to justify removal of the children as neglected. A rating of Unsatisfactory meant either that the children had been removed as neglected (there were ten such cases) or that their care was sufficiently poor to justify consideration of such action."

Table 13 indicates the relationship between adequacy of child care and mother's I.Q. It will be seen that with the exception of those with

TABLE 13. Relationship of Adequacy of Child Care to Mother's I.Q., in 86 Cases Where Known (208)

	Total Group No. %	I.Q. 30–49 No. %	I.Q. 50–59 No. %	I.Q. 60–69 No. %	I.Q. 70 and Over No. %
Satisfactory	35 41	3 30	16 46	11 42	5 33
Questionable	29 34 ⎰59	5 50 ⎰70	11 31 ⎰54	9 35 ⎰58	4 27 ⎰67
Unsatisfactory	22 25 ⎱	2 20 ⎱	8 23 ⎱	6 23 ⎱	6 40 ⎱
Total	86	10	35	26	15

I.Q.'s between 30 and 49, there is no particular relationship between adequacy of child care and the degree of the mother's retardation. The significance of this finding is that it suggests the importance of *nonintellectual factors* in social adjustment. This is revealed in other of Mickelson's findings: (1) There was a high positive relationship between adequate child care and harmonious marital relationships; (2) no mother in the satisfactory group presented a "serious mental health problem," whereas 3 in the questionable and 10 in the unsatisfactory groups presented such problems.

There are several factors which limit the degree to which one can generalize from Mickelson's findings and raise questions about their validity. First, 88 percent of the families came from rural areas. Unfortunately, Mickelson did not compare the families from rural areas with those from urban areas. It may well be that the cultural differences between these two areas are important in determining the quality of the defective's adjustment. Second, Mickelson's cases had been under the supervision of social agencies. If one assumes that such supervision aided the adjustment of these families, it becomes difficult to determine what the adjustment of these families would have been had they been "on their own." If one assumes that such supervision *was not* a factor, he may seriously question the diagnosis of mental deficiency in many of the cases because they would then appear to be socially competent. Another factor limiting the degree of generalization is the validity of the "subjective" estimates of adequacy of child care. These ratings, made on the basis of information supplied by welfare boards, raised two additional questions: the reliability of the original observations and the reliability of the judgments based on written records. It should also be noted that the original observations were made by different people. In addition, one can seriously question whether the criteria used to judge adequacy of child care focus attention on those aspects of parental behavior which have the most decisive influence on a child. With these limitations Mickelson's study suggests the following: (1) that under certain undetermined cultural conditions in a rural area a defective (according to test score) mother may be able to give her child "adequate" care; (2) that nonintellectual factors seem more influential in determining the adequacy of such care than degree of retardation as measured by a test. It must be emphasized that these findings are suggestive rather than conclusive. Future research will have to utilize more direct observational procedures, strive for more representative samples of the garden-variety defective population (institutional vs. noninstitutional, rural vs. urban), attempt to observe parent-child relationships as early in the child's life as possible, and employ valid and reliable measures as well as comprehensive and meaningful criteria.[5]

Thorne and Andrews (298) have furnished some data which indirectly throw some light on the present problem. Over a five-year period they studied parental attitudes toward institutionalized mental defectives "as measured by (a) number of visits by relatives to the child, (b) number of gifts received by the child, (c) aggressive and rejecting attitudes evidenced by the parents, and (d) other behavior which definitely menaced the welfare of the child." The subjects were 291 children who had been in the institution during the five-year period. Although the etiology of these cases is not given, it may be assumed on the basis of institutional population statistics that half or more would fall in the garden-variety category. The findings of Thorne and Andrews may therefore have some bearing on the nature of parent-child relationships among garden-variety defectives. "During the period studied, 25 per cent of the 291 children received no visits or gifts from their relatives even at Christmas time when it became necessary for the school to provide enough gifts so that no child would be forgotten. Forty-five percent of the children received gifts (usually at Christmas time) but had no visits, while 8 percent had visits but no gifts. Only 22 percent had both gifts and visits during the period under study. The significance of these data seems obvious when it is found that for all intents and purposes, one quarter of the children had been practically abandoned by their families which were the only persons in this world who could be expected to show them any affection." These data not

---

[5] Mickelson also presented some data on the intellectual status of the children in these families. Of 300 children, 33 percent were considered average or above, 23 percent retarded, 1 percent borderline or dull, 15 percent defective; the remainder were unclassifiable because of lack of data. The bases of these classifications were either an intelligence test score or school achievement and social adjustment data. Mickelson herself questioned the accuracy of these ratings, based as they were on secondary sources, and their validity is of a very dubious nature. It may be noted that the percentage of average and above-average children in this series is much higher than that reported by Halperin (127) on children in similar families and does not support his conclusion about the inheritance of the condition. However, in both the Mickelson and the Halperin studies the criteria of mental deficiency were either narrow or unreliable and conclusions based upon them are of questionable value (see p. 101).

only are revealing of parental attitudes toward the institutionalized child but are extremely suggestive of the nature of parent-child relationships *before the period of institutionalization*. The effect of these parental attitudes upon the child can be seen from Sarason's analysis (257) of the stories told by institutionalized defectives on the cards of the Thematic Apperception Test.[6] He found that themes of loneliness, desire for affection, fear of rejection, aggression, and ambivalence toward parental figures were the most frequent; these findings are similar to those reported by Abel (4). When the results of these investigators are viewed in light of the clinical descriptions presented earlier in this chapter, they cannot be considered as unusual or unexpected. The significance of these studies is that they emphasize the need for intensive observation of parent-child relationships in the early, formative years of the child.

The following hypotheses about child-rearing practices in defective families should be evaluated in the light of the paucity of relevant studies and the limitations of existing data. It is hoped that these generalizations will focus interest in this area and it is fully expected that they will be modified by subsequent research.

1. ` The defective mother does not *plan* to have a child, probably experiences its presence as an unnecessary annoyance, does not possess adequate knowledge of or receive guidance in child care, and is probably more concerned with her own than the child's needs. In other words, the defective mother is not adequately aware of or set to respond to the child.

2. Possessed of a negative or indifferent attitude toward her child, the mother would not be expected spontaneously to fondle, caress, or "play with" her child. The tension-reducing, hence gratifying, effects of mothering would only infrequently, if ever, be experienced by the infant. From the standpoint of the mother such responsiveness to the child does not have as much reward value for her as other forms of activity.

3. On those occasions when the child is distressed and cries, the defective mother probably does not respond promptly or with any appreciable degree of reassuring responsiveness. It is also likely that

[6] In these articles the etiological composition of the groups was not reported. Subsequent checking of the cases revealed that approximately 80 percent of the cases had been diagnosed as in the garden-variety category.

the mother's handling of the child on such occasion is inconsistent; she responds at one time in a perfunctory manner, at another with some attempt at reassurance, and at others in an abrupt, aggressive, "punishing" fashion. One might speculate about the number of times that the child's crying is not responded to at all because of the mother's absence or neglect. The amount of time during the day that the child receives no external stimulation is probably considerable.

4. In the case of feeding, the mother's intellectual limitations and behavioral pattern interfere with adherence to a schedule or making correct judgments about when the baby is hungry. The manner in which the baby is held, the amount of time he is allowed to suck, and the encouragement he receives are problems the importance of which the defective mother is unaware.

5. Since defective families are larger than families in the general population, the amount of attention which the infant receives is automatically reduced. It is also probable that in many such families its care is frequently entrusted to another sibling or siblings whose behavior toward the child would be expected to be even less adequate and consistent than that of the mother. In such a situation the child's learning of discriminatory responses to his environment is made more difficult.

6. The defective mother probably does not take pride in or encourage the child's initial attempts at verbalization or locomotion. One would not expect that she would reinforce the child's responsiveness by a display of enthusiasm or increased attention. In fact, the child's increasing powers of locomotion add responsibilities to the mother to which she probably reacts in a punishing and inconsistent manner. Activity which is neither punished nor rewarded at one time may result in physical punishment at another time. The child's responsiveness to people and objects is punished at a time when satisfying compensatory activities are beyond its powers.

7. Unlike children of normal parents, the offspring of defective parents do not enjoy the stimulation of toys, picture books, games, puzzles, building and alphabet blocks, etc. Whereas these cultural materials are used by many parents to encourage the acquisition of correct discriminatory responses—rewarding the correct response by enthusiasm and exclamation and extinguishing the incorrect one

by silence or facial expression—the child of defective parents does not encounter these learning situations.

If the above statements prove to be correct, it may be assumed that an infant reared in such a cultural setting would be unlikely to receive the degree and kind of maternal contact and stimulation, gratification and reduction of needs and tensions, consistency of parental response, and reinforcement of responsiveness to people and objects which have been found to be conducive for acquiring the patterns of response which are valued in other strata of society. It would not be expected that such a child would learn to want to inhibit impulses as a means of gaining parental affection, tolerate frustration of drives without arousal of undue aggression or anxiety, derive satisfaction from interpersonal relationships, acquire a questioning attitude toward ongoing activities, and acquire attitudes toward self and others which make for responsiveness to and not avoidance of new situations. It would be expected that in the behavioral pattern of the child reared in a "defective" setting, delayed or reflective thinking and sustained interest in activities or problems in which prompt reward is not forthcoming would be characteristics distinguished by their weakness. In short, whatever processes are subsumed under intellectual functioning would be seriously affected.

When one views the garden-variety defective in light of studies in child psychology, it becomes clear why the "ego formation" of such individuals cannot be understood without taking account of cultural factors. As Sherif and Cantril (271, p. 156) point out on the basis of their review of the literature: "The more we study, the more we find that the ego (the self) consists mainly of those attitudes formed during the course of genetic development: attitudes related to one's body, parents, family, school, profession, property, class, and the like. As attitudes are formed (learned) in the course of genetic development, the ego is formed. . . . Both the components of the developing ego and the speed of its development will vary in terms of the limitations of the physical surroundings: the kind of treatment (care, resistances, and encouragements) received from adults, opportunities for language development, contact with cultural products, symbols, norms, associations with age mates, and so on." The importance of these cultural and personal influences for the growing child may be gauged by the fact that his rate of development is very often evaluated on the basis of his reactions to people and objects. The following descriptions of behavioral norms are taken from Gesell and Ilg (*100*, p. 335):

"At *4 weeks* of age, the baby's face is generally passive. By *8 weeks* it breaks into a spontaneous social smile at the sight of another person's face. . . . By *28 weeks* he already reacts differently to a stranger's face.

". . . In the period from *1 to 2 years* there is an increasing amount of social reference. Although the infant-child is capable of long stretches of self-absorbed activity, he is also given to numerous social advances. . . . He extends a toy to a person; he holds out his arm for the sleeve; he says "ta-ta"; he hands the empty cereal dish to his mother. . . . By all these tokens and devices, he builds up a vast body of specific perceptual experience which ultimately enables him to draw the momentous conclusion that there are other persons in the world more or less like himself."

It should be noted that the responses which are expected of the growing infant presuppose that his experiences with people and objects have been of a certain degree and kind. The face of the eight-week infant does not break into a "spontaneous social smile" regardless of the nature of previous parent-child relationships. Whether the child between one and two years "extends a toy to a person" is a function of experiences with toys as well as people. Whether a child utters certain vocalizations in certain situations is a function of how and when these vocalizations have been rewarded by other people in the past. In other words, the behavioral pattern of the growing infant is a function of the degree and kind of stimulation and responsiveness provided by *his* cultural milieu. The importance of this conclusion for the understanding of the development and behavior of the garden-variety defective does not need to be labored. What needs emphasis is the fact that the culture of the garden-variety defective has not as yet been studied and analyzed in a systematic manner.

It may be profitable at this point to consider the implications of the role of biogenic needs (hunger, thirst, etc.) in children in understanding the garden-variety defective. Sherif's survey (*270*) of the literature in this area indicates that the earliest discrimination responses of the child are largely directed to people and objects that satisfy his needs. For example, children 3 to 5 years of age usually do not perceive or attend to the finer details in abstract patterns or notice irregularities in geometrical forms (*187*). As Sherif pointed out, however, young children, *when properly motivated,* are able to perceive very fine differences. Munn and Stiening (*213*) demonstrated that a 15-month-old child could discriminate between geometric designs, using candy as the reward for the correct discrimination. Their apparatus

". . . consisted of a box with two doors of equal size which were hinged at the top so that the child, by means of a small knob, could raise either of them. The configurations to be discriminated appeared on these doors. When the child raised the correct door he was rewarded by finding a piece of chocolate immediately behind it. If he made an incorrect response he was prevented from obtaining any chocolate until the next trial. This delay acted, in a sense, as a punishing factor. It was possible to change the background upon which a form appeared without in any way changing the form itself. One could also make any changes in the form without changing the background upon which it appeared."

The child was able to make the correct discrimination when the figure on the door containing the candy was rotated 45 degrees, when the background was changed, and when the "incorrect" door contained a different design. Gellerman (*97*) also demonstrated, using hunger as drive and food as reward, that very young children can learn to make relatively fine form discriminations. The significance of these studies is reflected in Sherif's conclusion (*270*, p. 55), "A comparison of these results with those obtained in studies in which no reward related to a biogenic need was given suggests vividly the primacy of biogenic needs in regulating the behavior of young children *and their importance in the learning process*" (italics mine).

The above findings and conclusions raise the following question: If the primary or biogenic needs of the young child are inadequately or inconsistently satisfied over a period of time, in what way is the learning process, its rate and content, affected? What effect does such deprivation of the needs of the infant have on his learning to make discriminatory responses to people and objects, acquiring language, and forming attitudes toward self and others? A partial answer to this question has already been given in the discussion of institutionally reared children. There it was seen that the conditions necessary for learning "normal" patterns of response were not present.[7] The objects

---

[7] The word normal is put in quotation marks to emphasize that it is being used in a relative sense. By normal is meant those patterns of response which are considered characteristic of the children on whom our present developmental scales have been standardized.

and persons which ordinarily have stimulus and reward value for the child, thereby serving as an aid in acquiring discriminatory responses, were conspicuously absent. Although the physical equipment to acquire normal patterns of response was present, environmental conditions extinguished rather than reinforced such tendencies.

When one compares the experiences of the infant in the defective setting with the deprivations encountered by the institutional child, some similarities seem apparent. In both cases there is little environmental stimulation and encouragement, inconsistent patterns of handling, and exacerbation of bodily tensions. In both instances responsiveness receives little reward and people and objects possess no consistent stimulus value. In both settings the patterns of response acquired during infancy interfere with rather than facilitate the development of those intellectual and social skills which other cultural settings value so highly. *In their own cultural settings* the behavioral pattern of these children is not unusual. It is only when they are judged by the value standards of other cultural settings—when they are forced to adjust to situations, i.e., school, in which they lack interest and the necessary social and intellectual skills—that their functioning is "inadequate." Just as it is unfair as well as unrevealing to judge the African native by the standards of any western culture, it seems equally pointless to compare the child reared by defective parents with one whose parents are not defective. That children of defective parents will obtain lower intelligence quotients than children of normal parents goes without saying. To attribute differences in test scores to differences between parents is to make the implicit assumption that cultural setting is a variable of little or no significance, an assumption which runs counter to current theories of behavior and research findings. To compare the test scores of normal and garden-variety defectives is to overlook the fact that the conditions of or opportunities for learning are by no means comparable. Until the relation between the behavior and the cultural setting of the garden-variety defective is more intensively studied from a psychoanthropological point of view, dogmatic statements about the etiology of garden-variety deficiency are not warranted.

A concluding note: If the researcher is to study garden-variety defectives in terms of their own cultural setting, he must be careful to prevent his own values and biases, acquired in his own particular cultural setting, from distorting or coloring his observations and interpretations. The following quotation from Herskovits states the importance of this point very clearly:

"The very definition of what is normal or abnormal is relative to the cultural frame of reference. As an example of this, we may take the phenomenon of possession as found among African and New World Negroes. The supreme expression of their religious experience, possession, is a psychological state wherein a displacement of personality occurs when the god 'comes to the head' of the worshiper. The individual thereupon is held to be the deity himself. He often exhibits a complete transformation in his personality; facial expression, motor behavior, voice, physical strength, and the character of his utterances are startlingly different from what they are when he is 'himself.'

"This phenomenon has been described in pathological terms by many students whose approach is non-anthropological, because of its surface resemblance to cases in the records of medical practitioners, psychological clinicians, psychiatrists, and others. The hysteria-like trances, where persons, their eyes tightly closed, move about excitedly and presumably without purpose or design, or roll on the ground, muttering meaningless syllables, or go into a state where their bodies achieve complete rigidity, are not difficult to equate with the neurotic and even psychotic manifestations of abnormality found in Euroamerican society.

"Yet when we look beneath behavior to meaning, and place such apparently random acts in their cultural frame of reference, such conclusions become untenable. For relative to the setting in which these possession experiences occur, they are not to be regarded as abnormal at all, much less psychopathological. They are culturally patterned, and often induced by learning and discipline. The dancing or other act of the possessed persons are so stylized that one who knows this religion can identify the god possessing a devotee by the behavior of the individual possessed. Furthermore, the possession experience does not seem to be confined to emotionally unstable persons. Those who 'get the god' run the gamut of personality types found in the group. Observation of persons in New World Negro groups who are interested in this religion and frequent the cults, yet who, in the idiom of worship 'have nothing in the head' and thus never experience possession, seems to show that they are far less adjusted than those who do get possessed. Finally, the nature of the possession experience in these Negro cultures is so disciplined that it may only come to a given devotee under particular and seemingly arbitrary circumstances. In West Africa and Brazil the gods come only to those who have been designated in advance by the priest of their group, who lays his hands on their heads. In Haiti, for an initiate not a member of the family group giving a rite to become possessed at a ceremony, is considered extremely 'bad form' socially and a sign of spiritual weakness, for this is taken as evidence that the god has not been properly propitiated, and is therefore not under the control of his worshiper.

"The terminology of psychopathology has been readily applied to these states of possession. Such designations as hysteria, autohypnosis, compulsion, have come to rest easily on the tongue. Employed solely as descriptive terms, their use in technical analysis of the possession phenomenon may be of some utility. But the connotation they carry of psychic instability, emotional imbalance, departure from normality recommends the use of other words that do not invite such a distortion of cultural reality. For in these Negro societies the interpretation given behavior under possession—the meaning this experience holds for the people—falls entirely in the realm of understandable, predictable, normal behavior. This behavior is known and recognized by all members as something which may come to any one of them, and is to be welcomed not only for the psychological security that derives from assurances of oneness with the powers of the universe it affords, but also for the status, economic gain, aesthetic expression, and emotional release it vouchsafes the devotee."[8]

[8] From M. J. Herskovits. *Man and his works.* Alfred A. Knopf, Inc., 1948. By permission of the publisher.

Chapter 7

CEREBRAL PALSY

CEREBRAL palsy may be defined as a "motor defect present or appearing soon after birth and dependent on pathologic abnormalities in the brain" (328). Motor defects which are due to lesions in the spinal cord, peripheral nerves, or muscles are not included in this grouping. The cerebral palsies may be subdivided as follows:

1. Monoplegia—paralysis of a single limb.
2. Hemiplegia—paralysis of one side of the body.
3. Triplegia—paralysis of three limbs.
4. Diplegia—paralysis of both arms and legs with equal involvement of opposing pairs, the paralysis being most marked in the legs.
5. Quadriplegia—in contrast to the diplegias all four extremities are involved in a more irregular fashion with equal or greater spasticity (constant muscular contraction) in the arms.
6. Paraplegia—in its pure form only the lower extremities are involved.
7. Cerebellar ataxia—impairment of the maintenance and regulation of postural activity which is complicated by voluntary efforts at correction.

The gross motor defects found in these cases point unmistakably to brain disturbances involving either the pyramidal or extrapyramidal systems or the cerebellum. Where spasticity is an outstanding feature, pyramidal involvement is most likely. Lesions occurring in the extrapyramidal tract or basal ganglia sometimes result in athetosis, a condition characterized by slow, wormlike, purposeless movements which are exaggerated by voluntary action. "Many cases show such diffuse lesions that they cannot be said to fall either entirely within or entirely outside the pyramidal tract. These diffuse cases are by far in the majority and there are very few which can definitely be described as pure spasticity or pure athetosis" (76, p. 33).

165

The Incidence of Mental Deficiency Among the Cerebral Palsied

Estimates of the incidence of mental deficiency among the cerebral palsied have varied rather widely. Little, whose classical work in 1863 stimulated interest in this area, reported that only 11 out of 63 cases suffered intellectual defect (*300*, p. 29). In a study of 50 cases Smith (*277*) found 22 percent normal, 16 percent morons, 40 percent imbeciles, and 22 percent idiots. Schroeder (*268*) reported that 66 percent of 146 children classified as cerebral palsied were mentally retarded. Ford (*84*, pp. 197, 205) states that in the diplegias "some degree of mental defect is usually present" and that in the hemiplegias "there is more or less mental deficiency." McIntire (*202*) reported that 26 percent of his series of 143 cases were mentally defective.

One reason for the diverse findings regarding the incidence of mental deficiency among cerebral palsy cases lies in the difficulty of administering standardized psychological tests to patients with marked motor disability, particularly when speech defects are present. In many cases the psychological examination cannot be conducted in the rigid fashion described in the manuals accompanying standardized tests. Data obtained by following the manuals are likely to reflect the degree of physical handicap rather than the individual's mental capabilities. However, the unfeasibility of adhering to procedures standardized on normal individuals is not obviated by relying on impressions and unsystematic observations as a basis for evaluation. What appears as "alertness" or "profound defect" to one examiner may not be so considered by another. For example, in a preliminary study of five cerebral palsy cases Lord (*189*) found that "one case only was unanimously diagnosed as an idiot. In the 4 remaining cases, the opinions of physicians, neurologists, psychologists, and parents varied from defective to normal. In one case there was a range from idiot to possibly above average; in another case there was a difference of opinion among the psychologists." Most studies of the cerebral palsied have either adhered to procedures which are standard for normals or relied on subjective estimates the reliability of which is unknown.

If it is difficult to evaluate the mental functioning of the cerebral palsied, it is even more of a problem to determine the extent to which personal and social isolation due to the severe motor defect existing from birth has affected intellectual growth. It is extremely difficult to separate behavior which is the direct result of brain injury from that due to development in the absence of locomotor and exploratory activity. Doll, Phelps, and Melcher have stated the problem clearly (76, p. 251):

"The development of intelligence cannot be successfully evaluated except in terms of its expression through speech and movement. A theoretical problem of the utmost importance is the extent to which handicaps of movements and speech may or may not hinder the growth of intelligence as a capacity, independently of its expressions. Assuming an underlying neuro-physiological basis for intelligence, it is important to know whether expressive activities increase in number, variety and complexity from physical improvement, or whether the neuro-physiological development makes progress in these regards inevitable (i.e., which is cause and which effect). If the social expression of an underlying physiological capacity is restrained by the difficulties of movement, then the removal of motor difficulties may be expected to be followed by a rapid increase in expressive intelligence, whereas if there is no such relationship, then rapid mental increase should not be expected with improvement in motor facility."

Despite the importance of this problem for a theory of intellectual growth, it will be seen later that the systematic research necessary for answering the question has yet to be done. Until this is done, the clinician cannot be too sure of the distinction he makes between capacity and functioning in the cerebral palsied child. If studies of institutional children who have no structural defects can be used as a guide, diminution in the opportunities for motor and exploratory activity can be expected to affect the rate of intellectual growth (see p. 139).

Another reason for the diverse findings regarding the incidence of mental deficiency among the cerebral palsied is that most studies have been limited to rather highly selected samples of cases. Schroeder, for example, obtained his cases from a larger sample of children who had been referred to a clinic for various behavior difficulties. Cases taken from such a sample cannot be considered representative of cerebral palsy cases in general. Smith's sample was heavily weighted with children under three years of age. Ford's estimates were based largely on observations of very young infants. McIntire's findings must be given most weight because his study appears free of sampling errors and his psychological evaluations were based on a pretest familiarization period, flexible test procedures, and supplemental interviews with people knowing the patient well. Mention should be made of the fact that his statement of psychological procedure is more detailed than those to be found in the studies previously cited. As part of a cerebral palsy project initiated by the New Jersey State Crippled Children's Commission, McIntire studied 146 of the first 161 individuals seen in the survey. The 15 excluded cases were eliminated because of a questionable medical diagnosis or a too incomplete case history. The cases came from fifteen different clinics in the state. The educational achievement and occupational status of the parents were found to be representative of families in the state, a finding subsequently confirmed with a larger sample of cases (222). The median age of the subjects was 10.7 years. Of 121 subjects of school age, 3 were scholastically advanced for their age, 18 were in the expected grade, and 100 were one or more grades retarded. The large incidence of academic retardation "is partially explainable, in that 24 of the subjects have never had any school opportunity because of the severity of their physical and/or mental handicaps. Also those who attended school entered late. The average subject was past his sixth birthday upon entering, while 25 percent were eight years or older before beginning school." Fifty-seven percent of the subjects had speech defects and 5 percent had no speech at all. Cases were subdivided as follows: monoplegias, 1 percent of all cases; hemiplegias, 16 percent; triplegias, 10 percent; diplegias, 14 percent; quadriplegias, 57 percent; not reported, 2 percent. McIntire's handling of the formal examination is given in the following:

"The first consideration in the selection of tests was the extent and degree of the child's physical handicap. In view of the wide variation in the nature of the subject's physical handicaps, as well as age and other factors, no attempt was made to use a set selection of tests. In a number of cases, the physical handicap was so mild or so distributed as to exercise no influence on the selection of tests. In a few cases the physical handicap was so severe and general that only tests requiring a minimum of motor response were found applicable. In general, tests requiring a verbal response, such as the majority of those found in the Stanford Revision of the Binet, were found most usable. In each case the range of mental functioning was established. The method of limits was employed, fixing the maximum and minimum of response and from this estimating the individual's mental capacity. From this, with impressions gained from the qualitative aspects of his response, and from the written and oral reports of his mental functioning, the diagnosis was made" (202).

McIntire was able to evaluate the functioning of all but 3 cases who were excluded because "the results were so meager or so conflicting that a diagnosis could not be made." The remaining 143 cases were classified as follows:

Gifted intelligence	None
Superior intelligence	7%
High average intelligence	12%
Average intelligence	29%
Dull normal intelligence	13%
Borderline	8%
Mentally defective	18%

When the borderline cases are included with the mentally defective the incidence is still lower than most previously published estimates. On the basis of these findings one may conclude that the majority of cerebral palsy cases are not defective.[1] When the defective group (including the borderline cases) was considered separately, 29 percent fell in the borderline classification, 27 percent in the moron, 22 percent in the imbecile, and 21 percent in the idiot. In institutions for the mentally defective the cerebral palsied represent approximately 6 to 8 percent of the population, with the diplegias the largest clinical group (233, 329). Approximately four-fifths of these institutionalized cases fall into the idiot and imbecile classifications.

PSYCHOLOGICAL STUDIES

From the time of Little's original work (188) in 1863 until the third decade of the present century, research in cerebral palsy was largely the domain of the medical specialist. Problems of etiology and pathology received the greatest attention. Although the relation between brain damage and intellectual functioning had always been of major interest to many medical workers, the mental functioning of the cerebral palsied received scant attention. This neglect was probably due to the psychological "inaccessibility" of so many of the cerebral palsied as well as to the unquestioning faith which the clinician had in the validity of his powers of observation. Even with the development of

[1] Phelps (235) reported that out of every 100,000 births seven were of the cerebral palsied type. Of these seven, one dies in infancy, two are mentally defective, and the remaining four are intellectually above the defective range.

standardized psychological tests, systematic research with the cerebral palsied has been distinguished by its absence.

The first published systematic and comprehensive attempt to develop psychological procedures for the evaluation of intellectual status and growth in the cerebral palsied was that of Lord (*189*) in 1930. From cases coming to a Muscle Training Clinic she selected 35 cases of diplegia and 7 of hemiplegia. For comparative purposes she also studied 25 cases of motor defect due to abnormalities outside the brain. Although Lord attempted to obtain an unselected sample of cases, this was not possible because cases "which seemed low-grade to the physician" did not reach the clinic and, in addition, preference for inclusion in the study was given to cases who came regularly for treatment. Lord attempted to secure subjects at as early an age as possible. In contrast to her control group, most of whom were seen before two years, in the cerebral palsied group "no child was examined under 12 months of age and only 3 under 24 months." Regarding the later age at which the cerebral palsied are brought for treatment, parental interviews revealed the rather surprising fact that in only 15 cases had the motor disability been noticed within a few days of birth; in 5 cases it was noticed at 3 months, and in 10 cases between 6 and 12 months. Of the 31 diplegias for whom data are presented, 12 were seen for one examination, 7 for two, 9 for three, 2 for four, and 1 for six examinations. The minimum interval between examinations was six months.

One part of the examination consisted of tests of balance, locomotion, manipulation, and vocalization. In the other part, the "mental test situations," the child's adjustment to strange and familiar people, sounds, and objects was noted. These situations were devised so that the severely crippled child could respond with a minimum of activity. Facial expressions and visual fixation to people, objects, and situations were the kinds of responses which were elicited and evaluated. Table 14 lists examples of the mental test situations. In both parts of the examination each type of test situation was put into a developmental series and the highest credit in each series was taken as the index of the child's mental level. The credit or age value assigned to each test situation was based largely on Lord's clinical experience and the reported work of others.

A comparison of the intelligence quotients of the two groups revealed that 19 of the 35 diplegias had quotients below 70, whereas only

TABLE 14.   Examples of Test Situations Used by Lord for Testing
Cerebral Palsy Cases

Test Situation	Response[a]
Report in regard to response to "no-no."	"No-no" (or tone) inhibits child's activity (12).
Examiner winks eye, shakes head.	Child imitates simple motions (15).
Child held before mirror in which are reflected self and examiner. Move away from mirror so that child must turn to keep image in view.	Child gives transient fixation to mirror image (4). Fixates on image and turns head to keep it in sight (5). Smiles (6).
"Animal Book" placed on table. Examiner slowly turns pages, noting difference in fixation to blank and colored page, taps page to gain fixation. Examiner names cat, dog, cow, etc.	Child indicates by fixation preference for colored page (5). Makes animal sounds indiscriminately (18). Child looks at, points, pats, or names either dog or cat correctly more than once (21).
"Book of children's activities." Examiner names a few details in pictures. Says on two appropriate occasions, "Where's the little boy eating dinner?" If child does not correctly fixate, Examiner points to picture and goes through book again.	Child looks steadily at page, shifts fixation promptly as Examiner points and names details (18). Look at "children eating dinner" (24).

[a] Numbers in parentheses refer to the age placement (in months) of the item.

5 of the 25 control cases had such low scores. In the diplegic group there were cases who obtained very high ratings but with relatively advanced motor control, and several cases who showed normal mental development up to a certain point but thereafter showed no progress at all. Lord also found that the locus of the brain injury, based on neurological findings, was not predictive of test rating. "In the group of 35 cases with cerebral lesion involving both hemispheres the mental status of 16 cases approximated their chronological age. On the other hand, in the remaining 19 cases showing evidence of mental defect 10 had the differential diagnosis of sub-cortical lesion. One child who showed no evidence of injury to the motor system at 19 months has the extremely low mental quotient of an idiot; whereas several children with bilateral [motor defect] involving the speech mechanism gave indication of mental superiority."

In evaluating Lord's pioneer study consideration must first be given to the reliability of her test procedures. One way of determining reliability is to compare the scores the subjects achieved on their first and final examinations. If there are marked discrepancies between the two scores, it would indicate that the test was not a dependable yardstick of whatever it purported to measure and could not be relied upon for predictive purposes. Although Lord did not compute the necessary statistics, the data necessary for their computation are available in Tables 2 and 3 in her monograph. When both of her groups are combined, there are 34 cases who were given at least two examinations. The rank difference correlation between the first and final examinations is .62, which cannot be considered high enough for predictive purposes. Within the diplegic and comparison group there were some large changes in test score. In the diplegic group there were 4 cases whose quotients decreased by 12 or more points, and in 4 cases the quotients increased by at least 20 points. In the control group there were 5 cases whose quotients decreased by at least 10 points and 7 cases whose quotients increased by at least 13 points. The relative unreliability of Lord's procedures is probably due in part to the lack of standardization of her test situations and to the age range of her group. Since there is abundant evidence (21, 118, 195) from the study of normal children that the predictive value of infant and preschool tests is low, the difficulties encountered in testing the cerebral palsied make predictions of their future status even more hazardous. That Lord was aware of these pitfalls is seen in her statement that "we are not prepared to say that the children who have a low developmental quotient will maintain a consistent rate." It is somewhat surprising to find a subsequent statement by her that "it is my impression that a low rating is indicative of an intellectual defect. . . ."

It is interesting to note that although "low-grade" cases were not referred to the clinic for treatment, 5 of the cerebral palsied group had quotients varying from 13 to 38. This indicates either that the referring physician or Lord was in error. That the latter's estimates are to be given more weight is suggested by the fact that in 3 of the 4 cases where there were reëxaminations little change in test score was found. It would be expected that the unreliability of subjective judgments would be greater than those based on well-defined, systematic procedures, even though the latter may not be as precise as one would like. Since cases of very severe mental defect cannot be expected to respond to muscle-training treatment, it is of more than academic interest to have a valid yardstick of intellectual development which can be used in formulating a treatment program.[2]

At the same time that Lord was studying young cerebral palsied children, Doll, Phelps, and Melcher (76) were conducting a similar study at the Vineland Training School. While Lord's subjects were not chosen because of a particular etiological factor, Doll, Phelps, and Melcher restricted their study to cerebral palsy cases due to birth injury which includes "those influences which are immediately traceable to the entire process of birth, regardless of their relation in point of time to the actual period of labor." Among their 12 subjects the physical conditions ranged from a very severe quadriplegia to no evidence of motor lesion. In contrast to Lord's study the subjects ranged in chronological age from 7 to 39 years; two of them were below 10 years, five were between 11 and 18, and the remainder were 22 or over.

In choosing a battery of intelligence tests to apply to their subjects Doll and his colleagues selected tests which had been widely and successfully used with both normal and defective children, which would allow a wide range of test performance, and which might bring out special abilities and disabilities. The tests chosen were the Stanford-Binet (1916), the Myers Mental Measure, the Goodenough Drawing Test, the Healy Picture Completion Test II, the Porteus Mazes, the Witmer Form Board, the Ohio Literacy Test, and Morgan's Mental Test. Before any testing was attempted the examiner established a personal relation with each patient and in those cases where there was a speech defect familiarized himself with the patient's articulatory peculiarities. That the authors were aware of both the dangers and advantages of utilizing test data is revealed in their statement (76, p. 82): "The fact that a test does not measure the same thing when applied to these children as when applied to physically normal children does not necessarily invalidate it as a test. Obviously the response cannot be compared with that of a normal child in estimating general intelligence, but the test may be repeated and the performance compared with previous performances of the same individual as a check of the growth

---

[2] As Strother (288) has pointed out, "The parent, the doctor or the teacher is interested in knowing the child's intelligence not to satisfy idle curiosity but to help them determine what to do for the child. The specific questions they have in mind are questions such as: Is the child able to profit from surgery or physiotherapy? Can he be taught to talk? Can he profit from education? Is he ready to enter school? Will he be able to get along in a regular classroom? Can he learn to read? What special materials or methods of instruction does he need?"

of that individual in capacity to succeed in that test. If the test is capable of indicating improvement, or if it differentiates between the ability of two physically handicapped children it may be valuable even though it may not be useful for comparison with the normal."

As a result of their analysis of test results the authors concluded that the Binet was the only test which gave a wide distribution of scores and on which all subjects, except one whose condition made testing of no value, were able to obtain a definite numerical score. On every other test there were always at least three subjects who could not achieve a minimum score or to whom the tests were not applicable. The difficulty in administering standardized tests to these cases is well illustrated in the following (76, p. 174):

"(Case 3) ... It was possible to use the standard tests in some instances, though they were considered as qualitative symptoms of genetic development rather than as quantitative measures of native ability. The Binet examination showed a mental age of 4.0 years, I.Q. 29. The tests were slightly altered in some instances to allow for the child's obvious disabilities. Gestures were accepted in the definitions according to use in Year V, and commissions were given within his reach from the chair in which he sat. He was given a doubtful plus on the comprehension of Year VI, since his gestures indicated that he understood the questions and the correct responses.

". . . He certainly understood all directions in the V-year Binet. At the VI-year level he did not appear to comprehend the requirements in number questions, nor, in fact, in this type of question at a lower level, but he persistently attempted response to the comprehension questions. He was successful in showing the motion of putting on a coat to the question, 'What must you do if it is raining when you start to school?' At the same time he articulated two syllables, which the examiner understood to mean 'rain-coat.' In Year VII the poor quality of his response and the apparent lack of interest as contrasted with a more positive emotional reaction to questions on the lower level suggested that he did not comprehend the questions. He understood the prepositions 'in,' 'under,' and 'behind.' He did not distinguish 'on,' 'beside,' or 'at.' The general level of his language comprehension in vocabulary and sentence structure was estimated at 4 to 5 years.

In Table 15 the gross results from the Stanford-Binet are presented. It will be seen that 4 cases had quotients above 82 and that the rest fell below that point. The fact that the average I.Q. of the subjects below 15 years of age was 51 whereas the mean for those above 15 was 79 was considered by the authors as evidence for the belief that the mental

TABLE 15. Gross Results from Stanford-Binet (1916) Examinations of
11 Birth-Injured Subjects Studied by Doll, *et al.* (76)

Chronological Age	Mental Age	I.Q.
7.1	3.0	42
8.9	7.3	82
11.1	5.7	51
12.3	6.0	49
13.7	4.3	31
15.3	10.3	74
18.9	13.1	94
22.2	9.4	67
23.9	8.2	59
33.6	12.7	91
39.7	12.6	90

development of such subjects "may continue to a later age than is the case with ordinary feeble-minded subjects and with average normal subjects." The authors presented further evidence for the concept of "delayed development" in their analysis of the mental growth curves of 8 of their subjects who had been in the institution for more than one year and had at least three Binet examinations. In a majority of these cases there was a noticeable tendency for mental age growth to continue over a longer period of time than the 14 years "which is generally assumed to be the limit of development for both normal and retarded individuals." The appearance of these cases in such a small sample was considered significant in the light of the finding (76, p. 190) that only 5 percent of institutionalized defectives showed such increase. The authors discounted the possibility that these increases were due to practice effects. They pointed out that even if their subjects profited more from practice than the ordinary feeble-minded group, "then that ability in itself must distinguish these individuals from the ordinary feeble-minded subject."

In evaluating this study one might begin by asking why all of the subjects were diagnosed as mentally defective. It will be remembered that 4 of the cases had intelligence quotients above 82, 3 of them being above 90. In one place the authors state that their diagnoses were based on "complete case studies, rather than on intelligence level alone," and in another place they say that "we are not entirely sure that all of our birth-injured subjects are really feeble-minded." Since the criterion of social competency was not discussed and could not be fairly applied to such subjects, it is not clear what criteria other than test score were used in labeling the entire group defective.

One of the most interesting findings in this study concerns the concept of delayed development. If the validity of this finding should be confirmed in studies with larger numbers of cases, it would mean that the clinician working with the younger cerebral palsied would have to exercise caution in predicting the course of a patient's intellectual development. From a theoretical standpoint it would be of significance to determine why some cases show this delayed development and others do not. The unpredictable relation between the focus of the brain lesion and the intellectual level indicates that anatomical factors may not be sufficient to explain the differences in the rate of intellectual growth. When one considers the possible effects of the presence of a cerebral palsied child on family structure and relationships, the influence of these factors cannot be disregarded. Not all parents react to the cerebral palsied child in an accepting, warm, consistently affectionate manner. The effects of such a child on the emotional stability of the parents are considerable, as Lord noted in her study. It seems reasonable to assume that parents of the cerebral palsied child react more realistically and less emotionally to his limitations and deformities when he is older than when he is younger. The number of parents who never "accept" their child is probably considerable. It is interesting to note that the children displaying delayed development in the Doll, Phelps, and Melcher study showed this growth after they had been admitted to the Vineland Training School. Although preadmission test data were not available, one might speculate about possible differences in the handling of the child at home and at Vineland and their differential effects on rate of development. The very high standard of care and individualized training for which Vineland is noted may well have been a factor in the delayed development of some of these children.

Another study which attempted to ascertain the diagnostic value of psychological tests with cerebral palsied cases was that of Sarason and Sarason (261). Their subjects were 18 defective institutionalized children ranging in age from 12 to 30 years. The 18 cases were distributed as follows: 5 spastic paraplegias, 8 hemiplegias, 4 diplegias, and 1 cerebellar ataxia. In only two cases was a speech defect present but in neither was there a testing problem. Each case was given the Stanford-Binet (1937 L), Arthur Point Scale, the Rorschach, and an electro-encephalogram. The method of analysis used by the authors was that employed in an earlier study of garden-variety defectives (see p. 126): those with Kohs M.A. 18 months above the Binet were put in one group; those with Kohs M.A. 18 months below the Binet were a second group; and the remainder constituted the third group. As was found in the study of the garden-variety defectives, the 4 cases who fell in the *Kohs-above-Binet* group had little or no difficulty with the Binet tasks (drawing a diamond, memory for designs, and paper cutting) in which other investigators found that cases of cerebral pathology had the greatest difficulty. On the Rorschach the form level of their responses was adequate and showed no indication of the so-called "organic" record. The test patterning of these 4 cases was very similar to that of the garden-variety, Kohs-above-Binet group, where no signs of brain disfunction were present. There were 12 cases in the cerebral palsied *Kohs-below-Binet* group, in 9 of which the test patterns were very similar.

"Not one of the nine, regardless of mental level, was able to approximate a correct drawing of a diamond, or achieve at least a marginal failure on paper cutting or memory for designs. In one case even the drawing of a square at the 5-year level was completely failed, and in several of the other cases their marginal success in the drawing of a square revealed their marked disability where the reproduction of form relationships was involved. Only two of these nine cases were able to complete the first Kohs designs and the remainder could not do any. On other Arthur sub-tests these cases did equally poor. In comparison to their mental level this group did relatively better on the vocabulary test. A comparison of these nine cases with the six cases in the [*garden-variety*] Kohs-below-Binet group suspected of some form of cerebral pathology reveals the striking similarity of their Binet-Arthur test pattern."

The remaining 3 cases in the Kohs-below-Binet group had a more variable picture. Although they did not do well on the Kohs designs, they did not show the complete inadequacy of the other members of the Kohs-below-Binet group. In addition, they also succeeded in two of the three Binet items on which all the other members of the group failed. These 3 cases, in addition to the 2 whose Kohs mental age was neither above nor below the Binet by 18 months, had a test pattern more characteristic of the unstable defective child than of one whose intellectual functioning is directly hindered by cerebral pathology. Like the unstable garden-variety defectives, and unlike the 9 cerebral palsy cases previously described, these 5 cases were not consistently poor in the visual-motor area, and the quality of their successes and failures suggested capacity for more efficient functioning. Their variability seemed to be a function more of instability than if disability.

In contrast the remaining 9 cases in the Kohs-below-Binet group gave vague and irrational responses, 3 of them resorting to color naming and description. Their records seemed more compatible with what has previously been described as the organic record. In grouping their cases on the basis of test performance, the intellectual functioning of the 9 cases in the Kohs-below-Binet group was considered primarily due to the damaging effects of their brain lesions; in the remaining cases the lesions were not considered primary. These groupings were based solely on the test analysis, the electroencephalographic examination being given after the groupings were made. "This procedure was adopted in order that the writers be uninfluenced in determining which cases in the Kohs-below and Kohs-equal-Binet groups had a test pattern more characteristic of instability than cerebral pathology. In other words, distinguishing between the test patterns of instability and cerebral pathology is made in some cases on qualitative observations so that dependence on and knowledge of non-psychological test data (such as the EEG) may hinder the clinical psychologist from giving a more precise basis to his conclusions." The inclusion of some of the Kohs-below and Kohs-equal-Binet cases in the grouping where the cerebral palsy was considered secondary was made on the basis of the following criteria: "(a) when there was variability in the Binet items requiring visual-motor coordination, (b) when there was evidence of the ability to handle the reproduction of diagonal lines, (c) when there was evidence that sloppiness and impulsiveness rather than a basic disability were affecting visual-motor performance, and (d) when the form level of the Rorschach responses varied noticeably, or the individual was obviously disturbed by the blots as a result of what seemed to be emotional factors."

Table 16 presents the EEG data. It is clear from the table that there is good agreement between the EEG and the test pattern. These results suggest that in the "primary" group the brain lesions were in the

TABLE 16. Electroencephalographic Data (261)[a]

	Normal EEG	Abnormal EEG
Cases where cerebral palsy is not considered primary	(N = 7)	(N = 2)
Cases where cerebral palsy is considered primary	(N = 2)	(N = 6)

[a] One case was not available for the electroencephalographic examination.

cortex, making interference with intellectual functioning likely, while in the "nonprimary" group the subcortical areas were involved. This interpretation raises a question as to the etiology of the mental deficiency in the "nonprimary" group. An examination of the family backgrounds revealed that the "primary" group came largely from intellectually average homes, whereas most of the "nonprimary" group came from backgrounds usually associated with the garden-variety defective. Sarason and Sarason concluded that "although evaluating family backgrounds from case history materials is hazardous, the cultural and intellectual subnormality of the backgrounds of those in whom cortical pathology is not considered primary lends weight to the suggestion that their retardation is on a familial basis rather than a result of cerebral pathology."

The Sarasons' finding that marked inadequacy on visual-motor tasks (i.e., drawing a diamond) is associated with cortical dysfunction is confirmation of Lord's observations on older cerebral palsied children (190). There is no satisfactory explanation why in many of these cases adequacy with tasks requiring visual-motor activity should be markedly affected. This inadequacy is even found in cases where the physical handicap does not interfere with test performance. Lord (190, p. 37) observed:

"The difficulty in drawing and writing is obviously not in motor control but in a sensory defect that causes confusion in the reproduction of direction. A child aged three years and nine months after considerable training with a pencil could draw a 'flag with a cross on it' on the basis of mental imagery, but he could not imitate the drawing of a cross because he could not reproduce the direction of lines. In the same way an older child could not copy a square or triangle, but could draw a 'window' and a 'tent' if she did not look at the model."

The paradoxical discrepancies in performance which Lord describes do not seem to be explained by assuming a sensory defect. The inadequacy of such an explanation can be seen in Goldstein's description of a man who suffered a brain injury from a bullet wound and who showed behavior similar to that described above by Lord in her cerebral palsy cases.

"The patient has the task to copy different simple forms, e.g., different angles, composed by two small sticks. He was able to do this only if he were allowed to trace the lines of the angle. Then he repeated this movement. Without tracing, he was unable to copy the angle. He could not even copy the position of a single stick presented in a definite direction if it were taken away so that he could not trace it. When two sticks were presented in the form of an angle he might produce an angle but not the right one. This is more astonishing in that the patient could copy quickly a little house with a door, a chimney, built of a number of sticks after he had looked at it for only a short time.

"At first sight these differences may seem totally incomprehensible. Further examination clarifies the situation. We have seen that the patient failed in the test with two sticks joined together in the form of an angle with the opening upward. It appears amazing at first that if we composed the same angle with the opening pointing down, the patient would reproduce the figure very well at the initial trial. When we tried to ascertain how this were possible, when we asked the patient how it happened that he could reproduce the second figure, but not the first, he said, 'This one has nothing to do with the other one,' and 'this is a roof.'

"These two replies lead us not only to an understanding of the patient's behavior in these tests but also of the fundamental change undergone by him.

"His first reply made it clear that the two objects with which he had to deal in these two tests were to him totally different from one another. The second answer showed that the angle pointing downward was apprehended by the patient as a concrete object of his own visual experience, and he constructed a concrete thing with the two sticks. A concrete apprehension and concrete behavioral action were sufficient to meet the condition of this test. In the former test, the two sticks did not arouse in the patient an impression of a concrete thing. He had to conceive of the positions of two meaningless sticks in a meaningless connection, one with the other. He had to regard the sticks as mere representations, indicating directions in abstract space. Furthermore, he had to keep these directions in mind and re-arrange from memory the sticks as representatives of such abstract directions.

"In the first test the patient needed to deal simply with a known object; in the second one he had to give an account to himself of relations in space, and act on the basis of abstract ideas. His action was not determined directly by a given concrete thing, but by a representative of an abstraction.

"The disturbance of the patient, it was apparent, lay in the circumstance that he was unable to assume an attitude toward the abstract, but was able to act in a concrete way. Therefore, he was unable to perform tests the execution of which demanded the abstract attitude. The angle, with the opening pointing down, did not demand it and the patient was able to execute it perfectly. For the same reason, he was unable to place a stick in a definite direction but was well able to imitate the constructing of the little 'house' which would seem to be much more complicated." [3]

Introspective analysis also seems to offer support to Goldstein's explanation rather than Lord's. When an individual is asked to copy a design, he begins to verbalize relationships to himself: "This line goes here, that line goes there, this one is shorter than that one, etc." In other words, the verbalizations refer to relationships in the stimulus material; that is, a conceptual process takes place. If for one reason or another an individual is unable to use language purposively, then the stimulus material cannot be translated into words on the basis of which a procedure adequate to the problem may be formulated. The stimulus material has little or no meaning in the sense of engendering little or no self-verbalization. However, if the nature of the stimulus task, because of past training or drill, minimizes the necessity of the self-verbalization or conceptual process, adequacy of response may be expected. The important point, as Goldstein has emphasized, is to understand the relation between the nature of the stimulus task and the mental set or "attitude" which it calls forth in the subject. It may be profitable at this point to recall the finding of Sarason and Sarason that the cerebral palsy cases whose mental deficiency was primarily due to brain injury had the greatest difficulty in visual-motor tasks where past training or drill was of no help but where self-verbalization of a procedure was necessary. The cases whose mental deficiency was not due to brain injury did not have such difficulty. Bender (30) also has noted that the designs drawn from a model by brain-injured defectives were different from those drawn by defectives with no brain injury but simliar to those drawn by nondefective individuals with aphasic disturbances.

[3] K. Goldstein, *Language and language disturbances*. Grune & Stratton, 1948, p. 212. By permission of the publisher.

In regard to the test functioning of the cerebral palsied there does not appear to be a characteristic test pattern which differentiates them sharply from all other diagnostic or etiological groups in which brain abnormality is present. Some cases have inordinate difficulty with tasks involving visual-motor activity and others do not; some cases have a relatively high vocabulary relative to mental age and others do not; some cases show a generalized lowering in the level of intellectual functioning, whereas in others the defect appears to affect performance in some tasks more than in others. However, since much of the psychological work with the cerebral palsied has been done with the pass or fail criterion, the obtained differences in test functioning may in some instances be more apparent than real. For example, the fact that one case gets a higher vocabulary score than another may on closer study reveal that both individuals are equally unable to utilize language in a conceptual manner. Without knowledge of previous conditions of and opportunities for learning, together with some idea of the individual's conception of himself and his adequacy in various stimulus situations, the psychological significance of a test pattern of successes and failures is questionable.

Hebb (*135*) has contrasted the effects of early and late brain injury upon test scores. His review of the literature in addition to his own findings led him to conclude that in cases of late brain injury (excluding aphasic cases) vocabulary was only slightly affected. To these adult cases with mental deterioration Hebb compared a series of 32 cases diagnosed as exogenous by Strauss at the Wayne County Training School. In these exogenous cases the vocabulary age *was practically always well below the chronological age*. Hebb concluded that "with vocabulary at least it appears that cerebral lesion may be deleterious at infancy and not at maturity, for such lesions at maturity do not affect vocabulary to a detectable degree." Hebb was aware that his exogenous cases might not be representative of the birth-injured population because they were without gross motor handicap and all cases with Binet I.Q.'s below 50 were excluded. In light of the discussion in Chapter 3 concerning the validity of Strauss' diagnosis of brain injury (exogeneity), the representativeness of Hebb's group is open further to question.

Another source of selection error is the absence of any cerebral palsy cases, a crucial group because one is very sure of the presence of brain abnormality and its existence from, before, or shortly after birth. Even if one were to exclude those cerebral palsy cases whose physical handicap would interfere with their Binet performance, there would remain an appreciable number whose test-score level could be considered a valid reflection of their capacity. It may well be that such cases, defective and nondefective, would not give the unequivocal results obtained from Hebb's exogenous group. It should be kept in mind that the low vocabulary level among the exogenous cases is relative to their chronological age. When mental age is used as the reference point, it is not unusual to find that the vocabulary age is above the mental age. In the Doll, Phelps, and Melcher study 4 cases passed vocabulary at or above their mental age while 2 failed below their level; the remaining 5 subjects had mental ages below eight years and their vocabulary-mental-age relationship could not be evaluated because the 1916 Binet does not give credit for vocabulary below the eight-year level. In the Sarason and Sarason study the majority of the cases had a vocabulary age at or well above their mental age. It would seem that one is warranted in concluding that in some cases of early brain injury *vocabulary is likely to be less depressed than other areas of functioning and that the reverse is true for other cases.*

Cotton (56) made "a qualitative analysis of the behavior of a group of spastic children in several test situations so devised that the effect of the physical disabilities of the children might be minimized while at the same time making possible some indication of the subject's ability to apprehend and to remember relationships differing in complexity." Her procedures were of four types: (1) sorting techniques similar to those used by Goldstein and others; (2) string pattern tests designed to test "acuity in spatial relationships"; (3) completion tests requiring generalization; and (4) a pattern-memory test. The sorting tests, which were the most extensive in the battery, are described as follows:

"A group of 32 objects, 54 leather, glass and cardboard forms and two lists of words, in varying combinations, made up 13 sorting test situations. The objects included toys, foodstuffs, and articles in common use. The forms were circles, squares and triangles in three-, two-, and one-and-a-half-inch dimensions. Cardboard forms were in four colors: yellow, blue-green, violet, and white. The same objects were used over and over in different contexts in an attempt to discover whether the subject could readily shift his associations to fit the new context or whether his responses would disclose a more stereotyped sort of behavior. In cases where two or three types of responses were, with the material presented, equally possible, the subject was asked to associate the articles in as many ways as he could. Procedure in each of the situations was essentially the same. The objects were placed on the table in front of the subject, unused objects being pushed out of the way although still within sight. The subject was then instructed to put everything together which belonged together and urged to use his own judgment in deciding the basis of belongingness."

Cotton's 27 cerebral palsy cases were matched with physically normal children for mental and chronological age. The chronological age range of the cerebral palsy group was from seven years and two months to thirteen years and one month, with a mean of nine years and seven months. The mental ages ranged from six years and nine months to twelve years and nine months, with a mean of nine years and three months. In contrast to subjects in other studies, Cotton's group appears to be intellectually normal. From her analysis of the results of the test situations, Cotton concludes that the cerebral palsied group differed from the control in three respects: "First a wider range of individual differences in type of response within any one test situation with bizarre or fantastic responses found only among the spastics; second a greater tendency toward more concrete types of response, with less ability to shift toward the more abstract forms of behavior; and third, a greater tendency toward stereotyped responses no matter what the nature of the test situation." She also found that "a severe speech difficulty was more often connected with stereotyped behavior, with 'fantasy' responses, and with difficulty with verbal (abstract) material than such categories as estimated mental age or type and severity of disability in general." Cotton concludes with the tentative hypothesis that her cases were "affected by their cortical injuries in somewhat the same fashion as are cases of brain injury after maturity." When one reviews Cotton's data, he is struck by the fact that there is a good deal of overlap between the two groups in many categories. Table 17 contains the results for the 13 sorting test situations. Although there are differences between the groups, it is apparent that the two groups gave an appreciable number of the same type of response. The lone exception is type 7 (fantasy and design), but even this is probably not a group characteristic because, as Cotton points out later, this type of response was largely due to 3 cases with severe speech difficulties. In the other kinds of test

TABLE 17.   Summary of Results in the Thirteen Sorting Situations Used by
Cotton with Cerebral Palsied and Normals (56)

Type of Response	Cerebral Palsied	Normals
1. Total classifications on the basis of color	40	19
2. Total classifications on the basis of shape	70	98
3. Total classifications on the basis of size	27	36
4. Total classifications on the basis of material	21	13
5. Total classifications on the basis of familiar associations	42	43
6. Total classifications on the basis of comprehensive relationships[a]	65	99
7. Total classifications on the basis of fantasy and design	30	1

[a] These totals include some of the color, shape, and material classifications totaled above.

situations also, the differences between the groups were not striking. Since there almost always were some individuals in the control group who exhibited behavior similar to that of some in the palsied group, the manifestation of the behavior in the presence of a cerebral injury does not necessarily mean the two are related.

A recent study by McIntire (203) seems to have implications for future psychological work with the cerebral palsied. In a study of 173 hemiplegics and 114 quadriplegics McIntire found a greater incidence of mental deficiency among cases whose motor defect involved or was greater on the right side of the body than among those whose left side was affected. When one considers that most people are right-sided, in which case the left hemisphere of the brain is dominant, whereas in left-sided individuals the right hemisphere is dominant, McIntire's results suggest that injury to the dominant brain hemisphere is more likely to eventuate in mental defect than if the nondominant one is involved. This helps to explain an earlier finding by Doll (67) that left-handedness was four times as frequent among the defective cerebral palsied as in a control group. In many of these cases the natural tendency to right-handedness has presumably been blocked by injury to the dominant left hemisphere. Clinical observations by Phelps (236) on the handedness of cerebral palsied children and their parents support the view that injury to the dominant hemisphere has a more deleterious effect on intellectual functioning than when the nondominant one is affected. That injury to the dominant hemisphere may have a profound effect in contrast to that when the nondominant hemisphere is involved has been demonstrated in other types of neurological disorders, the aphasias in particular (121, 124). In light of these considerations the relation in the cerebral palsied between test functioning or patterning on the one hand, and degree of damage to the dominant hemisphere on the other, warrants further research.[4]

In reviewing the psychological work which has been done with the cerebral palsied, one is struck by the paucity of studies. Aside from the pioneer efforts of Lord and Doll, the psychological problems, practical and theoretical, presented by the cerebral palsied have not been attacked. What studies have been made indicate that while psychological procedures are an indispensable part of the diagnostic armamentarium, there are wide gaps in knowledge concerning the intellectual and emotional growth of the cerebral palsied child; especially with the very young child is there need for refined procedures which will make early diagnosis valid and reliable. There has not been a single study in which a sizable group of cerebral palsied children has been followed from infancy to maturity. If such a study should be done, the factors making for individual variations in rate of development would probably become clearer. In setting up such a study it would be necessary for the psychologist to focus some attention on parent-child relationships. In the past the presence of the severe motor defect has obscured the fact that the cerebral palsied child is being responded to and stimulated by people whose behavior in turn is affected by the severely handicapped child. Although many cerebral palsied children are severely limited in exploratory and locomotor activity, it seems reasonable to assume that parental behavior may either accentuate or lessen the deleterious effects of such restrictions. Case studies by Thorne (295) and Gesell (98)

---

[4] The significance of handedness among mental defectives in general is seen in some incidental results which Abel (6) obtained from a comparison of matched pairs ($N = 15$) of institutionalized girls who differed in the degree of education achievement. Etiology was not considered in the selection of cases. Although the study was primarily concerned with differences in Rorschach performance, subsequent neurological examinations revealed that in the lower educational group 8 out of the 15 cases had definite or possible brain damage in contrast to 4 possible cases in the higher educational group. In addition, there were 6 cases in the former group who were left-handed in contrast to 1 in the latter. Abel did not indicate whether left-handedness was found only in the cases diagnosed as definite or possible brain damage. The significance of the findings of Gordon (119) and Mintz (210), that the frequency of left-handedness among unselected groups of defectives is well above that found in normals, bears further investigation.

demonstrate that parental attitudes toward and the handling of the cerebral palsied child can be important factors in intellectual growth. It must be concluded that the nature of the growth of intellectual behavior in the presence of a severe motor handicap existing from birth remains a fertile area for research. Until the relation between capacity and functioning is better understood, the clinician must be cautious in interpreting the significance of test findings.

ETIOLOGY

From the time of Little's original work until relatively recently, medical consensus has stressed factors at or surrounding birth in the etiology of cerebral palsy. Cerebral hemorrhage, instrument deliveries, abnormally difficult labor, obstetrical mishandling, and asphyxia are some of the factors that were considered important in producing the central nervous system impairment which resulted in motor defect (55, 76, 80, 268, 277). It was also held that the probability of the first-born having cerebral palsy was greater than in the case of other children, presumably because of the greater incidence of difficult labor in the primipara. In the past two decades there has been an increasing tendency to discount factors of birth as primary in the causation of cerebral palsy. One reason for this change in viewpoint is the increasing caution with which birth histories are evaluated. Since in most cases the evaluation of the details of a birth is a *post hoc* procedure dependent in many cases on parental reports, the unreliability of diagnoses based on such data is considered high. Maternal impressions of birth, influenced as they are by errors of memory, suggestion, cultural stereotypes, and superstitions, have not been demonstrated as sufficiently valid to be used as a basis for a diagnosis. In addition, when a mother reports that her labor was difficult, it does not follow that it was difficult for the child. Another factor that makes maternal statements an unreliable criterion is the frequent report of difficult and prolonged labor in cases where there were no untoward effects on the child. It has been pointed out that in many cases of cerebral palsy, where the motor defect is very severe, there have been no indications of an abnormal or complicated birth. Another reason for the deëmphasis on factors of birth is that the anatomical defects and malformations found in many cases of cerebral palsy are not of the type that one would expect as a result of birth injuries. On the contrary, these defects are of a nature that suggests that they occurred well before the birth process (*216, 241, 328*). For example, Yannet (*328*) concludes, on the basis of a study of 86 cases, that the high incidence of particular kinds of eye defects can be explained not as a result of birth injuries but rather in terms of prenatal malformation or maldevelopment. Quinn and Tagdell (*241*) also report that in their series of autopsies of cerebral palsied children there was anatomical evidence of malformation prior to any possible birth trauma. It has been suggested that these malformations may result in a difficult labor rather than vice versa. Recent studies (*200, 328*) of cerebral palsy among mental defectives have indicated the following:

1. The average age of the mother at the birth of the cerebral palsied child is significantly greater than that found in the general population.

2. "There is no significant difference between the percentage of affected children who were first-born and the percentage expected on the basis of chance selection. . . . There is, however, suggestive evidence that a greater proportion of the patients with cerebral palsy are born after the third pregnancy than should be expected on the basis of chance selection" (*328*).

3. In families of cerebral palsied children where there is more than one child, there is a slight tendency for another sibling to have a similar condition.

4. The incidence of mental deficiency among the nonaffected siblings seems to be greater than in the general population.

5. Cerebral palsy cases in which a definite history compatible with the diagnosis of birth trauma is present comprise approximately 10 percent of institutionalized cerebral palsy cases. The birth trauma group differs from the cerebral palsied cases in which the etiology is unknown in the following respects: (a) there is a higher proportion of first-born among the birth trauma cases; (b) the age of the mothers at the time of the birth of the birth trauma cases is significantly lower; (c) the head size of the birth trauma cases tends to be smaller; (d) there is a greater incidence of prematurity among the cerebral palsy cases in which the etiology is unknown.

Point 3 has been advanced as evidence for a possible genetic factor in some cases of cerebral palsy. Although such a possibility cannot be dismissed, recent work on congenital malformations in animals suggests that the presence of a similar physical condition in two siblings may not necessarily be the result of a genetic factor. Warkany (*308*) points out:

". . . that genetic as well as environmental factors may lead to malformations of the same type, to malformations of identical or similar anatomical appearance. This statement is of great practical importance, since it implies identical malformations may be hereditary in one case and non-hereditary in another. Thus in one case congenital cataract may be genetically determined and inherited as a dominant characteristic; but in another case may be due to prenatal German measles and not be hereditary. Cleft palate has been described in mice as a genetic aberration, but we have seen a similar type of cleft palate in rats induced by environmental factors: maternal riboflavin deficiency in one case and maternal exposure to roentgen rays in another. Syndactylism resulting from genetic factors has occurred in the well-known strain of mice investigated by Little and Bagg. However, syndactylism occurs also in the young of mothers fed a riboflavin deficient diet and in the young of mothers exposed to roentgen rays during pregnancy."

Stewart (*280*) has also suggested that nutritional deficiency may be an etiological factor in some cases of cerebral palsies. His microscopic analysis of the brains of 50 diplegics revealed structural changes similar to those found in avitaminosis.

It has been recognized that no single etiological factor accounts for all cases of cerebral palsy. Although all workers agree that birth injury accounts for some cases, they differ widely about the number of cases in which it is the etiological factor. If one were to consider only those cases which all workers consider *not* to be due to birth injury, he would have to conclude, on the basis of the available evidence, that the etiological factors are unknown.

Chapter 8

OTHER FORMS OF MENTAL DEFICIENCY

Hereditary (Primary Amentia)

Phenylpyruvic Oligophrenia

Phenylpyruvic acid is a chemical substance which is excreted in the urine when phenylalanine, an amino acid, is incompletely oxidized. Phenylpyruvic acid has never been reported in the literature to have been found in the urine of clinically normal individuals. In 1934 Folling of Sweden reported the presence of this acid in 10 idiots. This observation was confirmed by subsequent investigations of Penrose (232), Jervis (148), and others (20, 89, 214). In institutions for mental defectives approximately 1 percent of the population have this metabolic disorder. Jervis found 213 cases in a sample of 20,300 patients obtained from several institutions. "About 85 per cent of the individuals in whom this metabolic disorder occurs are markedly defective, being either idiots or low imbeciles. Practically all of the remainder are also defective but in the high imbecile or moron category. Rare cases have been found with intelligence quotients in the borderline classification. No individual of average normal intelligence or better has so far been found to excrete this acid in the urine" (148). On physical examination there are no characteristic central nervous system abnormalities which would set this group apart from others with similar degrees of mental defect. It is interesting to note, however, that approximately 80 percent of the affected individuals are blue-eyed and blond.

In regard to etiology Jervis has shown statistically that (1) the ratio of affected to normal sibs in families with normal parents, (2) the rate of consanguinity among parents of affected individuals, and (3) the distribution of the condition among ascendant and collateral relatives are in striking agreement with what one would expect from assuming the presence of a recessive gene. On the basis of his findings, Jervis suggests "that parents of affected children should be discouraged from having other children since one-fourth of these will be affected and one-half will be carriers. Whenever possible, parenthood should not be encouraged in brothers and sisters of affected individuals, since half of them are carriers. Consanguineous marriages among members of families of patients should particularly be prevented."

Cotzin (58), in an unpublished report, studied a case of phenylpyruvic oligophrenia whose intellectual level and behavior are at variance with the opinion that all such cases never have intelligence quotients above the borderline level. The following are some of the test results which Cotzin obtained from a phenylpyruvic male of 20 years:

Wechsler-Bellevue (Verbal): I.Q. 86
Wechsler-Bellevue (Performance): I.Q. 97
Wechsler-Bellevue (Full Scale): I.Q. 91
Terman-Merrill (L): M.A. 12–6, I.Q. 83
Terman-Merrill (M): M.A. 12–6, I.Q. 83
Chicago Non-Verbal: M.A. 12–4, Standard Score 96 (Average)
Army General Classification Test: Equivalent I.Q. 84
Army Alpha (Nebraska Revision): Equivalent I.Q. 92

In addition to the finding that this boy's test functioning is above the borderline level it is interesting that there are no psychological indications of brain injury. This is very unusual when one considers that such cases are considered to have diffuse brain damage. Because of this boy's background, test functioning, and social adequacy, Cotzin felt that there was a serious doubt about the validity of a diagnosis of mental deficiency. Since almost all the research with phenylpyruvic oligophrenia has been done with institutionalized cases, it may well be that a study of an unselected sample of the population might not confirm the opinion that this condition is invariably accompanied by mental deficiency.

Congenital Ectodermoses

This group, which includes tuberous sclerosis, neurofibromatosis, and cerebral angiomatosis, has in common the presence of neoplastic tissue in the central or peripheral nervous systems as well as various skin manifestations. This group accounts for approximately one-half of 1 percent of an institutionalized defective population. Yannet (329) found

5 cases in an institutional population of 1330. The following is Tredgold's clinical description of *tuberous sclerosis* (*302*, p. 218):

"As seen in institutions for defectives the three cardinal symptoms are *mental defect, epilepsy* and *adenoma sebaceum* [fatty tumors in the facial regions]. Where this combination is present it is practically certain that the patient has tuberous sclerosis of the brain. In the absence of adenoma sebaceum or other skin anomalies, a positive diagnosis cannot be made during life; although post-mortem examination may subsequently reveal the presence of tuberous sclerosis of the brain and tumors of various internal organs.

"Patients suffering from the condition are usually backward from birth, and sitting up, standing, walking and speech are all delayed. Many patients never learn to talk or walk properly. . . . Epileptic fits are usually present from the first year and continue throughout life. . . . They vary greatly in frequency; some patients have a number of fits every day, others have one or two only in the course of a year, others may have complete remission for several years. In very exceptional cases fits may be entirely absent. . . .

"The degree of mental defect is usually a pronounced one, most patients being idiots or imbeciles. . . . As they grow up, however, the majority lose their acquirements and undergo a progressive mental deterioration. In the course of this they may pass into a state resembling catatonic schizophrenia with flexibilitas cerea. A few survive to adult age, but most of them die before reaching maturity."

On autopsy hard, pale neoplastic masses are found in various parts of the brain, especially the cortex. In addition to these changes tumors in other internal organs are frequently found.

Although most authorities believe that tuberous sclerosis is transmitted by a dominant gene, clear-cut data supporting such an assumption are lacking. Penrose's statement (*231*, p. 134) about etiology bears repetition: "Genetic study reveals a high incidence of psychosis in families where epiloia [tuberous sclerosis] occurs but the familial incidence of the actual disease is low. It is rare to find more than one member of the family affected. The disease itself being very rare, however, the recorded familial incidence is greater than would be expected from mere chance occurrence. Cases have been described where the disease appeared in parent and child. Owing to the variety of clinical types, it is not always easy to determine whether a given member of the family was affected or not, on the evidence of a history, and the familial incidence may appear lower than it really is. Moreover, many cases are probably missed owing to the erroneous diagnosis of the facial eruption as 'acne rosacea.' At the present time nothing definite can be inferred about the causation of the condition, but the familial incidence points to some genetic mechanism." In subsequent studies Penrose pointed out (233, p. 48) that a single Mendelian dominant character or gene mutation may be causative factors in some cases.

Neurofibromatosis, sometimes called Von Recklinghausen's disease, is a disease characterized by the formation of tumors of the nerves. "The neurofibromata may involve any nerve, and vary in size from the smallest bead to grotesque overgrowths in extremities resulting in symptomatic elephantiasis. Peculiar pigmentary lesions are seen in the skin and characteristic osseous defects may be noted" (331). Since tumor formation in this disease does not usually affect the cerebral hemispheres, it is not surprising that only approximately 10 percent of those afflicted are mentally defective (231, p. 135). The fact that 10 percent is greater than the incidence of mental deficiency in the general population has been interpreted by some as indicating a causal relationship where these two conditions coexist. When mental deficiency occurs with neurofibromatosis the degree of defect varies from the idiot to the moron classifications. Studies by Penrose (233) and Preiser and Davenport (239) indicate that the genetic mechanism in neurofibromatosis appears to be similar to that of tuberous sclerosis.

Cerebral angiomatosis, sometimes referred to as either the Sturge-Weber syndrome or Brushfield-Wyatt disease, is a very rare cause of mental deficiency. In this disease angiomas, which are tumors formed of blood vessels, are present on the face and forehead and are associated with tumor formation of the cerebral cortex. Although these cases have sometimes been classified in the hereditary category, their family histories do not seem to warrant such a classification. For example, of 4 cases reported by Brushfield and Wyatt (43), 2 had negative histories, in 1 the grandmother had "fits," and in the other the mother, sister, and grandmother were psychotic. Tredgold (302, p. 225) reported that in the cases he had seen "there was a well-marked family history of insanity, epilepsy, or other psychopathic conditions." Such backgrounds do not seem to constitute an explanation of the angiomatosis. McCoy and Voris (198) recently concluded that "the symptom complex is undoubtedly congenital. While heredity is an important factor in the occurrence of other angiomatous conditions, it has been difficult to demonstrate any familial linkage in this particular entity. Cases have been reported from all over the world, the majority coming from Europe. This high European incidence may represent a true geographic relation, or it may indicate that the condition is recognized to a greater extent in Europe."

Amaurotic Idiocy (Tay-Sachs Disease)

Amaurotic idiocy is characterized by degeneration of cerebral neurons, progressive blindness, wasting of the limbs, and progressive mental deterioration. Two clinical varieties have been described: the infantile and juvenile types. "They differ essentially only in the age of onset. The infantile type begins in the first year of life, and is recognized by degeneration of the macular region of the retina, leading to progressive blindness. Concurrently, a flaccid paralysis develops, with wasting of the limbs and a progressive mental degeneration. The end-result is a profound type of idiocy, although the child may have appeared normal in early life. Affected children usually die at the age of two. In the juvenile type the onset is later and the course slower" (231, p. 136). This disease is invariably associated with mental deficiency. On autopsy the most notable change is the accumulation of lipoid or fatty sustance in the cerebral neurons.

In the original accounts (254, 255) and subsequent investigations the incidence of amaurotic idiocy in more than one sibling in a family has been noted as well as its appearance in several generations of a family. Its distribution in families indicates that a recessive gene is the etiological factor. Sjörgen's study (302, p. 268) of 59 affected families suggests that an enzyme defect analogous to that in phenylpyruvic oligophrenia may be the abnormality caused by the defective gene. Amaurotic idiocy and other rare forms of cerebral lipoidosis account for approximately one-half of 1 percent of an institutional population (329).

Epilepsy

Although convulsive disorders are relatively common in a defective population, in the great majority of cases the convulsions are a secondary manifestation of a pathological brain condition. Table 18 shows the incidence of convulsions in patients of varying levels and conditions. In a few cases, approximately 4 percent of an institutional population (329), the underlying cerebral pathology and genesis of the

TABLE 18. Distribution of Patients with Convulsive Disorder According to Diagnosis of Mental Defect (329)

	Moron	Imbecile	Idiot	Total	Percent
Familial defects	19	11	4	34	6.6
Undifferentiated defects	13	21	42	76	18.4
Cerebral palsy	6	5	21	32	32.3
Mongolism	...	2	...	2	2.2
Infection	6	5	10	21	41.2
Trauma	4	6	5	15	35.7
Craniofacial defects	...	...	5	5	15.2
Phenylpyruvic amentia	...	...	1	1	8.3
Cretinism	...	...	...	...	0
Cerebral lipoidosis	...	...	1	1	16.7
Muscular dystrophy	...	...	...	...	0
Congenital ectodermosis	...	1	2	3	60.0
Total	48	51	91	190	14.9

convulsions are not clear, but there is some evidence that the recurring convulsions over a period of years have impeded normal intellectual development. In most of these cases the convulsions started relatively early in the child's life and there were reasonable grounds for assuming that prior to their occurrence the child was developing normally.

It will be seen from Table 18 that approximately 7 percent of the familial cases, predominantly garden-variety defectives, also have convulsions. In the large majority of these cases the convulsive disorder is not considered the cause of the mental deficiency and does not have a deteriorating effect on intellectual functioning. It is a concomitant but not an etiological factor in the mental deficiency. The epilepsy in these cases is generally labeled *idiopathic* epilepsy in contrast to the *symptomatic* variety in which the convulsions are a secondary manifestation of a known pathological brain condition.

In recent years genealogical and electroencephalographic studies (155, 175, 176, 177, 178) have indicated that idiopathic epilepsy may be due to heredity factors. It has been found, for example, that the incidence of abnormal electroencephalographic records among the parents, siblings, and relatives of epileptic patients far exceeds the incidence of such records in nonepileptic families. Also, the incidence of epilepsy among monozygotic twins exceeds that found among dizygotic twins.

The fact that the incidence of mental deficiency among epileptics and of epilepsy among mental defectives is higher than the incidence of each in unselected populations has been considered as "rather definite evidence for some kind of biological relationship between epilepsy and mental deficiency" (155). Although there is evidence that hereditary factors may play a role in epilepsy, the method of hereditary transmission is by no means clear. It is also not clear why one member of a family should have convulsions, whereas other members who may have "epileptic-like" brain waves do not. Also, the by no means infrequent case of idiopathic epilepsy with a completely negative genealogy remains unexplained.

Although there have been numerous psychological studies (130, 197) of mentally defective children with epilepsy, the results have been anything but conclusive and in many cases contradictory. Some authors (51, 65, 86) find a progressive decline in I.Q. over a number of years, but others do not (16, 82, 139). Some workers (289) report that the earlier the onset of the seizures the more likely is deterioration to be found; other studies (52, 65) do not confirm these findings. Some studies (51) have shown that memory and word usage are specifically impaired in mentally defective children with epilepsy, a finding not substantiated in other studies (52, 86).

One difficulty in comparing studies in this area is the fact that some workers have considered their cases as homogeneous for etiology, not taking into consideration that in some cases the epilepsy is a secondary manifestation of underlying cerebral pathology (symptomatic) and that in others an underlying pathology is either not present or not ascertainable (idiopathic). If in the former the pathology is progressive in nature, the intellectual deterioration that may occur cannot be attributed solely to the convulsions because they are themselves the result of the brain condition. By lumping all cases together one can only obscure possible differences between the two general types of epilepsy. When this factor was considered, as in the study by Arieff and Yacorzynski (16), more symptomatic than idiopathic cases showed deterioration in functioning. The fact that the intelligence range of the cases in the studies cited varies considerably also makes comparison of results hazardous. Another difficulty in evaluating studies in this area is due to the fact that institutionalized cases have been largely used. This not only limits the degree to which one can generalize from results but makes it almost impossible to separate the effects of convulsions on intellectual activity from the effects of prolonged institutionalization. Studies of the effects of institutionalization (see pp. 139, 161) indicate that even in the absence of epilepsy a decrease in the intelligence quotient is by no means surprising. The type and dosage of medication, the type (petit mal, grand mal, psychomotor) and duration of the seizure, the age of onset, and the relation of time of testing to previous seizures are other important variables which have been considered either not at all or in varying degrees by investigators and have made the evaluation of results extremely hazardous. Until future studies control the relevant variables and employ the necessary control groups, the influence of seizures on behavior, in defective as well as nondefective cases, cannot be satisfactorily described.

As may be seen from the above, much of the psychological work with epileptics has been concerned with the problem of deterioration. The psychosomatic problem of the relation between convulsions and emotional factors has not received much systematic attention. To those who have had the opportunity to observe the institutionalized epileptic the importance of emotional factors has long been apparent. As Yannet (330) has pointed out: "In many cases it is the resulting emotional instability and anti-social behavior which precipitates the need for institutionalization, rather than epileptic spells themselves. It must be one of the prime functions of the residential school to help correct these undesirable psychogenic deviations which contribute so much to eventual social maladjustment."

It is by no means difficult to find cases who prior to institutionalization had very frequent seizures but afterward either had very few or none at all. More usual are the institutional cases whose seizures seem to follow some interpersonal difficulty. It is the writer's impression, based on psychotherapeutic treatment of several cases, that psychotherapy gives one the opportunity (1) to determine rather precisely the psychological conditions which are emotionally disturbing to the individual and seem to precipitate a seizure, (2) to utilize such information in effecting a change either in the child's program or in the manner in which he is handled by the other employees, and (3) to help the child acquire new habits of response. The institutionalized defective child would seem to afford the researcher many opportunities for careful study of the relation between somatic and psychological factors, and the way in which psychotherapeutic techniques may effect changes in the relation.

Medications which have been most widely used in the treatment of epilepsy are phenobarbital, dilantin, and tridione. Phenobarbital and dilantin, usually given in combination, have been found most effective with the grand-mal and psychomotor types of convulsions (*330*). Tridione, one of the most recent drugs to be used with epileptics, has been found most effective with the petit-mal type of convulsive activity (*174, 242, 296*).

In recent years there have appeared reports on the effectiveness of glutamic acid as an anticonvulsant. Price, Waelsch, and Putnam (*240*) and Waelsch and Price (*304*) reported that glutamic acid seemed to be effective in reducing the frequency of petit-mal seizures. It was also observed that there was an increase of mental and physical alertness in patients treated with glutamic acid and that the "degree of improvement in mental efficiency could not be correlated with the incidence of seizures." Studies (*10, 336*) on the effect of glutamic acid on maze learning in the white rat revealed that it significantly increased the rate of learning. Subsequent studies by Zimmerman, Burgemeister, and Putnam (*337, 338*) on human subjects indicated that patients given glutamic acid showed significant increases in test scores. In the major work (*338*) 69 patients, of whom 28 had convulsive disorders, were studied. Of the total group, 44 patients were mentally retarded. A control group of 37 mentally retarded or convulsive patients was "introduced to ascertain the effect of seizure reduction upon intelligence for varying periods of time and to determine the retest reliability of intelligence test scores prior to the glutamic acid period." In effect, the control cases were the experimental cases for whom there were test-retest data before they were given glutamic acid.

"Patients in the experimental group were tested at the beginning and end of a six months' period in which they received glutamic acid therapy. They ranged in age from 16 months to 17.5 years, and in intelligence quotient from below 30 to 131 at the time of first test, so that different measuring instruments were required for different age levels, as well as separate treatment of data. Prior to glutamic acid treatment, 60 were given the Stanford-Binet test, Form L, 1937 revision; 1 the Wechsler-Bellevue scale; and 8 the Kuhlmann-Binet test; 60 the Arthur point scale or Merrill-Palmer performance tests; and 48 the Rorschach ink-blots. Retests with the same battery were made after six months."

Those cases who fell below an I.Q. of 65 had an average Binet M.A. of 5 years 8 months and an average I.Q. of 49.08 before glutamic acid therapy. Six months later the average M.A. rose to 6 years 8 months and the average I.Q. to 55.39. The average, preglutamic acid performance test M.A. was 6 years 1 month and six months later it was 6 years 10 months. For the entire experimental group the increase in Binet M.A. was 13 months and in performance M.A. 12 months (see Tables 19 and 20).

The results with the 37 control cases who had been tested over a period of six months to eight years prior to glutamic acid therapy were as follows:

"The average chronologic age of the control group was 8 yrs., 4 mos., upon previous psychometric tests, with a mental age of 5 yrs., 5 mos., intelligence quotient 62.84. At the beginning of the experimental period the average chronologic age was 11 yrs., 3 mos., indicating an average interval of almost three years (2 yrs., 11 mos.) between the two sets of tests. During this time, however, the average mental age of the group increased only eighteen months to 6 yrs., 11 mos., thereby resulting in a slight reduction of 1.08 points in retest intelligence quotient, from 62.84 to 61.76, prior to glutamic acid therapy. . . .

"Because the time interval between psychometric tests is a large one which is not uniform, performance test scores for the control group are more difficult to interpret, due to the growth factor. An average gain of only 9.17 months in mental age during an interval averaging 2 years, 11 months between tests, however, suggests little improvement in motor skill prior to the glutamic acid period. In contrast to this, the control group gained 12.04 months in mental age during the six months of glutamic acid treatment.

Several problems arise when comparing the control and experimental groups. The first concerns the consistency of relationship between patient and examiner; that is, were the experimental and control cases tested and retested by the same or different examiners? If the experimental cases were tested and retested by the same examiner and the control cases were not, it might be that better rapport was established with the former than with the latter. The possibility that differences in degree of rapport influenced test scores would be strengthened in light

TABLE 19. Test Data on the Most Seriously Retarded Children Before and After Glutamic Acid Therapy (338)

Test	Before Glutamic Acid Therapy						After Glutamic Acid Therapy							
	Av. Age	Number	Mental Age 1	I.Q. 1st	σ	σ Av.	Mental Age 2	I.Q. 2d	σ	σ Av.	$\frac{D}{\sigma \text{ Dif.}}$	Change Mental Age	Point Change I.Q.	Chances of Real Difference
Stanford-Binet	11 yrs. 8 mos.	38	5 yrs. 8 mos.	49.08	8.75	1.43	6 yrs. 8 mos.	55.39	9.45	1.54	3.02	12 mos.	6.31	Certainty
Performance	...	36	6 yrs. 1 mo.	...	1.76	.29	6 yrs. 10 mos.	...	1.76	.29	1.88	9 mos.	...	96 in 100

TABLE 20. Test Data on the Entire Experimental Group Before and After Glutamic Acid Therapy (338)

Test	Before Glutamic Acid Therapy						After Glutamic Acid Therapy							
	Av. Age	Number	Mental Age 1	I.Q. 1st	σ	σ Av.	Mental Age 2	I.Q. 2d	σ	σ Av.	$\frac{D}{\sigma \text{ Dif.}}$	Change Mental Age	Point Change I.Q.	Chances of Real Difference
Stanford-Binet	11 yrs. 2 mos.	60	6 yrs. 10 mos.	62.67	23.40	3.02	7 yrs. 11 mos.	69.67	24.47	3.16	1.65	13 mos.	7.00	95 in 100
Performance	...	52	7 yrs. 3 mos.	...	2.89	.40	8 yrs. 3 mos.	...	3.63	.50	1.50	12 mos.	...	94 in 100

of the fact that the test-retest interval was much shorter for the experimental group than for the control group. Differences in test-retest interval also raise a question about practice effects. Are practice effects greater after six months than after two years? It should be noted that the test-retest interval for the control group ranged from six months to eight years. Zimmerman, Burgemeister, and Putnam do not state whether the control cases with the shorter test-retest intervals showed the same increases or decreases as those with longer intervals. McHugh (201) tested and retested 91 children before they entered kindergarten and after an average interval of 1.93 months. He found an average M.A. gain of 5.84 months and an I.Q. increase of 6.09 points. He attributed the gains to adjustmental factors associated with kindergarten attendance. There was also some evidence that better rapport and reduction in shyness and negativism were contributing factors. In light of Zimmerman, Burgemeister, and Putnam's finding that the most retarded of their subjects showed the most significant Binet changes after glutamic acid therapy, it is important to note that McHugh found that the lower the initial I.Q. the higher the increase on retest (see Table 21). Another factor about which data are lacking is

TABLE 21.   I.Q. Changes After an Interval of 1.93 Months (201)

Initial I.Q. Level	No. of Children	Mean I.Q. Points Change 1st to 2nd Test
125–134	3	−5.00
115–124	11	−1.18
105–114	16	+3.00
95–104	32	+8.03
85– 94	16	+9.05
75– 84	6	+9.17
65– 74	2	+15.00

the number of experimental cases who showed no increase at all. It would be of interest to know if the average increase in test score was a function of many cases showing similar increases or of a few cases showing disproportionately large ones. It would also be important to know if the convulsive and mentally retarded subjects showed similar test gains.

That the test-score increases may have been related to glutamic acid therapy is suggested by the study of Albert, Hoch, and Waelsch (*11*). Their subjects were 8 mentally defective individuals with I.Q.'s from 22 to 73. The subjects were tested after a period of glutamic acid medication and then after administration of placebos. These authors found that test scores increased during the glutamic acid period but decreased when placebos were substituted. The case history of 1 of the 4 cases for whom test results were given follows:

"N.C.—Family history negative. Patient is the first child; second pregnancy was an abortion. He has a brother three-and-a-half years younger who is normal.

"Childbirth was normal. Showed difficulty in feeding since birth. Refused breast at two weeks and was then fed artificially but gained poorly. Sat without support at seven months, stood alone at 15 months, spoke the word 'mamma' at 14 months but did not speak any more words until two years of age. He was restless in sleep, showed unmanageable bed-wetting and a peculiar gait affecting the right foot. Patient suffered poor health since birth: had many colds and sore throats, fell from a table when he was nine months old and was frightened but not injured. At the age of two he started to say a few words but pronounced them poorly; he was unable to form sentences or repeat anything in a sentence after his mother.

"Physical examination showed a poorly developed, undernourished child. The lower extremities showed a talus equinus. Intelligence test was given to him April 7, 1938. On the Stanford-Binet he had a mental age of 3 years, 3 months: I.Q. 50 (chronological age 6 years, 4 months). On the Merrill-Palmer his I.Q. was 49. Further tests showed a defect in general intelligence and manual skill. Patient was quite fearful during testing and insecure.

"A neurological examination was negative. In the Neurological Institute a diagnosis was made of hypoplasia of the brain with mental deficiency.

"Examination in the Psychiatric Institute revealed in October 1945 at the age of 13 years, 11 months an undersized, imbecilic boy. His speech was indistinct and consisted for the most part of two to three word phrases. A battery of psychological tests—intelligence, drawing, memory, manipulative skill and projective techniques—was administered, following which he was placed on glutamic acid therapy. When first tested his I.Q. was 42. Two months after treatment had begun, the I.Q. on Form M of the Stanford-Binet test had increased 9 points and at the end of three months, the I.Q. on Form L was up 8 points. On the Kuhlmann-Binet the rise was 6 points, on the Kohs Block test 5 points, and on the Goodenough 9 points. The only test on which there was no improvement was the Pintner-Paterson which showed a 5-point drop.

"In the seven and a half years (1938–1945) prior to glutamic acid treatment the patient's mental age had increased 2 years, 5 months, or an average of four and a half months' gain in mental age per year. In two months on glutamic acid medication the patient gained 1 year, 5 months in mental age, or two-thirds of his total gain in mental age during the previous seven and a half years.

"At the end of three months on glutamic acid the patient was given placebos. Retested one month later, his I.Q. had dropped to within 1 point of his original I.Q. Scores on the Kuhlmann-Binet, Bender Visual-Motor Gestalt and other tests showed corresponding losses."

Although the findings of Albert, Hoch, and Waelsch are very suggestive, it would seem that in future studies control should be exercised about the examiner's knowledge of which medication the child has been receiving. If the examiner knows that the child has been receiving glutamic acid, he may unconsciously react to the child in a way so as to bias his administration and scoring of the tests in the direction of obtaining higher scores. If the examiner knows that placebos rather than glutamic acid tablets have been administered, an unconscious bias producing lower scores may be operative. An added advantage in the examiner's ignorance of the type of medication is that clinical observations about changes in the child's general behavior will also be more objective.

The findings of the effect of glutamic acid on maze learning in the rat in addition to the suggestive psychological findings in human beings are sufficiently encouraging to warrant further and more controlled studies.

Hereditary Idiocy

From time to time there have appeared in the literature descriptions of families in which the frequency of idiot children was striking. Waggoner and Scharenburg (*305*) described a family with six idiots in one sibship, presenting pathologically a lack of development of the white matter of the brain. Allen, Herndon, and Dudley (*12*) described a family in which the mother and maternal grandmother of the members of the third generation were both said to have had one or more idiot brothers. In the third generation there were eight children, four boys and four girls; two of the boys were idiots. Two of the girls produced idiot sons, one sister having four idiot sons out of a sibship of ten, and the other sister one idiot son out of a sibship of three. The progeny of the fourth generation contained a number of idiot children. The authors concluded that "idiocy in this family may be inherited by sex-linked recessive or by dominant sex-linked transmission. In the case of a disease which is of sufficient severity to prevent the reproduction of affected individuals it is generally impossible to distinguish between these two mechanisms." Friedman and Roy (91) described a family which consisted of six low-grade children of parents of normal intelligence. In all the children speech was halting, all but one had foot or leg deformities, and all had bilateral positive Babinşki or Gordon reflexes. Electroencephalograms of all the siblings and the mother were very similar. The authors concluded that the defects of the children had been inherited through the mother.

INFECTION (SECONDARY AMENTIA)

This category includes those mentally defective cases in which the defect is due to some infection of the brain, meningitis and encephalitis being the chief etiological factors. It has been estimated that approximately 11 percent of all cases of mental deficiency fall in this category. In institutions these cases represent approximately 4 percent of the population. It should be understood, of course, that the majority of people who have had meningitis and encephalitis show no impairment of intellectual functioning, although physical sequelae are not unusual.

Meningitis

The meningococcous, a pathogenic microörganism causing cerebrospinal fever, most frequently results in the type of meningitis that gives rise to mental deficiency. The following clinical description is taken from Tredgold (302, p. 251):

"The history of these cases is usually as follows: the birth of the child was normal; his mental and physical progress was quite satisfactory until, at some time in infancy or early childhood, he was struck down by an acute illness. The illness was accompanied by a rise in temperature, vomiting, and signs pointing to involvement of the brain. In some cases there was stupor or coma, in others restless delirium; very often there was headache, some kind of paralysis, rigidity of the neck, and convulsions. The child was seriously ill for a fortnight or more; he had then begun to improve and he had gradually recovered. But it was found that he was not the same child. In some cases the paralysis did not clear up, in others he continued to have convulsions. In all of them his mental development was affected and his progress was either brought to a complete standstill or was greatly retarded. In some instances he had actually retrogressed, and had been robbed of the acquirements he had made and did not regain them. In others he had undergone an obvious change in his character and personality.

"As seen in later life, some of these sufferers from meningitic amentia are speechless, low-grade idiots who have to be fed, washed and dressed like infants. Others are somewhat less defective; but although they can do little things for themselves and may understand much of what is said to them, they remain incapable of saying more than two or three words. Sometimes incurable deafness is present, and not infrequently paralysis and epilepsy."

Mental deficiency due to meningitis accounts for approximately 1 percent of the institutional population.

Encephalitis

Encephalitis is a form of brain inflammation which may be caused by several different viruses. Occasionally the encephalitic condition develops after an acute fever brought on by influenza, whooping cough (pertussis), measles, mumps, etc. (*182, 220*). It is believed that the weakened condition caused by the fever makes the individual more susceptible to the encephalitis, no relationship having been established between the virus of the latter and the etiological factor of the former. In an institutional population encephalitis has been found to be an etiological factor in approximately 1.5 to 2.0 percent of the cases. Since only those cases with the most severe mental and intellectual sequelae are likely to be institutionalized, encephalitis probably accounts for a somewhat larger percentage of all defectives than institutional statistics indicate.

The encephalitic child who manifests pathological behavioral sequelae has already been described (*285*) in connection with Strauss' exogenous defective type. Although encephalitis is only one of several conditions included in the exogenous type, Werner and Strauss' psychological descriptions of exogenous children are generally similar to those of investigators who have studied encephalitic children only (*31, 182*) and will not be described further (see pp. 39 and 116).

Congenital Syphilis

Congenital syphilis appears to be a rare cause of mental deficiency. In an institutional survey Yannet (*329*) found less than 2 cases per

1000 in which there was definite evidence of central nervous system syphilis. When one considers that many congenital syphilitics die at an early age because of this condition, Yannet's finding is probably valid for older defectives. The proportion of defectives with congenital syphilis is of course larger than that indicated by Yannet's finding, which refers only to those cases in which the spirochete has invaded the central nervous system and presumably interfered with normal development. Tredgold (*302*) has estimated that 3 percent of all defectives have congenital syphilis.

German Measles (Rubella)

Gregg (*122, 123*) has shown that German measles in the mother during the first two months of pregnancy results in the birth of a severely defective child with the following physical characteristics: congenital cataracts, microphthalmos (abnormally small eyes), heart abnormalities, and deaf-mutism. Microcephaly is a developmental defect sometimes found in these cases. In his review of the literature dealing with the relation between rubella and congenital defects Parsons (*224*) concluded that although there was strong evidence for the relationship, its extent remained to be determined. He pointed out that in most of the recorded cases the inquiry as to the occurrence of rubella during pregnancy was retrospective, "having been made when a congenital deformity was found in the newborn child, and that there are only scanty data concerning mothers who had rubella during pregnancy but gave birth to normal children." Studies by Swan (*290, 291*) and Fox and Borten (*87*) do not support the thesis that the occurrence of rubella during pregnancy necessarily produces congenital malformation in the newborn. In the last series of cases ($N = 130$) studied by Gregg, who supplied his findings to Parsons, the findings were as follows:

No. of Cases	Deaf-Mutism	Congenital Heart Disease	Eye Defects
85	Present	...	...
17	Present	Present	...
5	...	Present	...
6	...	...	Present
8	...	Present	Present
8	Present	Present	Present
1	Present	...	Present

It seems reasonable to conclude that while there is a relationship between rubella and congenital defects, it is not known in how many cases rubella did not produce untoward effects. Parsons points out that "statistical investigations to confirm or refute the association between maternal rubella and congenital deformities are difficult to carry out adequately because large epidemics are infrequent and the section of the population at risk [pregnant mothers] on which they have to be carried out is a small one."

IRRADIATION AND MICROCEPHALY

Murphy (*215, 217*) has shown that therapeutic pelvic irradiation of pregnant mothers may result in mentally defective offspring. Fifty-one percent of the offspring of 53 mothers receiving x-ray treatment *during* pregnancy were abnormal in one way or other, 26 percent being microcephalic. Approximately 4 percent of the offspring of 256 mothers receiving such treatment *before* pregnancy were abnormal, only 1 case being microcephalic. It should be noted at this point that "true" microcephaly is not synonymous with small head size. The term microcephaly is usually reserved for those cases in which (1) the cephalic index is low, (2) the head is long and narrow, and (3) the length of the head is much nearer normal than either height or breadth. ". . . Some authorities define the condition in terms of a cranial circumference of less than about 440 mm., or a cranial content of less than about 1000 cc., or cephalic measurements below the norm for two years. Others emphasize cranial form as well as size, noting markedly receding forehead and 'sugar-loaf' form of head. Such a cranium can usually be encompassed within the adult hand" (*72*). When these criteria are applied, the small heads found among Mongolians and some cases of cerebral palsy are found to differ from the configuration of true microcephaly.

The incidence of microcephaly in an institutional population is between one-half and 1 percent. Yannet (*329*) found 14 cases out of an institutional population of 1330. The number of cases of microcephaly due to maternal irradiation is considered small. Although there have been reports of the familial incidence of microcephaly, interpretations of the findings have differed. Tredgold (*302*) states that "most cases of microcephaly are the result of a pathological variation of the germ cell similar to that present in ordinary primary amentia, although in some instances abnormalities [irradiation] of the foetal environment may possibly be present in addition." Yannet (*331*) includes microcephaly among the nonhereditary etiologies. Doll (*72*) maintains that the condition is "apparently due to reproductive anomalies rather than to ancestral transmission." According to Penrose (*231,* p. 126), "Although examples of familial incidence are to be found in the literature, it is not always clear that the traditional type is being referred to. In the writer's experience, the familial evidence of true microcephaly is low; where it has been observed, a recessive type of heredity is usually believed to be the cause. At the present time, however, this is unproved." Halperin (*126*) presented three pedigrees which support the hypothesis that microcephaly is due to a recessive factor.

MENTAL DEFICIENCY DUE TO UNKNOWN ETIOLOGIES

Mongolism

Mongolism represents approximately 10 percent of all institutionalized defectives. The following clinical description is taken from Yannet:

"The diagnosis of Mongolism is dependent on the invariable presence of severe mental retardation associated with certain pathognomonic clinical features resulting from a disordered growth of the skeletal system, especially the skull and long bones. Other findings due to defective development of other tissues and organs are frequent but not invariably present. The mental status is usually in the imbecile range. Infrequently idiocy is encountered, and rarely the mental status is of moron level. The disorder in the growth of the skull bones gives rise to most of the features which are characteristic. The skull is usually in the 10–20 percentile of normal circumference. It tends to be flattened anteriorly and posteriorly. The osseous orbits by x-ray are smaller than normal. An epicanthus is present in the younger child which differs from that seen in Asiatic races by being confined to the inner angle, rather than most of the upper lid. This tends to disappear after the tenth year. Chronic inflammatory changes involving the conjunctivae and lid margins are frequent. Cataracts are found in about 5–8 percent of cases. Strabismus is common. The external ears show frequent developmental anomalies. The tongue is usually protruded, due as a rule to the smallness of the oral cavity. It is usually fissured and furrowed except during the first six months of life. The nose is short, with a flat bridge due to underdevelopment of the nasal bone. In line with the general growth disorder, the teeth are delayed in eruption, small and abnormally aligned as a rule. The neck is short and broad and there is laxity of the skin at the lateral aspects. In the young child, the abdomen is prominent due to hypotonia of the abdominal muscles. The extremities are shortened, especially the phalanges, so that the hands and feet tend to be broad, flat, and square. The fifth finger is proportionally small, and tends to curve inward. The second phalanx of this finger in about 40 percent of cases, is rudimentary by x-ray examination. The space between the first and second fingers and toes is increased. In the foot this is associated with a prominent skin crease. The genitalia are underdeveloped, and the secondary sex characteristics are delayed. An interesting observation is the straight, rather silky quality of the pubic hair. There is no evidence to indicate that the Mongolian is ever fertile. The most frequent associated developmental anomalies are those of the eyes and heart. In the heart, defects of the interventricular septum are the most common anomalies. Generalized hypotonia is present but becomes less marked as the Mongolian gets older. Although considerable laboratory studies have been carried out, none of the findings are specific; neither do they indicate the presence of any significant endocrine or metabolic abnormality. The emotional development of the Mongolian child is on an extremely simple plane. They are easily regimented and institutionalized. They are usually pleasant and affectionate . . . and rarely exhibit temper tantrums or behavior disorders. In the absence of serious extra cerebral defects especially of the heart, and when given reasonably good medical care, their life span need not be as short as has been assumed in the past."[1]

One of the striking facts which has been discovered in connection with the etiology of Mongolism is that the average age of mothers at the birth of these children is significantly higher than the average age of mothers at the birth of normal children in the same families or in a large sample of the population. Van der Scheer (231, p. 103) found that the average age of mothers at the birth of 154 Mongols was 37.2 years and at the birth of their other children it was 31.2 years. Another finding from the same study was that the average age of the fathers at the birth of the Mongol children was 39.4 years, as against 33.8 years at the birth of the normal children. Although it has been noted that Mongols tend to be the last born in a family, this is not regarded as an etiological factor because the increasing maternal age would sufficiently account for this tendency (231, p. 104).

Despite the large amount of research which Mongolism has stimulated, there is relatively little agreement about its etiology. According to

[1] H. Yannet, "Mental deficiency." In A. G. Mitchell and W. E. Nelson (eds.), *Textbook of pediatrics*, 5th ed., W. B. Saunders, in press. By permission of the author and the publisher.

one theory (*183*), Mongolism is caused by some damage to the germ plasm. "This theory is mainly based on speculation following the study of twins, one or both of whom have been found to be Mongoloid. The possibility of a gametic mutation and the fertilization of an abnormal ovum not suited to produce a normal offspring has been suggested. Since it was found that there is a higher frequency of Mongolism in homozygotic as contrasted with heterozygotic twins, this was taken as an indication that the ovum or sperm is defective. However, this theory has been proven not to be valid in most cases, and multiple Mongolism is considered to occur as a result of the coincidence of several factors."

Another theory about the etiology of Mongolism assumes that the condition occurs mostly in the last child of a family especially if the mother is near the end of the childbearing period. A variation of this theory is that Mongolism may be caused by physical exhaustion of the mother, particularly when there have been short intervals between many pregnancies. Neither of these theories has gained much acceptance primarily because there are many cases where the mother was young and there were either few or no previous pregnancies. However, if one assumes that Mongolism may be caused by several different factors, these theories may prove to have some validity.

Another theory is based on some recent findings by Ingalls and Davies (*146*) on 7 cases. They found in 6 of the 7 cases that very early during pregnancy the mother had suffered from some kind of infection: rubella, mumps, influenza, pleurisy, etc. They concluded that maternal infection during pregnancy might be a causative factor in producing Mongolism, although they stated that if this were true only a small number of such cases could be so explained. As a test of this theory, Levy and Perry (*183*) studied mothers of a group of 64 Mongoloid children and a group of 83 feeble-minded subjects of unknown etiology. On the basis of their results they concluded "that intercurrent infectious disease occurring in the mother during pregnancy does not seem to have any influence on the subsequent development of Mongolism." Their data did confirm previous findings that (1) ages of the mother and father at the birth of the Mongoloid child are relatively advanced and (2) the Mongoloid child tends to be the last born. As was pointed out previously, the fact that the Mongoloid child tends to be the last born may be due to the fact that the mother's age may render her incapable of reproduction. Also, it may be that the mother who gives birth to a Mongoloid child may not desire any more children for fear that another such child may be born. However, Levy and Perry's data do confirm the relation between Mongolism and advanced age of the mother.

Benda (29), on the basis of extensive study of more than 300 cases, has concluded that Mongolism is the result of insufficient functioning of the pituitary gland. Just as the cretin is the result of hypothyroidism, so "Mongolism is a congenital hypopituitarism." Benda also maintains that the relatively advanced age of the mother sets the stage for an inadequate hormonal environment in which the embryo develops.

"Immediately after fertilization, before the placenta is fully developed, the corpus luteum is of special importance and its proper function is an essential factor for preventing abortion and guaranteeing a proper development of the fetus. In the last two-thirds of pregnancy, the placenta seems to take over numerous endocrine functions and the importance of the corpus luteum is decreased. It is known that faulty corpus luteum is one of the main causes of abortion in the first part of pregnancy. This is primarily due either to dysfunction of the ovary or to insufficient production of the [luteinizing hormone] action of the pituitary. The pituitary reacts to a pregnancy through development of the so-called 'pregnancy cells,' which are thought to produce some of the essential growth hormones. It is probable that in mongolism either the maternal pituitary or the corpus luteum itself is at fault. We have overwhelming evidence that the mongoloid child occurs mainly on the threshold of hormonal sterility, and one may call this 'ill-finished child' the unfortunate survivor of a threatened abortion" (29, p. 277).

Yannet's statement on page 209 that laboratory studies do not "indicate the presence of any significant or metabolic abnormality" may be recalled at this time to emphasize the disagreement that exists about the etiology of Mongolism.

Cretinism

Cretinism is a disease characterized by a deficiency in iodine secretion by the thyroid gland. Such cases account for approximately one-half of 1 percent of institutionalized defectives. The physical appearance of the cretin is superficially similar to that of the mongolian and the two conditions are sometimes confused. Table 22 presents differential factors in these conditions.

A high incidence of cretinism has been found in certain parts of England, Germany, and Switzerland where the water is deficient in

TABLE 22. Differential Factors in Mongolism and Cretinism (*331*)

	Mongolism	Cretinism
Recognizable	At birth	After 2 to 3 months
Body growth	Retarded	Retarded
Head	Brachycephalic	Normal size
Eyes	Upward, outward slant	Puffy
Osseus orbits	Smaller than normal	Normal
Epicanthus	Present at inner angle	Not present
Nose	Small; bridge underdeveloped	Normal
Tongue	Scrotal, may protrude	thick, large, protrudes
Hands	Short; incurved 5th finger	Short; square
Feet	First and 2nd toes widely spaced	Short; square
Skin	Occasionally dry	Very dry, pale, coarse
Hair	Variable	Very dry, and coarse
Tone	Poor, marked joint laxity	Unchanged
Constipation	Uncommon	Marked
Congenital anomalies	Frequent, heart and eyes	Umbilical hernia
Ossification	Slight or no delay	Marked delay
B.M.R.	Normal	Decreased
Serum iodine	Normal	Decreased
Cholesterol	Normal	Decreased

iodine. However, it is not at all clear why some members of a family are affected while others are not. Cretinism is also found in areas where insufficient iodine in the water is *not* a factor. Penrose (*231*) has suggested that the "thyroid apparatus of some individuals is more subject (on account of hereditary constitution) to the ill effects of infective processes or lack of iodine." There are no supporting data for this speculation.

Cranial Anomalies

Microcephaly, a cranial deformity, has already been discussed. Hydrocephaly is caused by the blocking of the outlets of the cerebrospinal fluid from the ventricles of the brain or its failure to be absorbed. The head gradually swells, the ventricles enlarge, and the brain is stretched and flattened. In most cases that do not succumb mental deficiency usually results, although this is not an invariable consequence (*293*). Macrocephaly is another condition which results in an abnormally large head. In contrast to hydrocephaly, macrocephalics have an enlarged face as well as the skull; the brain enlargement is due to an overgrowth of supportive tissue.

"The cause of hydrocephaly is sometimes congenital syphilis, but infective basal meningitis of different origin may block up the outlets of the cerebrospinal fluid and cause hydrocephaly to appear in infancy. Internal hemorrhage due to birth injury is believed to have the same result occasionally. It is quite probable that there are also developmental abnormalities which may lead to the same result. Familial incidence of such cases, however, is extremely rare and nothing can, at present, be said about an hereditary mechanism. Macrocephaly is of quite unknown origin" (231, p. 129). The etiological factors in other very rare cranial deformities (hypertelorism, oxycephaly, scaphocephaly) are also unknown. The group of cranial anomalies accounts for approximately 2 percent of the institutional population, microcephaly comprising about one-half of these cases.

The Undifferentiated

This grouping includes cases whose mental deficiency is due to cerebral abnormalities not classifiable in any of the recognized categories. The undifferentiated represent about 31 percent of the institutional population.

"Its relative importance at the different mental levels is indicated by the fact that among an institutional population admitting all types of mental defectives, this diagnosis was made in 6.5 percent of the morons, 32 percent of the imbeciles, and 60 percent of the idiots. Except for the mental defect, there are no characteristic physical abnormalities. Neurologically, there is frequently some increase in motor tone without palsy; the deep reflexes are hyperactive but equal; and occasionally the Babinski responses are extensor. An interesting observation is the finding of extra-cerebral malformation in about 10 percent of this group. These include defects of the eye and skeletal system primarily. Convulsive disorders occur in about 10–15 percent of this group. The central nervous system at post-mortem examination shows a wide variety of developmental defects including malformations of gyri, distorted cellular architecture, absence or imperfect development of various cerebral structures, generalized or focal hypoplasias, etc. Diagnosis is made entirely by the process of exclusion" (331).

Iso-Immunization (Rh factor)

The Rh factor is a property of the blood cells which is found in approximately 85 percent of all white individuals. When blood containing the Rh factor is injected into individuals whose red blood cells do not contain this factor, a marked sensitization or immunization process occurs. It has also been demonstrated (*179, 180*) that an Rh-negative mother bearing an Rh-positive fetus may become sensitized to the Rh antigen, the antibodies built up in the mother against the antigen passing back through the placenta into the fetus and causing destruction of the blood of the fetus. This process of sensitization is known as iso-immunization, a process which has been established as the etiological factor in the causation of the syndrome erythroblastosis fetalis, a syndrome characterized by jaundice, rigidity or spasticity, convulsive movements, and frequently vomiting, diarrhea, and respiratory difficulty. "Infants who survive these manifestations, in a severe or even a subclinical form, may after a period of months or years exhibit manifestations of a chronic neuromuscular syndrome consisting of retarded motor development, choreo-athetosis, ataxia, rigidity, spasticity or hypotonia, mental retardation—at times of a severe degree, emotional instability, convulsions and cortical blindness. The neurologic picture may vary considerably" (*323*). On the basis of clinical observations Yannet and Lieberman (*332*) hypothecated that iso-immunization might not always result in the clinical description given above and therefore the underlying mechanism might go unnoticed. Such cases would be expected to be found among the undifferentiated category rather than among those in whom a clear-cut diagnostic picture is already recognizable. These authors were able to obtain blood samples from 56 mothers whose children were classified as undifferentiated and 53 mothers of children in whom specific diagnoses could be made: Mongolism, infection, trauma, etc. Table 23 summarizes the findings.

TABLE 23.   The Incidence of Rh-Negative Mothers of Children with Mental Deficiency of Varying Etiology (*332*)

	Total Number	Mother Rh Negative Number	Mother Rh Negative Percent	Mother Rh Negative Patient Rh Positive Number	Mother Rh Negative Patient Rh Positive Percent
Mongolism	23	3	13.0	3	13.0
Miscellaneous[a]	30	3	10.0	1	3.3
Total	53	6	11.3	4	7.5
Undifferentiated	56	14	25.0	11	19.6

[a] Miscellaneous group includes spastic diplegia, 13 cases; birth trauma, 4 cases; postnatal infection, 8 cases; cranial anomalies, 3 cases; congenital cerebellar ataxia, 1 case; cerebro-retinal degenerative disease, 1 case.

It will be seen that the proportion of Rh-negative mothers among the undifferentiated is significantly larger than that reported in the literature for large random samplings and also larger than the percentage found in the control group. Similar differences are found if the combination of Rh-negative mother and Rh-positive child is considered. Yannet and Lieberman estimated that iso-immunization was an etiological factor in 3 to 4 percent of institutionalized defectives. Their findings have been supported by those of other investigations (278).

Yannet and Lieberman (333, 334) have also presented evidence which indicates that mother-child incompatibility in the the major blood groupings (A, B, and O) may be an etiological factor in some cases of mental deficiency. "The clinical picture presented by these possible cases of ABO iso-immunization differs in many respects from that seen in cases of Rh iso-immunization, and suggests a possible fundamental difference in pathogenesis of the fetal injury in Rh and ABO iso-immunization" (334).

Other Rare Conditions

There are a number of very rare pathological brain conditions which are sometimes associated with mental deficiency. Muscular dystrophy, Friedrich's ataxia, Schilder's disease, and Wilson's disease are examples of forms of progressive nerve degeneration in which mental deficiency may be a feature (124). Another rare condition is the Lawrence-Biedl syndrome in which obesity, hypogenitalism, retinal defects, syndactylism, and polydactylism are characteristic physical findings. Mental retardation has been considered an essential feature of this syndrome (22). Fröhlich's syndrome is another condition in which mental deficiency is sometimes found (266). There is general obesity which is more pronounced in the abdomen and hips, the sexual organs are infantile in character, hands and feet appear small and the fingers are long and tapering, and the face is infantile in appearance. The Lawrence-Biedl and Fröhlich syndromes have been considered due to pituitary dysfunction.

Two Clinical Syndromes Sometimes Mistaken for Mental Deficiency

One of the clinical syndromes sometimes mistaken for mental deficiency is early *childhood schizophrenia* (15, 32, 42, 66, 238, 327). In such cases the child's early years are not unusual but after this period there is a gradual change in his behavior. Rapport with the child becomes difficult, his affective reactions may be bizarre, stereotyped mannerisms are frequently found, withdrawal tendencies are manifested, variations in mood become pronounced, and a disturbance in thought processes is present.

"An early sign of great value and perhaps of pathognomonic significance is the inability of the child to form any real emotional attachment to anyone in his environment. The child seems to have no emotional warmth and moves in an atmosphere of his own, isolated from all contacts. One gets the feeling of talking to him but not talking with him. Without being necessarily aloof from his fellows, he seems separated from them and unable to enter into any real emotional rapport. The detachment from the other human beings is not only an impression of the observer—it is evidently felt also by the child himself. . . . These children [tend] to continue to refer to themselves in the third person long after the normal age of three when such discrimination is usually made and indeed, in later life, it is apparent that they frequently look on their own actions with a sort of distant and detached interest. Naturally they form few friendships with their contemporaries though they do better with adults. They pass among their seniors as shy, 'apathetic,' or sometimes merely as 'lazy.' They are inclined to be sensitive or submissive. Very often they are extremely 'good' children who never cause any trouble, are overlooked by their parents, given less and less attention because they seem to need so little supervision.

"Such a child is readily depressed and discouraged. When either in his environment or in his inner life things go wrong he sinks into despondency or bursts into tears instead of attempting to take action and such outbursts which may seem at first sight like typical temper tantrums differ in that they seem to have no externally conditioning object.

"This detachment from environment easily and usually rapidly passes from a mental to a physical one and the child becomes seclusive, staying in his room instead of playing with other children. Very often some queer hobby is developed as a reason for the seclusiveness but actually it is found that such children spend much of their time daydreaming instead of actually working. Often in spite of spending an increasing amount of time on their studies, their schoolwork slips.

"Peculiar mannerisms may be apparent either in simple motor phenomena or as behavioristic patterns. There is a tendency to use words for the sake of their sound rather than their meaning.

"Thinking difficulties are somewhat harder to elicit but as the disease progresses not only do the word forms become more obviously detached from their meanings but confusion is increasingly apparent.

"Neurotic complaints sometimes are a prominent feature; selfishness, and an unreasonable regard for their property and rights is common and, in direct contradiction to their earlier behaviour, they may become extremely resentful of authority, irritable, and easily provoked to assaultiveness. Suspicions and paranoid delusions are fairly common.

"These symptoms may merely develop slowly and insidiously over a period of time and gradually lead to a complete withdrawal from reality, in which case hallucinations of any sensory field may or may not be present, or they may be interrupted by an acute episode characterized by either overactivity and restlessness with an exaggeration of the bizarre behaviour or by posturing, rigidity or complete stupor. Usually such an episode is associated with sleeplessness and if the child will talk confusion of thought is very evident. Hallucinations frequently occur in the disturbed episodes and regressions to infantile behaviour in the habits of eating or a lapse of toilet training are usual and possibly even characteristic" (15).

It is not surprising that in a psychological examination some of these children receive low scores and show an intellectual inadequacy which superficially resembles that of the mentally defective child. The psychologist who looks beyond test scores, however, does not ascribe the child's peculiar behavior to the low scores but will attempt to relate both of these factors to the developmental history. Adherence to inclusive criteria of mental deficiency enables one to obtain the data which serve as a basis for a differential diagnosis: Is there evidence that constitutional factors are the basis for the behavior? Was the child's retardation apparent at or shortly after birth or did the disorder become manifest after a period of apparently normal development? Does the child's behavior seem to be due to a lack of capacity to develop normally or to an autistic process which prevents language and thought from being used in a realistic manner? In the schizophrenic child, language, which may be well developed in terms of extent of vocabulary and articulation, is not utilized either for communication or for the purpose of initiating and maintaining interpersonal relations.

Yakolev, Weinberger, and Chipman (327) have characterized the difference between mental deficiency and childhood schizophrenia as follows: "The difference is radical. The concept of mental deficiency implies *agenesis* of behavior in which the differentiation of all phases . . . is more or less uniformly arrested or impeded at different stages of organization of the total behavior. . . . In childhood schizophrenia in general, one deals with the *dissociation* of the evolved and the derived phases of behavior."

Kanner (*157*) described 11 children whose condition he ascribed to an *inborn autistic disturbance of affective contact.* "The combination of extreme autism, obsessiveness, stereotypy, and echolalia brings the total picture [of this condition] into relationship with some of the basic schizophrenic phenomena. . . . But in spite of the remarkable similarities, the condition differs in many respects from all other known instances of childhood schizophrenia." Kanner pointed out that whereas in childhood schizophrenia there was usually at least two years of essentially average life, "the children of our group have all shown their extreme aloneness from the very beginning of life, not responding to anything that comes to them from the outside world. This is most characteristically expressed in the recurrent report of failure of the child to assume an anticipatory posture upon being picked up, and of failure to adjust the body to that of the person holding him." In contrast to the young schizophrenic, Kanner's cases were able to establish and maintain a purposeful and "intelligent" relation to objects "but are from the start anxiously and tensely impervious to people, with whom for a long time they do not have any kind of direct affective contact." The course of development of these children also seems to be different from that found in early schizophrenia.

"The basic desire for aloneness and sameness has remained essentially unchanged, but there has been a varying degree of emergence from solitude, an acceptance of at least some people as being within the child's sphere of consideration, and a sufficient increase in the number of experienced patterns to refute the earlier impression of extreme limitation of the child's ideational content. One might perhaps put it this way: While the schizophrenic tries to solve his problem by stepping out of a world of which he has been a part and with which he has been in touch, our children gradually *compromise* by extending cautious feelers into a world in which they have been total strangers from the beginning. Between the ages of 5 and 6 years, they gradually abandon the echolalia and learn spontaneously to use personal pronouns with adequate reference. Language becomes more communicative, at first in the sense of a question-and-answer exercise, and then in the sense of greater spontaneity of sentence formation. Food is accepted without difficulty. Noises and motions are tolerated more than previously. The panic tantrums subside. The repetitiousness assumes the form of obsessive preoccupations. Contact with a limited number of people is established in a twofold way: people are included in the child's world to the extent to which they satisfy his needs, answer his obsessive questions, teach him how to read and to do things. Second, though people are still regarded as nuisances, their questions are answered and their commands are obeyed reluctantly, with the implication that it would be best to get these interferences over with, the sooner to be able to return to the still much desired aloneness. Between the ages of 6 and 8 years, the children begin to play in a group, still never *with* the other members of the play group, but at least on the periphery *alongside* the group. Reading skill is acquired quickly, but the children read monotonously, and a story or a moving picture is experienced in unrelated portions rather than in its coherent totality. All of this makes the family feel that, in spite of recognized 'difference' from other children, there is progress and improvement."

The only case in Kanner's series who did not follow this course of development was a girl who at the age of five had been "dumped" into a training school for the feeble-minded. Her behavior was markedly different from that of the other children in the school. Over a period of years there was no change in it, the institutional setting presumably making for a continuation of her behavioral pattern rather than a change in it. Several of the other cases described by Kanner had also been considered at one time as mentally defective but their development was as described above.

Whether the condition that Kanner describes is an inborn autistic disturbance of affective contact must be considered as problematical. Kanner generally saw the cases several years after birth; here again one wonders if the parental reports of early infancy and childhood can be considered valid. It should also be noted that the parents of these children were in some ways unusual.

"One other fact stands out prominently. In the whole group, there are very few really warmhearted fathers and mothers. For the most part, the parents, grandparents, and collaterals are persons strongly preoccupied with abstractions of a scientific, literary, or artistic nature, and limited in genuine interest in people. Even some of the happiest marriages are rather cold and formal affairs. Three of the marriages were dismal failures. The question arises whether or to what extent this fact has contributed to the condition of the children. The children's aloneness from the beginning of life makes it difficult to attribute the whole picture exclusively to the type of the early parental relations with our patients."

It would seem that before attributing the infant's behavior to an inborn inability for affective contact with people, the degree to which parental behavior *did* influence the infant would have to be more precisely determined. That parental attitudes may play an important role is suggested by Rank's description (*243*) of four children who showed many of the characteristics described by Kanner. In these cases the mothers tended to be highly intellectual prominent people in whom immaturity and narcism were marked. Rank's description of the psychological structure of these mothers and its effect on the child follows:

"The need to be a mother, the hope and expectation that through this experience she may become a real person capable of true emotions, is so desperate that of itself it may create anxiety, ambivalence, fear of failure. Because she is so barren of spontaneous manifestation of maternal feelings, she studies vigilantly all the new methods of upbringing and reads treatises about physical and mental hygiene. Her greatest fear is of 'spoiling' her child. Frequently she insists on an aseptic environment, and the child grows in an orderly, scientific atmosphere where routine and dietary prescriptions prevail. The sunshine which is radiated by the spontaneous, tenderly devoted mother is missing. The result may be passive inertia of the infant or at the other extreme, restlessness and sleeplessness. The passive child is less of a threat because he does not make exaggerated demands on the mother, who feels constantly in danger of revealing that emotionally she has little or nothing to offer, that she is a fraud. Parallel with this or independently, we may find in her personality structure the 'messianic idea,' not in the psychotic sense, but as a symbol of hope that through identification with the child, her own flesh and blood, she may experience vicariously the joys of real living, of genuine feeling.

"If then, as frequently occurs, she becomes aware that this is not the case, she is compelled to face the fact that she is really without magic. She fights desperately for control, no longer of herself perhaps but of the child. The struggles over weaning and toilet training are generally battles in which she tries to redeem herself. The child becomes the real victim—victim of the mother's helplessness which in turn creates an aggression in her that mounts to destruction. The only way for the child to survive is to retreat, to withdraw not only from the dangerous mother but from the whole world as well. A world of his own is created, a world of fantasy, but of fantasy so primary, so repetitious, so remote from our own feelings and experiences that he appears to us odd, bizarre, and dull intellectually and emotionally. He may then remain arrested in this stage, showing a scattered development, or regress even further to a complete breakdown of all social patterns. He becomes a restless wanderer in search of no one and no place, weaving about the room, swaying back and forth, circling the walls as if they were bars he would escape through; and he frequently does escape into the neighboring yard or the street, unconcerned with danger, absorbed in his own world. Unaware of the people he encounters, he stumbles over their feet or their most precious possessions. But all at once he may get panicky and in his fury and anguish throw himself to the ground when suddenly aware that his mother or mother-substitute is not at his side. It is as if he had been running away from her only to be able to return to her over and over. This special quality of pulling away and yet leaning on one, is one of his many enigmatic characteristics. Because he tries so desperately to be invulnerable in his own world, he is pathetically helpless at the same time."

It is Rank's conclusion that the chief source of the child's condition is "the tenuous relationship with an emotionally disturbed mother." Whether Kanner's or Rank's explanation of the condition is correct will probably be determined by direct observation of such cases during the infancy period. While these two author's *posthoc* explanations are suggestive, they cannot be considered conclusive.

Chapter 9

PROJECTIVE TECHNIQUES

IN the past two decades psychologists have become increasingly aware of the inadequacies of traditional terminology. It has been recognized that words like intelligence and personality refer not to *things,* as do words like pencil and clock, but to presumed relationships between overt and inferred behavior. It has also been evident that the phenomena to which the words intelligence and personality refer overlap to a large extent. The confusion that results from the implicit assumption that these words refer to different things can be seen in the tendency to put one kind of psychological procedure under "intelligence" testing and another under "personality" testing—as if one procedure is measuring one kind or variety of phenomena not tapped by the other. Although it might be argued that the use of these words has a practical value, it may be said that the semantic problem is a reflection of an inadequate atomistic theory of behavior which is bound by the compartments which it has prematurely set up. The student learns about intelligence in one course and personality in another, and it is the rare student who learns (by himself) to fit words to phenomena and not phenomena to words *(149, 150)*. The danger involved in implicitly assuming that one is observing intelligence or personality as if they were entities is that variables which are functionally related to each other may be arbitrarily or unknowingly separated.

Recognition of the inadequacy of utilizing intelligence test scores for explaining individual variations in behavior can be seen in the increasing attention given projective techniques by clinical psychologists. In contrast to the usual psychometric procedures in which the individual is presented with a clearly defined task to which there is a right or wrong or limited way of responding, the projective technique involves a more or less ambiguous stimulus situation to which he can respond in a wide variety of ways. For example, when an individual is asked, "What makes a sailboat move?" (Year VIII, Stanford-Binet, 1937, L),

222

he knows that there is a right answer which he is expected to give. He knows that he cannot respond with anything that comes to his mind and that the content of his response must conform to a predetermined right answer. When he is shown an ink-blot and is told that there are no right or wrong answers and that he is merely to tell what it reminds him of, what he sees in it, the content of his responses will be determined more by personal (internal or subjective) factors than by cultural, learned standards of correctness. If one were to give the Binet question to a thousand eight-year-old children the variability in response would be a great deal less than to an ink-blot. The greater the ambiguity of the stimulus task the greater the opportunity for personal as opposed to cultural factors to be reflected in the responses, thus increasing the variability. In other words, the more ambiguous the stimulus the more the individual will endow or project on to it aspects (attitudes, fears, motivations, deprivations, etc.) of the content of his mental life. In most instances he is unaware that what he says he sees "out there" is the result of his own psychological processes.

"Projection may be defined as the tendency of ascribing to the external world mental processes which are not recognized as being of personal origin, as a result of which the content of these responses is experienced as an outer perception. An extreme example of projection in the abnormal field is the mechanism of delusion or persecution. Normal manifestations of this tendency are found in the Rorschach test, for example, where the percepts reported by the subject appear to come directly from the ink-blot while in reality they are conditioned by attitudes and feelings which are characteristic of the individual and are projected into the ink-blot. For this reason, the same ink-blot may give rise to different percepts in different people" (339).

THE RORSCHACH TEST

The Rorschach ink-blot test is the projective technique which has received the widest use in the psychological study of the mentally deficient. The following from Klopfer and Kelley (167, p. 370) states the clinical purposes of the Rorschach:

"Another field which has been intensively studied by the Rorschach method is that of mental deficiency. Rorschach himself in *Psychodiagnostik* [252] concluded that the method is of value, not only in evaluating the intelligence level but also in the estimation of grades of mental deficiency. Furthermore, the method, since it results essentially in an evaluation of the total personality of the individual rather than in a quantitative determination of one particular aspect, is of value in depicting the influence of the patient's emotional life in inhibiting or expediting intellectual functions, and in demonstrating inherent but perhaps unrealized capacities in the personality of the subject."

When one contrasts the clinical purposes of the Rorschach with those of the Binet, it is understandable why the former has been so readily accepted by the clinical psychologist. The limited diagnostic value of the I.Q. for the understanding of a child's behavior, its inadequacies in explaining individual variations in behavior, the dependence of the Binet on learning opportunities and academic achievement, and its limitations for the understanding of the role of internal or subjective or emotional factors in the behavioral pattern of the child—this was the experiential background of the clinical psychologist which made him so ready to employ a test whose aim is to evaluate "total personality." Because of the increasing clinical use of the Rorschach in the study of the mentally defective child it is discussed first in this chapter.

The Rorschach test consists of ten ink-blots, five of which are achromatic, three chromatic; two contain both chromatic and achromatic colored areas. The cards are presented to the subject with the following instructions:[1]

"Have you ever played the game of ink-blot? You can take a piece of paper and drop some ink right in the middle, fold the paper in half, press down, and then when you open it up you can see all sorts of things there. Some people see this and some people see that. No two people see the same things. I have some ink-blots here which I am going to show you one at a time and I would like you to tell me the different things that you see in the cards. Now, remember, no two people see the same things. There are no right or wrong answers. I would just like you to tell me the different things that you see. When you are through with each card give it to me and I'll give you the next one."

After the subject has seen each card, during which time the examiner

[1] It is not the purpose of this chapter to describe the administration, scoring, and interpretation of the Rorschach in such detail so as to enable the reader to utilize the test in clinical practice. The reader who wishes to become competent in the use of the Rorschach will have to familiarize himself with the standard texts (25, 26, 27, 40, 167, 244). However, it is the writer's experience that merely reading these texts results in a dictionary-like approach to the material. It is recommended that the Rorschach be learned in a clinical situation under the constant supervision of a competent person. As will be seen later, the lack of rigorous standardization and validation procedures with the Rorschach makes it necessary for the student to be very cautious in the interpretations he makes.

has been completely neutral and has merely recorded what he has said, the cards are reëxposed with the following directions:[2]

"I would like to go back over the cards with you because I would like to know *where* it was in the card you saw what you said you saw and *what* it was about the card that reminded you of it. For example (re-exposing the first card), you said you saw . . . (here the examiner reads what the subject said when he had first seen the card)."

The aim of this question period is to determine for each response: (1) how much of the card was used, (2) the determinants (color, shading, movement, form) of the response, (3) the content of the response (animals, humans, objects, etc.), (4) and the frequency (very frequent or very infrequent) of the response. In Table 24 will be found brief explanations of some of the Rorschach scoring categories; *only those categories are described which are relevant to subsequent discussions.* Below is given the psychological significance which has been traditionally attached to some of the Rorschach factors:

1. *Form (F) Responses.* "The principal test factor through which the individual shows his ability to direct his thinking from his higher centers, i.e., with conscious attention and discriminating judgment, is the accurate or 'good' form response, the F+ percept. . . . The more intelligent the individual, the higher his F+ percentage" (*26*, p. 19).

2. *Human Movement (M) Responses.* Such responses have been considered indicative of creative thinking and related to wish-fulfilling, fantasy activity. "Adults in the higher intelligence ranges produce M that are in nearly all instances accurate form percepts (F+) and that are seen in major portions of the figure, i.e., in the whole or in the more prominent details. These are the good quality movement responses, M+. As one inspects the M responses in the next lower intelligence group, he will recognize them to be of about the same order as in the superior group, but there will be fewer of them. . . . The lower one goes in the intelligence scale, the fewer the M. But even feebleminded subjects, including those of the lowest grade, produce them. Their deficiency does not altogether preclude their engaging in some wish-fulfilling fantasy, small though the

---

[2] In the standard texts referred to in the preceding footnote the student will find that there is by no means complete agreement about the wording of the instructions to the subject. There are also differences as to when the question period or inquiry is to be conducted, some calling for it after the subject has finished with each card and others after all cards have been exposed. Whether these differences in instructions and administration produce different results has not been experimentally determined.

TABLE 24. Brief Descriptions of *Some* Rorschach Factors

How Much of the Card Was Used (Location)	Determinants	Content	Frequency
1. Whole (W) response—the response utilizes the whole card. 2. Usual Detail (D) responses—the response utilizes an area which is statistically among the most frequently used. 3. Unusual Detail (Dd) responses — the response utilizes an area which is infrequently used. 4. Space (S) responses—the response utilizes only the white space in the card. 5. Confabulation (DW)—a response in which the individual begins by using a D and then uncritically includes the whole card for the response.	1. Human Movement (M)—a response which contains an animal or human in a human-like activity. 2. Form-Color (FC)—a response in which the chromatic color is integrated with a form which has definite class characteristics (a green worm, a blue bird, etc.). 3. Color-Form (CF)—a response in which the chromatic color is used but is not integrated with a form as in 2. Rather the form is indefinite and may be found in a wide variety of shapes (splotch of blood, blue water, etc.). 4. Color (C)—a response in which only color is utilized with no attempt to give a form to the response. 5. Surface Texture (Fc)—a response in which the shading qualities of the blot are used in creating the impression of a mottled or differentiated surface and integrated with a form as in 2 (a furry animal, a bearskin rug, etc.). 6. Surface Texture (cF)—a response in which the shading qualities are used but the form is as in 3 (a bunch of fur, an animal skin with form not specified, etc.). 7. Form (F) responses—a response in which no other previously noted determinant is involved. The response is determined solely by the shape of the area used. Responses which are of good or recognizable form are scored F+ and those which contain irrational features are scored F—. Any response (M, FC, CF, etc.) which contains an intended form may be scored as either F+ or F—. Lists of F+ and F— responses have been compiled in some of the standard texts referred to in the footnote on page 224.	1. H—the whole human figure is seen. 2. Hd—part of the human figure is seen. 3. A—a whole animal is seen. 4. Ad—part of an animal is seen.	1. Popular (P) responses—the most frequently given responses. 2. Original responses — these are responses which occur about once in every 100 protocols.

total quantity may be, and meager in substance as each creation is" (*26,* p. 23).

3. *Color Responses.* "Response to color . . . presents information as to the individual's sensitivity to events known to be exciting to the healthy persons of his cultural group generally. . . . The undiluted color reaction, C, is the test's equivalent of the uninhibited feeling experience. It is an infantile response mode and thus not abnormal in the very young child. . . . The CF or color-form response is characteristic for a less impulsive but still highly labile reactivity. . . . The infantile reaction trend is being held in restraint by the F tendency, a force out of another psychic sphere —awareness of reality. . . . The FC or form-color association is a new developmental phase. In it F dominates C. In this reaction regard for form is the principal behavior determinant. The individual is activated by feelings, but even while responding to these he masters them, out of consideration for others" (*26,* p. 27).

4. *Whole (W) Responses.* The number of W responses is considered to be positively correlated with the individual's present functioning intelligence. Being able to respond to the whole card in a conceptual fashion with resulting good form is considered characteristic of the very intelligent person. As one goes down the intelligence scale W responses tend to be less well organized, vague, or undifferentiated.

5. *Usual (D) and Unusual (Dd) Details.* "The generic psychologic value of the D percept lies in exposing S's attention to the obvious; selection of Dd (rare detail) reflects interest in the minute, the usually overlooked elements. . . . Their usefulness stands out only when they are inspected in terms of the proportions in which D, Dd, and W contribute to the entire pattern. Thus W has value as an index not only of height of intelligence but also of *kind.* For the relative amounts of W, D, and Dd tell *how* an individual attacks his problems" (*26,* p. 13).

6. *Content.* "For some clue, usually not in very full perspective, as to personal needs, we look to the associational content. But content is informative also structurally, with reference to S's intelligence. Evaluation of content must therefore take account of breadth, or the number of different categories into which the content is distributed; of richness of originality; of quantity of human (H) and of part-human percepts (Hd); of quantity of animal (A) and of part-animal forms (Ad) . . ." (*26,* p. 41). It has generally been considered that a high animal percentage (A percent) reflects stereotyped thinking or limited intelligence or both. "Very high percentages are found in the feebleminded, not infrequently touching the maximum, 100 percent. These low grade minds

just do not have the mental repertory enabling them to match the blot stimuli with any content other than the most obvious" (26, p. 15).

7. *Organizational Activity (Z)*. Beck (24) observed that organizational activity was not restricted to W responses. He noted that such activity was present when the individual combined details into larger units. For example, an individual might respond to two noncontiguous details and relate them to each other in one response. Four kinds of organizations were identified in terms of frequency in each card and a corresponding sigma value given. A response which fitted into any of the four categories received a Z credit and an individual's Z score was the total of these credits. Beck (26, p. 12) considered the Z score to vary directly with intelligence and, therefore, to be an index of "intellectual energy."

In his original work Rorschach (252) studied the responses of mentally deficient individuals to the ink-blots. He found that their protocols, in contrast to those of nondefectives, were characterized by responses the content of which frequently did not fit the area of the blot chosen (F—), pure color (C) responses with little attempt at delineation of form, no human movement (M) responses, frequent confabulatory (DW) responses, few whole (W) responses, a very high number of animal (A percent) responses, and many oligophrenic details (Do), the last being a response in which the subject uses a small area of a body whereas others normally see the whole body.

A question that immediately arises about these findings concerns their diagnostic value. Are Rorschach's results "typical" of the defective? Several factors indicate that they are probably not representative of this group. The fact that Rorschach used only 12 cases in itself severely limits the degree to which one can generalize from his findings. In addition, the psychological criteria and procedures for determining mental deficiency were not given and etiological factors were not discussed. Also, the chronological and mental age ranges were not stated and whether the cases were institutionalized or not cannot be determined. As has been indicated many times, especially in Chapter 5, the institutionalized defective represents a small portion of defectives in general. The majority of defectives remain in the community, their adjustment being of a kind which does not bring them to the attention of authorities as candidates for segregation. In contrast, the institutionalized defective is one who has been unable to make a marginal or submarginal community adjustment; he has usually come to the attention of authorities because of his social rather than intellectual inadequacies. It follows that findings obtained from institutionalized subjects cannot be considered representative of defectives in general.

The inadequacies of this pioneer study are emphasized here because the results have been assigned normative importance by subsequent investigators. It is to Rorschach's credit that he realized that his study was empirical and clinical and that the results could be considered only tentative. Although Rorschach's findings cannot be used by the clinician as an aid in diagnosis, it should be noted that some of them are in keeping with our everyday observations of *some* defective children.

1. The defective child is generally not capable of sustained conceptual thinking which is adapted to the reality of the situation. He tends to respond impressionistically, concretely, and without much critical reflection or delay. In Rorschach's findings these characteristics are seen (a) in the high number of responses which do not fit the area of the blot chosen and (b) in the inability to respond to external stimuli (color) in a conceptual manner—giving the pure C rather than FC type of response.

2. In his relations to people the defective individual generally responds in what appears to be an emotionally superficial, limited, or stereotyped fashion, personal feelings and attitudes toward self or others being unexpressed. In Rorschach's findings these characteristics are seen (a) in the absence of those responses (human movement) which are reflections of internal, subjective, or personal factors and (b) in the very limited variety of content, animal responses predominating.

Despite these points of suggested correspondence between behavior and test findings it should be emphasized that defectives vary considerably in their behavioral pattern and that broad generalizations which one might make about them cannot be used as evidence of the validity of conclusions reached by such a procedure as the Rorschach. Not only do defectives vary in behavioral pattern but they differ in regard to the etiology of their condition as well as in such factors as cultural background and institutionalization. The generalizations about the behavior of defectives offered above are true for *some* but not all defectives. In order to be diagnostically helpful the Rorschach would have to distinguish between defectives with differing behavioral patterns and would also have to demonstrate that whatever Rorschach patterns differentiate these groups are only rarely found among nondefective groups.

Pfister (234) worked with 59 mentally defective adults of whom 9 were morons, 24 were imbeciles, and 26 were idiots. This classification was not based on any explicit psychological criteria or procedures. Aside from the increase in the number of subjects, the criticisms made of Rorschach's study are applicable to Pfister's. As did Rorschach, Pfister found a large percentage of poor forms, few whole (W) responses, and a predominance of animal forms. In contrast to Rorschach, Pfister found that some individuals gave human movement (M), the number of color responses tended to be small, oligophrenic details were by no means characteristic of the entire group, and shading responses were given. While Rorschach's findings suggested that defectives react uniformly to the ink-blots, Pfister's results indicate that this group was not homogeneous on the basis of their Rorschach performance. It is somewhat surprising that Pfister's study has been considered by some (160) as corroborating Rorschach's original observations. Since the etiological composition of the cases in both studies is unknown, the criteria for diagnosis not stated, the mental and chronological age ranges not given, and the number of cases too small to serve a basis for generalization, it is somewhat difficult to see how the two studies can be legitimately compared or their results given the status of norms.

Beck's study (23) represents an advance over earlier ones. He used 69 cases, all were institutionalized, and their intelligence level was determined by the Stanford-Binet (1916). His cases were not merely

TABLE 25.   Number of Cases at Each Mental Age Level in Beck's Study (23)

Mental Age	Number of Cases
2 years 6 months to 3 years 5 months	9
3 " 6 " " 4 " 5 "	6
4 " 6 " " 5 " 5 "	7
5 " 6 " " 6 " 5 "	6
6 " 6 " " 7 " 5 "	9
7 " 6 " " 8 " 5 "	16
8 " 6 " " 9 " 5 "	9
9 " 6 " " 10 " 5 "	7
	69

classified as morons, imbeciles, and idiots; the mental age range was kept continuous from 2 years 6 months to 10 years 5 months (Table 25). The mean mental age was 6 years 9 months with a standard deviation of 2 years 3 months. Chronological ages ranged from 5 years 10 months to 65 years 10 months, 47 subjects being under 16 years of age. In Table 26 are presented the averages for various Rorschach factors at

TABLE 26. Summary of Mean Response at Each Mental Age Level for All Rorschach Factors (23)

Mental Age (In Months)	W	F+	A	M	C	O	Do	Dr	R[a]
30–41	1.33	36.33	60.44	0.11	2.05	43.00	0.22	2.00	14.89
42–53	1.33	35.50	43.16	0.33	1.75	45.16	3.16	3.00	21.50
54–65	2.29	43.72	49.71	1.29	4.21	42.00	1.14	3.28	27.28
66–77	2.33	68.33	44.83	0.50	7.58	23.67	0.50	2.16	18.33
78–89	3.44	52.45	46.22	0.44	5.61	43.88	1.67	3.44	29.22
90–101	3.56	61.12	59.06	1.00	3.68	31.19	0.88	2.75	20.56
102–113	4.55	78.22	61.56	0.89	3.55	29.11	0.22	1.11	18.11
114–125	4.86	68.28	65.86	1.29	1.50	22.85	0.29	1.42	18.71

[a] R = response total for each subject.

each mental level. In discussing Beck's findings attention will be paid first to the factors which have been considered indicators of intelligence level: the number of whole (W) responses, the percentage of good form (F+) responses, the number of human movement (M) responses, the percentage of animal (A percent) responses, and the number of original (O) responses.

1. *Whole (W) Responses.* In contrast to Rorschach and Pfister, Beck found "a materially higher number of W's." The correlation of W and M.A. was +.474 with a P.E. of .06. He concluded that while intelligence was related to the production of W, the size of the correlation "is so low that we must regard intelligence as only a minor factor, or one of many factors."

2. *Form (F+) Responses.* Beck found the mean F+ percentage of the entire group to be 57.76 with a S.D. of 20.2. The correlation with M.A. was .64 ± .051. Although Beck considered his findings "confirmatory of Rorschach and Pfister," his results do not seem to substantiate such a conclusion. In contrast to Beck's mean of 57.76, Pfister's mean of 35 seems a good deal lower. From the way in which Rorschach presented

his data the mean for his 12 cases seems also to be much lower. The fact that these investigators found that the F+ percentage and M.A. are positively related must be tempered by the fact that their absolute values are different.

3. *Animal (A Percent) Responses.* The mean percentage of animal responses was 55.4 with a S.D. of 20.8. This is not in agreement with Rorschach's expectation that the mentally deficient should give an A percentage above 60. The correlation between the A percentage and M.A. was +.156 ± .079. "In short, our results are not confirmatory of a prediction as high as Rorschach's frequency of animal responses among feebleminded subjects, and nothing in them indicates any linear dependence of the number of such responses upon intelligence level" (*23*, p. 46).

4. *Human Movement (M) Responses.* Rorschach's finding that M is not found in the records of the mentally deficient was not borne out by Beck's findings. In 55 percent of Beck's cases there were no M's; in 26 percent there was one M; and in 19 percent there were two or more M. The correlation between M and M.A. was +.256 ± .079.

5. *Original (O) Responses.* These are responses which are found very infrequently in Rorschach protocols. It can be seen that what is "unusual" depends on the experience of the particular examiner; the more records he has seen the better he can spot an unusual response. Ordinarily a response which is found once in every 100 records is considered original. Aside from the absence of any comprehensive compilation of what have been considered original responses, another difficulty is that some originals are of good form (O+) and some of bad form (O—). Because of these difficulties Beck felt it "inadvisable to attempt statistical treatment of O— as against O+ pending more evidence in the basis of which to make this distinction" (*23*, p. 52). Beck's mean O percentage of 35.84, S.D. 15.10, refers to all originals regardless of form. The correlation between originals and M.A. was —.391 ± .068. Beck considered his findings confirmatory of those of Pfister—within the defective range of intelligence the higher the mental level the lower the percentage of originals.

In discussing the significance of these findings Beck (*23*, p. 65) states:

"The question may well be raised, however, regarding individual children who gave responses that materially deviate from the norm for feeble-minded? How about the cases of many W's? high F+ percentage? much M response? Were the Binet findings inaccurate and were these cases not feeble-minded? Or does the Rorschach test err in some cases sufficiently so to invalidate its diagnostic usefulness?

"Since there are five Rorschach indices to intellectual functioning (Whole responses, W; sharp forms, F+; inner creativity, M; high percentage of stereotyped thought, A; and originality, O), it was felt that a deviation to be considered as genuine must occur in two or more of these categories, and should be one standard deviation in the direction of higher intellectual level. Of such cases, there were eight or a total of 11.6 percent."

A question that immediately arises from Beck's discussion concerns the legitimacy of speaking of "the norm for the feeble-minded." In view of the small number of cases that Beck studied at each mental level (see Table 25), it is reasonable to question the advisability of referring to the results as norms. Even the total number of cases ($N = 69$) cannot be considered a large enough sample for establishing norms. As one would expect from a small number of cases, the variability or standard deviation which Beck found for each of the Rorschach factors was relatively large. This large variability is due to the disproportionate weight which a single or a few extreme cases have when the sample is small. The following example using Beck's data may illustrate this point:

Group with M.A. Between 30 and 41 Months

Case	No. of W Responses	
1	1	
2	0	
3	0	Mean (with case number 4 omitted) $= 1$
4	4	Standard deviation $= \pm .866$
5	2	
6	2	
7	1	
8	2	
9	0	

Mean $= 1.33$
Standard deviation $= \pm 1.25$

It will be seen from this example that when one is working with few cases a single extreme case may unduly influence the mean and the standard deviation. In the raw data that Beck gives in the appendix of his monograph, the variability at each mental age level for most determinants is considerable. If in repeating his study one were to triple or quadruple the number of cases, it would not be surprising if different results were obtained. It is for this reason that in the establishment of norms for a psychological test, such as the Binet, one of the aims has been to include as many cases as possible. This point is emphasized here because Beck considered an individual to be a "genuine" deviant if on two of the five intellectual factors he was one standard deviation above the mean. Using his "norms," Beck found that 8 cases were genuine deviations. With a larger sample of cases the results might well be different.

Another factor in Beck's study which limits the degree to which one can generalize from the findings is that the cases were institutionalized. The majority of defectives are not institutionalized and those that are represent a "select" group. Since his cases were institutionalized and data about length of institutionalization are not given, it is impossible to determine to what extent Beck's findings are related to this variable rather than to mental deficiency *per se*. Still another limiting factor in his study concerns the etiological composition of the group. Beck does not state how many of his cases were garden-variety defectives, brain-injured, undifferentiated, etc. In light of the importance of etiology one cannot assume that the different etiological groups would give the same Rorschach picture. It must also be noted that Beck excluded cases who gave less than 10 responses or perseverated—exclusions which make one question even more the representative nature of his sample.

The behavioral pattern of the defective and the Rorschach factors from which it was derived may be seen in the following (*23*, p. 58):

"In the group here studied the mean C^3 response was 3.73; S.D. 3.83. . . . The mean M response was 0.75, the difference between that and the mean C response is therefore 2.95. The ratio of this difference . . . is [statistically] a real difference. The interpretation according to Rorschach principles would be that the Randall's Island children showed a reliable difference in their tendency to be impulsive and exterior in their affective life, rather than introversial—a finding which certainly is not out of accord with the character of the feebleminded as observed by those who have had experience with them."

As was indicated earlier, generalizations about the behavioral pattern

---

[3] In this study Beck did not treat the various kinds of color responses (FC, CF, C) separately but totaled them. Ordinarily, impulsivity is associated with a preponderance of **CF and** C over FC, but whether this is the basis for Beck's conclusion cannot be determined.

of defectives usually overlook and obscure the heterogeneity that exists. That some, perhaps many, defectives fit the generalization cannot be denied; but whether the Rorschach differentiates these cases from those with other behavioral patterns has yet to be demonstrated. It may also be pointed out that the significance of the comparison between the sum of C and the average M is open to question because Beck did not obtain the relation of M to C for each individual but instead added up the number of such responses of the group, averaged them, and then compared them to each other. From such a procedure one cannot determine the number of *individuals* for whom his generalization holds.

Beck attempted to check the validity of his conclusion based on the M to C comparison by comparing 16 cases who were presumably unstable with 13 who were stable. He did not obtain a statistically reliable difference between the groups in their color score. These results, like those of Pfister, indicate that the Rorschach did not validly distinguish between individuals with differing behavioral patterns.

Other Rorschach studies (77, 94, 153, 154, 162) with mentally defective individuals are open to many of the criticisms which have already been presented. For the sake of emphasis the questions which one may ask about a study in this area are as follows:

1. What criteria and psychological procedures were used in making the diagnosis of mental deficiency?
2. Were the cases institutionalized or not? If institutionalized, was the length of institutionalization controlled in group comparisons?
3. What was the etiological composition of the cases?
4. Were sufficient cases used so that generalizations may be made with some degree of confidence?
5. Were the range and variability of the scores given so that one may determine the expected frequencies of certain scores?
6. Was the influence of chronological age determined?

The fact that some studies control for some of these factors while others do not makes comparison hazardous.

Sarason and Sarason (260) studied the heterogeneity in adjustment in an otherwise etiologically homogeneous group: the high-grade, garden-variety mental defective. The purpose of this study was to determine whether psychological tests could differentiate between those whose adjustment was relatively good or bad. The criteria for selection of cases were: (1) The neurological examination was negative; (2) only those cases were chosen in which more than one child in the family was in the institution; (3) all members of a given family had to have a similar degree of mental defect—all classified in the moron or border-line categories. Forty cases were obtained and each was given the 1937

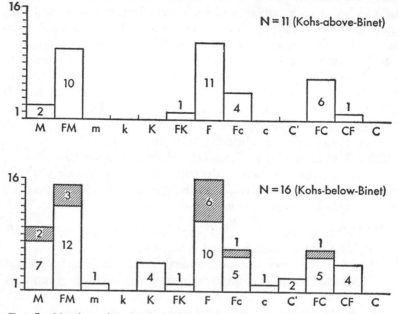

Fig. 5. Number of Individuals Giving at Least One Response in Various Rorschach Categories. Shaded areas indicate number of cases giving minus responses. (From Sarason and Sarason, 260.)

Stanford-Binet (L), the Arthur Performance Scale, an electroencephalographic examination, and the Rorschach.[4] All those cases who on the Kohs Block Designs test of the Arthur Scale had a mental age at least 18 months *above* the Binet M.A. were put in one group; those whose mental age on the Kohs was 18 months *below* the Binet M.A. were put into another group. With this criterion the former group (Kohs-above-Binet) was comprised of 11 cases and the latter (Kohs-below-Binet) of 16 cases. There was no difference between the groups

[4] This study has already been discussed on page 126. In the present chapter the Rorschach results will be discussed in greater detail.

in mental and chronological age. On the Rorschach (see Fig. 5) the following trends toward group differences were noted:

1. *Minus Responses.* No individual in the Kohs-above-Binet group gave a response which could be scored minus; that is, their responses did not contain irrational features. Nine individuals in the Kohs-below-Binet group gave minus responses. One gave eight such responses, one gave six, three gave two, and four gave one minus response.
2. *Human Movement (M).* Only two individuals in the Kohs-above-Binet group gave human movement responses, while nine gave such responses in the Kohs-below-Binet group.
3. *Form Responses (F).* Both groups gave form responses, although the Kohs below-Binet group gave more on the average than the other group. The value of *t* in this instance is 2.073, which is below the 5 percent level of significance.
4. *Form-Color (FC).* Six individuals or 54.5 percent of the Kohs-above-Binet groups gave FC responses, whereas six or 37.5 percent of the Kohs-below-Binet group had such responses.
5. *Whole (W) and Detail (D) Responses.* The Kohs-above-Binet group gave less such responses on the average than the other group, although the difference cannot be considered statistically significant.
6. *Number of Responses.* The Kohs-above-Binet group had on the average fewer responses than the other group. The value of *t* in this instance is 2.922, which is well below the 5 percent level of significance.
7. *Rejections.* The Kohs-above-Binet group tend to reject more cards on the average than the other group, although the difference is not statistically significant.

Sarason and Sarason conclude:

"The Kohs-above-Binet group seems to be the more stable of the two. Their social adjustment, which lacks depth, is relatively better than that of the Kohs-below-Binet group. Their smaller number of responses, frequent rejection of cards, in addition to the relative lack of spontaneity and imagination, should not obscure the fact that what they do see in the cards is seen with at least average form quality and is not marred by illogical elements. As a group they tend to react conventionally and cautiously to situations, seemingly overcontrolled emotionally so that their quiet, 'dull' appearance may easily allow one to miscalculate their capacities. In the institution they are the 'good' boys and girls who conform to their program quietly but well. Not one of this group has ever been in need of other than ordinary discipline; all are well liked by other patients and employees; and their work records are for the most part very good.

"The Kohs-below-Binet cases cannot be delineated as clearly in a composite picture as the other group. As a group they tend to be more introversive, have less adequate emotional control, and are more irrational. The institutional records of this group are in marked contrast to those with Kohs-above-Binet. Not only do they have poor work records but their behavior in many cases has necessitated frequent, extraordinary, disciplinary action. Irregular sex behavior, runaway, stealing, laziness, extreme childishness, silliness, and incorrigibility are some of the characteristics noted in their records. Not only are they considered as poor parole possibilities but when three of this group were paroled they had to be returned after a short time to the institution."

The Rorschach findings by Sarason and Sarason are suggestive of the following: (1) Within a group of defectives who are etiologically homogeneous there are marked differences in behavioral pattern; (2) differences in behavioral pattern (using extreme groups) are associated with different Rorschach patterns; (3) the number of human movement (M) and whole (W) responses is not a reliable indicator of intellectual efficiency since these responses appeared less frequently in those cases that did best on tests of conceptual thinking (see p. 237) and whose vocational efficiency was relatively good; (4) the number of minus or poor forms seems to be negatively correlated with intellectual efficiency.

In a subsequent study with a group of cerebral palsy cases Sarason and Sarason (261) corroborated the above findings (see p. 176). Their results emphasize not only how heterogeneous defectives are but, perhaps more important, that even within one etiological grouping heterogeneity in behavior pattern is marked. It should be remembered that these studies involved relatively few cases, extreme groups were used, and all were institutionalized. Further research is necessary in which larger groups will be used, institutional and noninstitutional cases studied, and more specific behavioral criteria employed.

Werner (314) studied two etiological groups of defective children, the endogenous or garden-variety and the exogenous or brain-injured, on Rorschach performance.[5] There were 19 cases in each group and each member of one group was closely matched for mental age and I.Q. with a member of the other group. Werner's administration of the Rorschach differed from the usual procedure in two respects. First,

---

[5] The endogenous-exogenous typology is discussed in Chapters 2, 3, and 5.

whereas the subject is usually questioned about his responses after he has gone through the ten cards, Werner questioned after each card. "These children frequently have a short memory span; it was not expected of them to remember their responses to a card too well, after other cards had been presented to them" (*314*, p. 54).[6] The second difference in procedure was the fact that Werner "probably prodded the children for responses more frequently than would many examiners" (*314*, p. 54). It can be seen that these differences in administration make comparison with other studies difficult.

Table 27 lists some of the major differences which Werner obtained between the two groups. On the basis of this and other studies (see p.

TABLE 27.   Differences Between Exogenous and Endogenous on
Certain Rorschach Factors (*314*)

	Exogenous > Endogenous	Exogenous < Endogenous
1. Number of responses		P = .01
2. Percentage of whole (W) responses	P[a]= .01	
3. Percentage of usual details (D)	P = .03	
4. Percentage of tiny details (dd)		P = .01
5. Percentage of oligophrenic details (Do)	P = .01	
6. Percentage of white space responses (S)	P = .01	
7. Percentage of animal movement responses (FM)		P = .01
8. Percentage of pure color (C) responses	P = .01	
9. Percentage of good form (F+) responses	P = .01	
10. Percentage of original (O) responses	P = .01	
11. Percentage of poor original (O—) responses	P = .01	

[a] The probability values were obtained from a chi-square analysis.

116), Werner concluded that the brain-injured defective differed from the garden-variety individual in the following "general traits" (*314*, p. 107):

[6] Investigators using the usual procedure of administration with defectives did not note that their subjects had difficulty in remembering their responses.

1. *"Lack of integration of elements into more comprehensive configuration* has been previously shown to characterize sensori-motor performance of brain-injured children. Indications of disintegrative tendencies [in the Rorschach] are the predominance of piece-like oligophrenic detail responses (Do, Hd, Ad).

2. *"Forced responsiveness to sensory stimulation or lack of sensory control* is a well-known symptom of a brain-injured organism. Reactions to perceptually conspicuous areas such as white parts may be considered a result of this behavior. Reversals in the normal relationship of figure and background appeared in the ink-blot situation as a tendency of brain-injured children to reach to the white spaces.

3. *"Lack of affective-motor control* demonstrating itself clinically in hyperactivity, outbursts, etc., was evidenced in the Rorschach test by abnormally strong reaction to color, and by a relatively small number of movement responses.

4. *"Lack of associational control* conveyed itself in the Rorschach test—as on previous conceptual tests—in the tendency of the brain-injured children toward strange and fantastic interpretations (O— responses).

5. *"Meticulous behavior* has been observed on all previous tests with many of the brain-injured children. Meticulosity of these children was evident by their attitude toward the ink-blot test: they took the task more literally than the other group, were often apologetic for an interpretation, if it did not completely fit the object. This meticulosity was probably partially responsible for their higher number of whole and plus form responses.

6. *"Pathological rigidity:* i.e., inability to shift, perseverations, are known to be symptomatic of brain-injury. Since rigidity, however, is not only a pathological trait but is characteristic of mental deficiency in general, it is not surprising that quantitative differences between the two groups have not been found. The form percentage was equally high with both types, indicating a high degree of rigidity. Similarly, perseverative tendencies in general were equally frequent with the two groups. On the other hand, there were some indications in the records of the brain-injured children of a pathological form of rigidity. In view of earlier studies, it seems reasonable to interpret the small total number of responses of these children as being at least partly caused by inflexibility in the shift from one interpretation of the ink-blot to another one. Furthermore, whereas the repetitive responses of the endogenous children were exclusively in the nature of a superficial stereotypy, the (very few) occurrences of perseverations caused by a deep-set inflexible mental attitude appeared only in the records of brain-injured children."

In earlier sections of this book some questions were raised about the validity of the criteria for brain injury employed by Werner and Strauss.[7] Aside from the question of the validity of the criteria it was also pointed out that in some of their studies it was difficult to determine how much overlap there was for a given kind of behavior between *individuals* in the two groups. In other words, how many individuals in the endogenous group responded in the same way and to the same degree as individuals in the brain-injured group? In Werner's Rorschach study, for example, it was shown that 20.7 percent of all *responses* of the brain-injured group were of the whole (W) variety, in contrast to 14.9 percent in the endogenous or garden-variety group. These percentages do not tell one how many *individuals* in the brain-injured group gave as many or as few such responses as individuals in the other group. If whole responses are to be given discriminatory value, one would have to have the data in terms of individuals. It may be, for example, that a few individuals in the brain-injured group are unduly influencing the percentage. Since only 19 cases were studied, one or two extreme cases can have such an effect. As was also pointed out earlier (p. 121), Werner's use of chi-square (see Table 27) is not justified because an assumption basic to the use of chi-square is that each entry in a cell be independent of all other entries in that cell—an assumption not met when one enters responses and not individuals in a cell. Since Werner used chi-square in this manner, one must be skeptical about the validity of his interpretations.

Werner's findings that the brain-injured, in contrast to the endogenous cases, give fewer responses, a higher percentage of good form responses, and about the same number of human movement responses seem at variance with the findings of Sarason and Sarason previously discussed. They found that some endogenous cases (Kohs-above-Binet) *in whom there was no evidence of brain injury* gave significantly fewer responses, more good form responses, and less human movement responses than other endogenous cases (Kohs-below-Binet) in some of whom there was *suggestive* evidence of brain injury. Werner's finding that his brain-injured group gave proportionately more good form responses is not supported by the results of other studies (*129, 221, 237*) of brain-

[7] It is pointed out again that the exogenous cases studied by Werner and Strauss "were free from gross motor defects. Their main overt sign of brain injury was mental impairment, not disturbance of gross motor function" (*314*, p. 53).

injury cases, defective or otherwise. Werner's explanation that the brain-injured "frequently displayed pedantic and critical behavior whereas endogenous children showed less concern about their interpretations" seems to be a restatement of the findings (higher F+ percentage) rather than an explanation. While one would expect criticalness in the healthy organism to result in form responses of high quality, one would not expect a brain-injured, defective organism to utilize such an attitude in an efficient, conceptual manner—at least no more so than the nonbrain-injured defective individual. Another explanation offered by Werner is "that the brain-injured children, though of the same mental age level as measured by a Binet test, actually function on a superior level, in comparison with the endogenous children." This also seems to be a restatement of the findings rather than an explanation of them. No objective non-Rorschach evidence for the statement is presented. At least one other explanation is possible. In light of their relatively high good form percentage (F+), which Werner noted was well above that ordinarily found in defectives, the efficient conceptual thinking which such a performance represents casts doubt on the diagnosis of brain injury. It should be emphasized that F+ is a reflection of an individual's ability to mold his perceptions in a conceptual and realistic manner to the areas of the blots chosen for the responses. The possibility that some of the exogenous group do not possess a brain injury can be decided only by further research.

In recent years the psychological pendulum seems to have swung from the Binet to the Rorschach as the basis for a diagnosis of mental deficiency. Several studies have appeared in which the evaluation of intellectual capacity based on the Rorschach has been considered more valid than that based on the Binet or other standardized psychometric procedures. Where discrepancies between the Binet and Rorschach have been found, the Rorschach indicating higher capacity, it has been interpreted as an indication that affective factors are interfering with full utilization of capacities. Sloan (274), for example, was concerned "with the problem of determining whether certain personality disturbances may appear to be mistaken for mental deficiency." He used two groups who differed only in I.Q. range, a defective group (N = 26) ranging from 44–79 and a nondefective group (N = 24) ranging from 80–100. Before institutionalization the nondefective group was considered to be defective by a judge and two physicians. "Evidently their social adjustment was sufficiently lacking to the extent that it resembled that of a mentally defective." The two groups were given the Rorschach and the record of each subject was evaluated in light of ten signs generally considered to be indicative of mental deficiency. The "norms" and the basis for their selection are given in Table 28. Sloan determined the extent of each subject's deviation from the "typical" pattern. The median number of deviations was 4.5 and 5.0 for the nondefective and defective groups respectively, the difference not being significant. The five factors which showed the most frequent deviation in the direction of higher functioning were A percent, F+ percent, F percent, R, and Z. Sloan concluded that "on the basis of these five most frequently deviating factors, one may suspect absence of mental deficiency when the Rorschach pattern shows a preponderance of these signs," and also that "personality disturbance" may be presumed to be present in both groups.

The steps whereby Sloan reached his conclusions are not clear and bear examination. Assuming at this point that there is a "characteristic" defective pattern on the Rorschach, the underlying assumption in his study, it can be concluded from the obtained deviations that both groups are not mentally defective. Sloan seems to reason that if one group, the nondefectives, show a particular pattern on the Rorschach, and another group, the defectives, also show the same pattern, then the latter may take on the characteristics of the former and can also be considered nondefective. Such a conclusion does not seem tenable. *In the absence of evidence to the contrary, it appears reasonable to assume that the defective subjects on whom the "accepted" norms were based were similar in composition to Sloan's own defective group. Yet Sloan's defective group differed significantly from the defectives on whom the norms were obtained. From these findings one might well question the validity of the original norms.*[8] It has already been shown that the reported Rorschach norms are probably neither valid nor reliable enough for clinical use. It may well be that in future studies of adequate and representative samples of the defective population the degree of deviation which Sloan obtained will fall within the range of the char-

[8] A hypothetical example from another field may serve to make this point clearer. Let us say there is a test on which schizophrenics are supposed to perform in *x* fashion. One then studies a group of schizophrenics and finds that his group does not perform in *x* fashion. Although he might be tempted to assume that the group was not schizophrenic, he might more justifiably assume that *x* fashion is not reliably characteristic of schizophrenics.

Table 28. Basis for Selection of Rorschach Norms by Sloan (274)

	W	M	Csum	F%	A%	Z	P	F%	App	R
Rorschach	1-3	0-2	4-7	45-60	60-80	...	...	...	D, Do	>15-30
Beck[a]	3-5	0-1.3	1.5-3.68	52-78	46-66	...	...	...	D, Dr	13-29
Beck[b]		0 or 1	...	<60	"Very high"	5-31 = lower ½ of normals	3.5	>80	D, Dd	...
Klopfer	"Slightly higher than Rorschach"	"Occasional M"	...	...	...	...	...	...	...	21 (quoting Pfister)
Sloan	...	86% with 0-1 M	64% with <2Cs.	55-81	37-70	5-18	2.8-5.6	...	...	11.4-23
Accepted norms	0-5	0-1	0-3	55-75	50-70	5-18	3-6	80-100	D, Dd	15-25

[a] From Beck's 1932 monograph (23).
[b] From Beck's text (26, vol. ii).

acteristic performance for such groups. It may also be that the Rorschach cannot be used for distinguishing defective from nondefective functioning. In any event one must agree with Sloan that "obviously, extensive research is both necessary and desirable for establishing norms for defectives and for refining the criteria tentatively proposed here as having diagnostic value for differentiation of mental deficiency and other clinical entities."

A study similar in purpose to Sloan's is that of Jolles (152): "We have to investigate the importance of personality adjustment as a factor in the etiology of mental deficiency." Jolles' 66 subjects were children between the ages of 10 and 15 with I.Q.'s between 65 and 79. Each child had been referred to a school psychologist in order to determine whether or not he should be placed in a special class. Jolles divided his cases as follows: "In Group I we have all the cases whose Rorschach patterns indicate clearly that these subjects are normal in mental ability. In Group II are placed all subjects whose Rorschach records include at least one factor which might possibly suggest normal mental ability although the pattern as a whole would suggest severe mental retardation. In Group III we have all cases whose Rorschach patterns give us no indication of normal mentality." The Rorschach signs contraindicating mental deficiency are nowhere explicitly stated by Jolles, but a close reading of his case studies indicates that the giving of M responses, a high Z or organization score, good W responses, "normal" interest range, and an F+ percentage around 60 were the Rorschach signs employed. Unfortunately, he does not state the exact extent of each sign that must be present in order to warrant calling it a "non-defective" sign. According to his analysis, 14 cases fell in Group I, 28 in Group II, and the remainder in Group III.[9] Jolles' conclusions may be seen in the following:

"In each of the 66 cases of this study we find that the Rorschach test reveals a severe emotional disturbance. There are many cases of anxiety neurosis, a number in whom there are definite schizoid trends, and many who present mixed symptoms of feelings of inferiority, depression, compulsions, and

[9] The first question which may be asked is why these cases were called familial. In order for the cases to fall in the familial category it would have to be demonstrated (1) that the neurological examination was negative and (2) that the parents and siblings were on a similar mental level as the patient. Since no medical histories were available and the parents and siblings were not observed, the diagnosis of familial deficiency does not seem warranted.

other forms of personality disorder. This raises several issues which may affect our concept of mental deficiency. The cases in Group I illustrate the fact that there is, perhaps, a greater incidence of normals functioning as mental defectives than clinicians have believed to be true, for many of these cases would not have been recognized without the use of the Rorschach test or some other projective technique. The cases in Group II bring out the possibility of an even greater incidence of such cases.

"The cases in Group III raise an even more crucial issue: Are these children, whose I.Q.'s and Rorschach patterns indicate mental deficiency, really potentially normal in intelligence? Could it be that the anxiety states and other emotional disturbances found in these children distort their personalities to such an extent that we are unable to discover their normal intellectual potential? Or are they mental defectives in the usual sense of the word and the personality disturbances merely coincidental with or caused by the retarded intellectual development? If there was at least one case among these 66 children in which the emotional disturbance was not severe, then the latter hypothesis might be preferred. However, such is not the case, and, therefore, it is essential for us to recognize the possibility that the former hypothesis may be the more acceptable one, although this study is too limited in scope to make it conclusive" (*152*, p. 186).

A serious limitation to Jolles' study is his assumption that the Rorschach signs indicating mental deficiency have a high degree of validity. Since Jolles relied entirely on Beck's studies, the limitations of which have already been discussed, one may question the validity of Jolles' conclusions. It should be pointed out that Jolles assumed that the signs contraindicating mental deficiency were each of equal importance, an assumption for which there is no evidence. For example, an F+ percentage *below* 60 was considered by Jolles to be compensated for by a "good" W response, although Vernon's review (*303*) of the literature indicated that the F+ percentage was by far the most valid Rorschach indicator of intelligence. It is interesting to note in this connection that 7 of the 14 cases in Jolles' "mentally normal" group had F+ percentages at or below the critical point; in the "possible" mentally normal group (according to the Rorschach) 16 of the 28 cases had an F+ percentage at or below the critical point. Jolles' use of the human movement response (giving more than two) as contraindicating mental deficiency is questionable because, as Beck pointed out, contrary to Rorschach, some defectives do give two or more human movement responses. To assume that two movement responses indicate mental deficiency while three do not is to assign a questionable degree of importance to a difference of one.

A serious limitation in Jolles' procedure is that he used some Rorschach signs (W, M, populars) in terms of absolute scores. For example, do three M responses in a record of 15 responses have the same significance as three in a record of 30; does one good W in a record of 15 responses mean the same as one in a record of 30? The Rorschach literature is replete with examples of researchers finding that raw scores did not have as good discriminatory value as when they were expressed relatively. For instance, when F+ responses are not expressed in terms of a percentage of all F responses, their diagnostic value is very slight.

That the Rorschach signs which Jolles used may not discriminate between defective and nondefective intelligence can be seen by his presentation of 8 problem cases with average I.Q.'s. In each case the Rorschach signs contraindicating mental deficiency *were absent.* Jolles concluded, however, that these cases "for all practical purposes" may be considered mentally deficient. It would seem that one is equally justified in concluding that the Rorschach signs employed may not be as discriminating between mental levels as Jolles believed. It will be remembered that a similar conclusion was offered in the discussion of Sloan's study.

Jolles' conclusion, similar to Sloan's, that mental deficiency is a sign of personality disturbance, seems to be based on two lines of reasoning. First, the fact that an individual is defective on psychometric tests but not on the Rorschach indicates that some personality disturbance must be present that is interfering with expression of intellectual capacity. As has been pointed out, this argument rests entirely on the questionable assumption that the Rorschach signs are valid. Second, the fact that some of these psychometrically defective cases give a Rorschach record containing features similar to those found in records given by schizophrenics indicates that the former have some of the personality characteristics of the latter. This seems to be reasoning by analogy. All Jolles' data may indicate is that some of his cases gave some schizophrenic-like responses. It does not follow that these responses have the same significance for both groups. Jolles' reasoning is akin to saying that since schizophrenics show a disturbance in conceptual thinking, any individual who shows such a disturbance is schizophrenic or has such tendencies. Jolles does not explain why some schizophrenics do not have the "characteristic" Rorschach signs. That mental deficiency may be a sign of personality disturbance is an intriguing assumption, but Jolles' data do not offer relevant proof. Other studies (*125, 151*) similar in design to those of Sloan and Jolles have the limitations just discussed.

Another feature of Jolles' study deserves discussion. Was there justification *before the Rorschach was administered* for assuming that the cases were mentally deficient? The fact that they obtained low test scores does not constitute an adequate basis for the diagnosis of mental deficiency. Were these cases socially adequate for their age? Was there evidence that they were always retarded? Could one assume that environmental factors were not related to the intellectual inadequacy? Did Jolles conclude that the condition of these children was incurable and that therapeutic procedures were not indicated? The data for answering these questions are not given. It may well be that with more comprehensive data about his cases Jolles would not have labeled them initially as mental defectives. Although he felt that without the use of the Rorschach the normal capacity of many of his subjects would not have been detected, it may be said that utilization of inclusive criteria of mental deficiency might also have indicated the presence of pseudofeeble-mindedness.

It is interesting to note that the psychological pendulum seems to have swung markedly. Whereas formerly the I.Q. was the sole basis for a diagnosis of mental deficiency, the Rorschach seems now to have been given this Herculean task. It may be anticipated that just as the uncritical acceptance of the I.Q. proved embarrassing to the psychologist, so will the Rorschach be shown to have limitations. It is indeed surprising how in the clinical literature little can be found about the limitations of the Rorschach. It cannot be denied that the problems to which the Rorschach has been applied are extremely important from a theoretical and practical point of view; the relation between "personality and intelligence" remains a central problem in clinical psychology. The Rorschach *may* give a better picture of this relationship than any other single technique. But until this has been demonstrated by scientific procedure and control, the value of the Rorschach remains an open question.

The studies which have already been discussed are largely concerned with the problem of determining intellectual level and capacity by means of the Rorschach. As was stated previously, comparing the Rorschach results to some kind of validating criterion was not a methodological feature of these studies. Patterson and Magaw's study (228) compared the behavioral pattern revealed by the Rorschach with an external criterion: a personality sketch of the individual written by a trained observer. The subjects were 30 institutionalized defective boys from one cottage, ranging in I.Q. from 37 to 79. The Rorschach was administered by a person who had no contact at any time with the subject other than during the Rorschach test period. None of the personality sketches written by the observer were read by the experimenter until after the Rorschach interpretations of all the subjects had been made.

"The personality sketch was based upon observation of the boy in question. The author of the personality sketches acted as an assistant supervisor of the cottage and had served in this capacity for a period of six months before any of the sketches were written. As an additional check upon his observation, he copied excerpts of opinions which had been recorded in the boy's clinical folder by the teachers, cottage workers, work supervisor, social worker, mental hygienist, and psychiatrist. The results of intelligence tests, performance tests, and educational achievement tests were also taken from the clinical folder. All reference to the physical appearance was omitted from the sketch, and, although reference was occasionally made to unusual incidents, no attempt was made to write a history of the boy's development."

The 30 subjects were arranged by the writer of the personality sketches into groups of five. A matching technique was then employed; the writer of the personality sketches matched the Rorschach interpretations against his sketches, and the Rorschach tester matched the personality sketches against the Rorschachs. The following results were obtained:

Number of Correct Matchings

Group	Tester	Observer
I	2	3
II	3	3
III	0	5
IV	1	3
V	1	3
VI	5	5
Totals	12	22

For both the tester and observer the number of correct matchings was significantly better than chance expectations, although the observer obviously did better than the tester. According to Patterson and Magaw, "The most probable explanation of this discrepancy that has occurred to us is that the observer knew more about the boys than he could possibly have conveyed in the personality sketches and consequently had more cues than the tester upon which to base his judgments. Since he possessed also some familiarity with the Rorschach technique, he had the further advantage of being able to make additional interpretations from the [Rorschach] psychogram." The authors conclude that "the test has sufficient validity to be used in the diagnosis of personality problems of individuals within this group." It should be noted that although the number of correct matchings made by the observer was high, the basis for his success cannot be determined. It would have been interesting to know what Rorschach cues he utilized which enabled him to match so much better than the tester. If the interpretive procedures of the observer could have been determined, valuable data might have been obtained about the relative value of the various Rorschach factors for an interpretation. Similarly it would have been helpful to know the interpretive procedures of the tester. The results of this study suggest that the validity of the Rorschach interpretation depends to an unknown extent on the interpreter. It is interesting to note that Patterson and Magaw found very little relationship between the actual I.Q. and the intelligence level estimated from the Rorschach.

Abel (5, 6) applied the Rorschach to the problem of determining the factors making for agreement and disagreement between school performance and intelligence rating among institutionalized defective girls. Fifteen pairs of moron white girls were matched for I.Q. and chronological age. There was a difference in school placement of two or three grades between the members of each pair. Abel found that "the better educational group gives the kinds of responses associated with greater integration of inner life (M, FM), more adequate control of environmental stimuli (FC), greater maturity as expressed by human content responses (H and Hd), and greater awareness of reality (Popular answers). Certainly these aspects of mental functioning are favorable to learning and adjusting to the school situation. The poorer group conversely reveals different aspects of mental functioning, greater withdrawal from a difficult situation (rejection of cards), less clear-cut and more confused perceptions (F—), greater egocentricity and stimulation from the external environment without adequate control of the situation (CF, C responses) and a more varied content (more responses in other categories than H and A)" (6). An additional finding of Abel was that there were more cases of possible brain damage in the lower educational group than in the higher one. One of the interesting features of this study is that it indicates the heterogeneity (educationally, neurologically, and behaviorally) among defectives of similar mental level. This heterogeneity among individuals of similar Binet level is probably one of the reasons why the standard deviations for the means of the Rorschach factors for a given mental level have been found high. It is not surprising, therefore, that attempts to correlate Rorschach factors with mental level have not been successful. While the Rorschach does not seem to differentiate between mental levels, it does seem to have value for differentiating between groups with objectively determined behavioral differences. Even this conclusion must await further research with larger numbers of cases in order to determine how valid Rorschach interpretations and predictions are in the individual case.

Until the necessary large-scale research is done, the value of the Rorschach as a diagnostic tool in mental deficiency must be questioned. In such research it will be necessary to judge Rorschach results by valid, reliable, comprehensive, *non-Rorschach* criteria. Clinical impressions and discrepancies with Binet scores are hardly adequate criteria for the validity of a Rorschach interpretation. If the Rorschach indicates a higher intellectual capacity than the Binet, detailed observations of behavior and the results of remedial or therapeutic procedures can determine which test is the better diagnostic tool. Wittenborn and Sarason (325) have indicated that defectives who give "good" responses not ordinarily expected by their Binet score are no more efficient or productive in their everyday functioning than those of similar level who do not give such responses. Their observations, however, were of a clinical nature and are only of suggestive value, emphasizing the need for reëvaluation of "accepted norms" and the necessity of research. That traditional Rorschach signs, derived largely from work with nondefective groups, may not be applicable to defectives is indicated by Sloan's study (275) of the differences between a group of institutionalized defectives who had adjusted successfully on placement and a group who had not. Seven Rorschach criteria considered by Beck to be prognostic of successful adjustment did not distinguish between the successful and unsuccessful groups.

Sarason (258) has cautioned about utilizing results obtained from normals:

"Results obtained on these tests from normal groups must not necessarily serve as validating criteria for data obtained from defectives. It should constantly be kept in mind that the defective child has usually had an unfortunate personal, social, and economic background, and encountered environmental pitfalls to which most normals have not been subjected. As a result, the defective child, especially the institutionalized one, more often than not approaches the test situation with fear, timidity, anxiety, or a feigned indifference; and the clinical psychologist must employ all his 'psychology' if he is to get from the defective child maximum effort and representative functioning. For example, it is standard procedure on the Rorschach for the subject, after he has told the examiner the different things he has seen in each of the ten cards, to be questioned as to where on the card he saw what he did, and what it was about the blot that made him think of it. It became apparent in the writer's work with institutionalized defective children, however, that when the patient was asked to point out precisely the section of the blot he was using, he would sometimes become vague, uncertain, and unable to make up his mind. If the examiner should finally point to a section of the blot and ask if it were being used in the response, suggestibility might well be manifested. Such reactions might be interpreted as being either the result of intellectual deficiency and/or the result of the fact that one is dealing with the much-tested child who is conscious of the importance of the 'brain-test' and is fearful of giving the wrong answer. Some light is thrown on this problem by the fact that if before any questions are asked the child is told to trace what he sees, less indecisiveness is shown and one obtains a clearer picture of what was intended than if questions are asked which may be interpreted by the child as indicating that the response was incorrect."

Since the evaluation of the form accuracy of Rorschach responses gives important data about the degree of "reality testing" present in the individual, it would seem that evaluation based on tracings would be affected less by the examiner's errors of judgment than when the individual's verbalizations are the sole data available.

THE THEMATIC APPERCEPTION TEST

The Thematic Apperception Test (TAT) (218, 219) is a projective technique which has also been used with mentally defective individuals.

It consists of a series of 20 pictures for each of which the individual is asked to make up a story. The content of the stories, especially the behavior of the "hero" or central character, furnishes important clues about the thoughts, feelings, and attitudes of the storyteller. Like the Rorschach, the TAT attempts to describe the behavioral pattern of the subject. Unlike the Rorschach the TAT has not been generally considered a test which can be used for determining intellectual level. In a study of psychotic patients (I.Q. range 73 to 136), Rotter (253) and Harrison (128) found a correlation of .78 between Binet I.Q. and estimate of level from the stories based on such criteria as "range of interests and general knowledge, types of stories told, whether the interpretation was bare or well-knit, productivity, vocabulary, and originality as opposed to stereotypy." Although these investigators felt that their results "pointed to the possibility of I.Q. estimation with a fair degree of accuracy from a Thematic analysis," research along these lines has not appeared.

Masserman and Balken (194) were among the first to apply the TAT to the mentally deficient. They did not report any cases or systematic findings but merely noted "that the phantasies of mentally deficient patients show a characteristic naïveté of material and dearth of imagery." Superior subjects, on the contrary, "produce phantasies rich in novelty and creative invention." Sarason (257) used the TAT with 25 institutionalized mentally deficient children, the majority of whom were of the garden-variety type. He found that such children generally gave plausible and coherent stories, although it was sometimes necessary for the examiner to repeat the directions and to make up a story for the first picture of the series as an illustration. Among the girls that he studied Sarason found that the two themes which occurred most frequently in their stories were concerned with feelings of aggression and desire for affection.

"It may seem paradoxical that these two seemingly antithetical thema should be found in such frequency, but logical analysis will reveal that one is a function of the other. It is not unusual in working with children to find that the aggression displayed by many of them stems from a situation in which affection was desired and given, but none obtained in return. The child, for example, who is suddenly displaced by a younger sibling feels such a lack of affection keenly and the aggression displayed by him toward the sibling and parents is a means of revenge, on the one hand, and an assertion of a desire to remain in the superior position, on the other. Aggression is used here as retribution for something not received. Thus the mentally deficient child, made to feel different from others, unable to compete on equal terms for the attention and affection of others, unconsciously grasps aggressive means as a way of breaking through a maze of frustrations."

Other themes which occurred frequently concerned rebellion against the parents, feelings of guilt, and feelings of loneliness.[10] Among the boys that he studied Sarason found similar themes.

"One finds again that aggression, rejection, ambivalence towards the parent, guilt, and fear of loneliness are the prevalent themas. The mother remains the key character: the individual from whom love and security are sought, and whose rejection of the child brings forth from it aggressive and destructive reactions. However, when one compares the stories of the girls with those of the boys a difference begins to emerge which analysis reveals to be one of degree and not of kind. That is, the stories given by the boys in response to the pictures, while similar in content to those of the girls, are not told with as much heightened feeling or emotional fervor. Stated in another way one could say that the boys, as a group, do not feel or do not express their more or less unconscious attitudes in as direct or obvious a manner as the girls. With the boys aggression is less specifically directed and more generalized, affection is not as eagerly sought, feelings of guilt less severe, and fear of loneliness not as poignant."

Sarason presented several cases to illustrate the clinical usefulness of the TAT. One of these cases is as follows:

The first case was an eighteen-year-old Negro girl of borderline intelligence who had been admitted to Southbury Training School in February, 1941, from an institution for delinquent girls. She made a good social and vocational adjustment at Southbury—getting along well with others and practically taking the place of an attendant in one of the cottages. Since her admission she had been most anxious to go home and was always asking about such a possibility. On a few occasions she had been allowed to go home for a day's visit with the mother or a cousin. The home is in a poor neighborhood in which this girl had become a part of a "wild" crowd. The child's father is deceased and the mother, who has frequent epileptic seizures, has given her poor supervision. In spite of the mother's neglect, the girl has given as a reason for her wanting to go home the fact that she could be of

---

[10] The significance of these themes for understanding parent-child relationships among garden-variety families is discussed on page 157.

aid to her sick mother. Her mother has requested the girl's placement at home for the same reason. In the opinion of the Social Service Department the homes of all relatives are not very suitable for placement and would have to be thoroughly investigated before visits would be even allowed. In August of this year, an attorney representing the family inquired about the girl's placement in the community. The psychological report which was written about this girl was largely based on the Thematic Apperception Test. The main thema which emerged from her stories indicated an ambivalent feeling toward the mother. On the one hand, there was a desire to be with and care for the mother, and on the other, there was a resentment of the fact that such care meant that she could not do the things she wished and could not spend time with her friends. This ambivalence was also noted in a religious conflict. The mother in the stories was pictured as very religious while the daughter was seen as stubborn, irreligious and indifferent. (In a later interview the autobiographical nature of this conflict was corroborated.) Another major thema concerned itself with a lack of affection from the mother which this girl felt very keenly. The following are some of the typical stories told by this girl:

"The mother was washing and she left the baby in the house while hanging out clothes—the baby fell out of the doorway—she ran and picked him up—she found the boy hurt and she is very sad—it will be a lesson never to leave him there again."

"A little boy—he lives in the country—and looks as if he had no home— he don't know where to go—he is cold—don't know whether to go to these two houses—he is standing and thinking whether to go in or not— he went in."

"Boy and mother—he has been running around with bad company—his mother has been hearing about it—he came from his room and told his mother he was going out—his mother asked him where?—he told her down the street—his mother said not to go to the pool-room boys—he said, I'm not going there, Ma—his mother told him if he leaves house she'll know he's going there—he still insists he should go—so his mother turned back and walked away."

"This looks like Virginia Weidler (child actress) saying—'My mother was very sick and I didn't go to school—every day I'd stay and see that she could have breakfast every morning—I'd go and pray to window for my mother to get well—and I was very sad and lonely because I wasn't able to go out and play with other children—I had to stay and see my mother had special care.' "

On the basis of the analysis of this girl's stories the writer recommended that it might be best that the girl not be placed in her mother's home—aside from the fact that this home is in an unfavorable neighborhood. A home should be found where instead of her caring for another she would be the recipient of attention, and where her desire to "belong" and to receive affection would receive outlets.

In this particular case the Thematic Apperception Test was useful in revealing some of the more unconscious attitudes of the patient which are necessary to know if the proper placement in the community is to be made. Many of these attitudes could not be gleaned from the case history in which the mother is one of the chief informants.

Kutash (*170*) administered the TAT to 60 inmates of an institution for defective delinquents who had also been diagnosed as psychopathic personalities by psychiatric interview. All cases had been institutionalized for a minimum of two years. Kutash found that the most frequent themes in the stories concerned anxiety connected with separation from family, family conflicts, guilt feelings, unconscious desire for punishment, death, depression and despair, aggression and assault, eroticism, and suicide. In regard to the most frequent theme, separation anxiety, Kutash remarked:

"There were numerous expressions of longing for loved ones at home—mother, wife, sweetheart, etc. The fact that most of the subjects came from insecure homes, many of them broken through death or separation of the parents, and others economically and socially unstable, no doubt contributed to insecurity feelings on the part of the subjects. Separation anxiety in their fantasy life may be an expression of fundamental insecurity and also the result of their actual separation from their families and homes. The inmates usually revealed feelings of having been rejected by their parents in early childhood which resulted in anxiety and insecurity."

In comparing the studies of Kutash and Sarason two points may be made. (1) In both studies the defective individual is shown to be deprived in a psychological sense; (2) in both studies there are indications that this deprivation is due not solely to institutionalization but is related to longstanding, psychologically unhealthy parent-child relationships. One important difference in the results of the two studies is the absence of suicide or self-aggression themes in Sarason's "ordinary" defectives and their relatively high frequency in Kutash's defective delinquents who had also been diagnosed as psychopaths. This difference seems to support the clinical impression that the psychopath "frequently unconsciously seeks punishment as a result of a guilt complex and commits his crimes which are psychically determined in order to be punished" (*170*).

Gothberg (*120*) studied two groups of 10 girls who differed in that the girls of one group had run away from the institution at least twice, whereas none in the other group had run away. The cases were matched for age, intelligence, and body build. Analysis of the thematic stories revealed that the following themes occurred to a greater extent in the runaway than in the control group: need for love and protection, conflict with parents, aggression to female figures, self-aggression, and a desire to conform. In discussing the factors responsible for the group differences Gothberg states:

"The majority of these children in both groups came from broken homes, many of them having spent years in foster homes and child caring institutions before coming to the Institution. For the majority there was no parental home to return to and in half of the cases not even a parent or sibling, no matter how disinterested, to whom they could turn or who paid any attention to them. Since these traumatic experiences were shared by both groups in and by themselves they cannot be said to be responsible for the running away or the remaining at the School. And as the School is shared by both groups it is not this, per se. It is rather that strange alchemy of personality which colors, distorts and interprets its environment into its own basic configuration, the organic potentiality or readiness to respond in the certain way when certain conditions occur. These differences in the personality patterns are to some extent revealed through the TAT."

One may question the justification for assuming that the quality of the past interpersonal relationships of both groups of girls was the same. The fact that many in both groups had spent their lives in foster homes or institutions does not mean that they had the same experiences. Not all foster parents react in the same way to their wards. The fact that some girls in both groups had come from broken homes does not tell one the child's age when the home broke up, the nature of the family relationships before it took place, and whether such a situation was equally traumatic for all. Before dismissing previous life situations as contributing factors, one should know much more about the details of the nature of childhood experiences (see Chapter 6). Gothberg does not present evidence which contraindicates the assumption that previous conditions of learning determine the nature of the individual's behavioral pattern. The concept of "organic" potentiality to respond in a certain way to certain situations seems to regard the individual as possessing a bundle of inborn response tendencies which await the proper situation in order to be expressed. Gothberg's statements have been scrutinized here because they seem to avoid the problem of the origin of individual differences, a problem which has not received the attention it deserves so far as the mentally deficient are concerned. Why does one mentally defective child crave love and affection much more than another? Why do two mentally deficient children who appear to crave love and affection to a similar degree manifest such needs differently and react dissimilarly when they are not satisfied? When one attempts to answer these questions by postulating differences in organic readiness to respond, he seems to be restating rather than explaining the problem.

Abel (4) used the TAT in one of her studies of Negro and white adolescent morons (2, 3). The 22 subjects she used were for the most part the ones to whom the Rorschach had been given in a previous study (9).

"The chief results of the Rorschach Test were that the white girls restricted their number of answers and gave few concrete details, while the performance of the Negro girls was more flexible and expansive. The performance of Negro and white boys was intermediate between that of the Negro and white girls, although the white boys were somewhat more expansive and showed more interest in concrete details than did the Negro boys. . . . The Rorschach Test corroborated in particular the observed behavior of the Negro and white girls in the institution, the Negro girls being aggressive and free in their activities, the white girls as a group more submissive and inhibited" (4).

On the TAT the Negro girls were much more expansive than Negro boys, their stories containing many more words and ideas. "This difference is in keeping with observed differences in everyday behavior in the institution. Even though they are in a considerable minority the Negro girls are in a favorable position in the institution in that they succeed in becoming aggressive toward and leaders of white girls and receive the admiration and love of the white girls. The Negro boys do not play the same role in their social relationships with white boys.

TABLE 29. TAT Themes Most Frequently Expressed by
Negro and White Defectives (4)

Card	Thema	N	W	Girls	Boys
1	Aggression	24	18	22	20
2	Aggression	15	14	15	14
3	Lonesome	14	16	21	9
4	Parent protests	25	26	24	27
5	Parents ask obedience	16	23	15	24
6	Climbs to escape	20	16	22	15
8	Resists parent	15	10	15	10
9	Parent cries over baby	26	25	28	21
10	Loss of loved one	24	28	31	19
11	Man attacks girl	21	24	24	21

They may be aggressive but they do not arouse the sex interest of the white boys, nor do they become their leaders." Abel also found (see Table 29) that loss of parents and loneliness were themes which were much more frequent among the Negro and white girls than among the boys. This finding was also noted by Sarason (257). Abel concluded that this sex difference was related to the different roles which boys and girls are expected to play in our culture. "A boy when he reaches adolescence is likely to be called a 'sissy' if he cries for his parents and admits he is lonely. According to the social structure of our society he is supposed to be a *man* and to some extent able and willing to fend for himself. A girl does not have as much social disapproval if she shows a desire to cling to parents."

In contrast to the Rorschach findings, the white girls were much more responsive to the TAT, giving more words and ideas in their stories than the Negro girls. Abel hypothecated that the Negro girls, being less inhibited about sexual matters, were not affected by the ink-blots which "reveal to some extent an individual's attitudes toward sex matters." The white girls, experiencing more sexual taboos than the Negro girls, were presumably more affected by the ink-blots. Abel concluded that since the TAT taps "some of the crucial attitudes other than sex of the white girls," they were able to be much more responsive than on the Rorschach. Abel does not offer data to support this conclusion. There have been no systematic studies which demonstrate that the ink-blots engender more sexual associations than the TAT.

The H-T-P Technique

Buck (*44*) has utilized the freehand drawing of a house, tree, and person as a projective technique for the study of defective and other groups.

"The H-T-P, freehand drawing of House, Tree and Person is a technique designed to aid the clinician in obtaining information concerning the sensitivity, maturity, flexibility, efficiency, and the degree of integration of a subject's personality; and the inter-action of that personality with its environment—both specific and general.

"The H-T-P is a two-phased approach to the personality. The first phase is non-verbal, creative, almost completely unstructured; the medium of expression is a relatively primitive one, drawing. The second phase is verbal, apperceptive, and more formally structured: in it the subject is provided with an opportunity to define, describe, and interpret the objects drawn and their respective environments, and to associate concerning them" (*44*, p. 319).

Basic to this approach is the assumption that what a person draws "is to be regarded as a self-portrait" in that the drawing contains characteristics which are in one way or another of personal significance to the drawer. The feelings exhibited before, during, or after the drawing of certain details or combinations of them, the care and concern regarding their execution, their proportion, and the subject's own interpretation of his productions are some of the factors which are considered as revealing the individual's behavioral pattern. Buck also maintains "that the H-T-P is a valid measure of adult intelligence, despite its restricted and unconventional approach to such measurement."

In standardizing the H-T-P technique Buck studied subjects ranging from the imbecile to the superior level. There were 20 subjects at each level. It was found that those items relating to detail, proportion, and perspective differentiated best between levels. Correlations between H-T-P and scores from standard psychometric procedures (Wechsler-Bellevue, Otis) ranged from 41 to 74. Buck concludes that his technique is not "a highly refined measure of intelligence." Since Buck himself feels that the validity of the method of analysis and interpretation which he presents has not been established by "adequate experimental evidence," one must reserve judgment about the H-T-P until such data are available. Studies of the validity of this technique will have to employ more subjects at each level, and more reliable and valid criteria.

That the H-T-P in its present form cannot be used as a substitute for standard tests of intelligence is indicated by Sloan and Guertin's study (276) of the relation between H-T-P and Wechsler-Bellevue I.Q.'s among mental defectives. They found that the scores obtained from the two tests were not comparable and that the H-T-P was in need of "a good deal of substantiation before results . . . can be taken as an accurate measure of intelligence."

SUMMARY

When one takes an overall view of the role of projective techniques in the study of the mentally deficient, he can only regret that these procedures have received relatively uncritical acceptance. Just as the Binet was once looked upon as the panacea for the psychologist's problems, so have projective techniques now been assigned this unenviable role. It may well be that the psychologist's disappointment with the Binet as a diagnostic instrument, especially with deviant groups and the problem of individual differences, set the stage for his eager acceptance of techniques whose aim it is to describe the relation between intellectual processes and behavioral pattern or, stated somewhat differently, between capacity and functioning. *However, one of the most significant contributions which projective techniques have made to the field of mental deficiency is that some people have been awakened to the fact that the behavior of the defective individual is not explained by pointing to an intelligence test score and that whatever is subsumed under intellectual processes is inextricably related to and affected by attitudinal or subjective factors which have been acquired as a result of earlier life experiences.* In other words, the defective individual, like the normal one, has fears, anxieties, wishes, and needs which may affect his intellectual functioning in varying degrees. It may be said that whereas the Binet gave the defective individual an "intelligence," projective techniques have given him a "personality."

One of the chief factors which has limited the significance of the conclusions drawn from the use of projective techniques with the mentally defective is the absence of convincing validating evidence. For example, the fact that the Rorschach frequently indicates higher intellectual capacity than do standard psychometric procedures requires some external evidence that the former is in fact a more sensitive instrument. Does the individual's everyday functioning corroborate the conclusion of higher capacity? Do remedial or therapeutic procedures bring out this latent capacity? Until such questions are answered by the necessary research, the scientific value of projective techniques in mental deficiency cannot be judged. Such techniques have focused attention on long-neglected problems in mental deficiency and it can only be hoped that they will be utilized in a rigorously scientific manner so that answers to these crucial problems will be obtained.

Chapter 10

PSYCHOTHERAPY

IT is generally assumed that the mentally defective individual is unable to benefit from a psychotherapeutic relationship. The paucity of studies in this area is witness to this assumption. The inability of such an individual to control or delay emotional expression, to seek and to accept socially appropriate substitute activities in the face of frustrations and restrictions, to view objectively the behavior of others, to adjust or to want to adjust to the needs of others, to realize the sources and consequences of his behavior—these have been considered the liabilities of the defective individual which make it difficult for him to comprehend and to adjust to the purposes of the psychotherapeutic interview. When one considers that language is almost the sole means of communication between therapist and patient and that the defective individual has inordinate difficulty in using and comprehending verbal generalizations, it is not surprising that the usual psychotherapeutic interview has been viewed as unfeasible with such individuals. For an individual to be aware that he "has a problem" implies that he has verbalized to himself or others his reactions to certain experiences and relationships; he sees or judges himself in terms of other people's behavior or standards. Without verbalization of the problem he is unable to take steps to solve it. This is implied in Allen's statement, (*13*) "The therapeutic process occurs as a unique growth experience, *created* by one person *seeking* and *needing* help from *another* who accepts the responsibility of offering it. This basic structure characterizes each potentially therapeutic setting irrespective of methods or techniques employed or of whether it is a child or adult who seeks assistance" (italics mine). It has generally been felt that the defective individual's inability to see or to verbalize (and to become aware of) the interpersonal nature of his problems makes him unable to seek help (to create the therapeutic relationship) or to understand the purposes of an individual offering it.

263

It should be clearly stated that the above conclusions about the unfeasibility of psychotherapeutic interviews with defective children have been based more on deductions from theoretical considerations than on systematic research findings. Many practical considerations have prevented research in this area. The tremendous demand for psychotherapeutic help, the scarcity of trained personnel, and the amount of time which such efforts entail have forced clinicians to give what little time they have to those cases which promise the most results in the shortest period of time.

The disposition of the defective individual referred to a clinic can be seen from Rogers' survey (250) of treatment measures used with 292 children. The data in Table 30 show that institutionalization is by far

TABLE 30. Recommended Environmental Changes as Related to Intellectual Level in 292 Clinic Referrals (250)

	Defective	Borderline	Dull Normal	Average	Superior
Number in group	29	48	94	102	19
To remain in present placement	24%	48%	43%	44%	26%
Foster home recommended	7%	21%	39%	42%	63%
Institution recommended	66%	18%	4%	4%	0%
Other change recommended	3%	12%	14%	10%	11%

the most frequent recommendation made in the case of defective individuals. Gaudet and Gaudet (96), in a survey of 1040 cases diagnosed as mentally defective in twelve mental hygiene clinics in New Jersey, also found that institutionalization was the most frequent recommendation. Rogers' statement that theoretical considerations suggest that the defective individual is "scarcely receptive to [psychotherapeutic] treatment" reflects the attitude of other clinicians (103, 132, 145, 193, 324). In their follow-up study of 400 cases treated at the Judge Baker Guidance Center, Healy and Bronner (132, p. 22) stated that "very rarely have we accepted for treatment any case that was graded as feebleminded." They found (Table 31) that the lower the I.Q. the greater the probability of a later unfavorable adjustment. That caution must be exercised in the interpretation of these findings is evident from the following statement by them (132, p. 34):

TABLE 31. The Relation Between Intelligence
Level and Later Adjustments (*132*)

I.Q.	Adjustment	
	Favorable	Unfavorable
70 – 79	5	10 (66%)
80 – 89	33	10 (23%)
90 – 109	157	42 (21%)
110+	128	15 (10%)
	323	77

"But we insist that there are many reasons for caution in interpretation. In particular no inference can be drawn that there is a direct causal relationship between the quality of the career and the I.Q. For example, in trying to determine why there was such a large proportion of unfavorable careers in the I.Q. 70–79 group we found other factors largely involved. In three cases the family and general social situation of the individual was so bad that it could not be modified; three others suffered from severe biological handicaps as well as from poor family circumstances; two had early established such prevailing patterns of delinquent behavior that they could not be broken; one was an abnormal personality; and the only individual with an I.Q. as low as 70 was so defective and had such a sense of inferiority and insecurity that he was not capable of responding to clinical treatment.

"On the other hand, in five cases of the same intelligence level the reasons for favorable careers were equally clear. Four of them came from families who were co-operative with us and fairly adequate in understanding—which was not true for any single one of those showing unfavorable careers. In one instance, after considerable attempt at treatment by the clinic much devoted work was done on the case by a probation officer."

Although each child in the study was seen for at least one interview, the range being from one to over a hundred, it is not possible to determine the number of times each of the children with I.Q.'s between 70 and 79 was seen. In the case of those who made favorable adjustments it would have been interesting to know the number of times each child was seen in an individual interview and the degree of therapeutic gain effected thereby. It may have been that these cases had relatively few interviews and that improvement in adjustments was effected through work with the parents. Since the exceptional case can be extremely instructive, it is unfortunate that the case with whom a probation officer did "much devoted work" was not elaborated upon. It is not clear from Healy and Bronner's discussion whether none, some, or all of the cases with I.Q.'s between 70 and 79 were mentally defective. They do state that two of their cases "were considered to be morons." Since all cases had an I.Q. of at least 70, it is not clear how the two cases were distinguished from nonmorons of similar I.Q. It may be that there were only two cases in the series who were considered mentally defective, but in the absence of explicit criteria this point cannot be clarified.

It should be stated here that one of the chief difficulties in evaluating the feasibility of psychotherapy with mental defectives is that the criteria for the diagnosis of cases so labeled either are not stated or are restricted to an intelligence test score. In other instances the use of test-score classifications beclouds rather than clarifies the problem. For example, Cooley (54) compared psychotherapeutic results with a group of dull and of bright children referred to a child guidance clinic. The bright group was comprised of 25 children with I.Q.'s above 115. The dull group consisted of 16 children with I.Q.'s between 76 and 84 and 9 with I.Q.'s between 61 and 74. Cases were matched for sex, age, and economic status. A question that immediately arises about the "dull" group concerns its homogeneity. With the use of inclusive criteria of mental deficiency, how many of these cases would have been diagnosed as mentally defective? Is the use of the label *dull* an indication that *all* these cases did not meet the inclusive criteria for mental deficiency? If these cases had been seen in other clinics, how many would have been diagnosed as defective, and of these how many would have been given psychotherapy?—a speculation intended to emphasize the disparity in criteria and practices employed by various clinicians and agencies. The data necessary for answering these questions are not given.

The importance of these questions may be seen from Cooley's results in Table 32. It will be seen from the table that there is no particular relationship between test-score level and adjustment at the close of psychotherapeutic treatment, a result similar to that obtained by Glassman (103) and Wegman (313).[1] "Over half of the children of inferior

---

[1] These findings do not support one of Rogers' criteria for suitability for psychotherapy, that the patient possess "adequate intelligence for coping with his life situation, with an intelligence rating of dull normal [I.Q. 80–90] or above" (251, p. 77).

TABLE 32. Comparison of I.Q. Groups with Respect to
Adjustment at Close of Treatment (54)

Adjustment Rating[a]	I.Q. 61–74	I.Q. 75–84	Total Below 85	I.Q. 115 or Above
A	1	3	4	2
B	2	4	6	9
C	5	5	10	6
D	1	3	4	7
E	..	1	1	1
Total	9	16	25	25

[a] The adjustment rating scale:

"A. Original problems have disappeared and no new problems have appeared. The child has friends of his age and sex, and interests normal for his age and intelligence. His school work is consistent with his ability. If on a job, he is a steady, reliable, interested worker; at home, he is a friendly, cooperative member of the family group.

"B. The problems for which the child was referred or which were revealed in treatment have very definitely improved though some traces of them may remain. His adjustment may be less than ideal on one of the criteria points—home adjustment, friends, school or work, but he is not markedly maladjusted in any of these spheres. Further treatment is not indicated.

"C. Some problems still exist, sufficiently marked to handicap the child in his adjustment with other children, or at school or work, or at home. Further treatment is indicated but there is no emergency need for such treatment (i.e., ideally; this statement does not take into account circumstances that may make further treatment impossible).

"D. The child shows definite behavior or personality problems (no or very little improvement over the situation as it originally existed); new problems may have appeared. He is in real need of further treatment and is definitely maladjusted in at least two of the three spheres of adjustment—home, friends, school or work.

"E. The child's problems are more severe than when he was referred or during treatment. New problems have probably appeared. He may be delinquent or show psychopathic traits. His adjustment is unsatisfactory in all of the three spheres mentioned above."

intelligence had from one to ten hours of therapy, while only four of the bright children had so few interviews with a psychiatrist. Only five of the children of low intellectual level had more than twenty hours of therapy, in contrast to thirteen, or over half, of the superior children. Since the outcome of therapy appeared to be equally successful with the dull group, it would appear that the children of inferior intelligence required no more and in many cases less expenditure of time in treatment than the superior children" (54). Although Cooley's results indicate that "dull" children are amenable to and benefit from psychotherapeutic interviews, the fact that only the I.Q. of the cases was reported sheds merely suggestive light on the feasibility of such procedures with mentally defective individuals.

Although in his study of psychotherapy with "fifty-five 'bad' boys" Hartwell (*131*) states that cases with mental defect were usually not selected for treatment, he does include one such case in his reports. This boy, who was classified as feeble-minded in the moron range, was referred to the clinic because of the appearance of psychotic-like symptoms: increased tendency to stay by himself and active daydreaming "which causes him suddenly to laugh aloud."

"In psychiatric interviews Melvin responded differently from most children with his mental equipment. He reached the rapport of personality contact very quickly. Because of his responses he has been encouraged to maintain this relation and has been seen regularly during the past two years. He has given during that time and in that rapport much interesting material to think about. In his slow, plodding way he has thought with me about many problems that most children with an intelligence quotient of 73 could not recognize as existing.

"Melvin has never been questioned deeply about his mental problems or urged to tell about them. He wants to do so, and at each visit he has new questions to ask and he asks the old ones over again, saying he has forgotten. But he has not forgotten. He likes to hear again such encouragement as someone whom he can trust may give him.

" 'Is there every any boys who can't learn like me who maybe get so they can learn fast?' 'Does an engineer on a train have to be smart?' 'Are you sure you know I can make my living when I grow big?' 'I wish I was big now, only I'm afraid I can't make my living.' 'How did my brothers learn to be smart?' 'What makes folks like my brothers better than me?' 'Does it hurt you to die?' 'Can anyone always be good if they try to?' On every occasion I have seen him, he has talked about and wished he were older and could earn his own living. Over and over again he says he does not want other folks to have to give him money. He never has failed to thank me at the close of the interview for talking to him.

"Melvin and I have thought about many practical things that might help him with his problems. (At one time we decided that it might help to make his home more pleasant if I were to see his brothers. Possibly this helped with the situation somewhat. The brothers willingly came. They proved to be intelligent boys who were anxious to help Melvin in any way they could. They had been noticing his increasing unhappiness and were concerned about it.) We thought about Melvin's unusual ability to find his way in strange places. He can be trusted to go from one part of the city to another, even though he has never been there before, as well as the average boy of his age or better.

"When I first knew Melvin, he was just entering a somewhat premature puberty. At that time he was disgusted and worried about some experiences he had had with another boy, who had attempted to teach him sex habits. Recently he has been more concerned about these old happenings and about his own developing sex emotions. He says: 'One reason I want to come and see you is that you will tell me more about these dirty things.' He badly needs someone to think both with him and for him concerning his sex problems. At his last interview he told me that he could not refrain from hunting for news dispatches about sex attacks and sex murders. He would find them and persist until his grandmother would read them to him. He says that the ones that tell about crazy men who perpetrate these attacks make him feel 'awful funny and bad.' He says: 'They make me feel like if maybe I would do such things some time, but then I won't. I'd be afraid. Anyway, it's wrong.' Melvin has never masturbated.

"He has always talked about suicide. At first it was simply because of an interest he had in it. More lately he has been thinking about suicide. He says: 'I might do it if I were not a coward, but I won't. It would hurt me, and I'm afraid.'

"One interesting thing about this boy is the fact that he is always happier and less worried and upset for a time after he talks with me. He is always anxious to come for an interview. He is very careless about his dress (though he is painstaking about most things) except when he is coming to the clinic, when he will dress himself with great care.

"*Results:* His parents feel that his interviews do him so much temporary good that they are of great help, both to them and to the boy. He seems less discouraged and a little more extroverted for a short time after them. He seems to do a little better in his school-work. (He is working in an ungraded class and making but little progress, though he always tries hard.) I have tried to encourage Melvin in every way I could without doing so in a way that would make him unhappy later. He considers me a very good friend and thinks I understand how he feels. While this latter belief, I fear, is not true to any great extent, it is one that may be encouraged without later doing him harm.

"The family believes that to some extent the boy's personality traits have been changed for the better. This is very doubtful. However, two definite things have been accomplished: one is that the boy has been made happier, and the other is that I have established myself in his and the family's confidence to the extent that if he becomes an institutional case, as he probably will soon, I may be of help to them in adjusting to the situation.

"During the year following my first interviews with Melvin the boy was for several months in a foster-home on a large farm. Here he did well, but finally became dissatisfied and is now at home again. He sees either Dr. Bronner or me occasionally. He desires these interviews. He still has remarkable' insight into his mental life for a boy who is presenting many definite psychotic symptoms. Perhaps if he can continue to have a little psychiatric bolstering up from time to time he may live always outside of an institution. But I feel that he will always be of potential danger to others as well as to himself." [2]

Hartwell's doubts about the boy's future adjustment should not obscure the fact that he considered the boy to have benefited from treatment. It would seem that this case at least allows one to ask the question whether other defective boys with nonpsychotic-like symptoms would have benefited even more from individual psychotherapy. It should be noted that aside from an I.Q. of 72 the data on which the diagnosis of mental deficiency was made are not given.

"He was eleven years old when first seen. His health has always been good, his physical development somewhat above the age average. The change in the appearance of the boy may be judged from the notes in regard to this taken from his first and last physical examinations. The first describes him as 'an active, healthy, good-looking youngster'; the last, 'a dull, coarse, irregular-featured boy.' The psychological examinations which have been made at intervals of about a year show a remarkable consistency in all respects. His intelligence quotient as first determined was 73, at the second test given him 72, and at the last two 73. This is particularly interesting because of the fact that the boy, in his appearance and somewhat in his responses, seemed to be gradually deteriorating. His school-work had always been below that of his mental age."

It is not clear from this account whether this boy's inadequacies represent the effects of developmental arrest due to presumed constitutional factors or are related to a not too well-understood psychological process.

Chidester and Menninger (47) reported a case of a supposedly mentally defective boy with whom psychoanalytic therapy was attempted.

[2] S. W. Hartwell, *Fifty-five "bad" boys.* Alfred A. Knopf, Inc., 1940. By permission of the publisher.

Because this study contains far more data on background and therapeutic technique than other reports, it is presented in some detail.

"Henry was the first of four children. Birth was normal. Artificial feeding was begun in the sixth month. He walked and talked at a normal age and was said to have been trained in toilet habits early. He was subject to frequent colds until his third year at which time his tonsils and adenoids were removed.

"At the time that Henry's parents were married his father was a university student and was unable to provide a home for his wife, who remained with her parents until several years after the child was born. When the patient was about four years old the mother went to her husband and they established a home of their own, but were persuaded to leave Henry with his grandparents. They had three more children, but Henry was never a part of that household. He continued to live with his grandparents and alone he occupied the room that he had formerly shared with his mother.

"A cousin was born into the household of the grandparents when Henry was in his fourth year and from birth was Henry's rival for the family attention.

"The grandparents first suspected that the patient was retarded when he repeatedly failed in school. During his first year in school, the grandparents made an extended trip, leaving him with his parents. While they were gone he did poor school work. A nurse reported his poor vision (16 percent) but his parents neglected to do anything about it. The child became increasingly unhappy and when his grandparents returned they found him acutely ill with appendicitis. Against his father's will they removed him to a hospital for an operation.

"Afterward the grandparents took the boy away with them, had his eyes fitted with glasses and started him in another school. He failed several times and passed twice on condition. He made excellent grades in reading and spelling, but his arithmetical comprehension was nil and writing was poor. After five years he was promoted to the third grade because of his ability to read. It was evident that he was wholly unable to compete with boys of his age even in their play. Therefore, he was placed in the Southard School at the age of eleven years.

"Entrance examination revealed little organic pathology except poor motor coordination and defective vision corrected with glasses. Our neurologist who later examined the child was of the opinion that he had acalculia due to definite organic lesion such as has been described by Gerstmann, Singer and Low. He scored an I.Q. of 62 (Stanford-Binet) and his emotional development gauged by his general interests, was equally retarded.

"He was a small boy who constantly hung his head as though abashed. His deep voice contrasted strangely with his immature appearance and he was exceedingly awkward. His face seldom lost its pleasant expression and he seemed unmoved by the struggles that went on around him. He appeared to like everyone at the school, but demonstrated no affection for them nor any desire for affection from them. Instead of loving people he seemed to attach his fondness to inanimate objects, and spent most of his time collecting indiscriminately such things as empty cereal boxes, tin cans, milk bottle stoppers, discarded auto tags, and other debris. Those he put in his room and carefully guarded them, and when any such possession was lost or discarded in the process of house cleaning, it was nothing less than a tragedy to Henry, who burst into tears as though a relative had died.

"He was tremendously selfish. He freely partook of the candy and toys of the other children, but his own he enjoyed in solitude. Though he demanded many gifts he was never grateful for them. In conversation he eagerly asked for information, but volunteered none and when asked the simplest questions was disinclined to give any information. His conversation was often so incoherent as to be unintelligible, and he was exasperatingly slow in all aspects of his behavior like a long drama in slow-motion pictures.

"During the first year at the Southard School he studied first grade arithmetic but was able neither to understand number facts nor to retain them from rote memory. His writing remained scarcely legible, but he read rather well and enjoyed the newspapers especially."

Because the boy had no appreciation of his problems it "was necessary to devote a period to wooing Henry's affection and confidence. The therapist saw him for an hour each day, during which time games were played and small gifts made to him. After this preparatory period the patient was instructed to lie down on a couch and to express freely any ideas that came to him. The psychologist sat a little distance from the head of the couch and out of the patient's sight." Many difficulties were encountered by this orthodox psychoanalytic procedure.

"There was little evidence of spontaneity, he exhibited no initiative in play, work or study; in general there appeared no eagerness to learn, he was not especially alert to his immediate surroundings and often could not evaluate what he did see. He produced no memories antedating his coming to the school. Instead of being pliable, his whole personality manifested a quality of inelasticity, a fact that was very discouraging to the therapists. And most of all his appreciation for reality seemed feeble as manifested by (1) his tendency to daydream excessively, (2) his lack of knowledge about and judgment concerning the objects of his most immediate environment, and (3) his frank delusions. His thought processes seemed exceedingly retarded so that his speech was monotonous, slow, and halting. He often required as much as fifteen minutes to complete one sentence."

These liabilities made it necessary for the therapist to present interpretations to the boy in a direct fashion.

"During the first few months much resistance was expressed in the form of sullenness, tardiness, silence, or constant questioning on the part of the patient. By Christmas the child was consciously resentful of having to come for treatment and at last he asked to be excused from it. He announced that he did not like the psychologist, and when questioned he gave as his reason the fact that she talked to the other children at the school. This admission of jealousy was an opening wedge for a strong relationship and hence, further treatment, for it was explained to him that someone else must have abandoned him for another child. Immediately he admitted that his mother had given him to his grandmother and he felt that the love she once bestowed on him was withdrawn and reinvested in his younger sister. Thus the boy was helped to see that the hostility that he expressed toward the psychologist was that which he felt toward his mother. After realizing this the child of his own accord decided to continue treatment, and was much more cooperative.

"He expressed great disdain for his father and for his father's profession and demanded to be called by the name of his grandparents rather than that of his father. At first he refused to speak of his mother and siblings, and when questioned about them, professed to have forgotten their names and ages, although he had visited them but a few months before.

"One day the psychologist came with a new permanent wave, and the boy refused to have anything to do with her. He said that her hair was too kinky and it reminded him of Negroes. When asked who else had kinky hair, he replied that his siblings had such hair. After much persuasion he showed their pictures to the therapist. They did appear to be Negroid and were much darker than others in the pictures. Henry made numerous remarks to the effect that these children were not smart, not pretty, and not good children.

"About this time he began to fantasy that he would like to have a child and be its mother and nurse it. He would want only the one child, he said, unless he got married, and then he might have three more. This was his idea of what his mother had done. That is, he believed himself to be illegitimate. . . .

"During the second period he began to relate his dreams and through their interpretations he began to be aware of his hostility toward his father and his desire to replace the latter in his relations with his mother. It was also by means of his dreams that he realized his tremendous hostility toward his cousin and his jealousy of the attention which his grandmother gave the boy. Following his awareness of hostility, he, once mild and passive, became very sadistic, kicking and beating the smaller boys with a ruler which he carried concealed in his trousers. At the same time he talked to the psychologist of the unfair treatment he had received from his cousin. She was able to correlate his behavior with the children at the school with his feelings of anger for his cousin and to interpret his sadism as meant for the cousin. Following this interpretation his sadism receded.

"As his confidence in the psychologist developed he began to confess his excessive night prowling. He said that he frequently woke in the night and went through the house and yard naked, touching his penis compulsively to the back of his teachers' chairs and going to the barn loft where he covered his feet and genitals with dirt. On other nights he tried to peep at the women and girls and stole their clothing, especially shoes, hose and pajamas. Sometimes he slept in these articles and fantasied that one of the women was in bed with him. The climax of these erotic fantasies was that they would expose themselves to each other and defecate and urinate together. How extraordinary it is to get such information and fantasies from retarded children need scarcely be mentioned!

"He bought a gaudy ring, wore red nail polish, carried a compact and demanded feminine lingerie. He reported fantasies of having babies and dreams of having intercourse with men. After seeing the moving picture 'State Fair' he identified himself with the beautiful trapeze artist and wished 'that I could have some nice looking man like that fall in love with me.' The realization that he wanted to be a woman and could not be one depressed him for days. As the depression subsided he began to relate fantasies involving sadistic treatment of women by him. He envied women their breasts and frequently expressed a desire to injure those of the psychologist so that men might cease to pay attention to her and turn to him."

In the beginning period of the second year of treatment the boy's interest in anal matters, masturbatory activity, and sexual fantasies became more and more marked. "During this period of anal indulgence, he was making excellent grades in his number work and for the first time he had been able to report quite a few perfect lessons in arithmetic. In general his school work seemed to have improved rapidly." When he returned to school after a month at home during the midwinter holidays, he displayed extremely aggressive behavior.

"Upon his return to the school two aspects of his behavior were prominent, his insistence on the monopoly of the bathroom and his sadism toward a smaller boy whom he kicked till the child was bruised from his hip to his ankle. But his conversation during the treatment period concerned only his tremendous envy and jealousy of the younger and brighter cousin, his old rival. When his mistreatment of the poor child was interpreted to him as his desire to hurt his cousin he told one of a number of delusions which he held, namely, that he had believed that when a boy left the school and later a new boy entered, the new boy was the old one disguised. The boy whom he kicked he had believed for many months to be the cousin in disguise who had come to spy on him.

"As a punishment for some of his aggression, he was denied the privilege of reading the newspapers for a time. Immediately he became sullen and less cooperative. In reporting this matter to the psychologist, he added, 'And I was as mad as a hungry bear.' At this same time he confessed that he had begun eating garbage and food that had been given a dog. Writing he had equated to the excretion and smearing of feces, and reading what someone else wrote seemed to be a mode of incorporating this valuable substance—a sublimation. And when this sublimation was denied him, he regressed to a more primitive stage, that of eating refuse or unclean matter.

"He had become much more insistent on monopolizing the bath. He said he spent much time trying to expel large quantities of feces and would stand and gaze at his excrement for considerable periods. He said he liked to see what large quantity he could get which was the exact expression he used in speaking of his collections of useless objects. He began to go to the bathroom as soon as it was vacated by others in order to ascertain the quantity of their excrement so as to compare it with his. Once after viewing that left by a girl he remarked disdainfully, 'That was much smaller than mine.' Thus it was possible to see that both his hoarding and his toilet interests were attempts to compensate for his fear of sexual inferiority. He was able to see that he was annoying everyone but said he wished to annoy the psychologist for having continued to see other children and that he wished to annoy his teachers for hurrying him with his number work in which he had become exasperatingly slow and exceedingly inaccurate. When asked what he objected to being hurried in doing, he said, 'I don't want to be hurried about my bowel movements.' He was told that arithmetic as well as some other things at which he insisted on taking his time were symbolic of the toilet activity. Again he began to do good school work. . . .

"At times he regressed in his arithmetic and in his bathroom habits. At such times he was often resistant to his treatment but it always turned out that he has been unable to stand seeing the teachers giving any quantity of attention to the other children and purposely failed in his arithmetic to provoke the teacher to nag and give him attention. Then he stayed in the bathroom long so that he would be punished, and thus absolve his guilt. With this interpretation both forms of misconduct decreased, and he began to show definite progress.

"One day the psychologist had an opportunity to watch Henry with his arithmetic. His teacher assigned his lesson, then those of the other children one by one. Then she returned to Henry, who had not written a thing, but who on hearing her approach, scratched his head, knitted his brows, bit his pencil and looked fixedly at his problems. The teacher began, 'Why, Henry, haven't you written a thing?' Henry shifted his position, scratched his head, leaned closer to the paper and made as though to write. The teacher then went to the next pupil. When she returned again Henry had made a few marks and spent most of the time erasing them. He was no farther along' than before. This time the teacher was a bit more severe. She stood by him watching him and told him to get to work. Henry went through all the appearances of profound cerebration, but produced nothing, offered no explanation, asked no help. Finally as the teacher became very insistent he slowly marked down some answers which were remarkably inaccurate. One was reminded of a mother who has set an infant on the toilet and insisted that he defecate. The child grunts and grimaces and gives all the appearances of making strenuous effort to defecate, when in reality he is trying hard not to."

During the third year of treatment there was a marked improvement in his attitude and relations with other children, an improvement which disappeared as soon as he went home for a vacation. He returned in bad humor and was very indifferent to treatment.

"In order to overcome his resistance, he was charged 10 cents a day for his treatment after March 1935, and the school offered to pay him 10 cents for various small jobs. That is, the psychologist unwittingly charged the child his total earnings, his entire childish fortune. He refused any work whereby he could earn the dime and became very resistant and day after day seemed to regress in the type of material he brought, in his school work, and in his general attitude. An eating disturbance appeared and although he was given five meals a day he steadily lost weight. In June 1935 when he was again given psychometric tests, he scored an I.Q. of 75 on the Stanford-Binet and much worse on the performance tests. In this regressed condition he went home for the summer. When he returned this fall he still scored very low on the tests and he seemed less able to adjust to situations around him. The psychologist felt that either there was an organic deterioration or more likely there was insufficient gratification to permit progress. It occurred to her that since she took as payment all the money he made, he was deprived of all the pleasure of the money he earned and hence the endless paying and working must seem futile to him. Therefore, she began returning to him a dime of his earnings each week, and praised him for his efforts. Very soon his interests improved and his psychomotor retardation lessened. He began to bring new aspects of his conflicts and seemed able to accept and assimilate interpretations. On tests given in his improved condition he scored a mental age of 13 years 2 months, and an I.Q. of about 90 on the Stanford-Binet, and a mental age of 15 years on the Porteus Maze tests. The performance tests were solved correctly but still a little slower than normal.

"For the first time he was aware that some situations appeared real and some unreal to him, and discovered that his participation in a situation, particularly if he were able to make decisions, enhanced its reality value for him. He began to see himself in relation to his environment and made definite efforts to be like others and to accept reality."

Results from the Binet which was administered periodically during the four years of treatment follow:

September	1931	I.Q. 62	April	1934	I.Q. 87
September	1932	I.Q. 65	September	1934	I.Q. 88
February	1933	I.Q. 73	March	1935	I.Q. 90
May	1933	I.Q. 77	June	1935	I.Q. 75
October	1933	I.Q. 80	September	1935	I.Q. 77
January	1934	I.Q. 84	November	1935	I.Q. 90

One of the questions that might be asked about the case reported by Chidester and Menninger concerns the validity of the original diagnosis of mental deficiency. This question may be raised because two of the criteria (see p. 8) of mental deficiency are that it is a condition that is likely to obtain at maturity and is essentially incurable. The problem may be posed as follows: Although before treatment this boy was socially incompetent for his age, very retarded intellectually, and showed indications of a brain lesion, was there evidence for believing that the condition was curable? If there was such evidence before treatment, the diagnosis of mental deficiency could be questioned. Although Chidester and Menninger stated that "the patient presented numerous symptoms indicative of a severe long standing emotional disturbance," they did not state whether they considered the disturbance the sole cause or effect of the boy's intellectual deficiency. The fact that they termed their study an experiment suggests that they entertained doubts about the curability of the case. In effect, their therapeutic efforts served as a test for their original diagnosis. *More important, perhaps, than the question of the validity of the original diagnosis is the speculation about the number of times that similar cases (low I.Q., social incompetence, positive neurological signs) referred to clinics have been diagnosed as mentally defective without any therapeutic test of the diagnosis.* Although clinicians are aware that the learning process may be seriously affected by emotional factors, the fact that a given case has a low I.Q. in addition to positive neurological signs (which are sometimes given undue weight) usually disposes the clinician to deëmphasize etiological factors of a psychological nature and to emphasize the organic factors. Had Chidester and Menninger considered their case as one of mental deficiency due to some organic factors (the exogenous type of defective) in which psychotherapeutic procedures were not indicated, their diagnosis would not have been questioned by most clinicians.

The therapeutic problems posed by the above case and the way in which they were handled deserve discussion. Since this boy had no appreciation of his illness and was not set to communicate his feelings and thoughts to other people, the necessity of a "wooing" period is clear. The therapist had to behave in a manner which would make the boy want to see her and which would engender and reinforce his dependence on her. This relationship had to be of a nature which would make responsiveness to the therapist more satisfying than avoidance. By utilizing her power of "reward," she was in a position to make the child inhibit certain kinds of responses while increasing the frequency of expression of others. The preparatory period, in effect, served to make the child begin to be aware of and to respond to *external* rather than internal stimuli, the beginning of reality testing. The technique of direct interpretation may be said to have served a similar function in that such statements put into words the boy's relation to and attitude toward others. For example, when Henry decided to discontinue treatment because the therapist was talking to other children in the school (see p. 273), the direct interpretation offered served to make him think of, to become more aware of, his feelings toward his mother (an external figure) as well as to reëvaluate his feelings toward the therapist (another external figure). His decision to continue treatment indicates that he was aware of external as well as internal factors. It should be realized, of course, that the therapeutic value of a direct interpretation depends on how and when it is offered, the degree of generality with which it is verbalized, and the number of times it is made. Many times it is extremely difficult to determine from published studies the degree to which acceptance of a direct interpretation is a function of the patient's uncritical acceptance of what is offered or the result of the patient's understanding the problem the way the therapist does.[3] In any event, direct interpretation as employed by Chidester and Menninger seems to have had results. Another feature of this case that bears discussion is the fact that the boy was treated in an institutional setting in which he was sympathetically but consistently handled, his activities observed and controlled, and the family situation in which his difficulties arose absent. It is reasonable to assume that the fact that this boy was in a strange setting made it easier for him to respond to the therapist's friendly overtures. In effect, the therapist had no competitors for his affection and confidence. It goes without saying that an institutional setting which does not provide parental substitutes or some kind of consistent and satisfying interpersonal relationships will more often than not have a retarding rather than an accelerating effect on intellectual-social growth (see Chapter 6).

It will be obvious to the reader that the improvement shown in the above case took place over a long period of time (four years) and was the result of painstaking efforts. It might be argued that the amount of time spent on this one case could have been employed in the treatment of many children with lesser difficulties and more favorable prognoses. While this practical objection may be true, it cannot be denied that this case is of great value in that it challenges the validity of some prevalent diagnostic practices and underlines the necessity for research in an area which has been neglected for too long. Since mental deficiency is considered an incurable condition which responds in only a limited way to various types of educational and vocational training, it is surprising that psychotherapy as a test of the validity of the diagnosis of mental deficiency has received scant clinical and research attention.

[3] Clark (49) reported on the psychoanalytic treatment of institutionalized defectives, but his criteria for diagnosis are not at all clear. In describing his cases he gives little background material, neurological data, and psychological test results. Most of Clark's reports consist of a very involved theoretical formulation of the "instinctual" basis of the behavior of his cases, for which there is no validating evidence. His therapeutic procedures are not presented clearly and their effects are difficult to evaluate. It is Clark's conclusion that psychoanalytic therapy is feasible with defectives. Although the case presented by Chidester and Menninger seems to support this conclusion, it is difficult to say whether Clark's data are corroborative evidence.

There are few published data on the use of and benefits from individual psychotherapy with institutionalized defectives. This is not surprising when one considers that the institutionalized defective has usually been viewed as either a medical-custodial or a narrowly conceived educational-vocational problem. The lack of attention which the institutionalized defective has received from psychologists and psychiatrists can be seen from Humphreys' survey (*141*) of the publications of the American Association on Mental Deficiency. The survey, done in 1935, covered 59 years of the Association's publications. Humphreys (*142*) "found that of the six hundred and eighty-one papers studied according to content, nearly 19% could be classified under 'Psychology and Psychiatry' but the percentage of papers dealing with analytical studies of the emotional life of the individual defective amounted to only 1.5% of the total papers of the Proceedings. The statistical and psychiatric trend survey of the paper showed that no matter what the exact percentages may be, or what psychiatric activities may be included under the general term of custodianship, very little well integrated psychiatric work has been done in the American State Schools. However, a recognition of increasing interest in psychiatry in relation to the study of mental deficiency, was clearly shown." This increased interest, however, has not been reflected in the area of psychotherapy with these cases, although the need for such work has been emphasized by Humphreys (*143*).

Thorne's report (*297*) of the results of systematic psychotherapy with institutionalized defectives is one of the few in this area. In setting up the psychotherapeutic program the usual institutional manner of handling problem children was changed. "Under previous administrations disciplinary problems at the schools had been handled by repressive methods involving rather strict punishment including occasional corporal punishment for serious offenses. The old plan of training was oriented toward the general objective of making each child into a compliant institutional inmate who was supposed to submerge individuality in becoming a cog in an impersonal organization." The basic objectives of the psychotherapeutic program involved "(a) accepting the mental defective as being a worthy individual in spite of his defects, (b) permitting expression and clarification of emotional reactions, (c) patiently teaching him methods for resisting frustration and achieving emotional control, (d) outlining standards for acceptable conduct within the ability of each individual child, (e) building up self-confidence and respect by providing experiences of success, and (f) training the child to seek help intelligently through counseling when faced with unsurmountable problems."

The psychotherapeutic methods employed by Thorne were suggestion, persuasion, advice, and reassurance. Nondirective methods were also found effective at certain times:

"In our experience, the nondirective methods developed by Rogers are very effective in certain stages of treatment when the objective is to assist the child to express and clarify his feelings and emotions. When dealing with the child who is emotionally upset, it is desirable to listen quietly to the initial outburst of feeling, reflecting and clarifying feelings nondirectively. If the child quiets down within a reasonable period of time, counseling goes to a discussion of what can be done to solve the difficulties. In many instances, nondirective handling alone is sufficient to solve the difficulties. If the child is so disturbed as to be completely unapproachable, he is placed in isolation until the emotional storm has subsided and he is willing and able to discuss the situation reasonably."

In Table 33 are presented some relevant data about the cases reported by Thorne. The causes for referral for psychotherapy were insubordina-

TABLE 33. Showing the Sex, Age, and Intellectual Level of a Group of Institutionalized Mental Defectives Who Received Intensive Counseling and Psychotherapy Because of Behavior Problems (297)

Ages	Male			Female		
	Imbeciles	Morons	Borderline	Imbeciles	Morons	Borderline
0–9		2			1	
10–19	3	9	3	2	7	2
20–29	4	6	1	3	10	3
30–39				3	3	
40–49	1	1		1	2	
Totals	8	18	4	9	23	5

tion, fighting and quarreling, elopements, severe temper tantrums, stealing, and sex problems. In evaluating the results of psychotherapy the following factors were considered: conduct record, number of breaches of discipline, school and work records, and clinical judgments.

With these criteria, 45 cases were considered improved, 16 unchanged, and 7 worse.

The difficulty which the clinician encounters in setting up a psychotherapeutic program can be seen from the following statement by Thorne: "The most difficult obstacle to the accomplishment of this program is to convince all concerned that it can be done. At the beginning of the program the older employees made dire predictions and stated that nobody could handle these cases without strict and repressive punishments. Corporal punishment died a hard death. . . . Perhaps most difficult is to convince employees that they largely make their own problems through failure to use psychological methods of studying and handling the children under their care." The significance of Thorne's conclusion that psychotherapy with defectives is both possible and profitable and that an extensive research program should be undertaken to exploit its possibilities has not been recognized by many institutional administrators.

The following two cases treated by the writer are presented in some detail in order to emphasize the role of psychotherapy with institutionalized defectives and to illustrate some technical problems that arise.

THE CASE OF LOTTIE

Lottie was born in 1922. She was committed together with her mother and brother to the State Institution for Defectives in 1929. Lottie was committed "because of neglect at home and low mental rating. Before admission she was living with her parents and younger brother on the Town Farm. The mother is reported to have left school at 15 years of age. She had reached the fifth grade and was profane, quarrelsome, fault-finding, and totally incapable of caring for her family. She could not cook, take care of a house and the children were filthy." The father was described as a drunkard who was completely irresponsible. The following excerpt is from an institutional report written several months after admission:

"Lottie is an able-bodied, attractive-looking, seven-year-old child with a mental age of four years, six months, and an intelligence quotient of 74. Her mother is also a patient in this institution. She is very tidy, careful of her clothing and very clean in her personal habits. She is most attentive to her teeth and nails. Mrs. B. reports that in her opinion she is nearer normal than any other child in the institution. She talks a good deal and usually in a quiet, sensible way. She mixes well with the other children, and is a leader in all her games. Her manner is polite, and her table manners excellent. She knows how to use her head. She shows fair judgment and reasoning powers. Insofar as a child of her age is able, she can make herself very useful. Often in the evening she will report incidents of the day, happenings at school and sometimes her remarks are very shrewd, and cute. One evening while her group was being undressed for bed, an announcement was made that the superintendent was making rounds with visitors. Mrs. B. was downstairs in the clothes room, and for a few minutes there was much excitement and confusion in an endeavor to get things straightened out, clothing readjusted, etc. After everything was put in order she said: 'Oh Mrs. B. I was so scared that everything wouldn't be all right until I saw you coming. Everything went off just fine, didn't it?' On another occasion she was kept in quarantine for a few days. When released she wouldn't allow other children to come close to her, 'for fear they might get it too.' This child has undoubtedly promising possibilities."

The following was written one year after admission.

"This little girl of eight years is very attractive in appearance and plays like a normal child. She plays quite well with the group of children her own age, occasionally shows a very naughty disposition. If unable to run things as she wishes, she will sulk and has lately been biting her hands when angry. She did this the other day because another child refused to come into the building and get her a drink of water. When questioned concerning her behavior, she said that she bit herself because she had seen other children do the same."

It was also noted in the history at this time that the older girls in the institution were inclined to make a pet of Lottie and that there was a tendency for her to be spoiled. The following is typical of later institutional reports:

(School report for 1936) "Lottie has very little ability for academic work. She is impertinent and makes disturbances in class. She talks loudly, gets angry instantly, and it is difficult to make explanation to her at times as she sees things her own way. Conduct is unsatisfactory, very moody, doesn't accomplish much, has shown a slight improvement in personality the last few months. In leader work, she gets excited easily. When criticized she becomes sulky, cries and carries on, mean and nasty to her classmates, quarrels with them often, striking them, disobedient, sassy and troublesome, bad tempered, boisterous, swears frequently.

(1938) "Lottie has been moody this year. One day she is interested in her work and the next day she is ready to give up. She grumbles and complains constantly, is very silly and boisterous, seeks attention from older girls by becoming sulky and disagreeable, quarrelsome, carries stories and trys to start trouble. Her work hasn't been as good as it has been in other years."

In 1940 Lottie was transferred to a new institution for defectives. Again one finds in institutional notes mention of surliness, insolence, and bravado. A more rounded picture of this girl is given in the following excerpt from a report written by a schoolteacher toward whom Lottie had always seemed unusually well disposed:

"When Lottie was admitted here in 1940, she appeared to be a very unhappy, discouraged, contrary girl. She was extremely untidy and discouraged about her appearance, feeling that it was useless to bother as she felt herself very homely and queer-looking and that no amount of fussing would change her looks. She also felt that no one cared about her appearance, happiness, or future. In fact, she felt that her only future was here in the institution and that she was even too 'dumb' to get a decent job here. She was inclined to be sulky and when spoken to would act very rudely in order to hide her embarrassment. She would very deliberately break rules to prove her braveness. She would repel any overture of friendliness for fear that you were being sorry for her. She would be insolent to any one being kind to her so that no one could feel she was currying favor.

"She was very fond of her brother (who together with the mother had also been transferred), but beyond a very superficial interest, he paid no attention to her. She took little if any part in athletic activities and yet at heart is rather a tomboy. She visited her mother in the T.B. unit whenever possible but worried after every visit. One of her major fears is being left alone without friends or family."

The following are the intelligence quotients reported from different examinations: in 1928 an I.Q. of 59, in 1929 an I.Q. of 74, in 1939 an I.Q. of 45, in 1942 an I.Q. of 48, and in 1944 an I.Q. of 51. Lottie had always been diagnosed as a familial (garden-variety or endogenous) defective.

The decision in September, 1945, to attempt psychotherapeutic interviews with Lottie stemmed from her refusal to take some psychological tests. The psychologist had come to her classroom to take her to his office, but when the teacher asked her to accompany him she refused to do so. She sat in her seat muttering to herself and indicating with facial expressions that she did not want to go. After some prodding by the teacher, which had no effect on Lottie, the psychologist said somewhat angrily that if she did not want to take the tests she did not have to and he left the classroom. Later in the day the psychologist sent for Lottie to come to his office. When she came in, it was obvious that she had been crying a great deal. However, she was very sullen and unresponsive and answered routine questions in a barely audible tone, never once looking at the psychologist. Shortly after the administration of a test was begun, tears came to her eyes. She tried to keep them back but soon she was crying very hard. The psychologist let her cry for several minutes, after which he asked her if she would tell him why she felt as unhappy as she did. Lottie, who kept her head down on her chest, merely shook her head. The psychologist then asked her if she would accompany him to the school canteen where they could get some ice cream. Lottie, her face still out of sight, did not answer and when the psychologist came over to her and took her hand she very meekly accompanied him. During the walk to the canteen she kept her face buried in her chest but held the psychologist's hand very firmly. In the canteen she was very ill at ease and said that she did not want anything but when ice cream was placed before her, she began to eat it in a very self-conscious manner. When the psychologist jokingly asked her why she always had her face down on her chest (making the eating of the ice cream quite a feat), she said, "My face is nothing to look at." When the psychologist said that he disagreed with her, she obviously appreciated the comment. In answer to a question about whether her brother had written to her from the Army, Lottie shook her head and when the psychologist expressed surprise she said, "I'm disappointed and not disappointed at Tom for not writing me—he did that before." During the walk back from the canteen the psychologist said that he felt badly about the fact that Lottie was so unhappy and he would like very much to help her, if Lottie thought he could help her. Would she like to come to see him regularly and talk things over? Lottie nodded and the psychologist went on as follows:

"It's probably going to be hard for you to talk about some of the things that bother you but unless you do tell me what's on your mind I won't be able to be of much help to you. I've got to know how you feel, why you do and did certain things, and what you think will make you happy. I want to tell you now that when we talk things over I may not always agree with what you have said or done. Because I don't agree with you doesn't mean that I don't like you. Just as I always want you to feel that you can talk to me about anything, I want to feel that I can tell you what I think. I don't want you to keep anything back because you think I'm 'Staff' and I might tell others what you tell me. Whatever you tell me stays with me—that's something between you and me and it will be no one else's business. I expect, of course, that whatever we talk over you will also keep to yourself. Unless we trust each other we are not going to get very far. Again I want to say that if I tell you that I think you've done something wrong, I'm telling it to you not because I don't like you or I want to make you feel bad but because I want to help you. Sometimes I'll probably be wrong in what I say but I want to feel that I can tell you what I think. If you feel that you will not be able to talk to me about what bothers you, then I wish you would tell me now. If you decide that you want to come to see me regularly, I'll set aside some time three days a week when we'll get together. That time will be for you and no one else. Another thing, any time you decide you don't want to see me any more all you have to do is say so. Don't feel that if you decide not to come I'll be angry and hold it against you. Regardless of whether you come or not I'll always be ready to help you in any way that I can."

When asked if she wanted to assent to the "agreement," Lottie nodded. Appointments were made for stated times on three days of the week.

One of the most difficult obstacles in establishing a "give-and-take" relationship with this girl was her fear and unwillingness to verbalize feelings and attitudes. During the initial interviews she would sit with her head either down on her chest or turned to the side—anything in order not to look at the psychologist. When she came into the office she would say hello in a friendly manner, but as soon as she sat down in the chair the "avoidance" behavior would begin and she would be unable to talk. If the psychologist said nothing, long periods of silence would ensue during which Lottie might occasionally look furtively at the psychologist, giggling embarrassedly when he registered mock surprise at her attempt. During the first seven interviews this girl could not initiate a conversation and it was necessary for the examiner to adopt a very direct approach. The first "problem" attacked was why she could not look the psychologist (and other people) in the face. Her replies to these inquiries were, "If you were like me, you couldn't look people in the face either." She would not and could not elaborate on this reply. When the psychologist said that the reason he thought she behaved this way was that she felt she was not pretty and that people would not like her, she remained silent for some time and finally nodded her head in agreement. When the opinion was expressed that she was a rather attractive girl and that there were people who had said that they liked her a great deal, Lottie became very embarrassed and although she denied the validity of the statements she obviously was pleased by them. She would react similarly when the psychologist said that he liked her.

Sometimes she would mutter something that was inaudible but when she was asked what she had said she would shake her head or say that she had said nothing. On one of these occasions the psychologist thought that Lottie had said, "I'll always be unhappy. You can help it but it will never happen to me." Questioning did not result in any reply. When this occurred the psychologist would remind her of the original agreement between them about "talking" and would indicate his disappointment and displeasure at her failure to adhere to it, statements which sometimes resulted in a sort of hostile silence. When this occurred during the seventh interview, the psychologist said that he could not be of help to her until she felt that she could talk to him. Lottie sat in silence for the rest of the allotted interview time and when the psychologist indicated that the time was up she walked out of the office in an aggressive fashion banging the door after her. When she came in the next time, she appeared like a penitent child. After a period of silence she said, "Why didn't you look at me at breakfast?[4] You looked at the floor but you didn't look at me. You wanted to show me how bad it is not to look at a person." At the end of this interview Lottie, for the first time, looked directly at the psychologist when she said goodbye. She appeared somewhat flustered and self-conscious because she knew she was doing something she never had done before.

There were many opportunities for discussion of Lottie's fear and avoidance of people. When Christmas time came, she reported that she had refused to participate in the school pageant. "I refused to be in the pageant. I don't like people staring at me. That's why I stand with my head down in the dining room. I'm shy." At another time the psychologist was conducting some visitors around the institution and when they entered the unit in which Lottie was working, she turned her head away and never once looked at the psychologist or the visitors. When this problem was discussed with her Lottie would usually react in a somewhat sullen and hostile fashion, saying that it didn't matter how she acted, that she would always be in an institution, and that she just didn't want people looking at her. It was invariably pointed out to her that her avoidance of contact with people was due to unrealistic attitudes toward herself and that the effect of her behavior was to give people the wrong impression of her. "You're afraid that people will think you are not pretty and that you are not smart. So you are afraid to look at them and talk to them because then you would be giving them a chance to see that you are neither pretty nor smart. But by acting that way people will really think that you are not smart—which is the one thing you don't want them to think." In answer to this Lottie once remarked, "The next time you bring visitors around I'm going to dig a hole and hide till they go away." Another time she said, "I may look dumb but I'm not."

When it was pointed out to her that her fear of meeting people would make it difficult for her when she left the institution, Lottie's feelings of hostility and futility were blatantly expressed. She would laugh sarcastically at the idea that someone thought she "would ever get out of here." "It may happen to somebody else but it will never happen to me. What difference does it make how you act if you never get out of here?" This girl's conviction that she would never leave the institution ("They'll carry me out in a

---

[4] Lottie helped as a waitress in the dining room for the breakfast and supper meals. During the day she worked in the sewing room.

box") was so deep-seated that encouragement and reassurance by the psychologist had no effect. Lottie's attitude was, of course, completely understandable. She had been told innumerable times that "some day" she would be sent out of the institution. She had seen other children leave it and could never understand why she had been ignored. She had never been given a concrete indication that plans were being made for her to be placed in the community. With this background of institutional promises it is understandable why it was less painful for her to believe that she would never be placed than to entertain a hope which was inevitably followed by disappointment. From this attitude of futility it was only one step to the formula: "If they won't do anything for me, why should I do anything for them? If you're bad you don't go out and if you're good you don't go out." This created a most difficult therapeutic problem. As long as Lottie believed that she would never leave the institution the therapist was powerless to influence her behavior. If she could not believe that the psychologist's reassurance about placement had any likelihood of occurrence, then there was no reason for her *to want* to follow his suggestions and advice.

The manner in which this problem might be handled was largely determined by the nature of the relationship between Lottie and the psychologist. There were many indications of her attachment and fondness for him. For example, on several occasions when disapproval or disappointment was expressed at her behavior (sullenness, angry spells, difficulty with supervisors, refusal to talk, etc.), Lottie would say, "You really don't like me. You like to criticize me." Sometimes this would be said in a worried tone of voice and at other times in a manner as if to say, "You see, you really don't like me the way you said. You never meant it. I can't believe you." On several occasions after interviews in which Lottie either petulantly refused to talk or expressed pride in having acted aggressively toward her supervisors, or had announced her unwillingness or inability to change her behavior, the therapist received a note from her asking forgiveness and hoping that he would want to see her again.[5]

[5] The following letter was sent by Lottie after an interview in which she had reported in a flippant manner some misbehavior, resented the psychologist's expression of disapproval, and left the office without saying goodbye.

"Dear Dr.

"Just a few line to said that I'm sorry that I did not said goodbye to you. You think that I don't blieve you what you said to me. but I bleive you what you tell me.

"I no that you give up talk to me. but you think that I won't act like a lady but some day you will be glad that I act like a lady.

"I hope you have a nice time read this letter so please let me know what you think about it.

                              From
                              Lottie"

One day Lottie came to the office wearing glasses, something which the therapist had never seen her wear before. He expressed surprise at the glasses and inquired about how she had found out that she was in need of them. To his surprise Lottie replied that she had had the glasses for a long time.

PSYCHOLOGIST: How come you are wearing them today?
LOTTIE: The cottage matron said I was supposed to wear them and that I couldn't go out today until I put them on.
PSYCHOLOGIST: Why haven't you worn them before?
LOTTIE: (*At this point her head went down on her chest, a movement which the psychologist had learned to recognize as an indication that she did not want to answer the question.*)
PSYCHOLOGIST: (*After several minutes' silence.*) The reason I asked that question, Lottie, is that I was puzzled about why you haven't worn glasses before today. Now I'm puzzled about why you don't want to answer the question. You remember our agreement about talking. It may be hard for you to answer the question and so I'll give you as much time as you need to answer it. Until you show me that you will stick to the agreement, there's nothing I can do or say.
LOTTIE: (*After approximately ten minutes of silence.*) Because the girls called me four eyes.
PSYCHOLOGIST: When the girls call you four eyes, it reminds you of what you think about yourself, that you are not pretty. (*Nods her head in agreement.*) But I still don't understand why it was so hard for you to answer the question. Why couldn't you tell it to me?
LOTTIE: (*After another ten minutes of silence.*) Because you wear glasses.
PSYCHOLOGIST: (*Somewhat recovered from his surprise.*) You thought that I would be hurt the way you were by what the girls said.
LOTTIE: Yes.

The girl's fondness for the therapist was also revealed by cottage and work reports which indicated that she talked inordinately about how much she liked him, kept tabs on all his activities, and became impatient when the time for the interview approached. It was also indicated that she was very proud of the fact that she had regular appointments with the psychologist (and could make others if she felt it necessary) and was not above flaunting the relationship as a sign of distinction to other girls. As might be expected, in the interviews Lottie could express her fondness only in the most indirect manner. It was the therapist's impression that as Lottie's fondness for him increased, the fear of being rejected and unliked by him also increased, making it more likely that she would "find" in his statements and mannerisms

290 PSYCHOLOGICAL PROBLEMS IN MENTAL DEFICIENCY

evidence for her fear. It also seemed to the therapist that much of Lottie's aggressive and petulant behavior in the interviews was a way of testing his feelings toward her. Whenever he felt that these attitudes toward self and therapist were behind her behavior, he would reiterate his fondness for her and emphasize that because he disagreed with or criticized her should not be taken as an indication of dislike.

Lottie's growing fondness for the therapist and her dependence on him as a source of satisfaction were utilized by him as a means of shaking her conviction that she would never be given an opportunity to return "to the outside." During an interview in which she cried and repeated her belief that she would always be in the institution, the psychologist forcefully replied: "If you really believe that, then it means that I haven't been of help to you. I have told you time and time again that you will be given a chance to go out, but I suppose you think that I just tell it to you to make you feel good. What I haven't been able to make you understand is that if I thought you would never go out, I wouldn't waste my time seeing you. There are other boys and girls whom I could see who would be willing to try to change their behavior so they could do a good job when they go out. You deserve to go out but there is a lot you have to learn first. But since you don't believe you're ever going out, you're not willing to try to change yourself. I feel very badly that you feel it's all hopeless because it means I've failed to help you. I haven't been able to make you see that you will go out if you will only make an effort to act differently in some ways. I'm sorry that I've failed because I like you and I wanted to help you. If I didn't like you and I thought I couldn't help you, I never would have started to see you. Since you can't believe what I say about going out, I suppose you ought to stop coming to see me because I don't see how I can help you. Unless you believe what I say and really try to change some of your actions, I suppose we ought to call it quits. What do you think? It's your decision." Lottie remained silent for several minutes and then said that she believed what the psychologist said about going out and she wanted to continue seeing him. After this statement from Lottie the psychologist stated what proved to be the chief theme of all subsequent interviews: that he would help her in every way to help herself.

In the subsequent months there was a marked change in Lottie's behavior. Her work supervisors and cottage matrons noted that her angry spells and sullenness had noticeably decreased in frequency and that her relationship with other girls was also more smooth. In the interviews she was more spontaneous and frequently reported in a proud manner her own awareness of a change: "I don't mutter anymore." "I try to look at people when they talk to me." "It's hard but I keep my temper." During a period when the psychologist was ill, he received the following note from Lottie:

"Dear Dr:

"I was very sorry to hear that you wher sick in bed but I hope you will get butter soon.

"I am still keep my head up that some day I will get what I wish for. I am try to be a good girl for you wild you are sick in bed. So please don't think that I am be a bad girl girl wild you are sick.

"Please stay in bed wild you are sick. And I can wait for you to get butter so don't think of me wild you are sick in bed. I will close. I hope that you get butter.

"From your friend
"Lottie"

The following is from a report of Lottie's continuation schoolteacher:

"She is very much improved in several ways. She is no longer insolent in the dining room. She is courteous and agreeable and her reserved manner is friendly now rather than repellent. She is trying very hard to obey laws pleasantly and quietly without the undercurrent of muttering that always accompanied her objections. She feels that she is not hopeless and can really learn something and so she has doubled her endeavor. Her progress in Continuation school has been good. Her greatest progress has been made recently.

"She will read aloud now in the presence of strangers where before she would read only if I would take her alone. She is still afraid of new situations but she will attempt to solve rather than ignore them. Arithmetic is very difficult for her but for the first time in her life she is really attempting to do it."

The following is from a report of the supervisor of the employees' dining room in which Lottie worked:

"Five months ago her attitude was so indifferent, one can hardly believe today's girl is the one who then went into a rage at the slightest upset. To suggest a divergence from routine brought an outbreak of words in such an awful voice there seemed no way to calm her. Then followed such melancholy I pondered much on how to break it. With these came many jealous spells which could scarcely be broken. At that time she could only handle six or seven people at mealtime.

"Now rarely, very rarely, does Lottie have a suggestion of nerves. It is weeks since an unpleasant vocal outbreak. There is no evidence of jealousy, much greater goodwill for the girls, and an ever readiness to fulfill any request of mine. Daily she serves thirteen people for lunch. When an emergency arises, let it be hard work, an errand, or an employee party, Lottie will exclaim, 'Let me do it. I can do it.'"

Although there was a noticeable change in Lottie's institutional adjustment, on more than one occasion her relation with the psychologist resulted in a return of her sullenness and aggressiveness. In one interview (seventh month) Lottie was obviously, for some undetermined reason, feeling very aggressive. She avoided looking at the psychologist, gazed indifferently out of the office window, and responded to questions about her actions in a tart and hostile manner. After several minutes of silence during which she was the picture of feigned disinterest, the therapist said: "I wish I knew why you feel the way you do and why you are acting this way toward me. Since you feel the way you do, maybe you would rather cut things short today and leave." To this she replied testily: "If you want me to leave, I'll leave. Goodbye." She banged the door after her. The next day the psychologist received a call from her supervisor, who reported that Lottie was upsetting the unit, was refusing to do as she was told, and was as negativistic as she had been months before. When Lottie came in for her interview on the following day, she was obviously somewhat depressed. When the psychologist said to her, "You felt pretty angry toward me the last time, didn't you?" Lottie readily agreed. She was silent for a while, then said, "Why are they always saying that they're going to tell you what I do? They're always saying, 'I'll tell Dr. Sarason about that. I'll tell Dr. Sarason.'" Lottie's imitation was, to say the least, caustic.

PSYCHOLOGIST: When these people say that, it gets you pretty angry. When that happened a couple of days ago, you let it out on me. I sort of have the feeling that underneath it all you're angry at me too because I tell you when I think you're wrong.

LOTTIE: (With feigned annoyance.) They tell me these things as if I'm your daughter and you're my father.

PSYCHOLOGIST: Can it be, Lottie, that the reason you acted up yesterday was because after you left last time you felt I didn't like you?

LOTTIE: I know you don't like me because of the way I act. I can't help it.

PSYCHOLOGIST: (Sighing.) Maybe I'm expecting too much.

LOTTIE: (A little scared.) I can change if I want to.

PSYCHOLOGIST: It would make you and me happier if you did.

During the eighth month of interviews the psychologist informed Lottie that plans were being made to secure her a placement and that it might be a good idea for them to discuss some of the problems that she might encounter. The possibility that she would be leaving the institution in the next few months produced mixed reactions in Lottie. On the one hand she felt elated, and on the other she was apprehensive about how she would make out. The psychologist told her in a direct fashion that her chief difficulties would be (1) feeling of unlikability, (2) fear of rejection, (3) fear of new people and situations, (4) and inability to communicate feeling to other people. "You've lived in an institution for most of your life. You're going to see new people and places. You're going to be asked to do things that you may not have done before. At first you're going to be frightened at the newness of being outside. You're going to be lonesome. You may even cry at the beginning. But you must remember and always be sure to remind yourself that when you feel frightened and lonesome and unsure of yourself that it is perfectly natural for you to feel that way. If I were in your place, I would feel that way too. At the beginning everything is going to be new to you but that will wear off. After awhile you're going to wonder why you were ever scared." The attitudes which placement engendered in Lottie may be gleaned from an excerpt of an interview in which she was not "in a talking mood."

PSYCHOLOGIST: I'm wondering what you're going to do when the woman you work for asks you questions.

LOTTIE: I won't answer her.

PSYCHOLOGIST: For example, what if she asks about your mother?

LOTTIE: I'll say I haven't any.

PSYCHOLOGIST: You think that's a good answer?

LOTTIE: That's what they used to tell me. When I lived with my grandmother they told me that. Wouldn't it be good for the woman I work with if she didn't have to talk to me?

PSYCHOLOGIST: You still think that no one could like you and that people will think you are not smart.

LOTTIE: Other girls *are* smarter than me. They can talk to people. It's hard.

PSYCHOLOGIST: I don't think I agree with you. You're just as smart as the other girls and you can do the things they do. But the important thing is not what I think but that you think the way you do about yourself. That's why it's so hard for you to talk to people. You're afraid they won't like you and that they will think you're not smart. That's why it was so hard for you to talk to me at first. But you got over that with me and you have to get over that with other people.

LOTTIE: It's hard. You don't believe me. (*Is silent for several moments and then says with difficulty.*) I've been locked up for so long that it's hard for me.

PSYCHOLOGIST: But it's not hard as it used to be.
LOTTIE: No. But it's still hard. But I'm trying.

The following excerpt is from an interview which took place the day after the psychologist had visited Lottie's work unit in the course of showing a visitor around the institution. The visitor had spoken to Lottie about her work and she had responded with no sign of discomfiture—in marked contrast to her reactions to a similar situation several months previous (see p. 287).

PSYCHOLOGIST: How do you think you acted yesterday?
LOTTIE: All right. I wasn't afraid. I didn't want you to think I was scared.
PSYCHOLOGIST: I certainly did not think you were scared. You really showed me that you can talk to people. Don't you think that it will be easier for you on the outside when you meet people?
LOTTIE: That's different.
PSYCHOLOGIST: Why?
LOTTIE: I'll be working for the lady.
PSYCHOLOGIST: So?
LOTTIE: Maybe she'll be all right for a few days and then she won't like me any more.
PSYCHOLOGIST: You worry a great deal about that?
LOTTIE: Yes. I hope we'll understand each other.

In the last month of interviews the psychologist presented to Lottie in a direct fashion the kinds of problems she would encounter on placement, her probable initial reactions, and the manner in which they might be handled. A realistic picture of what to expect was always accompanied by reassurance and support.

Lottie's placement was viewed with some misgivings. Although there was little doubt that her handling of interpersonal relationships had improved, it was recognized that this change took place in a restricted environment in which she was the recipient of special handling. The fact that she was going "outside" to a world in which she would be a stranger meant that she would encounter situations which could only arouse anxiety. She had grown up in a restricted geographical and psychological atmosphere. She was being put into a situation which would be taxing to an individual of higher capabilities and more varied experience. Against these considerations were the following opinions: (1) She was as prepared to go out as she would ever be, (2) prolonged institutionalization would make placement in the future more hazardous, (3) even if she failed on this placement she would benefit from having had direct contact with another world, an experience which would make the probability of success of future placements greater. It should be noted at this point that the psychologist had told Lottie on many occasions that if she had to be brought back to the institution, it would not be considered that she failed.

Lottie was placed in the home of a middle-class family. There were several children in the home, the youngest being a newborn. The following is from an early report of the social worker:

"Employer said patient was very slow, was sluggish in walking and in all her actions, did not have a way with children. Employer thought she might make trainable material but her work was not of good quality. Employer has been tied up with the baby in the morning and so had to let patient go ahead on her own but she showed no initiative. Employer says she is a rather sweet girl but very shy, tended to be a little nervous and did not seem to let down and mix well in the family group. The worker interviewed Lottie, who said she liked the home but naturally found it strange. She said she was lonesome the first few days and cried a little. Is trying hard to work satisfactorily. She did not seem to know what to do with herself during her free time."

Two observations recur in later reports: not knowing what to do with her leisure time and being frightened and unable to "unbend and relax." Homesickness and lonesomeness were also frequently noted. "The worker took Lottie out with some other girls on placements and the worker noted that Lottie in comparison to some of the others was quiet and had not learned to unbend." Because the employer could not give Lottie individual attention and expected her to be able to carry on by herself, the placement was considered by the employer and worker as unsatisfactory. Another placement was secured, this time on the farm of an elderly woman and her daughter. The social worker reported as follows:

"Lottie took the change in placement as a personal defeat. Her first employer reiterated that if someone could spend a great deal of time with Lottie she had great possibilities. The worker explained to the new employer that Lottie was not too well trained but the worker thought that she was quite trainable but would need quite a bit of patience. The employer did not like this too well. There was great confusion in the home when Lottie got there and when the worker left Lottie was crying a great deal."

The placement did not work out very well and Lottie was returned to the Training School. The social worker's concluding note stated that she "did not feel that Lottie was entirely to blame for her failure in the last home as the worker is not yet sure just what type of woman the employer was."

In evaluating Lottie's adjustment to placement the following should be borne in mind: (1) From the time that Lottie left the institution she was under the supervision of the Social Service Department which at that time was located quite a distance from the institution; (2) although the psychologist had acquainted the social worker with his experiences with Lottie, the worker's knowledge of Lottie was second-hand; (3) because of the pressure of her case load the worker was able to visit Lottie only on the average of once a week; (4) people who take institutional children to work in their homes generally expect to receive rather than to give service.[6] These factors indicate that Lottie was placed in environments wherein she did not receive the reassurance she needed *in the consistent way in which she needed it* if feelings of insecurity, inadequacy, and rejection were to be avoided.

The crippling effects of prolonged institutionalization upon Lottie are best revealed by the following incidents. In her second placement Lottie was given a room on the second floor of the house, the employer and her mother sleeping on the ground floor. Each morning the employer would find Lottie asleep on the living room couch on the first floor. When questioned by the employer, Lottie said that she was afraid to sleep upstairs by herself. Despite the employer's disapproval, Lottie always came downstairs to sleep on the couch after the others had gone to bed. When several weeks later the psychologist was discussing this with her, Lottie said, "Of course I was afraid. All my life I've slept in dormitories with a lot of other girls. I can't sleep alone." In her notes the social worker several times referred to Lottie's complete amazement at traffic lights, large trucks, juke boxes, etc. On one occasion when the worker took her out for the day, Lottie was so overwhelmed by these sights and asked so many questions that she herself said to the worker, "You're going to be tired of answering all my questions." It may be assumed that aside from the visit of the social worker Lottie did not feel free to ask a fraction of the questions which came to her mind.

The primary purpose of presenting the case of Lottie is to demonstrate the feasibility of psychotherapy with a defective child in an institutional setting. At the end of ten months of interviews this girl's periods of sullenness and depression had noticeably decreased, she was more spontaneous, she did not avoid new people and situations with as much apprehension, her efficiency at work had improved, and she did not

---

[6] The majority of working placements are successful. In most of these cases, however, the configuration of problems which Lottie presented is absent. Whereas the fourth factor might not be crucial in other cases, in Lottie's case it was of great importance.

feel as personally isolated as previously. That this girl "failed" in her placement cannot be used to evaluate the effects of the psychotherapy. The placement notes indicate that procedures which were successful in other cases were not adequate for Lottie's needs. That Lottie needed special handling seemed to be due more to the effects of prolonged institutionalization than to an intellectual deficiency *per se*.

In a preceding paragraph Lottie was referred to as a mentally defective child. The reader may be interested in some of the writer's feelings toward and opinions about Lottie. Never once during the interviews was he ever aware that Lottie was defective. That she was very immature was painfully evident. In fact, he never regarded her in terms of her chronological age. He felt toward her and undoubtedly acted toward her like a big brother—a fact which did not prevent Lottie from regarding him as a father. It is the writer's opinion that his being unaware of Lottie's defectiveness was due not only to the fact that he responded to her as one would to a younger child, but also to the fact that *he considered her intellectual, social, and personal inadequacies not as being due either to a deficiency which existed at or shortly after birth, or was of constitutional origin or of a nature which precluded normal development.* Many times he was surprised at the degree of insight which Lottie had about her own behavior. Although she had difficulty in communicating feeling, it was not because she did not know how to express feeling or thought but because she did not want or was afraid to verbalize it. When she did express herself it was always coherent and to the point. She had no difficulty in understanding the generalizations of others and in formulating her own on the basis of her own experience. Her conception of time and space, as is to be expected from one institutionalized for such a long period, was unrealistic. She knew only certain kinds of people in certain kinds of roles and her fantasies about the "outside" were undoubtedly bizarre. Her absolute fund of knowledge was pitifully small. What she could not comprehend seemed to be due to lack of experience rather than of capacity. What constantly surprised the writer was not what she did not know or could not do but what she did know and how quickly she grasped the nature of problems with which she was faced. His attitude toward Lottie might be formulated as follows: "If I experienced what she did, I'd be what she is today." He did not feel that Lottie's inadequacies were the result of an initial lack of the potentiality for normal growth.

The validity of this opinion may be questioned, although, as was pointed out in Chapter 6, the data necessary for its proof or disproof are not available and the question will be decided only by future research. From the standpoint of the therapeutic relation, however, it may be said that the fact that the psychologist felt the way he did about the girl was reflected in his actions toward her, actions which made it easier for her to respond and adjust to the realities of her environment.

THE CASE OF STEPHEN

Stephen was born in 1929 at the State Farm for Women where his mother had been committed. His mother, who had an I.Q. of 45, was noted for her promiscuity. The paternity of four of her six children was never clear. When she became pregnant with Stephen, the putative father is supposed to have made arrangements to marry her but they never materialized and he left the state before Stephen was born. It is not clear from the history how long Stephen remained at the State Farm, but it appears that at a very early age he was transferred to a Catholic orphanage where he remained until his commitment to the State Training School for defectives.

There were few developmental data in the case history. At birth Stephen was noted as having a microcephalic head, but later examinations did not mention anything unusual about the size or shape of his head. He walked at eighteen months. On only rare occasions did he ever have an outside visitor. The following is taken from the admission report:

"Stephen has threatened to damage the oil burner at the orphanage by throwing matches in it. He threatens the sisters in the institution in general. He lies and disappears from the grounds. He also steals other chil. dren's belongings and sells them for a few cents. Since Stephen is considered an extremely troublesome and dangerous child, the sisters have asked to make arrangements for his commitment as soon as possible. Although only 13 years old, he is large for his age.

"He has no control of social situations, shouts in classroom at school, leaves the room and wanders about. He is untrustworthy, lazy, sloppy, friendly, heedless and indifferent. His reading ability is good but in other respects he has not made academic progress.

"He loves to work [in the orphanage] in the kitchen and he enjoys doing this because he knows that after he has helped bake pies he will get two of them which he shares with other boys at the orphanage. He enjoys everyone being well fed because he himself likes to eat. He shares what he takes from the kitchen with others. He cares for the younger children at the orphanage, entertains them quite well and reads stories to them. He is a leader and loves to get up amateur shows. The little ones respect him very much. He plays the piano by ear fairly well and as he plays the piano the little children follow him in song. He loves to play games with the children."

Stephen was admitted to the training school in 1943. The initial diagnosis was garden-variety deficiency. On psychological tests he received an I.Q. of 63 (1937 Binet), a Kohs Block Design score at the 11-year level, and academic achievement scores between the third- and fourth-grade levels. His institutional program consisted of half a day in a vocational assignment and the remainder in the academic school. Two years later he was given a full day's work assignment (bakery) and went to the continuation school one evening a week.

The possibility of attempting psychotherapeutic interviews with Stephen was raised in 1945 by his schoolteacher. She had noted that he was moody and unhappy; he complained of his dissatisfaction with his cottage placement and did not seem to get along too well with the others boys. It was the teacher's impression that "if his feelings could be straightened," he could function more efficiently and at a higher level. It was suggested to her that she sound out Stephen about wanting to talk to the psychologist. If he indicated that he wanted to come, the teacher was to tell him that she would try to arrange for an interview. The aim of this procedure was to make Stephen feel that he was seeking out the psychologist, and not vice versa. Stephen expressed a strong desire to see the psychologist and an interview was arranged. An incident which occurred two years earlier during the initial psychological examination probably played a role in Stephen's eagerness to come. During this initial examination the psychologist was called away from the testing room for several minutes. In this interval Stephen had gone through the therapist's desk and taken a stop watch. When the psychologist returned, the examination was resumed and it was not until later in the day that the watch was missed. Stephen was not questioned directly, but his cottage father was asked to look through his things. The watch was found, irreparably damaged, among his clothes. In accordance with institutional rules he was put in isolation for several days. On his release the psychologist called him down to his office. When he entered the office it was obvious that he considered the worst punishment was yet to come. When the psychologist said that he was more worried about Stephen than about the watch, the boy was visibly surprised. The fact that the psychologist hoped that Stephen would always feel free to come and talk to him when things bothered him and that he would always be ready to help him in any way that he could had a profound effect on the boy. Stephen left the office feeling he had gained a friend.

In the first psychotherapeutic interview it was clear that this boy would have no difficulty in communicating his problems. He was ill at ease for several minutes, shifted uneasily in his chair, and tended to avoid looking at the psychologist.

PSYCHOLOGIST: Mrs. K. was telling me that you wanted to talk to me about some things that were on your mind.
STEPHEN: Yes. Where should I start? I don't know where to begin. There's a lot.
PSYCHOLOGIST: Start wherever you want. I know it's hard to begin.
STEPHEN: I'll tell you about myself.

Stephen then began to recount the story of his life. He talked so fast that it was very difficult to distinguish one sentence from another. He went into such minute detail and went from one event to another so that it was extremely difficult to follow him. Every now and then he would pause for a moment, ask a question, usually answer it himself, and then go on with his stories. For the first half-hour of this interview, the psychologist did not say a word. This silence was as much due to bewilderment at the mass of detail as it was to technique. The following are some of the things that the boy related:

1. He came to the orphanage when he was two years old.
2. He was always stealing things. "I was sneaky. I did slicky things. I did things behind the nuns' back. Now I know that if I keep busy I don't get itchy fingers. I used to steal money from the poor box. Once I took the money and bought a pair of shoes. I used to steal a lot of food too."
3. He was not sure about his relationship to his mother, present stepfather, and siblings. "My mother used to visit me when I was small. She visited me in the summer. I'd get excited when she'd come. She stopped because her legs bothered her. She limps on one foot." At another time he said, "I don't know who my father was. My mother has pictures of my father in the coffin. She married again. I got a sister and there's Tom and Richard but I don't know if they are my brothers. I thought they were but I don't know." He also described his stepfather, who was a drunkard and fought constantly with his mother. "I'm ashamed to tell you these things but maybe you heard worse cases. Is he my real father? Is she my mother? I don't know if he's my stepfather. Sometimes he doesn't come home at all. I don't want a stepfather like that. I once saw him try to stab my mother. I was in the struggle. I got the knife away."

When the psychologist agreed that Stephen had many problems and that it might be a good idea to talk more about them the boy said he would like very much to come again. Appointments at stated hours three times a week were scheduled.

In the second interview Stephen began to talk as fast as before and it was difficult to follow him. The psychologist said that it was difficult to follow him and wondered if he always spoke that way. (The psychologist knew that it was not his usual manner of talking.) Stephen replied, "I don't always speak that way. But I'm nervous."

PSYCHOLOGIST: Why do you feel nervous now?
STEPHEN: Because I'm embarrassed because what I tell you. I think maybe you would change toward me. I never told anybody these things before.

Stephen was reassured about the psychologist's attitude toward him and the confidential nature of the interviews was explained. He then began to speak about his mother but referred to her now by her full name; for a moment the psychologist did not know to whom he was referring.

PSYCHOLOGIST: Who is A_____ H_____? Is that your mother?
STEPHEN: That's it, I don't know. She don't act like my mother.
PSYCHOLOGIST: Is it that you don't want to believe it is your mother?
STEPHEN: Yes. She doesn't act right. She drinks. She yells and fights. She told me I should get training here so I can get a job and give her money. But I said to myself that I'm not. I'll get a job with people and have a good time.

Shortly after this discussion Stephen said that he had a question he would like to ask. He had overhead his cottage parents say that "he had his brain tested and he's a lowgrade. There's something wrong with his brain."[7]

STEPHEN: Is there something wrong with my brain? I don't think so. The boys make fun of me because I'm in a low-grade cottage but I don't care.
PSYCHOLOGIST: We certainly do not feel that there is anything wrong with your brain. We feel that you are going to get a lot from your training here and that you will do a good job when you go out.

Stephen then returned to the discussion of his mother. His earliest memory was of "this woman" coming to see him. "She came with a little baby and a strange man." Then she stopped coming and he did not see her again for a

---

[7] When Stephen was admitted, he was placed in a cottage for imbecile boys, an unfortunate placement which was later rectified. The fact that he was not placed with boys like himself reinforced his belief that something was wrong with his brain. As will be seen later, this belief was longstanding.

long time. The other children in the orphanage used to taunt him because
he had no mother and no one came to see him. "Then she started coming
again. I was ashamed when she came and I wouldn't go to her until she
called me." Stephen used to visit her home but he never had a good time
there.[8] There were always fights and his mother was always telling him to
take money from the pockets of his drunken stepfather.

STEPHEN: (Thoughtfully.) I don't know. I'm like them.
PSYCHOLOGIST: How do you mean?
STEPHEN: I used to see them [mother and siblings] take money and my
    mother would give them some but not me. So I took. I would get nervous,
    but when I didn't get punished I'd do it again.

The next several interviews were largely used by Stephen for discussing
the nature of his relations with the other children in his mother's home and
his ambivalent feelings toward his mother. The more he talked about his
mother the more his hostility toward her overshadowed his feeling that a
son ought to love his mother. "She didn't act like a mother. If she did she
would have tried to get me out of the orphanage. Sometimes when she came
she would tell me to get some flower plants for her. I would tell her I couldn't
but she would say I could if I wanted to. She used to tell me to steal things."
    Following an interview in which his stealing had been discussed, Stephen
came in the next time and spontaneously began talking about the reasons
he took things.

STEPHEN: I figured it out and now I know why I took things. I would want
    something and there was no way of getting it so I stole it. I wouldn't get
    caught so I would do it. Like when I took your watch. I opened the drawer
    to get a pencil and I saw the watch. It was in me—temptation—I said I
    needed a watch. I was going to bury it in the ground in a box till they
    forgot about it.
PSYCHOLOGIST: When else have you taken things?
STEPHEN: I never took things when the Allens [cottage mother and father]
    were on duty. I was afraid he'd swing at me.
PSYCHOLOGIST: What do you mean?
STEPHEN: He's older and stronger. He could smack you and hurt you. I
    was afraid.
PSYCHOLOGIST: Who else are you afraid of?

----

[8] The data supplied by the orphanage do not indicate that Stephen was allowed to visit
his mother, who lived in the same city. While such visits may have been allowed, it is
probable that many of them were not sanctioned and were either substitutes for going to
school or mere absences from the orphanage.

STEPHEN: I'm afraid of Tony H. [a boy who worked in the bakery with him] He's always fighting and I'm afraid of him.

PSYCHOLOGIST: You feel that Tony is stronger than you are? [Stephen was approximately six feet tall and Tony was about five feet six.]

STEPHEN: (*Hesitatingly.*) He's got big muscles and he's good at fighting. I'm afraid of him. He's the champ boxer in the whole village. Mr. K. never says anything wrong about Tony. He's always saying how he'll make a good boxer out of him.

PSYCHOLOGIST: You're afraid of Tony the way you are of Mr. K. and Mr. A.

STEPHEN: Yes. I'm afraid they'll swing at me.

PSYCHOLOGIST: How long have you been afraid of people this way?

STEPHEN: I wasn't afraid before I came to the Training School. When I first came in the cottage I saw husky people and I never saw a cottage master before. At the orphanage the nuns took care of you but here there is a man and you've got to do as he says or else you get it. (*Reluctantly.*) When the nuns came after me at the orphanage I'd sometimes hit them.

For the next several months the interviews were concerned largely with Stephen's hostility toward Tony and his fear of acting aggressively toward him. Tony, who was known to be the bully type of boy, tyrannized Stephen, took advantage of him, and on several occasions made him take the blame for incidents with which Stephen had nothing to do.

STEPHEN: I don't want to be a sucker or a stooge. Once you're that way you always are. It's like when you're hypnotized and you do what they tell you. Even with little guys I get afraid when they say something nasty to me.

PSYCHOLOGIST: You want to hit back at Tony. You want to fight him and get even. You feel you shouldn't be afraid but you are. You feel that unless you fight back you'll never have a good opinion of yourself.

STEPHEN: That's right. But I think I'll smack them someday. Then they'll be afraid of me. I'll get even sometime.

PSYCHOLOGIST: You feel that once you fight back you won't be afraid any more.

STEPHEN: Yes. I know I should fight.

In all of these discussions the psychologist, by restatement and clarification of Stephen's own statements, attempted to reinforce his belief that he could and should fight back. In view of his position in the institution the psychologist could not tell the boy in a direct manner that he should fight back. Telling him this probably would have increased his feeling of shame without increasing the strength of his determination to fight back. Direct expression of the psychologist's feelings would have posed the problem for this boy before he himself was ready to act.

The strength of Stephen's conflict about the expression of aggression may be seen from the following dreams which he related on request of the psychologist.

Dream 1. Tony and Joe Abbot were fighting. I butted in and Joe and I pounced on Tony and beat him up.

(What comes to your mind when you think of that dream?)

It shows it could be done. It says the same thing we were talking about.

Dream 2. This was about Mr. K. A notice came in that nobody should be hit. Mr. Mc. came in and kicked him out. The boys were very happy because I told in the office about Mr. K. They were told they could smoke in the cottage.

(What comes to mind when you think of that dream?)

Someday it might come true when something will really happen. It shows I don't like Mr. K. I dreamed it because I don't like him.

Dream 3. I got kicked out of the bakery because Tony bossed me around. I walked out. They locked me up. When they needed help the boss baker came with his keys and let me out. He said he was sorry. At first I thought they would send me to the farm as punishment. But they gave me ice cream and pie and I worked with the boss baker. Next day there was ice cream missing. They blamed it on me. But I knew that Tony took it. I told the boss baker that. Tony admitted it. He went to the farm. The bakery was clean. Mr. K. said he would take me to his home.

(What comes to your mind when you think of that dream?)

I felt bad because they sent me to the lock-up. Tony thought he was big but they found out he wasn't. I wished that dream comes true. That's what I always say.

(What do you think these dreams show?)

It shows that I had something in my head that something would be done about Tony. You want to fight back but you're scared and then you have a good dream. But when you wake up it's the same and you wonder what's the use of living.

As time went on there were concrete indications that Stephen was expressing aggression to other boys in a direct manner. He came in one day and proudly reported a fight he had with a boy in his cottage. The boy had tried to interfere with Stephen's playing of horseshoes and tried to take them away from him. Stephen resisted, hit the other boy, and pushed him to the ground.

STEPHEN: I'm glad I stood up for my own rights. I'm not going to be a sucker any more. I was surprised when I got the horseshoe away from him. I thought he was stronger than me. I'm going to be different. You'll be hearing good things about me.

PSYCHOLOGIST: You feel that maybe you've been wrong about how weak you thought you were. You're stronger than you thought and you're not going to let the fellows bulldoze you.

STEPHEN: That's right. The other day some of the boys kidded me. I'm not afraid. I feel it coming. I'm going to swing one of these days.

One month after this discussion (in the fourth month of interviews) Stephen walked into the office with a wide grin on his face and the psychologist knew that "the" fight with Tony had taken place. He was very proud of himself and enjoyed relating how Tony was surprised when Stephen fought back after having been taunted by him.

STEPHEN: I wanted to hit him more. They stopped me. I didn't want to stop.

PSYCHOLOGIST: It didn't turn out the way you were afraid it would.

STEPHEN: No. The strangest thing has happened. Tony has respect for me now. I can see where I've been wrong. When I was a kid I was afraid. When I wanted something I'd steal it quick without thinking. I'd be afraid of hitting somebody. I'd say let him hit me first.

For the next several interviews Stephen relived his triumphant fight. Tony was now playing up to Stephen and the latter now wanted to fight the former in the boxing matches. Stephen kept saying, "I used to be afraid but I've learned not to be. Gee, I've changed."

In the subsequent months Stephen returned again in the interviews to his feelings toward his mother, stepfather, and siblings. The two problems which concerned him most were (1) why he was sent to the orphanage and (2) the conflict between how he felt and how he thought he ought to feel toward his mother. In regard to the first problem, Stephen once said, "I thought my mother put me away because she wanted more children. (*Pause.*) I thought maybe it was because she had no money. (*Pause.*) Then I thought that maybe she took me to a doctor who said there was something wrong with my brain." Stephen's attitude toward his mother was sharpened at this time by her renewed interest in him. She sent him letters and food and would visit him more frequently than before. Stephen's reactions to her visits were similar to those he experienced when she visited him at the orphanage. He felt embarrassed because of her slovenly appearance, could not respond to her attempts to show him how much she cared for him, and felt relieved when she left. Stephen would always relate to the psychologist how his mother would urge him "to get a lot of training here so I can get a good job and help her out." These visits usually served to recall his mother's past behavior. He would relate in great detail how she never kept her promises to him, urged him to steal from the orphanage and the stepfather, and sometimes spent what little money she had on drink. Following the recounting of these stories, Stephen would sometimes say, "I feel bad that I speak about my mother this way. It means I don't like her. But I do like her. Maybe she is different now." Aside from the fact that he wanted to believe that his mother had changed, the possibility that she might take him out of the institution heightened his feelings of ambivalence.

In the sixth month of interviews Stephen's mother requested the institution to release him in her care. This request produced mixed reactions in Stephen. Initially he was overjoyed at the prospect of leaving the institution, but this was followed by the fear that he would be unhappy in his mother's home. It was surprising and gratifying to see how realistically this boy approached the problem. The mother's request for placement was turned down, but a week's vacation at Christmas time was granted. When Stephen was told this by the psychologist, he was disappointed at first but spontaneously said that he understood why the institution might not want to send him to his mother's home permanently. When the psychologist said that a week at home might enable Stephen to resolve one way or the other his conflicting attitudes toward his home, he said, "When I go home I'll write down everything that happens so I won't forget. Then we can talk about it." He also said, "When I go home I'd like to visit the orphanage. I'll be embarrassed because of the things I did there. You understand that, don't you? It wasn't the nuns who was wrong. It was me. But I'm different now. I didn't have anyone like you to talk to at the orphanage."

When Stephen came in for the first interview following his return from the vacation, he was depressed and for the first time had difficulty in talking. He revealed that his mother's home was far more filthy and disorderly than he had imagined. Both his mother and stepfather drank heavily. His mother kept repeating her desire that Stephen get a job and make money for her. The night before Stephen was to return to the school his stepfather became so drunk and abusive that it was necessary to call a policeman to quiet him. Stephen was very firm in his conviction that he did not want to return to his mother.

While he was at home Stephen questioned his mother very carefully about his real father. He insisted that she tell him his name and whatever she knew about him. At first his mother refused to do so, but on the boy's insistence she told him the name of a family in town who had known his father. When

Stephen visited this family and told them who he was, he was surprised at the warmth with which he was received. In answer to his questions they said that they had known his father and, contrary to Stephen's belief, he was not dead. They said, however, that they did not know where he was. The family apparently took a great liking to Stephen and insisted that he come and visit them several times.

The fact that his mother had lied about his father served to increase his disappointment in and hostility toward her. However, the more aware he became of his hostility and the necessity of "forgetting" his mother, the more he feared her retaliation when she found out his feelings.

PSYCHOLOGIST: You say you've decided that you never want to be with your mother. You can't trust her and you know that she's interested in you because maybe you will be able to make money for her some day.

STEPHEN: Yes. How shall I tell her how I feel?

PSYCHOLOGIST: I'm not sure I know what you mean.

STEPHEN: She'll be mad.

PSYCHOLOGIST: You're afraid of her?

STEPHEN: Yes.

PSYCHOLOGIST: What do you think she'll do?

STEPHEN: I don't know. She writes me letters and I don't want to answer. But I'm afraid to stop writing. When she gives me things it makes me feel bad because she doesn't know how I feel. If she did, she might do something.

PSYCHOLOGIST: I sort of have the feeling that your being afraid of your mother is like your being afraid that Tony will hurt you.

STEPHEN: I thought maybe she'll get Freddie [stepfather's son] to do something.

When the psychologist said that there was nothing that his mother or anyone else could do to him now or whenever he was placed in the community, Stephen felt reassured and then revealed that he had also been afraid that because of his mother he would not be put out on placement.

Since his return from vacation Stephen had been in frequent correspondence with the family who had known his father. Much to his amazement they wrote him that they were related to Stephen's father; they knew where he was and enclosed an address to which they suggested he write. Stephen's joy knew no bounds. He kept saying, "Maybe he cares for me." Stephen wrote a letter to his father, who lived in a midwestern state. He received a letter in which his father expressed his delight at having heard from his son and promised that he would come and visit. Shortly after, the father and his wife visited Stephen. Before allowing the father to see his son, the psychologist talked with him. During the interview the father, to whom Stephen bore a remarkable resemblance, expressed his guilt at having neglected his son, cried bitterly, and promised to do whatever he could for the boy. He wanted to take Stephen home with him. In a separate interview, the father's wife revealed how distraught he had been ever since he had received Stephen's letter and said that she knew he would not be happy unless Stephen came to live with them. When Stephen's background and needs were explained to her, she expressed her complete willingness to make his transition from the institution to the community as easy as possible. Since a social service investigation had revealed that the father and his wife could provide a good home for Stephen, it was decided to place the boy with them. This was done and according to the latest available reports the placement is working out very satisfactorily.

At the time that Stephen left the institution he had had interviews with the psychologist for one year. Shortly before he left he was given a psychological examination. It will be remembered that upon admission three years before, in 1943, Stephen, who was then 14 years old, had obtained an M.A. of 8 years 8 months on the Stanford-Binet (L), an M.A. of 11 years on the Kohs Block Designs, and academic achievement scores between the third- and fourth-grade levels. In 1946 Stephen obtained an M.A. of 11 years 4 months on the Stanford-Binet (L) with an I.Q. of 76, an M.A. of 17 years 1 month on the Arthur Point Scale with an I.Q. of 114, and academic achievement between the seventh- and eight-grade levels. In fact Stephen's achievement scores were the highest in the school and it was necessary for his teacher to give him books from her own library in order to satisfy his needs. The strength of Stephen's desire for knowledge, the need to be correct, and the way in which they aroused attitudes which interfered with intellectual efficiency are revealed in his test performance:

"Stephen viewed the tests as an intellectual challenge and, as a result, he was somewhat tense and kept saying that he was afraid that he would not do well. He appeared to be so aware of the need to grasp all that the examiner said that he would sometimes get lost in details and would lose the larger significance of a particular question. If he thought he had failed an item, he would continue to think about it when the next item was given, thus reducing his efficiency. Several times he spontaneously requested if he could go back to a previous question. After an item which he thought he had failed, he once said, 'It makes me feel bad. I'll have to read more.'

"Stephen passed all items on the Binet at the nine-year level and failed all at the fourteen-year level. Of the ten items which he failed (excluding year fourteen) five of them were memory ones, failures which seemed due to the 'fear of forgetting' which the instructions for these items engendered. That memory *per se* was not a factor was suggested by his performance on the Reading and Report item at the ten-year level. He read the passage in 14 seconds without an error. Although he seemed to read the passage for speed rather than comprehension, when he was asked to tell about the passage from memory he was able to do so and get credit for the item. The pattern of successes and failures in this record suggest that the obtained level and quotient are not valid reflectors of the boy's intellectual capacity. It is interesting to note that the day after the examination Stephen came to the psychologist's office with a paper on which he had written down revised answers to some of the items which he failed. Some were right and some were still wrong. He had also used a dictionary to learn some of the vocabulary words which he had been unable to define.

"On the Arthur Point Scale Stephen functioned more efficiently than on the Binet. While on the Binet visual cues for determining procedure are usually not given the subject, this does not hold for this performance type of test. Stephen worked quickly and efficiently with a minimum of trial and error activity. It would seem that in the face-to-face type of test situation, as in the Binet, affective factors are more likely to interfere with his functioning than when the face-to-face aspect of responsiveness is minimized. This examination does not support a diagnosis of mental deficiency."

In evaluating the effect of psychotherapy with Stephen, the most outstanding feature seems to be that this boy was helped to change his pattern of behavior in certain kinds of situations in a way that was satisfying to him. By facing rather than avoiding certain problems, he was able to resolve conflicts which had previously reinforced unhealthy attitudes toward self and others. He was not plagued as much by feelings of guilt and worthlessness, he achieved a more realistic conception of his physical adequacy, and he received the reassurance and support necessary to minimize his long-standing feelings of rejection.

In a preceding paragraph it was stated that Stephen was not a mentally defective boy. This conclusion was based not only on evaluation of his test functioning but also on his unusual academic achievement, his realistic appraisal and handling of his problems, and the behavioral indications that he would be socially and vocationally adequate in the community. There were little, if any, data in this boy's developmental history to indicate that his intellectual retardation was due to constitutional rather than environmental factors. That Stephen was born and reared in an institution, received no consistent display of attention and affection, and experienced rejection from his mother, are grounds for assuming that his capacity for growth was stifled. There is little evidence for assuming that it was limited because of constitutional factors.

In Lottie's case a doubt was also raised about the validity of the diagnosis of mental deficiency. *Questions about validity of diagnoses should not obscure the fact that Lottie and Stephen are by no means rare cases in an institutional population and, perhaps more important, that they are amenable to and benefit from psychotherapy.* Even though one may disagree with the writer's evaluation of the original intellectual capacity of these two children, it should not be overlooked that psychotherapy enabled them to respond more adequately to their environment, a result which institutional routine did not achieve and, in fact, may have made more difficult. How many and what etiological types of an institutional population are amenable to and can benefit from psychotherapy cannot be answered at this time because of the absence of the necessary research. What evidence is available suggests that a fair number of cases diagnosed as mentally defective are in need of and respond favorably to psychotherapeutic procedures.

Earlier in this chapter it was stated that intensive psychotherapy has not been utilized as a test of the assumption of essential incurability. The problem is more complicated than this statement may imply. Present-day psychotherapeutic techniques are not so effective as to allow one to assume that negative results necessarily mean that the diagnosis of mental deficiency has been confirmed. In the case of the garden-variety defective there is another factor which in many cases may be a barrier to psychotherapeutic gain, namely, the fact that an acquired behavioral pattern which has been continuously reinforced throughout an individual's life cannot be unlearned or markedly changed. The problem may be put in the form of a question: If a child has been reared for the first ten years of his life in a Kallikak-like cultural atmosphere, is one justified in assuming that through psychotherapy (or even marked environmental change) he can become "normal"? In other words, it may be that his mode of response makes it difficult or impossible for him to acquire those attitudes and motivations which facilitate learning. It may be instructive at this point to recall Gold-farb's finding (see p. 140) that children who experienced severe and prolonged deprivation during infancy are psychotherapeutically un-reachable. Freeman, Holzinger, and Mitchell's finding (see p. 35) that the intelligence level of children of defective parents was related to the length of time they remained in the family emphasizes the deleterious effect that early deprivation may have on subsequent de-velopment. It may also be recalled that in Skodak's study (p. 31) children of defective parents were placed in foster homes before six months of age. It seems reasonable to assume that their subsequent favorable development was related to their early removal from their families.

The degree to which psychotherapy can effect a change in the be-havior of the defective individual must remain a problem for future research. It may be said that for idiots, imbeciles, and some morons (especially the brain-injured type) psychotherapy is neither feasible nor indicated. With the remaining cases, particularly the garden-variety defective, research in psychotherapy is indicated for both its diagnostic and its therapeutic possibilities.

Before leaving the problem of individual psychotherapy in an insti-tutional setting, some suggestions may be made about situational factors which seem to favor beneficial results.

1. The therapist should not be overburdened with routine institutional work. He should be available most of the time for children who wish to see him.[9] It is also important for the therapist to have time to go around the institution, talk to the employees, engage in some of the children's activities, and give substance to the impression that he is there to help them.

2. The therapist should have administrative authority to recommend and carry out changes in a child's program (change his job, cottage, etc.). Unless the children learn that the therapist can do something for them, they are not likely to want to come to him. It is the writer's experience that once the children learn that the therapist wants to

---

[9] Abel and Humphreys (7) described several cases of unstable institutionalized defec-tives who were in need of psychotherapy but who did not receive it because of lack of facilities and adequate staff. Too often the psychiatrist and psychologist have too many rou-tine or administrative duties to allow them to see children individually, regularly, and over long periods of time.

and can help them, the problem of rapport is minimized to a fair extent.

3. Children should be allowed to see the therapist whenever they wish. The therapist's relation with the employees must be such that they will want to send a child to see him and not be afraid that he will hold against them the information a child may relate. It follows that the "psychological" education of the employees is a function of the therapist, a function that requires a degree of diplomacy which sometimes taxes his patience. Since rapport is facilitated by having the initiative for an interview come from the child, the employee can be of decided help to the therapist.

4. It should be understood by both children and employees that the therapist does not have a punitive function. If the idea of punishment is associated with him, his rapport with the children will probably be on a very superficial level.

Although the need for psychotherapeutic service and research is very great in institutions for defective children, the reluctance of states to expend the money necessary to obtain the trained personnel needed for such work has been a barrier to the development of this area. Perhaps more serious obstacles are the relative lack of attention which the mentally deficient has received from psychology and psychiatry and the absence of attempts to study new procedures. As Humphreys (142) has said, "Too little scientific investigation has been extended into the possibilities of the development of psychiatric techniques both with the individual and the group. In many ways, a new type of psychiatry is needed in approaching institutional and community problems of the mentally deficient."

GROUP PSYCHOTHERAPY

The tendency to build state institutions housing from one thousand to several thousand children has pointed up the necessity of employing group psychotherapeutic procedures. As Humphreys (142) stated:

"How can one or a few men meet the personal needs of these thousands? Obviously, it is impossible. The answer lies in the development of intimate relationships among the psychiatric and other services of the institution, namely in the development of group techniques in psychotherapy. On visiting a group of patients one morning, the writer talked with certain members of a group. In hurrying on, he omitted one young cripple who could barely walk or talk. The cripple hobbled after him, pulled his coat and said, 'Me too.' It is this 'me too' relationship that the psychiatrist must ever be alert not to miss in the world swirling around him. But the psychiatrist is forced to include the total institution group in his system of institutional psychiatry if he is going to care for the 'me too' among the thousands. The sheer mass of patients, therefore, calls for the development of group psychiatric work within the institution."

Despite the need for developing group psychotherapeutic procedures with the mentally deficient, very little work has been done. The consensus among workers seems to be that group psychotherapy with the mentally defective individual is contraindicated (225, 226). In order to test this conclusion Cotzin (57) studied nine mentally defective institutionalized problem boys in a group situation. The average chronological age of the boys was 14 years 5 months, I.Q.'s ranged from 50 to 79 with a mean of 62, length of institutionalization varied from approximately two to six years, and all had been referred to the psychologist repeatedly as classroom problems. Ten therapeutic sessions were held over a three-week period.

In the first session, during which the therapist adopted a neutral role, the boys' behavior was well-nigh unmanageable. "All inhibitions apparently were thrown to the winds. The children kicked one another under the table, challenged and swore at one another, called names as regards race differences and differences of physical condition. They made unreasonable demands of the therapist and ran helter-skelter about the room." In order to channelize their diffuse aggressiveness the therapist suggested boxing, in which "the children were paired off according to mutual hostility and consent." This activity seemed to make for a more cohesive group and reduced the boys' aggressiveness to one another.

"The second and third sessions followed the trend of the first session with the exception that there were longer periods of time in which the group was quiet and in which the children seemed to respect one another and the therapist. Behavior began to become somewhat more purposeful and more disciplined. Progress of the therapy demanded that the therapist take an active role but in an indirect way. Stimulation of continued collective and coöperative behavior required that the therapist initiate programs for the children. Some of the initial programs, henceforth designated as 'warming-up sessions,' were the following: each child in turn was allowed to tell a story; to act something out; to do something of his own personal interest, that is, to write letters, draw pictures, complete his classroom work; to build aeroplanes or work with clay; to do his best on the Goodenough-Draw-a-Man test. Programs were suggested at the beginning of a session but carried out by the children. In turn, each child served as the therapist's assistant. Opportunity for observation by the therapist was prime.

"As each session proceeded, it was noted that the children lost some of their diffuse aggressive behavior, respected each other a little more, made fewer critical remarks about one another, spent more time on a given task without interruptions, came to succeeding clinics with less resentment and initial negativism, and left each session looking forward more pleasantly to the next one."

After these warming-up sessions a "courtroom scene" procedure was used:

"This represents the main part of the therapy and has a two-fold objective: first, it uses the group as an indirect means of giving each individual insight or release, in so far as may be possible, into his own behavior when viewing and assessing the behavior of other individuals in the group; and secondly, it is an indirect method of having the therapist, as a part of the group, gain further knowledge diagnostically about each individual.

"This 'courtroom scene' was set up so that the therapist acted as the judge, each child in turn was the defendant on the stand, and every other child in turn acted as prosecutor, with the remaining children serving as gentlemen of the jury. After a child had been selected to be the defendant, each child in his role of prosecutor stated what he knew about the defendant. No coaching was given as to what the prosecutor was to say about the child. He could make any remarks that he wished about the defendant in his knowledge of him in the cottage, in the classroom, and in recreation. The defendant himself had to wait while the prosecutor was speaking and then had his chance to defend himself on the basis of what the prosecutor had said. The remaining children, as members of the jury, had to listen to the testimony of both the prosecutor and the defendant.

"The group, as a whole, was very much interested in this setup and group participation was at its height. Initially, the procedure did not run off smoothly. The defendant was very quick to interrupt the prosecutor and defend himself against the remarks which the prosecutor made; the members of the jury spoke out of turn either in confirming what the prosecutor said or in defending the defendant. Initially, also, it was noted that the prosecutors started off by making critical remarks about the defendant.

The first session of this courtroom scene covered only one defendant since there was considerable interruption by all members of the group.

"However, as these sessions continued, changes took place so that the proceedings ran along more smoothly. The defendant waited until the prosecutor had finished; the members of the jury did not speak out of turn; the prosecutors changed from initial derogatory remarks about the defendant to more relevant, constructive criticism and praise for the defendant, where indicated, and even criticized previous prosecutors. The last of the 'courtroom scene' sessions had decorum established early. The children seemed to be getting insight about themselves on the basis of the remarks which were made by the members of the court. There was no overt hostility or aggression present. Diagnosis by the therapist was definitely facilitated and the dynamics of each child more clearly understood. Needs for leadership, affection and acceptance, the child's rejection, his aggressive, hostile, and suspicious attitudes, his drive for security, were all made much more apparent, certainly to the therapist and possibly to the child, through the 'courtroom scene.'"

The main purpose of this exploratory study was not to evaluate the therapeutic effects of the sessions, the number of sessions being considered too small to effect any significant behavioral changes. Its main purpose was to determine the diagnostic value of this approach and the problems which it posed with these children. "The greatest value came from the better understanding by the therapist of the inherent bases of the behavioral difficulties that the children showed." As a result of his observations the therapist had the institutional programs of three of the boys changed, and definite improvement in their behavior followed. The concrete way in which the sessions enabled the therapist to obtain a more adequate picture of a boy's behavioral pattern and change his program accordingly can be seen in the following:

"*Johnny.* Johnny, the boy who came from an unstable home atmosphere which was dominated by a dull and excitable father and who had become aggressive, hostile, destructive, and defiant, definitely showed, within the sessions, that he needed an understanding parent-substitute who would take a keen interest in him in his everyday life in residence at the training school. He did not necessarily have to be the leader of any group, but it was noted in the sessions that when he was given the role of the therapist's assistant there was a remarkable change in his attitude and behavior. The therapist at the moment was a parent-surrogate. Johnny was, therefore, given a Big Brother in the person of the institution's electrician. Johnny's program was altered so that he is now in half-day attendance at school and the remainder of the time is the youngest member of the electrician's crew. The electrician has taken a fatherly and sympathetic interest in the boy and is helping him to feel he is achieving something concrete and now has some one whom he can respect and to whom he can come in time of need. It is found at the present time that Johnny is much more docile and respectful in the classroom."

One of Cotzin's conclusions from his exploratory study is that group psychotherapy with mental defectives seems feasible, diagnostically and therapeutically, and is in need of systematic study by psychologists and psychiatrists.

Schaefer-Simmern (262) has demonstrated the therapeutic value of artistic activity with mentally deficient children in individual and group situations. The primary purpose of his studies was to observe the nature and development of the artistic form in the efforts of defective individuals.[10] Although a child was allowed to draw what he wanted, it was not the aim of the procedure to give him an opportunity for "free expression." The child was requested to look over his drawing, to express how he liked it, to ask him what he would like to change, and to encourage him to try it again embodying whatever new he wanted to include. The case history of Selma (262, 263) may be used to illustrate Schaefer-Simmern's approach.

"At the time of admission in 1927 [the study was begun in 1944 when Selma was 30] to an institution for mentally defective children, Selma was living with her aunt. The father had died when she was ten, and the mother when she was twelve. At the age of three Selma had been burned over a large part of her body, and extensive scars have remained. According to informants, the aunt frequently and severely maltreated the girl. She would

[10] By the artistic form Schaefer-Simmern refers to the *pictorial data only*, independent of the likes or dislikes of the particular observer. The artistic form refers to a pictorial production in which all parts are functionally and indissolubly related, one part depending on another so that the removal of one destroys the unity of form. "Artistic form is usually recognized only where it appears in highly evolved works of art. However, it can also be found in simple beginnings, such as the pictorial achievements of prehistoric man and of primitive tribes, in folk art, and in the spontaneous drawings and sculptures made by children. Recent studies . . . have revealed that children's drawings not yet distorted by external methods of teaching or by imitation of nature possess a definite structural order which in essence is similar to that of more developed works of art. This configuration not only expresses general human attributes but also embodies them in an indissoluble relationship of form. . . . This unified structure, simple though it is, may be recognized as the 'seed' of the artistic form" (262, p. 9).

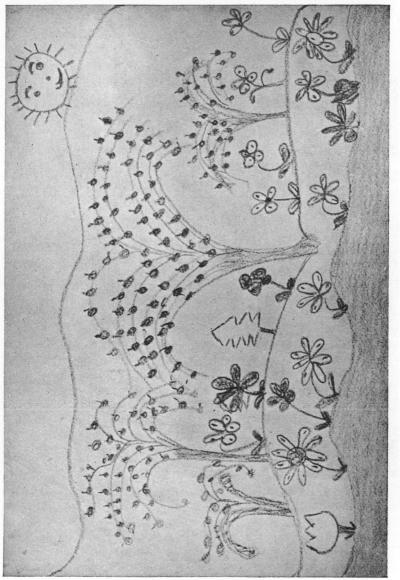

Fig. 6. Selma's First Drawing, Done with Colored Crayon. (From H. Schaefer-Simmern. *The unfolding of artistic activity*. University of California Press, 1948.)

Fig. 7.   Selma's Second Drawing. (From H. Schaefer-Simmern. *The unfolding of artistic activity*. University of California Press, 1948.)

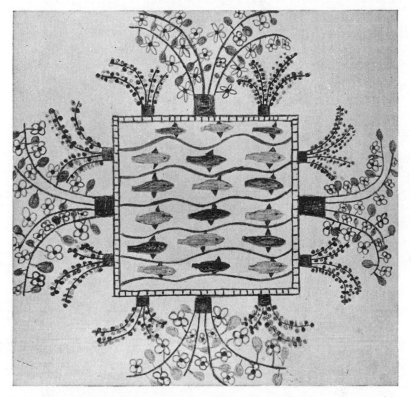

FIG. 8.   Pond with Fish, Bordered by Trees. Selma's first large drawing (22 by 21 inches) done with colored crayons. (From H. Schaefer-Simmern. *The unfolding of artistic activity*. University of California Press, 1948.)

Fig. 9. Selma's Tablecloth. Selma concentrated all her efforts for weeks on this tablecloth (20 by 30 inches). She designed and embroidered it herself. (From H. Schaefer-Simmern. *The unfolding of artistic activity.* University of California Press, 1948.)

hit her on the head, whip her unmercifully, and call her all kinds of names. The aunt frequently drank. At one time she dragged Selma by the hair and beat her. There is little known about Selma's parents except that both drank a good deal, also. The aunt wanted to get rid of Selma and was responsible for her institutionalization. After admission, Selma received only one visitor during the first five years and in 1943 there is record of another. Her institutional behavior was poor and she was considered quiet, deceitful, peculiar, and possibly hallucinated because she talked to herself and grimaced and smiled in a strange fashion. She was always assigned the most routine and simple tasks, which she would complete only under close supervision. In 1942 she was transferred to the Southbury Training School (p. 56).[11]

". . . She had an I.Q. of 49 . . . [and] at the time of her admission to an institution for mental defectives she had only attended special classes. She showed little inclination to learn and was reported by her teachers to be 'lazy and indifferent.' At the time of her entrance into the Southbury Training School she was 'unresponsive, inarticulate and phlegmatic.' She was sloppy, fat, unattractive in appearance, and had a vague empty stare. Her response to all questions consisted of a shake of her head or a groan. She would obey a direct command, she never caused any trouble or disturbance but she showed absolutely no initiative in making friends or social contacts. She would prefer to withdraw to the fringe of a crowd and be a spectator and never a participant in cottage activities" (p. 33).

Selma came to the workshop one day a week for 15 months. When she was requested to show her first drawing

"her feelings of inferiority, her shyness, and even a certain anxiety gripped her. Turning her face away, she submitted her drawing with trembling hands. She obviously feared attention and criticism. Selma's first picture (Fig. 6)—according to her own statement, the only one she had ever done— indicates that even a mentally deficient person can create in a modest degree an ordered pictorial whole. It was astonishing that she was able to accomplish even so simple a pictorial result, and the writer praised her for her work. Her reserved attitude disappeared at once and a big smile spread over her face; apparently a word of encouragement was what she needed. Another fact was still more astonishing. While the writer was engaged in supervising the work of the other girls belonging to the same group, Selma took some drawing paper from the desk and started a new picture (Fig. 7). She repeated almost the same subject. . . . Except for a little more careful execution of her drawing, there is no further development in the organiza-

[11] H. Schaefer-Simmern. *The unfolding of artistic activity.* University of California Press, 1948. All quotations from this book are reprinted by permission of the publishers.

tion of form. But two essential facts must be noted: the smaller trees show a different application of the stage of variability of direction of lines, a variation of form invented by herself; and furthermore, the fact that she drew this picture spontaneously indicated the possibility of an unfolding of energies that no one expected" (p. 35).

Although throughout the period of the study the content of Selma's artistic efforts was limited and repetitive, there was a marked tendency for her configurations to become more varied and complicated.

". . . As she little by little modified and even enriched the structural organization of her pictures by new differentiations of form, her repetitions showed some signs of an increase in the acquisition of visual cognition. Repetition which contains within itself elements of change and development, irrespective of their minuteness, is formative activity. It was only through this step-by-step enrichment within the pictorial processes that Selma acquired the capacity of mastering a more complex creative configuration."

Selma's work, shown in Figs. 8–11, is concrete evidence that, although there is a narrow content, the complexity of her configurations increases in an orderly, highly unified manner.

Concomitant with her artistic growth was a change in behavior.

". . . Prior to her participation in the course, it would have been impossible for her to carry out a commission outside the workshop, especially since she had a poor spatial orientation of the layout of the institution. She was obviously confused by the many different buildings and the many paths leading to them. It was difficult to persuade her to do errands which would require her going to other parts of the institution. Little by little, organized work that was in full conformity with her mental capacities, the exercise of a constant visual control, developed in her a visual orientation combined with clearness of thought. After nine months of her art activity, she was asked one day to go to the office of the psychologist in the administration building to call for a hooked rug which she herself had made. At first she hesitated and became embarrassed, but after repeated requests she reluctantly made up her mind, and when another girl offered to accompany her she rejected any help. This was the first time since her admission to the institution that Selma revealed such courage and determination in accomplishing an assignment outside of the workshop and her daily routine. Obviously encouraged by this experience, she two weeks later took over the responsibility of guiding another girl, who was unable to orient herself on the institution grounds, to the same office.

"Before participating in the experimental group, Selma lived a barren existence filled only with daily routine work. The simple tasks she performed were the result of manipulations that had been drilled into her. They brought her neither interest nor stimulation. There seemed to be no place where she could fit into the life of the institution. Constantly indifferent, unable to establish any contact between her occupation and her needs, she developed a chronic apprehension and shyness that made her so restless and insecure that she avoided the smallest difficulties. After sixteen years of institutional life, this was her state. Through the opportunity of participating in the experimental group, a basic function of her mental existence to conceive and to grasp her own world by images, and even to realize them in a well-organized fashion, had been awakened and developed within her in conformity with her natural capacity. Through these processes, her entire interest, her feeling and thinking, her physical behavior, her personality as a whole, had been affected. At the beginning of her activity in the experimental group, Selma was indecisive and insecure about what to do with herself. She wandered helplessly through the studio. Seven months later, she started her work spontaneously; she had definite ideas about her pictorial themes; she was determined in the execution of her pictures as well as in the manipulation of her material. Little by little her former nervous impulsiveness was replaced by a controlled and quiet determination. If she made mistakes, such as spoiling the order of form, she changed her color drawing independently until she reëstablished the pictorial organization. All these spontaneous actions indicated an increased self-assurance and a gain in her inner security, through which she reached a greater amount of freedom. In the first few months of her activity in the course she was reserved, silent, and shy; she even avoided any kind of conversation. After nine months she frequently initiated conversations with her co-workers. She always looked forward impatiently to making new designs" (p. 54).

Selma's artistic and behavioral growth brought her many rewarding comments from other children and employees. As a result, it was decided to have an "exhibition" of her work in her own cottage. This had a profound effect on Selma. Her happiness at having people come to see *her* work and the way in which she reacted to them were in striking contrast to her behavior at the beginning of the study.

"It might be said that the change in Selma's behavior could be attributed to the fact that she was receiving praise and attention to an extent which never before had been given her. That praise and attention played a role cannot be denied. Such an interpretation, however, disregards the fact that there is in her work an observable orderly development of gestalt formation. What seems to be basic in this case is that this girl was given an opportunity to merge in one activity emotional satisfaction, full utilization of energies, planning and foresight, and well-configurated visual expression. It is the educational and therapeutic significance of the genuine artistic process that it embodies in an indivisible manner so many different aspects of human functioning.

"The significance of Selma's case is that it demonstrates the importance of basic educational and therapeutical procedures on the individual's natural potentialities for organized development. To ask a person to reproduce, either from model or memory, a particular scene or object neglects the fact that such a task may well be foreign to the individual's interest and needs as well as beyond his particular level of visual conceiving. In such a case the discrepancy between task and result does not allow the individual to identify himself with what he has done; no opportunity has been given to 'grow into his work.' One might generalize and say that unless work stems from the natural growth of abilities it will have little effect on the personality" (p. 55).

Schaefer-Simmern also studied the artistic activity (Figs. 12, 13) of mentally deficient children in a group situation. "At the beginning of the experiment each child worked alone, and it was only after several months that the children worked together on a theme of their own choosing. When working in a group, each member carefully watched the others so that nothing would be done to spoil the coöperative work. They would caution each other, admonish each other when laxity was evident, and in general displayed a high level of group responsibility. When one keeps in mind the fact that these children were in similar stages of development of visual conception and so 'understood more easily the work of others,' and that all derived a sense of pride from their work, it becomes clear how each member of the group was able to identify with the others. This level of social interaction is, to say the least, unusual among feebleminded children" (p. 59).

Schaefer-Simmern's studies seem to have implications beyond the field of artistic activity. They corroborate a principle often neglected in practice, namely, that the work an individual does must be of such a nature and at such a level as to engender a feeling of adequacy in relation to it and to allow him to observe his own growth process in it Reward in the form of praise from others is important, but unless the individual receives satisfaction from his own realization of change the

Fig. 10. One of Selma's Hooked Rugs. This rug (25 by 32 inches) was designed and made by Selma.

Fig. 11.   Another Hooked Rug (25 by 32 inches) Designed and Executed by Selma.

therapeutic effects will be temporary. Praise from others, like reassurance, is usually of small value when unaccompanied by insight. When Schaefer-Simmern's procedures are contrasted with those ordinarily employed in occupational therapy units in institutions for defectives, one wonders whether a reorientation in thinking is not indicated. In these occupational units

"the patient may attain control over his hands, he may even learn perfect manipulation of a tool, he may become so used to this occupation that he is able to execute it without personality participation in it, he may even feel at ease in doing it, but the compulsory attention and concentration repeated over and over will throw him into a mental and emotional rigidity worse than before. He may become more or less adept at making things, but his personal relationship to them remains external because the work does not have its origin within him; it does not reflect himself. The performance is not related to the nature of his organism as a whole, as a psychobiological unity. Merely manual execution employs only a very small fraction of the total organism, and the attention and concentration it demands are not a result of the patient's inner decision. Only when the innermost core of interest voluntarily determines the applying of one's energies, when one feels that the work being done is an indivisible part of oneself (a condition which requires, of course, that it be in full conformity with one's own stage of visual conception), and when one is aware that attention and concentration are indispensable in order to realize oneself—only then does work become constructive" (*262*, p. 47).

ITARD'S WILD BOY OF AVEYRON

Before concluding this chapter mention should be made of one of the most detailed and illuminating reports dealing with an attempt to rehabilitate a defective child—Itard's study, *The Wild Boy of Aveyron* (*147*), published in 1801. The subject of this study was a boy, eleven or twelve years of age, who for a period of years had been living in the woods without contact with other people. On one occasion he had been seen completely naked seeking acorns and roots to eat. In 1799 he was seized by three sportsmen "as he was climbing into a tree to escape from their pursuit. Conducted to a neighboring hamlet and confined to the care of a widow, he broke loose at the end of a week and gained the mountains, where he wandered during the most rigorous winter weather, draped rather than covered with a tattered shirt. At night he retired to solitary places but during the day he approached the neighboring villages, where of his own accord he entered an inhabited house situated in the Canton of St. Sernin" (p. 3).[12] When he was seen in Paris by the famous authorities of the day, he was pronounced an incurable idiot. Some even stated that his "wildness" was a fake and that it was inconceivable that such an idiot had fended for himself for years in the forests. Itard, however, believed that the boy's condition was curable and that his condition was due to the lack of intercourse with people. The boy was placed under Itard's care. His description of the boy follows:

"Proceeding first with an account of the sensory functions of the young savage, citizen Pinel showed that his senses were reduced to such a state of inertia that the unfortunate creature was, according to his report, quite inferior to some of our domestic animals. His eyes were unsteady, expressionless, wandering vaguely from one object to another without resting on anybody; they were so little experienced in other ways and so little trained by the sense of touch, that they never distinguished an object in relief from one in a picture. His organ of hearing was equally insensible to the loudest noises and to the most touching music. His voice was reduced to a state of complete muteness and only a uniform guttural sound escaped him. His sense of smell was so uncultivated that he was equally indifferent to the odor of perfumes and to the fetid exhalation of the dirt with which his bed was filled. Finally, the organ of touch was restricted to the mechanical function of the grasping of objects. Proceeding then to the state of the intellectual functions of this child, the author of the report presented him to us as being quite incapable of attention (except for the objects of his needs) and consequently of all those operations of the mind which attention involves. He was destitute of memory, of judgment, of aptitude for imitation, and was so limited in his ideas, even those relative to his immediate needs, that he had never yet succeeded in opening a door or climbing upon a chair to get the food that had been raised out of reach of his hand. In short, he was destitute of all means of communication and attached neither expression nor intention to his gestures or to the movements of his body. He passed rapidly and without any apparent motive from apathetic melancholy to the most immoderate peals of laughter. He was insensible to every kind of moral influence. His perception was nothing but a computation prompted by gluttony, his pleasure an agreeable sensation of the organ of taste and his

[12] J. M. G. Itard. *The wild boy of Aveyron* (trans. by G. and M. Humphrey). Appleton-Century, Inc., 1932. All quotations from this book are used by permission of the publishers.

intelligence the ability to produce a few incoherent ideas relative to his wants. In a word, his whole life was a completely animal existence" (p. 5).

In working with the young savage Itard was aided by a woman who handled the boy "with all the patience of a mother and the intelligence of an enlightened teacher." The detail with which Itard describes the handling of the boy, the innumerable experiments he conducted with him, and the various ingenious pedagogical procedures employed make condensation difficult. The following excerpts may give the reader some idea of Itard's attitude toward and handling of the boy as well as changes in the latter's behavior in light of the preceding description of him:

"It is admitted by physiologists and political theorists that the inhabitants of the South owe their exquisite sensibility, so superior to that of the northerners, entirely to the action of heat upon the skin. I employed this stimulus in all possible ways. Not only was he clothed, put to bed, and housed warmly, but every day I gave him, and at a very high temperature, a bath lasting two or three hours during which frequent douches with the same water were administered to him on the head. I did not observe that the warmth and the frequency of the baths were followed by the debilitating effect attributed to them.

"I should even have been glad if such had happened, convinced that in such a case the nervous sensibility would gain by the loss of muscular strength. But if the one effect did not follow, at least the other did not disappoint my expectations. After some time our young savage showed himself sensitive to the action of cold, made use of his hand to find out the temperature of the bath, and refused to enter when it was only lukewarm. For the same reason he soon began to appreciate the utility of clothes which until then he had only endured with much impatience. This utility once recognized, it was only a step to make him dress himself. This end was attained after some days by leaving him each morning exposed to the cold within reach of his clothes until he himself knew how to make use of them. A very similar expedient sufficed to give him at the same time habits of cleanliness and the certainty of passing the night in a cold wet bed accustomed him to get up in order to satisfy his needs. To the administration of the baths I added the use of dry frictions along the spine and even ticklings of the lumbar region. This last means was more exciting than most. I even found myself obliged to reject it, when its effects were no longer limited to producing movements of pleasure but appeared to extend further to the generative organs and to add the threat of perversion to the first stirrings of an already precocious puberty.

"To these various stimulants I had to add emotional stimulants which were no less exciting. Those to which he was susceptible at this time were confined to two, joy and anger. The latter I only provoked at long intervals, for its attack was most violent and always apparently justified. I remarked sometimes that in the force of his passion his intelligence seemed to acquire a sort of extension which furnished him with some ingenious expedient in order to get himself out of trouble. Once when we wanted to make him take a bath which was as yet only lukewarm and our reiterated entreaties had made him violently angry, seeing that his governess was not convinced of the coolness of the water by the frequent tests that he made with the tips of his own fingers, he turned towards her quickly, seized her hand and plunged it into the bath.

"Let me relate another act of the same nature. One day when he was in my study sitting upon a sofa I came to sit at his side and placed between us a Leyden jar lightly charged. A slight shock which he had received from it the day before had made him familiar with its effect. Seeing the uneasiness which the approach of the instrument caused him I thought he would move it further away by taking hold of the handle. He took a more prudent course which was to put his hands in the opening of his waistcoat, and to draw back some inches so that his leg would no longer touch the covering of the bottle. I drew near him a second time and again replaced it between us. Another movement on his part, another adjustment on mine. This little maneuvre continued until, driven into a corner at the end of the sofa, he found himself bounded by the wall behind, by a table in front, and at my side by the troublesome machine. It was no longer possible for him to make any movement. It was then that, seizing the moment when I advanced my arm in order to guide his, he very adroitly lowered my wrist upon the knob of the bottle. I received the discharge.

"But if sometimes in spite of the intense interest this young orphan inspired in me I took upon myself to excite his anger, I let no occasion pass of procuring happiness for him: and certainly this was neither difficult nor costly. A ray of sun reflected upon a mirror in his room and turning about on the ceiling, a glass of water let fall drop by drop from a certain height upon his finger tips while he was in the bath, and a wooden porringer containing a little milk placed at the end of his bath, which the oscillations of the water drifted, little by little, amid cries of delight, into his grasp, such simple means were nearly all that was necessary to divert and delight this child of nature almost to the point of ecstasy" (p. 16).

". . . I took him not long ago to the country house of citizen Lachabeaussière in the valley of Montmorency. It was a most curious sight, and

Fig. 12. Four Streams, Bordered by Different Trees, Meeting at a Central Island. This is a coöperative work (30 by 40 inches) done in colored crayons by five mentally defective women, aged 20, 24, 29, 30, and 34. (From H. Schaefer-Simmern. *The unfolding of artistic activity.* University of California Press, 1948.)

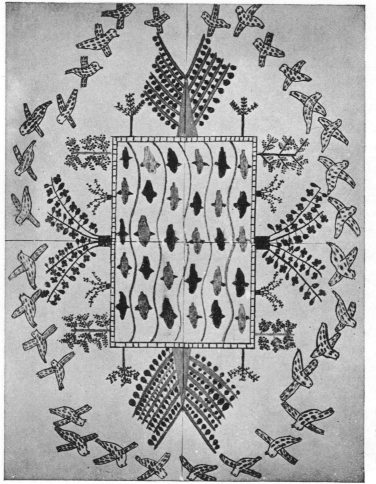

Fig. 13. Pond with Fish, Bordered by Different Trees and with Birds Flying About. This is a coöperative work (30 by 40 inches) done in colored crayons by four mentally defective women, aged 20, 29, 30, and 34. (From H. Schaefer-Simmern. *The unfolding of artistic activity.* University of California Press, 1948.)

I venture to say one of the most touching, to see the joy that was pictured in his eyes at the sight of the little hills and woods of that laughing valley. It seemed as if the eagerness of his gaze could not be satisfied through the windows of the carriage. He leaned now towards the one, now towards the other, and showed the liveliest anxiety when the horses went more slowly or were about to stop. He spent two days in this country house and such was the effect of these outside influences, of these woods, these hills, with which he could never satisfy his eyes, that he appeared more impatient and wild than ever, and, in the midst of the most assiduous and kind attention and most affectionate care, seemed to be occupied only with the desire to take flight. Entirely captivated by this dominant idea which absorbed all his faculties and even the consciousness of his needs, he scarcely found time to eat. He would get up from the table every minute and run to the window in order to escape into the park if it was open; or if it was shut, to contemplate, at least through the panes, all those objects towards which he was irresistibly attracted by still recent habits and perhaps even by the memory of an independent life, happy and regretted. I therefore resolved never again to submit him to similar tests. But in order not to sever him entirely from his country tastes, he was taken continually to walk in some neighboring gardens, of which the straight and regular arrangement had nothing in common with the great landscapes of which wild nature is composed, and which so strongly attach primitive man to the place of his childhood. Thus Madame Guérin took him sometimes to the Luxembourg and almost daily to the Observatory gardens where the kindness of citizen Lemeri has accustomed him to go every day for a lunch of milk. By means of these new habits, of certain recreations of his own choosing and finally, of all the kind treatment with which his new existence was surrounded, he finished by liking it all. This was the beginning of the intense affection which he has acquired for his governess and which he sometimes expresses in a most touching manner. He never leaves her without reluctance nor does he rejoin her without signs of satisfaction.

"Once when he had escaped from her in the streets, he shed many tears on seeing her again. Some hours after, he still had a high and broken respiration and a kind of feverish pulse. When Madame Guérin reproached him, he interpreted her tone so well that he began to weep. The friendship which he had for me was much less strong, and justifiably so. The care which Madame Guérin takes of him is of a kind which is immediately appreciated, and what I give him is of no obvious use to him. That this difference is unquestionably due to the cause indicated is shown by the fact that there are times when he welcomes me and they are the times which I have never used for his instruction. For example, when I go to the house in the evening just after he has gone to bed, his first movement is to sit up for me to embrace him, then to draw me to him by seizing my arm and making me sit upon his bed, after which he usually takes my hand, carries it to his eyes, his forehead, the back of his head, and holds it with his upon these parts for a very long time. At other times he gets up with bursts of laughter and comes beside me to caress my knees in his own way which consists of feeling them, rubbing them firmly in all directions for some minutes, and then sometimes in laying his lips to them two or three times. People may say what they like, but I will confess that I lend myself without ceremony to all this childish play.

"I shall perhaps be understood if my readers will remember the paramount influence exerted upon a child's mind by the inexhaustible delights and the maternal triflings that nature has put into the heart of a mother and which make the first smiles flower and bring to birth life's earliest joys" (p. 23).

"I ordered to be printed as a big character upon a piece of cardboard two inches square each of the twenty-four letters of the alphabet. I had an equal number of spaces cut in a plank a foot and a half square. Into these the pieces of cardboard could be inserted, without the use of paste, so that their places could be changed as required. I had an equal number of characters of the same dimensions made in metal. These were meant to be compared by the pupil with the printed letters, and were to be arranged in their corresponding places.

"The first trial of this method was made, in my absence, by Madame Guérin. I was very much surprised on my return to learn from her that Victor distinguished all the characters and arranged them properly. He was immediately put to the test and performed his task without any mistake. Though delighted with such an immediate success I was still far from able to explain its cause, and it was only some days after that I discovered this by noting the way in which our pupil proceeded to make this arrangement. In order to make the work easier he devised of his own accord a little expedient which in this task allowed him to dispense with memory, comparison and judgment. As soon as the board was put between his hands, he did not wait until the metal letters were taken out of their places but he himself took them and piled them upon his hand, following the order of their arrangement so that the last letter, after all were taken from the board, was the first on the pile. He began with this and finished with the last of the pile, thus beginning the board at the end and proceeding always from right to left. Moreover, he was able to improve upon this procedure; for very often the pile collapsed, the characters fell out and he had to straighten everything up and put it in order by the unaided efforts of attention. So the twenty-four letters were arranged in four rows of six each, making it easier to lift them up by rows only, and even to replace them in the same way by taking letters from the second row only when the first was replaced.

"I do not know whether he reasoned as I suppose, but at least it is certain that he executed the performance in the manner described. It was then a true routine, but a routine of his own invention, and one which was perhaps as much to the credit of his intelligence as was a method of arrangement hit upon shortly afterwards to the credit of his discernment. It was not difficult to set him off by giving him the characters pellmell whenever he was given the board. At last, in spite of the frequent transpositions to which I submitted the printed characters by changing their places, in spite of insidious arrangements, such as the O beside the C, the E beside the F, etc., his discrimination became infallible. In exercising it upon all these letters, the end I had in view was to prepare Victor for a primitive but correct use of the letters, namely the expression of needs which can only be made known by means of speech. Far from believing that I was already so near this great step in his education, I was led by the spirit of curiosity rather than the hope of success to try the experiment which follows:

"One morning when he was waiting impatiently for the milk which he always had for breakfast, I carried to him his board which I had specially arranged the evening before with the four letters L.A.I.T. Madame Guérin, whom I had warned, approached, looked at the letters and immediately gave me a cup of milk which I pretended to drink myself. A moment after I approached Victor, gave him the four letters that I had lifted from the board, and pointed to it with one hand while in the other I held the jug full of milk. The letters were immediately replaced but in inverted order, so that they showed T.I.A.L. instead of L.A.I.T. I indicated the corrections to be made by designating with my finger the letters to transpose and the proper place of each. When these changes had reproduced the sign, he was allowed to have his milk.

"It is difficult to believe that five or six similar attempts were sufficient, not only to make him arrange methodically the four letters of the word *Lait* but to give him the idea of the connection between the word and the thing. At least this is the justifiable inference from what happened a week later. One evening when he was ready to set out for the Observatory, he was seen to provide himself on his own initiative with the four letters in question, and to put them in his pocket; he had scarcely arrived at citizen Lemeri's house, where as I previously said he goes every day for some milk, when he produced them and placed them on a table in such a way as to form the word LAIT" (p. 45).

Itard's expectation that the wild boy could be trained into a normal civilized being was by no means confirmed. During the five-year period during which the boy was studied he never learned to utter more than a few words, his comprehension of abstract symbols was meager, his emotional expression was crude and diffuse, and his responsiveness to his environment was determined largely by biological needs. In light of Itard's original ambitious hopes it is understandable why he was disappointed with the results of his efforts. Itard's summary of his experiment, contained in his report to the French Minister of Interior, is distinguished by his attempt to evaluate his failures as scrupulously as his successes.

". . . I have made it my duty to present [the facts] without distinction, and to relate my reverses as scrupulously as my successes. Such an astonishing variety of results adds an element of uncertainty to any opinion which can be formed of this young man, while the conclusions that can be drawn from the facts related in this memoir consequently present a certain lack of harmony.

"Thus, bringing together those facts which are scattered through [the report], one cannot help concluding: first, that by reason of the almost complete apathy of the organs of hearing and speech, the education of this young man is still incomplete and must always remain so; secondly, that by reason of their long inaction the intellectual faculties are developing slowly and painfully, and that this development, which in children growing up in civilized surroundings is the natural fruit of time and circumstances, is here the slow and laborious result of a very active education in which the most powerful methods are used to obtain most insignificant results; thirdly, that the emotional faculties, equally slow in emerging from their long torpor, are subordinated to an utter selfishness and that his puberty, which was very strongly marked and which usually sets up a great emotional expansion, seems only to prove that if there exists in human beings a relation between the needs of the senses and the affections of the heart, this sympathetic agreement is, like the majority of great and generous emotions, the happy fruit of education.

"But if the happy changes occurring in the state of this young man are recapitulated . . . , one cannot fail to consider his education in a more favorable light. The following conclusions are then perfectly justifiable. First, that the improvement of his sight and touch and the new gratification of his sense of taste have, by multiplying the sensations and ideas of our savage, contributed powerfully to the development of his intellectual faculties; secondly, when one considers the full extent of this development, among other real improvements he will be found to have both a knowledge of the conventional value of the symbols of thought and the power of applying it by naming objects, their qualities, and their actions. This has led to an extension of the pupil's relations with the people around him, to the faculty of expressing his wants to them, of receiving orders from them, and of effecting a free and continual exchange of thoughts; thirdly, that in spite of his immoderate taste for the freedom of open country and his indifference to most of the pleasures of social life, Victor shows himself sensible to the care taken of him, susceptible to fondling and affection, alive to the pleasure of well-doing, ashamed of his mistakes, and repentant of his outbursts; fourthly and finally, my Lord, looking at this long experiment from any point of view, whether it be considered as the methodical education of a savage or as no more than the physical and moral treatment of one of those creatures ill-favored of nature, rejected by society and abandoned by medicine, the care that has been taken and ought still to be taken of him, the changes that have taken place and those which can be hoped for, the voice of humanity, the interest inspired by such a complete desertion and a destiny so strange—all these things recommend this extraordinary young man to the attention of scientists, to the solicitude of our administrators, and to the protection of the Government."

Despite his disillusionment with the final results, Itard made the significant observation, "To be judged fairly, this young man must only be compared with himself. Put beside another adolescent of the same age he is only an ill-favored creature, an outcast of nature as he was of society. But if one limits oneself to the two terms of comparison offered by the past and present states of young Victor, one is astonished at the immense space which separates them; and one can question whether Victor is not more unlike the *Wild Boy of Aveyron* arriving at Paris, than he is unlike other individuals of his same age and species" (p. 53).

Itard's study has been included in the present chapter because it illustrates the degree of behavioral change which can be effected by efforts which are planned, intensive, personalized, and therapeutically oriented. The words personalized and therapeutically oriented refer to Itard's efforts to give the wild boy the kind of environment which would make changing his behavior to the requirements of others rewarding and pleasurable. Had the boy been treated in accord with the diagnosis made by the authorities of the day there probably would have been no change in his behavior, a finding which then would have been utilized as proof of the validity of the diagnosis of incurable idiocy. The hopeless attitude which is expressed today regarding the defective individual's amenability to psychotherapy seems also to be a result of diagnostic labels. Once an individual is diagnosed as mentally deficient it is generally assumed that the psychotherapeutic procedures applicable to the normal person are not feasible with him. Consequently, those procedures most effective in producing behavorial changes have never become part of the "training" programs set up for the deficient person in institutions and special classes. When one considers that the relatively few published studies in this area indicate that the mentally deficient respond to psychotherapy (individual and group) and benefit much from it, he is surprised that more systematic research has not been carried out and that the results of available studies have not influenced current practices to any noticeable degree.

Chapter 11

INTERPRETATION OF MENTAL DEFICIENCY TO PARENTS

THE failure adequately to communicate to parents the nature and implications of a diagnosis of mental deficiency probably causes more unnecessary problems and suffering than any other factor, with the obvious exception of those factors which originally produced the mental deficiency.[1] By the word "communicate" is meant not only the imparting of facts but, in addition, the attempt on the part of a qualified person to help parents recognize and adjust to the realities of their child's condition. The imparting of facts does not insure that parents either will recognize or adjust to the child's condition. Resistance, anxiety, despair, hostility, and frustration—these experiences and reactions are not quieted or eliminated by a recital of facts. One might even say that when the nature of the child's condition is explained to the parents, their tendencies to resist the explanation and to react in an emotional way are strengthened rather than decreased.

Before becoming specific about the handling of the interpretation of mental defect to parents, the following statements about the goals of such a situation should be made explicit:

1. The parents should be completely informed about the probable causes of the child's condition, the severity of the mental defect,

---

[1] The writer cannot point to a study to support this statement. It is based on the writer's experience as well as on the fact that he has never heard any other worker deny that inadequate communication with parents is much more often than not the rule rather than the exception. That such a situation exists and should not be viewed with surprise may become more apparent to the reader in Chapter 13 when the inadequacies of professional training for handling the problem are discussed. It is only recently that workers in the field have become aware of the "parent problem" and one can only hope that in the future systematic studies of the efficacy of various approaches to the problem will be available. At the present time we are operating in the realm of opinion—a realm which includes the next three chapters. It is because the handling of parents of defective children is fraught with so much danger that it is so important that our assumptions, practices, and alleged results be subjected to scientific study.

and the probable course (educationally, vocationally, socially) of the child's development.

2. A specific program geared to the needs and capabilities of the child should be explained, discussed, and planned with the parents.
3. The personal problems of the parents, caused or exacerbated by the child's condition, should be dealt with in a manner so as to maximize the probability that parents and child will be able to function in a socially constructive and self-satisfying manner.
4. Provision should be made for periodic discussion with the parents and observation of the child in order to check on the nature of the child's and parents' adjustment and to re-evaluate the correctness of the initial program.

With these goals in mind, what follows is an attempt to describe in some detail the problems one frequently encounters and the ways in which one might handle them.

THE SETTING

In discussing here the interpretation of mental defect with parents it is impossible to take into account all the different settings in which such a problem is encountered. The physician in his office, the teacher in the school, the psychologist or social worker in the clinic—these and other professional specialists are called upon to handle the parents of the defective child. In each case the setting is different in terms of various diagnostic services, availability of case-history material, previous experience with the problem, knowledge of community resources, and time available for any one case. For the purposes of the present discussion we shall assume that the parents have brought their child to a clinic where psychological, medical, and social work facilities are available. We shall further assume that the child has been comprehensively examined, background data secured, and a diagnosis of mental defect made. The problem now is to communicate the findings to the parents.

SOME PRELIMINARY CONSIDERATIONS

In arranging for the interview it is extremely important to have *both* parents present. One must never assume that both parents have the same conception of the problem, the same attitudes toward the child, experienced a similar degree of frustration, or possess a similar degree of stability and maturity. By working only with the mother, as is most frequent, one may never find out, for example, either that the parents quarrel violently about the handling of their child, or that the father rejects the child, or that he now rejects the mother. One simply cannot assume that the mother's report is a necessarily valid or complete one, *even though she may be motivated to give what she thinks is an objective presentation of the facts.* Since carrying out a recommended program successfully depends in large part on a harmonious relationship between the parents, it is imperative that at the outset one be in a position to evaluate the nature of that relationship. In more than a few cases the primary problem is not the defective child but unhappy, mutually aggressive parents who have become emotionally distant from each other. To focus on the defective child not only overlooks important influences on his behavior but increases the likelihood that a recommended program will fail completely or fall short of its mark.

Another difficulty in working with one parent, say the mother, is that she may not communicate to her husband the contents of the interview in an undistorted fashion. She may forget to relate certain aspects of the discussion, distort others, and attempt to answer questions posed by the husband which had not been discussed at all with the counselor. *The tendency to perceive and report in a selective manner is a human characteristic which appears to become increasingly operative when strongly felt, personal problems are aroused.* It is for this reason that so much emphasis has been and will be given here to the recognition and prevention (as far as possible) of selective perception and reporting by parents of mentally defective children.

Another advantage in having the father at the interview is that he is then more likely to share the responsibilities of caring for the child. In our culture the primary responsibility in child rearing falls upon the mother. One can say with no hesitation that rearing a defective child is certainly one of the most difficult tasks which can confront a mother. In many cases, especially when the child is severely defective, it is too much to expect the mother to handle the problem by herself; it can be done but with the likelihood that the health of the mother sooner or later deteriorates. A sickly, irritable, frustrated mother is not likely to be a satisfactory wife. Where such a problem exists an attempt should be made to get the father to see the nature of the situation and *to want* to share the responsibilities.[2]

One of the most obvious cautions to be observed in arranging for the interview is that the child should not be present. This caution is necessary not only to protect the child but to enable the parents to discuss the problem without the distracting presence of the child.

STRUCTURING THE INTERVIEW

In working with parents of defective children one must never lose sight of the fact that they have experienced keen frustration and hardship, have generally previously been given ambiguous or contradictory advice, and have been given little or no opportunity to unburden their anguish and disappointment. Unfortunately, there are too many professional specialists who give parents the feeling that they have little or limited time in which to discuss the problem with them, conduct the interview in the form of a monologue so that the parents are seldom given an opportunity to ask questions, communicate in a technical jargon which effectively confuses and overwhelms the parents, and in general manifest little or no interest in the personal problems or reactions of the parents. Unless one is able to identify with the problems and feelings of the parents one is likely to conduct the interview in an impersonal, superficial, routine fashion—a fashion which may be considered "successful" by the specialist but is frustrating and confusing to the parents. In working with the parents of defective children—in fact, in working with the parents of any problem child—one must not only be able to experience vicariously the nature and strength of their frustrations but also to structure the relationships so as to enable one to facilitate change in parental attitude and practice.

The following represents the writer's way of structuring the interview:

Before we discuss in any detail the conclusions we have reached about

---

[2] The words "to want" have been italicized in order to emphasize that the aim of the interviewer is to try to avoid telling the father that he should share responsibilities with the mother, but rather to attempt to get the father to recognize that his own as well as his wife's present and future welfare require sharing of responsibilities. The distinction in technique is again between reciting facts, on the one hand, and clarifying and changing attitudes, on the other hand. The husband who is told what he should do is not likely to be as helpful as one who has decided for himself, on the basis of a discussion of the problem, what he should do.

your child there are a few things I would like to say by way of introduction.
The first thing is that I hope that you will feel free *at any time* to ask questions or express an opinion—or disagreement. If I should say something you do not understand, please ask me about it immediately. All of us, you know, do not always say things as clearly as we should, so that if something is not clear to you I hope you will not feel that it is your fault and be afraid to ask questions. Sometimes we have found that parents have had important things they wanted to say or ask but for some reason they thought we might think them silly. The more questions you ask and we discuss the more help we can be to you. If I should use a word or phrase which you do not understand please interrupt and tell me. Sometimes we forget that words which mean something to us do not mean anything to another person. So I will look upon it as a favor if you will tell me when you do not understand something. One more thing: in the hour or so we have at our disposal it may not be possible for us to go over every problem in great detail. We have found in the past that it is not always possible to discuss everything in one session. So at the end of our talk today I will be happy to make another appointment when we can talk some more. You may find that when you go home questions will occur to you which you forgot to ask, or what seemed clear to you now may not seem so clear later, or you may find yourself disagreeing with our conclusions. Whatever it is, I hope you will not feel that today is the only time you will have to discuss your problems with us. We will be eager to see you as many times as you think we can be of help to you.

The significance of the above lies not in the words employed or the order in which the statements are made but rather in the attempt to engender in the parents the following set or attitudes:

1. It is not only "permissible" for them to talk and ask questions but *it is expected of them.*
2. They are talking to someone whose manner does not suggest that he is impatient to get on to what is next on his appointment calendar.
3. Parents have something important to contribute to the discussion.

Needless to say, parroting words or phrases will not necessarily produce the desired effects. The words and phrases must reflect personal conviction and feeling—if they do not, the parents are likely to recognize the insincerity and react accordingly. The tone of one's voice, one's facial expression, and the manifestation of a genuine desire to understand and help—these are the media by which the words one utters gain their force.

Obtaining Parental Attitudes, Practices, and Goals

Having attempted to establish the kind of relationship described above, it has then been found helpful to determine parental attitudes about the etiology of their child's condition, how they have handled the problems he has presented, and goals they have set for him. *Without knowledge or consideration of these factors the extent to which the parent's personal problems and, consequently, the child's particular problems can be helped will be minimal.* It has been the failure to consider these factors which has caused so much ineffective planning, wasted effort, and continued disappointment and frustration. Advice about child-rearing, schooling, institutionalization and similar problems must take into account parental behavior and attitudes if such advice is to have a reasonable chance of success.

At this point in the interview the writer has found the following statements helpful:

Although we have studied your child very carefully from many points of view—which we will discuss in a little while—I think you will understand when I say that our examinations do not always give us all the information we would like. In our experience we have found that at this point parents can be very helpful to us about certain questions. You know your child longer than we do and you have observed him in a way that we have not. We have learned from many cases in the past that by sharing our experiences and conclusions we might see things somewhat differently than before. You might have talked some of these things over before but it would be very helpful to all of us if you could do it again.[3] For example, I wonder if you might tell me what *you* have thought was the cause of your child's condition? From time to time several possible answers have probably occurred to you and I wonder if you could talk about them—even though you might have thought they were silly or, as sometimes happens, too unpleasant to think about. Whatever these were, it would be extremely helpful if we could talk about them.

[3.]In a clinic setting it is likely that the parents were initially seen by a social worker and that some aspects of the parental problem have been discussed. In the writer's experience, however, the intake history is relatively unrevealing of parental attitudes. Many parents do or would find it difficult to be personally revealing in this initial contact. Whatever the limits of this initial contact, however, the sensitive social worker can make observations which can be extremely helpful to the counselor whose job it will be to work with the parents.

It is clear that these statements are intended to get the parents to verbalize *their* conception of the etiology of the child's condition. The havoc which can be wrought by parental misconceptions about etiology has been nicely pointed out by Kanner and Tietze (269):

"Popular notions regarding heredity have provided a handy means of transferring the blame to some afflicted relative. If the hunt for a skeleton in the family closet did just that, it would serve a fairly useful function of absolving the parents from a feeling of personal guilt. But often enough a parent comes to believe, or is made to believe by hostile in-laws, that the present or past existence of such a relative is his or her own fault and contribution to the child's condition. The in-laws thus wash their hands of any complicity. The clan members of the accused spouse cannot remain idle. They usually manage, sometimes after considerable search worthy of a genealogist, to uncover some conjugal counterpart of the skeleton, and mutual recriminations are the order of the day. Psychotherapeutic consideration of the parents of retarded children cannot afford to disregard such bickering arising between and within families from the desire to put the stigma and odium of an ancestral culprit on either parent."

Misconceptions about heredity are not the only ones which parents may harbor. Some mothers have concluded that they were too active during pregnancy, or that they had experienced some frightening situation during pregnancy, or that they did not feed their child adequately in his early days, or that they did not obtain for him prompt or proper medical attention, or that the child had once slipped or fell from the mother's arms and had then cried most excessively. Parental explanations are many and varied but they usually have three characteristics in common:

1. They sound plausible and *may* contain a germ of truth; in other words, it would be difficult for a professional specialist to say that these factors have never been a possible factor in any case.
2. In the individual case the parental explanation usually cannot explain *their* child's condition. For example, an infant may receive a brain injury because of a fall, but when the neurological findings point unmistakably to early embryonic disfunction the parental explanation obviously loses its etiological relevance.
3. The parental explanation usually involves self-plaguings and feelings of guilt.

When one bears in mind to what extent parental misconception about etiology can adversely affect parental happiness and adjustment, the importance of determining the nature of such conceptions is clear. In order to disabuse parents of misconceptions and thereby give them a basis for relinquishing unrealistic and irrational attitudes it is first necessary for parents to verbalize their feelings.

The next area about which parents should be encouraged to talk might be indicated in the form of a question: "What are the main problems you have had to face as your child has developed and how have you coped with them?" Here one is interested in specific child rearing practices and problems: *When and how* did they try to teach their child to talk, walk, eat, and control toilet functions? When and how did they try to teach their child letters, words, and numbers? How did the parents handle the problem of their child's inability to play and compete with others? What are the attitudes of siblings toward the child? Of neighbors? Have the social activities of the parents been in any way affected by the condition of their child? One of the main considerations giving rise to these questions is the importance of determining the degree of emotionality which the parents experience in responding to the problems which their child has presented. Have the parents accepted his limitations or have they pushed him? Do they feel that other children and neighbors are unfair in their response to the child? Have the parents restricted excessively their own activities in order to devote their energies to the child? Do the parents see eye-to-eye on the handling of these problems? Are there indications that the parents have been unable to take advice offered previously by other agencies?

The last area about which parents should be encouraged to talk concerns their expectations of or goals for their child. What have they hoped that this child will be able to do? What are their expectations or hopes about his schooling? About his social and vocational activities? *It is through parental report about their hopes and aspirations for their child that one can best determine how realistic an understanding of their child's abilities the parents have. At the same time one can also evaluate the extent of one's task in helping the parents to adopt a more realistic approach.* A parent who says that he does not expect his child to go to college but would like him to finish high school reveals not only an unrealistic conception of his child but very frequently also a need to avoid accepting the child's limitations. The parent who says that he is not interested in the child's academic schooling but only wants him to be able to learn a trade and to maintain himself independently is also revealing a lack of understanding. The difficulty parents experience in accepting their child's limitations has been well described by Kanner and Tietze (269):

"During the past centuries our culture has put a special premium on good cognitive endowment, in an increasing degree. Our communal life is so constituted that to people with sufficiently high intelligence quotients go, of necessity, the functions of governing, the jobs with good incomes, the respect of contemporaries. They are the acknowledged inheritors of the earth. They are the cream of society. To have a child with a lower-than-average I.Q. means that his parents must from the beginning expect that he will be excluded from leadership, riches and esteem. Regardless of everything else, the low I.Q., as such, marks the child as socially inferior. Physical attractiveness, good manners, emotional stability and manual dexterity may create attenuating circumstances, but even though they are all combined in one person, if the I.Q. does not measure up to the existing requirements, they still fail to admit the bearer to a seat among the elite.

"It is, quite understandably, difficult for many parents, especially those who themselves have been blessed with a good I.Q., to accept their child's intellectual retardation as an Act of God, as something unpredictable, inevitable and unalterable. There comes often a search for the possibility of parental contribution to the child's inadequacy. The question, 'Why do we have such a child?' soon assumes the form of 'What have we done to have such a child?'

"Some parents do their best to escape the discomforts of trying to find an answer by flatly refusing to recognize the fact as such. The feeling, not ever verbalized, goes something like this: 'If my child were really retarded, I should be forced to ascribe his condition somehow to some shortcoming or transgression of my own. But I simply refuse to admit that he is retarded.' Then comes a hunt for excuses, usually looked for in the child's physical health. The child's admittedly poor performance must be based on unrecognized poor eyesight, glandular anomaly or something pressing on the brain. If the doctors could only find the somatic culprit, then the child will be all right and the parents will have reason to feel exculpated. If it is not an organ of the child's body, then it must be the teacher's lack of understanding, the crowded class, or the faulty school system. And if it isn't that, then the tester didn't know his business, or didn't know how to handle the child, or the child wasn't in the proper mood just then. It would be wrong to attribute this attitude, as is often done, to parental stubbornness, wicked and disrespectful lack of cooperation, or mental dishonesty. Such parents need the kind of guidance which makes it possible for them to express their feelings, frees them of any implied necessity of considering themselves personally responsible for the child's retardation, and thereby helps them to lift their heads from below the ostrich sand pile."

The point which deserves emphasis is that parental misunderstanding and overevaluation of their child's behavior and capabilities stem not from stubbornness but from a need to avoid wounding their own pride and facing self-devaluation. The conception which a parent has of his child is a reflection of his conception of himself. To admit that his child is "stupid" is very likely to arouse in the parent thoughts of his own limitations.

THE INTERVIEW TO THIS POINT

Thus far we have endeavored to engender in the parents a set of attitudes toward the counselor and the interview, and we have also attempted to get the parents to talk about themselves in relation to their child. *In the latter attempt the emphasis has been on what the parents have to report, the counselor adopting a relatively passive role in which he expresses no opinions but attempts in as nonleading a way as possible to get the parents to clarify and elaborate upon their thoughts and feelings.* Without the parental report it is difficult to identify oneself with them: to understand why they have reacted to their problem in the way they have and how their reactions have influenced their child. In addition, *by obtaining the parental report one is then in the position to utilize the diagnostic findings to help the parents achieve a more realistic basis for their conceptions, practices, and goals.*

COMMUNICATING THE DIAGNOSTIC FINDINGS

At this point in the interview the writer has said the following to the parents:

I find that what you have told me is extremely interesting and has given me a better understanding of what you have been thinking and experiencing. Now I would like to share with you the results of our studies. As you know we have studied your child from many points of view and we have come to certain conclusions. Before telling you of our conclusions I would first like to tell you of some of our experiences with other parents. Sometimes parents are at first disappointed at what we have to say and sometimes do not want to accept our findings. *This is very understandable to us —no one likes to hear that his child will always have certain limitations which other children will not have.* It is not easy to accept the fact that your child will never be able to do certain kinds of activities. But we feel that it is our obligation to speak with you as frankly as we can—as we feel you would want us to do. Again I would like to remind you to ask questions whenever they occur to you, and to disagree if that is how you feel. And please remember that we will be glad to talk with you further—we will always be glad to make an appointment to discuss any matter that you want.

These statements are intended to achieve the following:

1. To reward parents for their participation and to reinforce the feeling that they have something to contribute.
2. To prepare the parents, in those cases where it is indicated, for what will be conflict-arousing information.
3. To facilitate for the parents the experiencing and verbalizing of feeling. Anxiety, hostility, disappointment, and despair—these are the feelings one should enable parents to express rather than inhibit. While the inhibition of such feeling makes for a more "pleasant" interview, it also reduces the amount of help that one can be to parents.

It is not possible to describe in detail how the diagnostic findings are presented to the parents because the order in which they are presented and the degree of emphasis which they receive are determined by the problems arising from the parental report. As was said before, *the diagnostic findings are used as the bases for helping parents give up erroneous ideas and adopt a more realistic approach to their own and their child's problems.* For example, if the diagnostic findings offer no support for parental conceptions of etiology, then this point must be made explicit—and emphasized. It is not enough to tell parents that they are "wrong"; one must not give them the impression that their conceptions are silly. One must make parents feel that one understands why they arrived at their particular conceptions—but that the findings offer no support for their convictions. If parents have unrealistic anticipations about their child's future schooling, then this should be explicitly discussed. To parents who would like their child at least to finish public or high school it is not enough to say that this is not possible; one must state the basis for one's conclusion and give as explicitly as possible the probable lower and upper limits of the child's academic achievements.

In many cases parents have already indirectly revealed that many of the day-to-day problems which they experience in relation to their child stem from highly emotionally-tinged attitudes which in turn adversely affect their child's behavior. It is difficult for these parents to see that such attitudes defeat, or at the least interfere with, the goals which they want to achieve. *In discussing this with parents one must be careful to avoid making them feel guilty. One must explicitly recognize and verbalize that what the parents had been doing, however ineffective, was based on "good intentions," as indeed it usually is.*

The Importance of a Specific Program

One of the most important functions of the interview is to offer to and discuss with parents a specific program for their child. A great deal of unnecessary unhappiness has resulted from the failure to give to the parents detailed advice about the handling of their child. Parents of defective children need guidance and emotional support. It is not enough to tell them that their child is defective and they should not expect much from him. The following is a list of questions which parents frequently ask—the questions, of course, varying with the age of the child, severity of defect, degree of physical handicap, etc.:

Should I try to teach my child to walk now? Am I teaching him the right way?
How can I get other children to refrain from teasing him?
Is there any way I can train my child to stop being as destructive as he is?
Should I punish him the way I do my other children?
When should he start school? Is there a school for him?
Should we institutionalize him? Where are these institutions? Are they expensive?
Should we have other children? Will my child be a bad influence on my other children? My other child who is normal resents him—what should I do about it?

One could list a great many more problems for which parents seek guidance. Some of the problems require a detailed knowledge and understanding of the child, parents, and family constellation. Other problems require, in addition, a knowledge of community resources: educational, recreational, and institutional. But in discussing any problem with parents one must wherever possible give specific advice and guidance. For example, if a mother is bothered because her child is frequently teased by neighborhood children, one must attempt to outline concrete steps which might be taken by the mother to cope with the problem. One should, of course, first determine how the mother has previously handled the problem: Has she "bawled out" the other children? Has she asked their parents to punish them? If the parent has reacted in this way then one must point out why such an approach is likely to be self-defeating. One might then suggest that the mother have a talk with the children and explain to them that her child cannot do some of the things that they can, that he needs a little more consideration and protection, that he is not as able to protect or defend himself as they are, and that she is discussing the matter with them because she knows that if they understood her child better they would not tease him. Another suggestion concerns discussing the matter in a similar vein with the parents of the neighborhood children.

One should not give the parent of the defective child the impression that one's suggestions are sure to work after one application. In addition, one must avoid giving suggestions which, while correct in general, cannot be properly acted upon by the parent because of their excessive emotionality.

If the problem concerns the future schooling of the child one should acquaint the parent with the nature of local facilities, the people who administer them, and the requirements for entrance. One should urge the parents to visit the facilities and, if possible, arrange for the visit and for a later discussion of parental reactions and questions. Too frequently parents have had to find out about local facilities in a trial-and-error kind of way, during which time their feelings of frustration and helplessness have mounted.[4]

[4] In the next chapter the problems involved in discussing institutionalization with parents will be taken up. These problems are given separate treatment because they are among the most thorny to handle and illustrate clearly how the problems of child and parents are interrelated.

THE INTERVIEW TO THIS POINT

Thus far we have attempted to do four things: (1) engender in the parents a particular attitude toward the interview, (2) identify the nature of the parents' problems, (3) utilize the diagnostic findings in order to help the parents adopt a realistic conception of their child's condition, and (4) formulate and discuss with the parents a specific attack on their child's and their own problems.

As was indicated before, it is not always possible or desirable to achieve all the goals of the interview within one session. The availability and advisability of another session or sessions should be again pointed out to the parents, the decision about returning being left to them. In terminating the interview one must convey to the parents that the need for further visits is not due to a present lack of interview time but to the need for the parents to digest what has been discussed, raise new questions or problems which usually occur to them after an initial visit, and to give the interviewer more time to mull over the discussion and the problems raised.

SOME CAUTIONS

The reader should not conclude that by following the contents of this chapter he will always be able smoothly and painlessly to achieve the goals outlined earlier. Parents do not always say or do what we would like or expect. The fact that one attempts to get parents to talk about their conceptions of the origins of their child's condition does not mean that they will do so. One may try to make parents feel free to talk and raise questions but the attempt does not mean that they will act accordingly. In some cases it is not until the second or third interview that a parent will really feel free to talk and raise questions. In working with parents one must be ready to change one's approach and, with unusually emotional or unstable parents, even to narrow one's goals. But in these cases extreme care must be taken to insure that a change in approach or narrowing of goals is not the result of one's own emotional reactions. For example, *some parents seem so hostile or resistant that one reacts similarly to them, reactions which then enable the parents to continue to be hostile and resistant. In working with parents (as in therapeutic work with anyone) it is self-defeating to respond emotionally to the deliberate or unwitting provocations of those whom one is trying to help.* The task is to recognize the hostility and to help the parents see its lack of justification in this situation.

The subjective reactions of the counselor can be an interfering factor in those instances when he fears the reaction of the parent to what will probably be highly disappointing news—the interviewer wants and yet does not want to state the truth. As a consequence he will sometimes relate the findings in an ambiguous manner so that the parents can interpret them in any manner that they choose—the interviewer unknowingly speaks out of both sides of his mouth. The writer has spoken to physicians who have frankly said that they did not "have the heart" to tell parents that their child was defective. Others have adopted the position that ignorance is bliss and "they (the parents) will find out for themselves later on." Both attitudes reveal a need to avoid an unpleasant situation, an avoidance which may make life more pleasant for the physician but creates undue hardship, now and in the future, for parents and child.

Interpreting mental defect to parents is not a simple or pleasant task and cannot be approached in a perfunctory way. In Chapter 13 the problem of who should handle such tasks and what the requisite training should be will be discussed.

THE "UNTREATABLE" PARENTS

As has been pointed out elsewhere (248), there are always parents who are unable to face the problems brought up in the interview despite all of one's efforts. In such cases the counselor must neither lose patience nor take it as an affront. Terminating the relationship with such parents, however, should not necessarily be looked upon as a negative step. The following information should be conveyed to the parents:

1. That one understands that it is not easy to accept and to adjust to the problems and conclusions which have been discussed. Should the parents at any time in the future desire to resume discussion, or feel that the agency can in any way be of help to them, they should not hesitate to call for an appointment.
2. Should the parents feel that they would like to take their child to another agency for evaluation, it might be helpful if they were given a list of agencies or professional specialists who are competent to make such an evaluation.

It is clear that the last statement represents an attempt to insure that parents, if they are "to shop around," go to reputable and competent specialists and agencies. In more than a few cases shopping around among recommended agencies has helped parents to accept conclusions which were discussed with them earlier. In other cases, of course, the shopping around never has any beneficial effects.

It is sometimes forgotten that although parents may achieve new insights during the interview and may give clear indications that their attitudes are beginning to change, the crucial test of the efficacy of one's efforts is if after the interview the parents can *act* on the basis of what they have learned. It is unusual if inter- and intrapersonal conflicts can be resolved either during or because of a single interview. What is perhaps more usual is that after the interview previous conflicts are experienced in their original or increased strength. One must remember that strongly held beliefs, unrealistic or not, are maintained because they are in one way or other satisfying to the believer. These beliefs serve the purpose of enabling the individual to defend himself against recognizing what for him would be an unpleasant or even impossible situation. It is because such beliefs serve this defensive purpose that they are not easily given up even when adherence to contrary beliefs is apparently being achieved. It is because of these considerations that emphasis has been given to the need for several interviews. In addition, these considerations contain the implication that in those cases where parents have achieved new insights the counselor should actively aid the parent wherever possible to follow through on their new insights. In some cases, for example, a visit to the home might not only reinforce more realistic parental behavior but might allow the counselor to be of more concrete help to the parents—a suggestion which Yepsen and Cianci (see page 350) have shown to possess marked therapeutic possibilities.

Chapter 12

THE PROBLEM OF INSTITUTIONALIZATION

A DECISION concerning the institutionalization of a child must take into account a wide variety of factors. Too frequently the recommendation is made perfunctorily and without systematic attention to factors which might contraindicate institutionalization or reduce the difficulties which parents frequently experience in accepting and following the recommendation. Perfunctory handling of the problem usually raises far more psychological problems than it solves.[1]

Because the nature of one's recommendation always involves the use of some criteria, implicit or explicit, attention will first be given in this chapter to a formulation of comprehensive criteria for institutionalization. Following a discussion of the criteria the problem of how to communicate the recommendation to parents will be taken up.

CRITERIA FOR INSTITUTIONALIZATION

Family Factors

A. *Marital relationship.* One of the most important things to determine concerns the effect of the defective child on the marital relationship. Do the parents quarrel about the child? Has it interfered with their enjoyment and sharing of social activities? Have their personal or

---

[1] Although we are primarily interested in the psychological aspects of the problem of institutionalization, one should not overlook its social-economic ramifications. In almost every state in the country institutional facilities are considered inadequate in the light of the number requiring institutionalization. When one considers the millions of dollars it takes to build and to maintain a well-equipped and adequately staffed institution, it is not surprising that the demand exceeds the supply. Even when a new institution is built one soon finds not only that it is full to capacity but that it possesses a lengthy waiting list—and it is not long before some are clamoring for a new institution. To anyone who has had to listen to the insistent and pathetic pleadings of parents whose children are desperately in need of institutionalization but for whom no beds are available, it becomes abundantly clear that the social-economic ramifications generate additional psychological problems. In light of this unfortunate situation it is somewhat surprising that so little attention has been given to the adequacy of or justification for the usual criteria for institutionalization. As we shall see later on in this chapter, it is only recently that attention has been given to ways of obviating or postponing the need for institutionalization.

347

vocational ambitions been frustrated? To what extent are the parents, willingly or not, sacrificing their own lives for that of their defective child? By posing these and similar questions one endeavors to focus on the degree to which the marital relationship has been impaired by the presence of the defective child. The next difficult question to answer concerns the likelihood that the child's removal will make for a more happy and constructive marital relationship. *That the above questions have been phrased in a somewhat "pessimistic" way should not obscure the fact that more than a few parents are only minimully affected by their defective child.* These parents can and want to take care of their child in the home as long as possible and they are puzzled and upset by a recommendation that they institutionalize their child as early as possible. It would be indeed interesting to know how many children have been institutionalized not because they could not be taken care of satisfactorily in the home but because the parents were told or made to feel that defective children should be institutionalized as early as possible.

B. *Other children.* If there are other children in the family, it is necessary to determine how they are affected, if at all, by their defective sib. The attitudes of the other children to the defective sib are usually a reflection of parental attitudes. If the parents are ashamed to have people visit them for fear that their "blight" will be seen and discussed, it is likely that the normal children will react similarly with their friends. Frequently the normal child will resent the fact that the defective sib receives extra attention or is not punished as he is for transgressions. In some cases the mother has to devote so much of her time and energies to the defective child that the other children receive too little discipline and guidance. In other cases the normal child prematurely has to assume household obligations which in effect rob him of the companionship of his peers. But again one must caution against uncritically assuming that the presence of a defective child must or will have a deleterious effect on the normal sibs. The question must be decided by study and not preconceived opinion.

C. *Financial factor.* A factor which deserves attention might be called a financial one, especially important in those cases where the child is grossly defective, bed-ridden, and in need of constant and special attention. Are the costs of maintaining such a child in the home of such a magnitude that what the parents can allot for themselves or their other children is considerably affected? What is perhaps more frequent are the cases where parents, unwilling to have their child in a public institution, have placed them in a private institution, the cost of which impoverishes the family resources—the welfare of parents and normal sibs again being sacrificed. Here the problem is obviously to get the parents to consider public institutions. The handling of this problem will be discussed later.

D. *Effectiveness of home environment.* A most important criterion might be put in the form of a question: *How effective is or can this home be in meeting this child's present needs, developing what assets he possesses, and preparing him for adulthood?* Whereas previously we were primarily concerned with the developmental possibilities of the parents and the normal children, here we focus on the defective child's possibilities for growth in a particular setting. If the defective child is obviously or subtly rejected by his family, or is overindulged and pampered, or is responded to by parents in an unrealistic way which does not appear modifiable—if the developmental possibilities of the child are interfered with by such conditions, then removal from the home should be considered. However, as was pointed out before, it is sometimes overlooked that in some cases the home is better able than an institution to meet the child's needs, at least up until a certain age.

E. *Age of parents.* The final factor under the general heading of family factors concerns the age of the parents. This factor is particularly important when the parents are at or near middle age or one or both of them is in ill health. The problem, of course, is to make provision for the care of the child when the parents will no longer be able to do so. Most parents are concerned with the problem but few take active steps to make provision for future emergencies. In some cases parents hope that another child will take over responsibility for the care of the defective sib. More frequently than not either the parents have not discussed the matter with the normal child or the latter is unwilling or most reluctant to accept responsibility. In other cases the middle-aged parents impoverish themselves in order to save money which will enable their child to be placed in a private institution. Here again the problem is not institutionalization but the type of institutionalization.

Neighborhood Factors

In the previous chapter we discussed how the aggressively toned attitudes of neighborhood children and parents might be handled. At this point our focus is on the seriousness of the problem in terms of the welfare of the defective child and that of the neighboring children.

Although frequently the defective child is adversely affected by attitudes based on prejudice and ignorance, it is not infrequent that the behavior of the defective child provokes counter-aggression and social rejection. When one remembers that the defective child has difficulty forming and maintaining social relationships, that he does not comprehend at all well the motivations of others, that he is likely to have difficulty controlling strong feeling, that he frequently feels frustrated and rejected, and that these factors are operative in combination, it is not surprising that the defective child will provoke adverse reactions in others. If, in addition, the parents of the defective child are themselves unstable and have unrealistic conceptions about their child's abilities, the neighborhood situation can indeed be explosive, to the detriment of the defective child and his normal peers. In some cases the relationship of the defective child and his parents to those in the neighborhood has deteriorated to such an extent that the origin of the difficulty becomes somewhat of an academic question. In any event, one must determine the nature and seriousness of the neighborhood problem, if any, and the likelihood that it can be resolved or ameliorated by procedures involving the continued presence of the defective child in his home.

Community and School Resources

A. *Home training program.* In the case of grossly defective children it has usually been the practice to recommend early institutionalization. The experience of the Home Training Program in New Jersey clearly indicates that such a recommendation is not necessarily warranted. This program, begun in 1943, was developed by Yepsen and Cianci (*335*) as a means of aiding parents of defective children (usually on the idiot and imbecile levels) who could not be admitted to custodial institutions because of the lack of facilities.[2] The following statement by these workers bears repetition:

"The problem is fundamentally one of education and training children and parents. It was the belief of this Department that the work should be

[2] As Yepsen and Cianci point out: "Vacancies in institutions providing custodial care because of the very limited mental development of the patients admitted usually occur only in case of death. The turnover is, therefore, slight and the waiting lists increase from year to year instead of decreasing. This means that there are many children in every state of limited ability who never receive any training and whose chance of ever being admitted into an institution is very slight."

carried out by a person trained as a teacher who will consider the problem from the teacher's point of view and uses teaching methods. The philosophy which governs this work is simple. The teacher in order to be successful in his work must have the firm conviction that every child regardless of his mental level is entitled to as much training and education as will aid him in developing to his maximum capacity. He must also believe that the parents of these children are entitled to every consideration and aid which will help them lead a normal life, and most important of all, he must truly believe in home training as a means of making the child adjustable in the family. He must discard the idea that every feebleminded child must be taken out of the community and put into an institution. This last statement cannot be emphasized enough for there are still many well-meaning people who influence and misguide parents into believing that the institution is the ultimate and only solution to the problem presented by the mentally deficient child."

The function of the teacher was twofold: (1) to work with the child in order to effect elementary habit training, speech, self-help, emotional control, and play activities aimed at developing muscular coordination; and (2) to guide the parent in the handling of the child. "Such parents need to be guided in the right attitude and they must be made to realize that the time spent in training the child is time well spent. Parents are given simple directions on how to proceed in establishing these correct habit patterns and advantages which will result from this training are pointed out to them. The mother must be advised that teaching these children will be a long-time process and can be accomplished only by a systematic established routine."

The value of the Home Training Program may be seen from the following data on 24 cases:

	Before Home Training	After Home Training
No. of parents who wanted child in an institution	17	6
No. of parents who did not want child in an institution	5	18
Undecided	2	0

As a result of the program parents achieved a more realistic picture of their child's limitations, and clarified their doubts, misconceptions, and fears about his condition. Mothers enthusiastically welcomed the support and guidance they received and they were able to handle their children in a much more constructive manner.

B. *School facilities.* The public schools divide defective children into two groups: (1) the educable who are usually in the moron range and who in special classes with specially trained teachers are considered able to profit to *some* extent from academic instruction, (2) the uneducable defectives who are usually in the imbecile range and who are considered unable to profit from any academic instruction. There are more than a few communities which provide no facilities for either group, although, in general, classes for the educable defective far outnumber those for the uneducable ones. Unfortunately, classes for the educable defective range from those which are held next to the boiler room and are conducted by an untrained teacher (or the least promising member of the faculty) to one which in every respect is the equal of classes for normal children. *The fact that a community provides facilities for the educable defective cannot be assumed to mean that they are adequate and will satisfy the needs of a particular child.* Frequently, the educational facilities of the institution are superior to those in the community—a fact used by some communities to justify their continued failure to improve their own inadequate facilities. Some community officials ask: Why should we spend money for facilities which the state has already set up?—a question which reveals a rather complete lack of understanding of the psychological problems involved. Here, too, it would be interesting to know how many children have been institutionalized not because of an inability to adjust to or benefit from a community program but because the institution was the only place where a program existed.[3]

In recent years, largely because of parental pressure, some communities have provided physical facilities and a nonacademic program for the noneducable defective. The effect of such a program, like the Home Training one, is to enable the child to remain in the home and to avoid the necessity of early institutionalization, at the same time that one at-

---

[3] Here again one might point with surprise to the absence of studies in which criteria for institutionalization have been evaluated. As a result, it is difficult to say to what extent institutional facilities are really inadequate in meeting the demand for bed space. It is clear that one's conceptions of inadequacy will vary with one's attitudes toward community responsibility and maintenance of family unity, with one's knowledge of the effects of institutionalization, and with one's values towards fiscal expenditures. In short, one's criteria for institutionalization determine one's definition of inadequacy.

tempts to develop the child's motor coördination, self-care potentialities, and socialization techniques. In regard to educational facilities one can only conclude that *consideration of institutionalization must take into account the scope and quality of a community's educational resources.*

C. *Recreational facilities.* A defective child, like a normal one, who has no one with whom to play or socialize is likely not only to be an unhappy child but a source of other people's unhappiness. Although some attention has been given to the need for community recreational facilities for the school-age defective, very little has been done for the older one. In more than a few cases a prime factor behind institutionalization is the desire to give the child the opportunity to engage in activities with other defectives, an opportunity completely absent in his community. Another aspect of the problem can be seen in those cases where the child has been institutionalized and then returns to the community only to experience loneliness and social isolation, feelings which make more than a few long for their institutional companions and activities. A community's recreational facilities must be carefully considered when studying the advisability of institutionalization for a particular child.

The Institution

There are many lay and professional people who harbor the belief that a private institution is always to be preferred to a public one. As a result, some parents literally impoverish themselves in order to maintain their child in a private institution, even though the public one in their region may be equally or more adequate. It cannot be overlooked that, in general, the public institution is better able to afford adequate facilities and personnel. It cannot be denied, however, that in some regions the private institution is to be preferred. *Although finances is an important aspect of the problem, the decision should be largely influenced by the quality of the program offered.* Beautiful shrubbery, attractive living quarters, breath-taking views, a "refined" atmosphere, and compulsive cleanliness—these factors do not guarantee that the institution, public or private, has an adequate program; they do not mean that the institution has appropriately trained personnel and a therapeutically and individually oriented program. It is banal but true that one cannot tell an institution by its appearance.

One other factor deserves mention at this point, although one is not usually able to do much about it. Reference is made here to what might be called a "geographical" factor: the tendency for institutions to be built in such relatively inaccessible places that geographical distance makes for "psychological distance" between child and family. In the case of the grossly defective child this usually is not a particular problem, but with higher grade defectives who have many ties with their own families, and who have been dependent upon them, separation from the family together with infrequent visits can produce severe feelings of rejection with consequent behavior problems. Some children show no untoward reaction to separation and infrequent visits from their family, but in many other cases the psychological effects are profound.

WEIGHTING THE CRITERIA

Because cases differ so markedly in terms of complexity, severity, and acuteness of the presenting problems, it is not possible or desirable to describe in detail what weights should be assigned in the individual cases to each of the criteria. In one case family factors might be given the most weight in making the decision while in another case community resources might be the most important factor. It is only after considering all the criteria that one is able to judge which of them should be given most weight. In addition, by systematically paying attention to all of the criteria, one is not only achieving a comprehensive picture but putting oneself in a position to make a recommendation which will have a beneficial effect for the greatest number of people involved in the case.

ASSUMPTIONS UNDERLYING THE CRITERIA

The reader may have already become aware that certain assumptions or values underlie the criteria. Since these assumptions or values determine in part the kind of data one seeks and the way in which they will be used, it would seem important to state them explicitly:

1. The defective child cannot be studied (or be understood) apart from the family and community in which he lives.
2. The problems, adjustment, and potentialities of the defective child's parents and siblings deserve as much attention and treatment as those of the defective child.

3. Institutionalization should not be recommended unless the results to be achieved by such a move cannot be attained by the continued presence of the child in the home.
4. It is the obligation of the community to provide those facilities which will either make institutionalization in many cases unnecessary or postpone it for as long as the child can benefit from the community program.
5. When the defective child for one or another reason adversely affects the functioning of normal people in his environment one should not accept the situation but should attempt to ameliorate the situation without removal of the child from that environment. When attempts at such amelioration have proved unsuccessful, the needs and potentialities of the normal people should be given precedence over those of the defective child.
6. A decision about institutionalization should be made by someone who has more than a superficial knowledge of the type and quality of available community resources. Whether the decision is to institutionalize or not, such a decision must be based on an intimate knowledge of the institution's goals, program, and effectiveness.

The Interview with the Parents

The following sections should be considered as a continuation of the procedures outlined in Chapter 11 since a discussion with parents about institutionalization usually follows that concerned with diagnostic findings.

In communicating the recommendation it is important that the various plans or programs which one has considered should be presented and explained to the parents together with the reasons why one has concluded institutionalization to be the best solution. If the recommendation is based on the conclusion that the child is in need of the kind of educational, vocational, or therapeutic program which only an institution offers, this should be explicitly stated together with the reasons why a program based on local facilities is not possible or desirable. If the recommendation is based on the conclusion that a more stable and healthy family constellation will be effected by the child's institutionalization, this should be clearly presented. On this point the writer has sometimes said to parents:

When parents bring their child to us, our interest is not only in the child but in his parents and other members of his family. When we make recommendations we take into account not only the child's needs and problems but also those of the parents. We feel that everything possible should be done for the child *but we also feel that this should not be done by sacrificing the health and happiness of his family.* If we conclude, after studying all the facts, that by institutionalizing the child his parents will be able to lead more normal lives, be of greater help to each other, and be better able to contribute to the happiness and welfare of others who are dear to them and who can benefit from their help—if we feel that these things cannot be accomplished by the child remaining in the home, we would not be doing our job if we did not say this openly and clearly.

There are several reasons for informing parents clearly and fully about the nature and justification of one's recommendation: (1) one has led parents to expect a complete explanation; (2) a full report makes less likely the parental reaction that one's approach has been cavalier, superficial, unsympathetic, and impersonal; and (3) a complete report may help some parents to become aware of facets of the problem of which they were formerly unaware.

Following the communication of the recommendation the parents should be given an opportunity to voice their reactions and ask questions. In those cases where the parents presumably have never considered institutionalization, the writer has said:

The recommendation I have made may be one to which you have never given thought or very little thought. In that case what I have said may have come as somewhat of a surprise and I hope you will feel free to tell me about your reactions and ask any questions which come to your mind. Sometimes parents disagree with us, sometimes they have difficulty getting used to the idea—I fully realize that this may be a difficult situation for you but I think that if we can talk over your feelings we can be of more help to you.

In those cases where there is evidence that the parents have already considered and rejected the idea of institutionalization, the following might be said:

I know that you have already thought about this matter and that you were opposed to putting your child in an institution. I do not know whether you feel differently having heard what I have to say. It would be helpful if you could tell me what your reactions are—whether you feel the same or different and why.

Too much emphasis cannot be placed on the importance of (1) facilitating parental verbalization about their attitudes to the recommendation; (2) avoiding any display of impatience or hostility when parents ask questions or disagree with the recommendation, and (3) reiterating the recommendation always in terms of the considerations which gave rise to it.

Because institutionalizing one's child is not a pleasant prospect or task to which one quickly adjusts, certain steps can be taken which may facilitate parental acceptance and adjustment:

1. Arrangements should be made for the parents to visit the institution and become acquainted with its program, personnel, and facilities.
2. The parents can be introduced to other parents whose children have been previously institutionalized with subsequent beneficial effects. If there is a local group of parents of defective children, they should be urged to join. In both instances the parents are given an opportunity to observe and talk with others who have had similar problems, a cathartic and therapeutic effect usually being achieved. More than a few parents are literally amazed when they discover that there are others like themselves with similar problems.
3. The parents should be invited to return for another interview after they have taken either or both of the above steps. Such an interview gives the parents an opportunity to ask questions based on their new experiences and to explore further their attitudes towards institutionalization of their child.

SOME FREQUENT PARENTAL REACTIONS

Many people believe that to institutionalize a member of their family is a "bad" or hostile act which "good" people avoid. To "put a child away," many believe, is "inhuman" and is an act which should be censured: "good parents simply do not do such a thing to their child." When such attitudes are operative, it is not difficult to understand why the prospect or act of institutionalization arouses strong guilt feelings in parents. *When the defective child has been an unusual burden to the parents and a source of keen frustration, it is likely that the parents have had hostile and destructive fantasies about the child, fantasies which in turn engender the reaction of guilt. In many of these cases the prospect or act of institutionalization is reacted to as if it were equivalent to the fulfillment of earlier hostile and destructive fantasies.* Parental guilt feeling might be reduced in several ways. The steps outlined in the previous section (visiting institution, joining parental groups) frequently enable parents to see the irrational basis for their feelings.[4] They frequently say: "It's not the horrible place I thought it would be. If it was, I couldn't live with myself if I put my child there." "I spoke with Mrs._____, who is a very nice lady, and she didn't like the idea of putting her child in the institution but she told me it was the best thing that could have happened for her and her child." By identifying with others whom they respect and who have institutionalized their child the guilt feelings of some parents are noticeably reduced in strength.

Although guilt feelings may be a potent factor in the parents' attitude, they may be unable to verbalize them. In such cases direct questioning usually further inhibits the parents because they are not sure how the interviewer will judge their answer—or they are sure that he will form a bad opinion of them. What the writer has frequently done is to raise the problem in terms of how "some" parents react to the problem, why a guilt reaction is understandable, but why it is not warranted. By verbalizing their feelings in terms of "others," some parents then feel free to verbalize their own feelings. In handling parental guilt feelings, verbalized or not, perhaps the most important thing to emphasize is the importance of conveying to parents that one understands why they may have developed guilt feelings but that such feelings are neither objectively warranted nor beneficial to parents or child.

Many parents resist institutionalization of their child because they imagine that he will experience the same feelings that the parents would

---

[4] In recommending that parents visit the institution one must, of course, be convinced that the particular institution is adequate for the child and, in addition, that an appropriately trained staff member guides and talks with the parents. The visit should not consist only of a tour of the buildings but should also provide opportunity for parents to observe in detail the unit where their child *may* reside, talk with the personnel who will be responsible for his welfare and training, and to discuss the rationale of the program. The tendency of parents (as well as institutional personnel) to be most impressed by the physical features of the institution should be counteracted. This is especially important where the institution may not give a striking appearance but where the program is a good one. *The closer the relationship between the institution and the referring agency or counselor the more beneficial can the visit be for the parents.*

if they were being institutionalized. In short, they identify with their child and project onto him feelings and attitudes which they harbor. They assume their child will be as lonely, cry as much, be as depressed, and feel as rejected as they would if they were in his place. To commit their child, therefore, is the same as if they were to be institutionalized. In many cases the nature of the child's condition or the severity of his deficiency clearly indicates that he is incapable of experiencing the feelings which his parents project onto him. In such cases the unrealism of parental anticipations should be discussed. *However, although a defective and normal person comprehend and experience a given stimulus situation differently, one should not overlook the fact that some defective children will react to institutionalization in a way approximating that imagined by the parents.* Some children will become depressed, feel rejected, cry bitterly. One should not try to convince parents, as is sometimes done, that their anticipations are groundless and that their child will immediately experience the institution as a heaven. To deny that the child may have difficulty, or to avoid discussing the matter with parents, not only may make for later increased difficulty for the parents but in some cases has resulted in the removal of the child from the institution when the parents' anticipations about the child's reactions are confirmed by his behavior. In discussing the matter with parents it is best to admit, especially where the evidence is confirmatory, that the child may have some difficulty, that the parents' own adjustment will not be made any easier thereby, but that the long-term benefits to be derived from institutionalization will more than offset temporary or transient difficulties.

Up to this point we have discussed parents who resist the recommendation of institutionalization. Not infrequently one encounters the parents who come to the agency for the express purpose of enlisting its aid in institutionalizing their child, a move which study reveals to be indicated. In some of these cases, however, the parents' conception of what the institution will do for their child is highly unrealistic. *Because parents heartily concur in the recommendation should not be taken to mean that they are concurring for the proper reasons.* If parental conceptions are unrealistic, they are likely not only to experience disappointment at some future date but to become hostile toward the institution which did not do what they expected. In any aspect of work with parents one must determine their motivations toward and anticipations about any recommended decision. The resolution of present problems must not be done in a way which insures the creation of future ones.

The Major Aim

The chief aim in this and the previous chapter has not been to give the reader a step-by-step guide to the problems posed but rather to indicate the complexity of the problems, the goals which one should set, and the nature of the relationship with parents which one should effect. In the majority of the cases many of the problems one encounters would never have arisen if the ramifications of the problem had been recognized and handled when the diagnosis was first made. One cannot cure mental deficiency but one can prevent many of the unhealthy consequences which are too frequently the lot of parent and child. It may be more correct to say that the major aim of this and the previous chapter has been to alert the reader to his obligation to ameliorate present problems and prevent future ones.

Chapter 13

THE PROBLEM OF PROFESSIONAL TRAINING

THE reader may have already concluded from a reading of the last two chapters that handling the problems posed therein requires not only knowledge of certain facts but an understanding of what is essentially a psychotherapeutically-oriented situation: a sustained attempt on the part of some trained person to understand the motivations of parents, their frustrations and hopes, and by virtue of such understanding, as well as by previous training, to enable parents to accept more realistic and satisfying attitudes. To be of help to people in this manner requires more than good intentions and the possession of a particular professional title. The fact that one is a pediatrician, psychiatrist, psychologist, or teacher does not necessarily mean, as we shall see later, that one is equipped with the knowledge and training required for the handling of the problems posed in the last two chapters. A great many of the difficulties which are encountered in working with the defective child and his family can often be traced directly to the previous failure of many of these professional people to recognize and handle the psychological aspects of the problem. *It is the thesis of this chapter that this failure is in large part due to the kind of training which these workers received in their student days.* We may anticipate a later conclusion by stating here that mental deficiency in general and its psychological aspects in particular have suffered from "professional disinterest," an attitude which not only minimizes the complexity of the problem but perpetuates practices which raise more problems than they solve.

The following case can serve well to illustrate the significance of the statements made in this and the previous two chapters. The child, parental behavior, and professional practice are not atypical:

". . . I received a call from the secretary of a local organized group of parents of cerebral palsied children. It seems that one of the mothers had

361

been trying to get her seven-year-old daughter into the kindergarten of one of the public schools. The school had refused admission because the child was not considered eligible. The mother, believing that the child was eligible, took her for a psychological examination to the out-patient clinic of one of the state training schools. The psychological report was sent to the secretary who was calling me and who had suggested that the mother arrange for a psychological examination in order to use it as evidence for her belief that the child should be in kindergarten. The psychological report contained the following: (a) a diagnosis was deferred because the child did not talk and the suggestion was made that the child should be seen again when she had learned to talk; (b) on those test items which could be given to the child her mental level seemed to be around three years; (c) the child should not be institutionalized at this time; (d) she should be entered into a kindergarten class if she was considered eligible by the school. The problem with which the secretary of the parent group confronted me was what should she tell the parent?

"The above situation is by no means infrequent, and in my own experience is the rule rather than the exception. In trying to understand these frequent situations we might ask this question: How do these situations come about? Before trying to answer this question we first have to ask other questions: What is the nature of the situation here and now? What are the problems with which we should be concerned? Briefly stated, here is what I think are the important aspects of the situation:

1. We are dealing with a parent who has certain beliefs about what her child can learn to do.
2. The mother's beliefs are not shared by school authorities.
3. It is very likely that the mother has a very hostile attitude toward the schools because she feels that they are being unfair and discriminatory.
4. It is also likely that the school authorities consider the mother to be unrealistic and aggressive—in short, a nuisance.
5. It is a fact that the schools do not consider this child to be *their* problem.
6. The psychological report does not support the mother's beliefs about the child's capacities.
7. The psychological report contains a recommendation about kindergarten which makes little sense in light of the earlier refusal of the school to admit the child.
8. The psychologist did not discuss his report with the mother.
9. No one, except the local parent group, considered the parent to be their problem, or understood, let alone tried to handle, the deep anguish she undoubtedly was experiencing.

"Let us now make one assumption: the mother has an unrealistic conception of her child's capacities. If this is so, it is difficult to see how anything done—by the school or the psychologist—was oriented toward helping this mother achieve a more realistic attitude. Telling a mother that her child is not eligible for school may be a valid statement, but in no way does this solve the mother's problem. In fact, making such a statement to a mother is evidence of the fact that the school assumes that only the child is a problem. Telling a mother that her child is not eligible for school without at the same time making concrete proposals concerning the child's training obviously does not help the child, but, just as obviously, increases the severity of the mother's problem. In the case of the psychological examination apparently no attempt was made to convey anything to the mother. The function of a psychological examination is not only to collect data about a child and his problems, but to use these data to help parents react realistically to the child. If the psychologist, for example, had only conveyed to the parent that the child was severely retarded, then he would have been as superficial in his approach to the problem as were the school authorities."[1]

One other fact about this case deserves mention: this eight-year-old child had previously been seen by numerous medical specialists none of whom considered the parents a problem or apparently attempted to insure that the parents had a realistic conception of their child's condition.

One could present case after case illustrating the failure of various specialists to handle the defective child and his family in such a manner as to reduce the strength of the anxieties associated with current problems and to prevent the occurrence of future ones. That mental deficiency is an incurable condition should not obscure the fact that many of the psychological and social problems to which it gives rise can either be prevented or greatly reduced in strength. In the following pages we shall see that the failure to recognize and handle such problems is in large part a function of the inadequate training which the various specialists have received.

In the following discussion of the training of those professional workers who come into contact with the defective child and his family *we shall only be interested in the adequacy of such training for meeting the psychological problems we have been discussing in the previous two chapters.*

MEDICAL PERSONNEL

A. Medical school and intern training. The medical student is not in

[1] S. B. Sarason, Aspects of a community program for the retarded child. *Training School Bulletin* (Vineland, N. J.), 1952, *48*, 201–207.

any formal or systematic way exposed to the psychological aspects of mental deficiency. Much more frequently than not he learns to define mental deficiency in terms of a test score. He is not prepared for or closely supervised in his contacts with the parents of defective children, and is unaware of the psychological, familial, educational, and community aspects of the problem. What has just been said is a reflection of a more general problem which is beginning to concern some medical educators: medical education today does not train students to approach the patient as an organism which in addition to having physical symptoms also possesses a psychological system which has functioned and continues to function in a particular familial and social setting. To focus on the physical symptoms results in a narrow view of the case, making the recognition of present and the prevention of future problems difficult if not impossible. Insofar as the field of mental deficiency is concerned medical education shows the following lacks:

1. The student does not learn how to conduct an interview which has as its purpose the evocation of parental attitudes, goals, and anxieties in order to help them achieve a more realistic conception of and adjustment to their problems. To learn such interviewing techniques requires supervised experience which the student does not now receive. It is this lack which not only limits the amount of help which parents can receive from their contact with the physician but also has the effect of creating new or exacerbating old problems.

2. The student learns almost nothing about the educational aspects of mental deficiency: the relation of mental level to academic achievement, the nature and goals of special classes, and an understanding of the pedagogical-psychological problems confronting the special class teacher. Too frequently parents are led to expect a level of educational achievement from their child which is out of keeping with his capacities.

3. The student is not acquainted with the nature of community facilities or the criteria by which their quality can be judged. Physicians in general do not know whether the local school system has special classes for the educable and noneducable defective, whether there are special recreational facilities, or whether there is a local organization of parents of defective children.

When one realizes that parents frequently first learn about their child's condition from a physician, and that this initial contact is of prime importance in shaping their thinking, the significance of the lacks in medical education is clear.

    B. Pediatric training. Although pediatric educators have become increasingly aware of the necessity for the student to become a psychologically sensitive observer and counselor, the detailed instruction and supervision necessary to achieve such a goal are seldom provided. Very rarely does the pediatrician in training learn to understand the techniques and problems involved in therapeutically-oriented interviews with parents.[2] The kind of interviewing with which we have been concerned is not of the fact-finding variety in which one person asks and the other answers questions—if it were, one could print the questions and have the parent write out his answers. The kind of interviewing which we have been discussing requires more than a superficial knowledge of personality dynamics or an earnest desire to be of help. It requires a degree of self-understanding and a knowledge of the tactics necessary to influence another person's behavior which are best learned under the supervision of a more experienced person.[3] The pediatrician is seldom exposed to such a learning experience. In cases of mental deficiency it is also necessary to be aware of the familial and educational ramifications of a case—an awareness which the pediatrician generally does not have for the rather simple reason that he has not been taught to become aware of such factors. Where the pediatrician has such aware-

    [2] This is not to suggest that pediatricians, or any of the other personnel discussed in this chapter, should be or become psychotherapists. What is being suggested here is that these personnel should possess a sufficient understanding of personality dynamics and the psychotherapeutic process to enable them to meet the problems which by tradition and practice are brought to them. If one maintained the position (for which there is no particular justification) that only psychotherapists can adequately handle the problems raised in chapters 11 and 12, then the future in this field, in light of the dearth of psychotherapists, is indeed gloomy.

    [3] The reader has undoubtedly become aware of the importance which the writer attaches to supervision. There are several reasons for this emphasis: (a) students differ in the degree to which they are aware of how they strike or influence other people, (b) the beginner is not the best judge of the relation between what he did and what he wanted to do, (c) without some independent observer "wrong" techniques cannot be recognized and unlearned, (d) the welfare of the patient requires that the beginner's handling of the situation be controlled in some fashion. To conduct competently a psychotherapeutically-oriented interview cannot be learned from books, lectures, or even by observing an experienced person. One learns by doing under critical supervision. Without close supervision practice may result in the perfecting of inadequate techniques.

ness more often than not he does not possess the training in interviewing technique which would enable him to capitalize on his understanding. What further handicaps the physician in general and the pediatrician in particular is their lack of knowledge of the training, procedures, problems, and contributions of the psychologist or teacher. What knowledge they possess is usually based on a few lectures which by their nature are not likely to be revealing or helpful. As a result the pediatrician often does not understand (1) the contributions and limitations of a psychological examination, (2) the dangers involved in giving or reading a psychological report to parents, (3) the psychologist's need for time to interpret and integrate his findings, and (4) the importance of a detailed discussion between pediatrician and psychologist concerning the significance of the test findings in light of other knowledge of the case.

Another result of these "token" lectures is that the pediatrician is usually unaware of the pedagogical problems with which the teacher is faced in working with the defective child. Practically every special class teacher can point to several cases in which a problem arose with parents because of a pediatrician's unwarranted statement about a child's educational potentialities. This situation is probably due to two factors: the pediatrician's lack of knowledge of the relation between mental level and educational achievement and his failure, due to lack of previous experience, to effect an adequate liaison with the teacher. In more than a few cases a conference between teacher and pediatrician might have resulted in a more effective program for the child. The need for such conferences has long been recognized by the teacher but their value has not yet been adequately recognized by the pediatrician and general practitioner.

C. Psychiatric training. Although the psychiatrist in training receives a long and supervised training in conducting therapeutically-oriented interviews, his clinical experience is only in small part with the defective child and his family—witness how much of his training is in a state hospital or other agency where the patient population is predominantly composed of neurotic and psychotic individuals. In addition, because the training experiences of most psychiatrists are largely with adults his knowledge of children in general, and the defective child in particular, is relatively meagre. His criterion of mental deficiency is usually that of a test score, and his knowledge of the practices, goals, and problems of special education is equally superficial. Although the psychiatrist could be a key person in handling the adjustment problems of the defective child and his family, his training does not give him knowledge, derived either from lecture or clinical contact, of the problems in the field. As a result, when the psychiatrist does encounter the mentally defective child and his family, it is not surprising that his contribution is usually not much greater or more comprehensive than that of the specialists already discussed.[4]

The reader should bear in mind that the criticisms which have been made of medical education were made only in terms of its adequacy in preparing the practitioner for meeting the problems raised in the previous two chapters—problems of which the great majority of medical personnel are only dimly aware and unprepared to meet. If the failure to meet these problems did not overlook old and create new adjustment problems for child and family, then the lacks in medical education would obviously not be of serious import. The obligations of medical training may be put in this way: if a particular condition (e.g., mental deficiency) brings into play familial, educational, and community problems, then it should be the aim of training to enable the student to recognize and handle such problems.

The Clinical Psychologist

Although clinical psychology as a discipline grew out of attempts to identify, educate, and train the mentally defective child, the clinical student today gets very little experience with the defective child. Psychological theory, diagnostic testing, interviewing and psychotherapeutic techniques, clinical experience with a variety of adjustment problems— these are some of the course and experience requirements which the clinical student must meet. It is the rare graduate department of psychology which has as a requirement course instruction in or clinical experience with the psychological problems in mental deficiency. Too

---

[4] It is sometimes overlooked that work in the area of mental deficiency requires special knowledge and training, a fact which only the educators seem to have recognized and to have acted upon, witness the differences between the curricula and training of special class and other teachers. In medicine and psychology there are no special prerequisites which the student must complete before becoming a practitioner or specialist in the field of mental deficiency. Perhaps a more correct way of describing the situation would be to say that neither the field of medicine nor clinical psychology recognizes mental deficiency as areas of specialization.

frequently the clinical psychologist views the mental defective in terms only of psychological test scores—in light of his training there is little reason why he should adopt any other point of view.

Consequences of Inadequate Professional Training

The following comments may serve not only as a summary of what has so far been discussed but also may give the reader some idea of the consequences of the inadequacies of professional training. Although these comments were meant to characterize the past attitudes of the professions, they are applicable to the situation today.

". . . although tests were developed by psychologists, the field of psychology did not train students for work with the defective individual. The same situation existed in other fields whose members in one way or other came into contact with the defective individual. The general practitioner, pediatrician, psychiatrist, and social worker—none of these professionals received in their student days more than a most superficial understanding of the psychological problems of the subnormal individual. To the great majority of these professional people the defective child was one who received a low score on a psychological test. The community aspects of the problem, the parental conflicts and despairs, the lack of educational opportunities— these were the areas which were either overlooked or underemphasized. *It was only the educator who was aware of these problems, but in the main his concern was with the school aspects of the problem. The help and support which the educator needed from these other professional fields were not forthcoming. There was no real teamwork or understanding and the educator was left to grapple with a problem which had important medical, psychological, psychiatric, and sociological ramifications. Is it any wonder that the defective child was called the "forgotten child" in American society?*

"It is true that many institutions were built for the care of the subnormal child. But in many instances these institutions were built not because they reflected a new idea or approach, or reflected an attempt to cope with this many-sided problem, but because there were either no facilities in the community or because some well-intentioned but misguided individuals believed that all such children should be in institutions. Institutionalization may have solved what the community felt to be a problem but it obviously did not solve the problems of many parents and in many instances it did not solve, but rather added to, the problems of the child.

"When one looks at some of the tremendous edifices which were built, bearing in mind the relatively small professional staffs which they contained, one does not have to labor the point that much more often than not the particular needs of a particular child were either not recognized or satisfied.

"Not only did such institutions contain small professional staffs but the quality of such staff left much to be desired. In the student days of these professionals they were barely exposed to the psychological problems in the area. What is most likely is that they learned to view the subnormal child as a truly dull problem for study. If the psychiatrist in training was interested in research it was most unlikely that his interest would be focussed on the subnormal child. *How could one become interested in something to which one has been only barely exposed, and exposed in a fashion which would quickly extinguish rather than reinforce any awakening interest?*

"In addition, why should a budding professional take a job in an institution, where research was not supported, for a salary which would be far less than he could obtain in noninstitutional work? Although one could point to exceptions, the leaders in these various specialties would probably agree that those of their colleagues who have worked in institutions have not been of the best or near-best quality. This is not to say that the institutional child did not receive adequate medical care but rather that the other equally important aspects of his problem were neglected.

"One of the most serious consequences of the above situation has been the absence of basic research concerning the psychological aspects of the problem. Without such research practice becomes routinized and superficial, innovation and experimentation meet with resistance, and the field more and more becomes divorced from the mainstream of scientific advance. It takes money and time to do research, a distasteful fact to some people, but not to support research guarantees that our energies and monies will be wasted."[5]

THE TEACHER

It is clearly the teacher who spends the greatest amount of time with the defective child and frequently has the most contact with his parents. That the teacher, particularly the special class one, faces more than a pedagogical problem, can be seen from the following problems which are by no means rare:

1. Communicating to parents, who have not been so informed before, that their child is either mentally defective or retarded.

[5] S. B. Sarason, The psychology of the exceptional child. In *Proceedings of the 1952 Conference of the Child Research Clinic of the Woods Schools* (Langhorne, Pa.), 1952.

2. Informing parents that the school has no facilities for their non-educable defective child.
3. Explaining to parents why preschool predictions about their child's academic achievement were overly optimistic.
4. Discussing with parents why institutionalization is preferred solution for the needs and problems of their child.

As has been indicated before, many of these problem situations would never have arisen if those who had earlier seen the child had handled the defective child and his family more sensitively and comprehensively. What frequently happens is that the parents become hostile to the school personnel: accusing them of discriminatory practices, lack of understanding, and, not infrequently, sheer ignorance and incompetence. "My doctor told me that he would be able to go to school," "Nobody ever said there was anything wrong with my child," "How will he ever learn to read and write if you will not let him in school?" —these are a few of the statements which parents of defective children direct to school authorities.

Although it is clear that the teacher comes into close contact with parents, and is in a position to be of help to them, teacher training does not prepare the student for the proper handling of such relationships. While teacher training requires supervised teaching, there is no such requirement for the handling of parental problems and attitudes, even though teachers are becoming more and more involved in such situations. Whatever is required today for becoming a skilled teacher does not necessarily fit one for appropriate handling of the kinds of problems which we have been discussing.

The Future

There is little reason for believing that professional disinterest in the psychological aspects of mental deficiency is likely to change in any noticeable way in the near future. To expect such a change it would be necessary to assume that educators in the various fields are aware of the discrepancy between the nature of training and the problems inherent in a case of mental deficiency—an assumption for which there is little justification. In order for a change to be effected the following attitudes and practices will have to be combated:

1. Working with the mentally defective individual is dull and unrewarding—a professional "dead-end."
2. From the psychological and psychiatric point of view there are no major or fascinating research problems in the area of mental deficiency.
3. To handle adequately a case of mental deficiency does not require any special knowledge or training.
4. The possession of a particular professional title or training thereby equips one to assume responsibility in program planning for the mentally defective child.
5. One can make recommendations for the mentally defective child without working with the parents or having a knowledge of educational practices and facilities.

What has been said in this chapter represents conclusions based on the writer's clinical and teaching experiences. They, therefore, represent opinions—a class of data which is not always true or convincing. *What is very much needed in this area is a systematic and objective evaluation of the adequacy of professional training for meeting the problems we have discussed.* Such a study should attempt to answer the following questions:

1. At different stages of training or specialization within a professional area, with what kinds of *facts* about mental deficiency is the student or practitioner acquainted? With how many cases does he actually come into contact?
2. What is the nature and extent of formal instruction? How much of such instruction involves a consideration of the training and contribution of other professional specialists who work with the mentally defective child? How much actual contact is there among the various specialists?
3. What does the student learn about the nature and scope of community facilities?
4. Within any one discipline what are the attitudes of the student or practitioner towards the value of working in the field of mental deficiency? What are the bases for such attitudes? Why do some go into and others stay away from this area of work?

5. What does the student or practitioner feel about his competency in this area? What does he feel is or was lacking in his training?
6. How are cases actually handled? Are there any differences in handling between the pediatrician, psychologist, general practitioner, teacher, etc.?
7. What are the reactions of parents to their contacts with these professional specialists?

To conduct a study along the above lines would obviously not be a small undertaking but the results of such a study could go a long way in effecting a change in the nature and goals of professional training for those who are called upon to handle the psychological problems in cases of mental deficiency.

BIBLIOGRAPHY

1. Abel, T. M. A study of a group of subnormal girls successfully adjusted in industry and the community. *American Journal of Mental Deficiency*, 1940, *45*, 66–72.
2. Abel, T. M. Negro-white interpersonal relationships among institutionalized subnormal girls. *American Journal of Mental Deficiency*, 1942, *46*, 325–339.
3. Abel, T. M. Dominant behavior of institutionalized subnormal girls: an experimental study. *American Journal of Mental Deficiency*, 1943, *47*, 429–436.
4. Abel, T. M. Responses of Negro and white morons to the Thematic Apperception Test. *American Journal of Mental Deficiency*, 1945, *49*, 463–468.
5. Abel, T. M. The relationship between academic success and personality organization among subnormal girls. *American Journal of Mental Deficiency*, 1945, *50*, 251–256.
6. Abel, T. M. The Rorschach test and school success among mental defectives. *Rorschach Research Exchange*, 1945, *9*, 105–110.
7. Abel, T. M., and Humphreys, E. J. Institutional biographies of unstable subnormal girls. *American Journal of Mental Deficiency*, 1942, *46*, 514–518.
8. Abel, T. M., and Kinder, E. F. *The subnormal adolescent girl.* New York: Columbia University Press, 1942.
9. Abel, T. M., Piotrowski, Z., and Stone, G. Responses of Negro and white morons to the Rorschach test. *American Journal of Mental Deficiency*, 1944, *48*, 253–257.
10. Albert, K., and Warden, C. J. The level of performance in the white rat. *Science*, 1944, *100*, 476.
11. Albert, K., Hoch, P., and Waelsch, H. Preliminary report on the effect of glutamic acid administration in mentally retarded subjects. *Journal of Nervous and Mental Diseases*, 1946, *104*, 263–274.
12. Allan, W., Herndon, C. N., and Dudley, F. C. Some examples of the inheritance of mental deficiency: apparently sex-linked idiocy and microcephaly. *American Journal of Mental Deficiency*, 1944, *48*, 325–334.
13. Allen, F. H. *Psychotherapy with children.* New York: W. W. Norton & Company, Inc., 1942.

14. Anderson, V. V., and Fearing, F. M. *A study of the careers of three hundred twenty-two feebleminded persons.* New York: National Committee of Mental Hygiene, 1923.

15. Angus, L. R. Schizophrenia and schizoid conditions in students in a special school. *American Journal of Mental Deficiency,* 1948, *53,* 227–238.

16. Arieff, A. J., and Yacorzynski, G. K. Deterioration of patients with organic epilepsy. *Journal of Nervous and Mental Diseases,* 1942, *96,* 49–55.

17. Arthur, G. *A point scale of performance tests.* New York: Commonwealth Fund, 1930, vol. i.

18. Bakwin, H. Loneliness in infants. *American Journal of Diseases of Children,* 1942, *63,* 30–40.

19. Baller, W. R. A study of the present social status of a group of adults who, when they were in elementary schools, were classified as mentally deficient. *Genetic Psychology Monographs,* 1936, *18,* No. 3.

20. Bates, R. M. Three cases of phenylpyruvic oligophrenia. *Journal of Mental Science,* 1939, *85,* 273–275.

21. Bayley, N. Mental growth during the first three years. In R. G. Barker, J. S. Kounin, and H. F. Wright (eds.), *Child behavior and development.* New York: McGraw-Hill Book Company, Inc., 1943.

22. Beck, H. G. The Laurence-Biedl syndrome. Reports of two cases in one family. *Endocrinology,* 1929, *13,* 375–387.

23. Beck, S. J. The Rorschach test as applied to a feebleminded group. *Archives of Psychology,* 1932, No. 136.

24. Beck, S. J. Configurational tendencies in Rorschach responses. *American Journal of Psychology,* 1933, *45,* 433–443.

25. Beck, S. J. *Rorschach's test.* New York: Grune & Stratton, Inc., 1944, vol. i.

26. Beck, S. J. *Rorschach's test.* New York: Grune & Stratton, Inc., 1945, vol. ii.

27. Bell, J. E. *Projective techniques.* New York: Longmans, Green & Company, Inc., 1948.

28. Benda, C. E. The familial imbecile or oligo-encephaly as a morbid entity. *American Journal of Mental Deficiency,* 1944, *49,* 32–42.

29. Benda, C. E. *Mongolism and cretinism.* New York: Grune & Stratton, Inc., 1946.

30. Bender, L. A visual motor gestalt test and its clinical use. *Research Monographs of the American Orthopsychiatric Association,* 1938, No. 3.

31. Bender, L. Post-encephalitic behavior disorders in childhood. In J. B.

Neal (ed.), *Encephalitis, a clinical study*. New York: Grune & Stratton, Inc., 1942.

32. Bender, L. Childhood schizophrenia. Clinical study one hundred schizophrenic children. *American Journal of Orthopsychiatry*, 1947, *17*, 40–56.

33. Bender, L., and Yarnell, H. An observation nursery: a study of 250 children in the psychiatric division of Bellevue Hospital. *American Journal of Psychiatry*, 1941, *97*, 1158–1174.

34. Benedict, R. *Patterns of culture*. Boston: Houghton Mifflin Company, 1934.

35. Bice, H. V. Mental deficiency, moron level. In A. Burton and R. E. Harris (eds.), *Case histories in clinical and abnormal psychology*. New York: Harper & Brothers, 1947.

36. Bijou, S. W. The psychometric pattern approach as an aid to clinical analysis—a review. *American Journal of Mental Deficiency*, 1941, *46*, 354–362.

37. Bijou, S. W. A genetic study of the diagnostic significance of psychometric patterns. *American Journal of Mental Deficiency*, 1942, *47*, 171–177.

38. Bijou, S. W. An experimental analysis of Arthur performance quotients. *Journal of Consulting Psychology*, 1942, *6*, 247–252.

39. Binet, A., and Simon, T. *The development of intelligence in children*. Baltimore: Williams & Wilkins Company, 1916.

40. Bochner, R., and Halpern, F. *The clinical application of the Rorschach test*. New York: Grune & Stratton, Inc., 1945.

41. Bolles, M. M. The basis of pertinence. *Archives of Psychology*, 1937, No. 212.

42. Bradley, C. *Schizophrenia in children*. New York: The Macmillan Company, 1941.

43. Brushfield, T., and Wyatt, W. Hemiplegia associated with extensive naevus and mental defect. *British Journal of Children's Diseases*, 1927, *24*, 98–106, 209–213.

44. Buck, N. J. The H-T-P Technique: a qualitative and quantitative scoring manual. *Journal of Clinical Psychology*, 1948, *4*, 317–396.

45. Cardwell, V. E. *The cerebral palsied child and his care in the home*. New York: Association for the Aid of Crippled Children, 1947.

46. Chapin, H. D. Are institutions for infants necessary? *Journal of the American Medical Association*, 1915, *54*, 1–3.

47. Chidester, L., and Menninger, K. The application of psychoanalytic methods to the study of mental retardation. *American Journal of Orthopsychiatry*, 1936, *6*, 616–625.

48. Cianci, V. Home supervision of mental deficients in New Jersey. *American Journal of Mental Deficiency*, 1947, *51*, 519–524.
49. Clark, L. P. *The nature and treatment of amentia.* London: Brailliere, Tindall, and Cox, 1933.
50. Cobb, S. Personality as affected by lesions of the brain. In J. McV. Hunt (ed.), *Personality and the behavior disorders.* New York: Ronald Press, 1944.
51. Collins, A. L. Psychometric records of institutionalized epileptics. *Journal of Psychology*, 1941, *11*, 359–370.
52. Collins, A. L., Atwell, C. R., and Moore, M. Stanford-Binet response patterns in epileptics. *American Journal of Orthopsychiatry*, 1938, *8*, 51–63.
53. Cook, R. C. The Rh gene as a cause of mental deficiency. *Journal of Heredity*, 1944, *35*, 133–134.
54. Cooley, J. M. The relative amenability of dull and bright children to child guidance. *Smith College Studies in Social Work*, 1945–46, *16*, 26–43.
55. Cornell, W. S. *Health and medical inspection of school children.* Philadelphia: F. A. Davis Company, 1924.
56. Cotton, C. B. A study of the reactions of spastic children to certain test situations. *Journal of Genetic Psychology*, 1941, *58*, 27–44.
57. Cotzin, M. Group psychotherapy with mentally defective problem boys. *American Journal of Mental Deficiency*, 1948, *53*, 268–283.
58. Cotzin, M. Unpublished data supplied to the author (1948).
59. Crissey, O. L. Mental development as related to institutional residence and educational achievement. *University of Iowa Studies in Child Welfare*, 1937, *13*, No. 1.
60. Crothers, B. *Disorders of the nervous system in childhood.* New York: D. Appleton-Century Company, Inc., 1926.
61. Davies, S. P. *Social control of the mentally deficient.* New York: Thomas Y. Crowell Company, 1930.
62. Davis, A. American status systems and the socialization of the child. *American Sociological Review*, 1941, *6*, 345–354.
63. Davis, A., and Dollard, J. *Children of bondage.* Washington: American Council on Education, 1940.
64. Davis, A., Gardner, B. B., and Gardner, M. B. *Deep south.* Chicago: University of Chicago Press, 1941.
65. Dawson, S., and Conn, J. C. N. The intelligence of epileptic children. *Archives of Diseases of Childhood*, 1929, *4*, 142–151.
66. Des Lauriers, A., and Halpern, F. Psychological tests in childhood schizophrenia. *American Journal of Orthopsychiatry*, 1947, *17*, 57–67.

67. Doll, E. A. Psychological significance of cerebral birth lesions. *American Journal of Psychology*, 1933, *45*, 444–452.
68. Doll, E. A. The Vineland social maturity scale. *Manual of directions*. Vineland, N. J.: The Training School, 1935.
69. Doll, E. A. An annotated bibliography on the Vineland social maturity scale. *Journal of Consulting Psychology*, 1940, *4*, 123–132.
70. Doll, E. A. The essentials of an inclusive concept of mental deficiency. *American Journal of Mental Deficiency*, 1941, *46*, 214–219.
71. Doll, E. A. Practical implications of the endogenous-exogenous classification of mental defectives. *American Journal of Mental Deficiency*, 1946, *50*, 503–511.
72. Doll, E. A. The feebleminded child. In L. Carmichael (ed.), *Manual of child psychology*. New York: John Wiley & Sons, Inc., 1946.
73. Doll, E. A. Is mental deficiency curable? *American Journal of Mental Deficiency*, 1947, *51*, 420–428.
74. Doll, E. A. Feeble-mindedness versus intellectual retardation. *American Journal of Mental Deficiency*, 1947, *51*, 456–459.
75. Doll, E. A., and Murphy, D. P. A case of microcephaly following embryonic Roentgen irradiation. *American Journal of Psychiatry*, 1930, *9*, 871–878.
76. Doll, E. A., Phelps, W. M., and Melcher, R. T. *Mental deficiency due to birth injuries*. New York: The Macmillan Company, 1932.
77. Dubitscher, F. Der Rorschachsche formendeuteversuch bei erwachsenen psychopathen sowie psychopathischen und Schwachsinnigen Kindern. *Zeitschrift für die Gesamte Neurologie und Psychiatrie*, 1932, *138*, 515–535.
78. DuBois, C. Attitudes toward food and hunger in Alor. In L. Spier (ed.), *Language, culture, and personality*. Menasha, Wis.: Sapir Memorial Publication Fund, 1941.
79. DuBois, C. *The people of Alor*. Minneapolis: University of Minnesota Press, 1944.
80. Ehrenfest, H. Birth injuries of the child. *Gynecological and Obstetrical Monographs*, 2nd ed. New York: D. Appleton-Century Company, Inc., 1926.
81. Fairbank, R. E. The subnormal child—seventeen years after. *Mental Hygiene*, 1933, *17*, 177–208.
82. Falk, R., Penrose, L. S., and Clark, E. A. The search for intellectual deterioration among epileptic patients. *American Journal of Mental Deficiency*, 1945, *49*, 469–471.
83. Fernald, W. E. Standardized fields of inquiry for clinical studies of borderline defectives. *Mental Hygiene*, 1917, *1*, 211–234.

84. Ford, F. R. *Diseases of the nervous system in infancy, childhood and adolescence.* Springfield, Ill.: Charles C Thomas, 1944.

85. Ford, F. R., Crothers, B., and Putnam, M. C. Birth injuries of the central nervous system. *Medicine Monographs* No. 11. Baltimore: Williams & Wilkins Company, 1927.

86. Fox, J. T. The response of epileptic children to mental and educational tests. *British Journal of Medical Psychology,* 1924, *4,* 235–248.

87. Fox, M. J., and Borten, M. M. Rubella in pregnancy causing malformation in newborn. *Journal of the American Medical Association,* 1946, *130,* 568–569.

88. Frazeur, H. A., and Hoakley, P. Significance of psychological test results of exogenous and endogenous children. *American Journal of Mental Deficiency,* 1947, *51,* 384–388.

89. Frazier, R. L. Phenylpyruvic amentia. *American Journal of Mental Deficiency,* 1947, *51,* 577–586.

90. Freeman, F. N., Holzinger, K. J., and Mitchell, B. C. The influence of environment on the intelligence, school achievement, and conduct of foster children. Bloomington, Ill.: Public School Publishing Co., *Twenty-seventh Yearbook of the National Society for the Study of Education,* 1928, I, 101–217.

91. Friedman, A. P., and Roy, J. E. An unusual family syndrome. *Journal of Nervous and Mental Diseases,* 1944, *99,* 42–44.

92. Fries, M. E. Diagnosing the child's adjustment through age-level tests. *Psychoanalytic Review,* 1947, *34,* 1–31.

93. Fulton, J. F. *Physiology of the nervous system.* London: Oxford University Press, 1938.

94. Ganz, E., and Loosli-Usteri, M. Le test de Rorschach appliqué à 43 garcons anormaux. *Archives de Psychologie,* Genève, 1934, *24,* 245–255.

95. Gardner, L. P. Responses of idiots and imbeciles in a conditioning experiment. *American Journal of Mental Deficiency,* 1945, *50,* 59–80.

96. Gaudet, F. J., and Gaudet, H. The problem of the feebleminded patient in the mental hygiene clinic. *The Training School Bulletin* (Vineland, N. J.), 1940, May–June, 1–20.

97. Gellerman, L. W. Form discrimination in chimpanzees and two-year-old children. I. Discrimination of form *per se.* II. Form versus background. *Journal of Genetic Psychology,* 1933, *42,* 1–50.

98. Gesell, A. A behavior study of birth injury. *Proceedings of the American Association on Mental Deficiency,* 1938, *43,* 37–43.

99. Gesell, A., and Amatruda, C. S. *Developmental diagnosis.* New York: Paul B. Hoeber, Inc., 1947.

100. Gesell, A., and Ilg, F. L. *Infant and child in the culture of today.* New York: Harper & Brothers, 1943.

101. Gibbs, F. A., Gibbs, E. L., and Lennox, W. G. Electroencephalographic classification of epileptic patients and control subjects. *Archives of Neurology and Psychiatry,* 1943, *50,* 111–128.

102. Gill, M. Problems in clinical research. *American Journal of Orthopsychiatry,* 1947, *17,* 215–222.

103. Glassman, L. Is dull normal intelligence a contraindication for psychotherapy? *Smith College Studies in Social Work.* 1945, *13,* 275–298.

104. Goddard, H. H. *The Kallikak family.* New York: The Macmillan Company, 1912.

105. Goddard, H. H. *Feeble-mindedness: its causes and consequences.* New York: The Macmillan Company, 1923.

106. Goddard, H. H. In defense of the Kallikak study. *Science,* 1942, *95,* 574–576.

107. Goldfarb, W. Infant rearing and problem behavior. *American Journal of Orthopsychiatry,* 1943, *13,* 2, 249–265.

108. Goldfarb, W. The effects of early institutional care on adolescent personality. *Journal of Experimental Education,* 1943, *12,* 106–129.

109. Goldfarb, W. The effects of early institutional care on adolescent personality. *American Journal of Orthopsychiatry,* 1944, *14,* 441–447.

110. Goldfarb, W. Psychological privation in infancy and subsequent adjustment. *American Journal of Orthopsychiatry,* 1945, *15,* 247–255.

111. Goldfarb, W. Effects of psychological deprivation in infancy and subsequent stimulation. *American Journal of Psychiatry,* 1945, *102,* 18–33.

112. Goldfarb, W. Variations in adolescent adjustment of institutionally-reared children. *American Journal of Orthopsychiatry,* 1947, *17,* 449–457.

113. Goldfarb, W., and Klopfer, B. Rorschach characteristics of "institution children." *Rorschach Research Exchange,* 1944, *8,* 92–100.

114. Goldstein, K. *After-effects of brain injuries in war.* New York: Grune & Stratton, Inc., 1942.

115. Goldstein, K. Concerning rigidity. *Character and Personality,* 1942–1943, *11,* 209–226.

116. Goldstein, K. *Language and language disturbances.* New York: Grune & Stratton, Inc., 1948.

117. Goldstein, K., and Scheerer, M. Abstract and concrete behavior. An experimental study with special tests. *Psychological Monographs,* 1941, *53,* No. 2.

118. Goodenough, F. L., and Maurer, K. M. *Mental growth of children from two to fourteen years.* Minneapolis: University of Minnesota Press, 1942.

119. Gordon, H. Lefthandedness and mirror writing especially among defective children. *Brain,* 1920, *43,* 313–368.

120. Gothberg, L. C. A comparison of the personality of runaway girls with a control group as expressed in the themas of Murray's Thematic Apperception Test. *American Journal of Mental Deficiency,* 1947, *51,* 627–631.

121. Granich, L. *Aphasia: a guide to retraining.* New York: Grune & Stratton, Inc., 1948.

122. Gregg, N. M. Congenital cataracts following German measles in the mother. *Transactions of the Ophthalmological Society of Australia,* 1941, *3,* 35.

123. Gregg, N. W. Rubella during pregnancy of mother with its sequelae of congenital defects in the child. *Medical Journal of Australia,* 1945, *1,* 313–315.

124. Grinker, R. R. *Neurology,* 3rd ed. Springfield, Ill.: Charles C Thomas, 1946.

125. Hackbusch, F. The contribution of projective techniques to the understanding and treatment of children psychometrically diagnosed as feeble-minded. *American Journal of Mental Deficiency,* 1946, *51,* 15–34.

126. Halperin, S. L. Three pedigrees of microcephaly. *Journal of Heredity,* 1944, *35,* 211–214.

127. Halperin, S. L. Human heredity and mental deficiency. *American Journal of Mental Deficiency,* 1946, *51,* 153–163.

128. Harrison, R. Studies in the use and validity of the Thematic Apperception Test with mentally disordered patients. II. A qualitative study; III. Validation by the method of "blind analysis." *Character and Personality,* 1940, *9,* 122–138.

129. Harrower-Erickson, M. R. Personality changes accompanying cerebral lesions. *Archives of Neurology and Psychiatry,* 1940, *43,* 859–890; 1081–1107.

130. Harrower-Erickson, M. R. Psychological studies of patients with epileptic seizures. In W. Penfield and T. C. Erickson (eds.), *Epilepsy and cerebral localization.* Springfield, Ill.: Charles C Thomas, 1941.

131. Hartwell, S. W. *Fifty-five "bad" boys.* New York: Alfred A. Knopf, Inc., 1940.

132. Healy, W., and Bronner, A. F. *Treatment and what happened afterward.* Boston: Judge Baker Guidance Center, 1939.

133. Heath, S. R. Rail-walking performance as related to mental age and

etiological type among the mentally retarded. *American Journal of Psychology*, 1942, *55*, 240–247.

134. Heath, S. R. Clinical significance of motor defect with military implications. *American Journal of Psychology*, 1944, *57*, 487–499.

135. Hebb, D. O. The effect of early and late brain injury upon the test scores, and the nature of adult intelligence. *Proceedings of the American Philosophical Society*, 1942, *85*, 275–292.

136. Hegge, T. G. Occupational status of higher grade defectives in the present emergency. *American Journal of Mental Deficiency*, 1944, *49*, 86–98.

137. Herskovits, M. J. *Man and his works*. New York: Alfred A. Knopf, Inc., 1948.

138. Hetzer, H., and Wolf, K. Baby tests. *Zeitschrift für Psychologie*, 1928, *107*, 62–104.

139. Hilkevitch, R. R. A study of the intelligence of institutionalized epileptics of the idiopathic type. *American Journal of Orthopsychiatry*, 1946, *16*, 262–270.

140. Hoakley, P., and Frazeur, H. A. Significance of psychological test results of exogenous and endogenous children. *American Journal of Mental Deficiency*, 1945, *50*, 263–271.

141. Humphreys, E. J. Investigative psychiatry in the field of mental deficiency as shown by the proceedings of the American Association in Mental Deficiency. *Proceedings of the American Association on Mental Deficiency*, 1935, *40*, 195–206.

142. Humphreys, E. J. The field of psychiatry in relation to the work of the state school. *Proceedings of the American Association on Mental Deficiency*, 1938, *43*, No. 1, 80–89.

143. Humphreys, E. J., and Howe, S. Range of psychiatric material within the state school. *American Journal of Psychiatry*, 1942, *98*, 482–488.

144. Hutt, M. L. "Consecutive" and "adaptive" testing with the revised Stanford-Binet. *Journal of Consulting Psychology*, 1947, *11*, 93–103.

145. Hutton, L. Length of treatment in child guidance clinics. *Journal of Mental Science*, 1945, *91*, 511–517.

146. Ingalls, T. H., and Davies, J. A. V. Mongolism following intercurrent infectious disease in pregnancy. *New England Journal of Medicine*, 1947, *236*, 437–438.

147. Itard, J. M. G. *The wild boy of Aveyron*. (Trans. by G. and M. Humphrey.) New York: Appleton-Century Company, Inc., 1932.

148. Jervis, G. A. The genetics of phenylpyruvic oligophrenia. *Proceedings of the American Association on Mental Deficiency*, 1938–39, *44*, No. 2, 13–24.

149. Johnson, A. B. *Treatise on language.* Berkeley: University of California Press, 1947.
150. Johnson, W. *People in quandaries.* New York: Harper & Brothers, 1946.
151. Jolles, I. A study of mental deficiency by the Rorschach technique. *American Journal of Mental Deficiency,* 1947, *52,* 37–42.
152. Jolles, I. The diagnostic implications of Rorschach's test in case studies of mental defectives. *Genetic Psychology Monographs,* 1947, *36,* 93–197.
153. Juarros, C., and Soriano, M. Le Psychodiagnostik de Rorschach chez les enfants anormaux. *Conference Internationale de Psychologie de Paris,* 1927, 595–605.
154. Juarros, C., and Soriano, M. Comparative results of normal and abnormal children on the Rorschach test. *Archives Españoles de Pediatria,* 1929, *13,* 609–613.
155. Kallman, F. J., and Sander, G. The genetics of epilepsy. In P. H. Hoch and R. P. Knight (eds.), *Epilepsy.* New York: Grune & Stratton, Inc., 1947.
156. Kallman, F. J., Barrera, S. E., Hoch, P. H., and Kelley, D. M. The role of mental deficiency in the incidence of schizophrenia. *American Journal of Mental Deficiency,* 1940–1941, *45,* 514–539.
157. Kanner, L. Autistic disturbances of affective contact. *The Nervous Child,* 1943, *2,* 217–250.
158. Kardiner, A. *The individual and his society.* New York: Columbia University Press, 1939.
159. Kardiner, A. The concept of basic personality structure as an operational tool in the social sciences. In R. Linton (ed.), *The science of man in the world crisis.* New York: Columbia University Press, 1945.
160. Kelley, D. M., and Barrera, S. E. The Rorschach method in the study of mental deficiency. *American Journal of Mental Deficiency,* 1940–1941, *45,* 401–407.
161. Kennedy, R. J. R. *The social adjustment of morons in a Connecticut city.* Hartford: Mansfield-Southbury Training Schools (Social Service Department, State Office Building), 1948.
162. Kerr, M. The Rorschach test applied to children. *British Journal of Psychology,* 1934, *25,* 170–185.
163. Kinder, E. F., and Abel, T. M. A comparative study of institutionalized and noninstitutionalized subnormal girls. *Proceedings of the American Association on Mental Deficiency,* 1939, *44,* 169–177.
164. Kinder, E. F., and Hamlin, R. Consistency in test performance pattern

of mentally subnormal subjects. *Proceedings of the American Association on Mental Deficiency*, 1932, *42*, No. 2.

165. Kinsey, A. C., Pomeroy, W. B., and Martin, C. E. *Sexual behavior in the human male*. Philadelphia: W. B. Saunders Company, 1948.

166. Kirk, S. A. An evaluation of the study by Bernadine G. Schmidt entitled: Changes in personal, social and intellectual behavior of children originally classified as feebleminded. *Psychological Bulletin*, 1948, *45*, 321–333.

167. Klopfer, B., and Kelley, D. Mc. *The Rorschach technique*. Yonkers-on-Hudson: World Book Company, 1942.

168. Kounin, J. S. Experimental studies of rigidity. I. The measurement of rigidity in normal and feebleminded persons. II. The explanatory power of the concept of rigidity as applied to feeblemindedness. *Character and Personality*, 1941, *9*, 254–282.

169. Kounin, J. S. The meaning of rigidity: a reply to Heinz Werner. *Psychological Review*, 1948, *55*, 157–168.

170. Kutash, S. B. Performance of psychopathic defective criminals on the Thematic Apperception Test. *Journal of Criminal Psychopathology*, 1943, *5*, 319–340.

171. Lamm, S. S. Asphyxia as a cause of mental deficiency. *American Journal of Mental Deficiency*, 1943, *48*, 131–136.

172. Lantz, B. Some dynamic aspects of success and failure. *Psychological Monographs*, 1945, *59*, No. 1.

173. Laycock, S. R., and Clark S. The comparative performance of a group of old-dull and young-bright children on some items of the Revised Stanford-Binet scale of intelligence, form L. *Journal of Educational Psychology*, 1942, *33*, 1–12.

174. Lennox, W. G. The petit mal epilepsies. *Journal of the American Medical Association*, 1945, *129*, 1069–1074.

175. Lennox, W. G. Sixty-six twin pairs affected by seizures. In *Epilepsy* (Research Publications of the Association for Research in Nervous and Mental Disease). Baltimore: Williams & Wilkins Company, 1947.

176. Lennox, W. G., Gibbs, E. L., and Gibbs, F. A. Inheritance of cerebral dysrhythmia and epilepsy. *Archives of Neurology and Psychiatry*, 1940, *44*, 1155–1183.

177. Lennox, W. G., Gibbs, E. L., and Gibbs, F. A. Twins, brain waves and epilepsy. *Archives of Neurology and Psychiatry*, 1942, *47*, 702–706.

178. Lennox, W. G., Gibbs, E. L., and Gibbs, F. A. The brain-wave pattern, an hereditary trait. *Journal of Heredity*, 1945, *36*, 233–243.

179. Levine, P. Role of iso-immunization in transfusion accidents in preg-

nancy and in erythroblastosis fetalis. *American Journal of Obstetrics and Gynecology*, 1941, *42*, 165–166.

180. Levine, P., Katzin, E. M., and Burnham, L. Immunization in pregnancy: its possible bearing on etiology of erythroblastosis fetalis. *Journal of the American Medical Association*, 1941, *116*, 825–827.

181. Levy, D. M. *Maternal overprotection.* New York: Columbia University Press, 1943.

182. Levy, S., and Perry, H. A. Pertussis as a cause of mental deficiency. *American Journal of Mental Deficiency*, 1948, *52*, 217–226.

183. Levy, S., and Perry, H. A. The role of maternal illness during pregnancy in the etiology of mongolism. *American Journal of Mental Deficiency*, 1948, *53*, 284–293.

184. Lewin, K. *A dynamic theory of personality: selected papers.* (Trans. by Donald K. Adams and Karl E. Zener.) New York: McGraw-Hill Book Company, Inc., 1935.

185. Lewinski, R. J. The psychometric pattern: I. Anxiety neurosis. *Journal of Clinical Psychology*, 1945, *1*, 214–221.

186. Lewis, E. D. Types of mental deficiency and their social significance. *Journal of Mental Science*, 1933, *79*, 298–304.

187. Line, W. The development of visual perception. *British Journal Psychological Monographs*, 1931, No. 15.

188. Little, W. J. On the influence of abnormal parturition, difficult labors, premature birth, asphyxia neonatorum, on the mental and physical condition of the child, especially in relation to deformities. *Transactions of the Obstetrical Society of London*, 1862, *3*, 293–342.

189. Lord, E. E. A study of the mental development of children with lesions in the central nervous system. *Genetic Psychology Monographs*, 1930, *7*, 365–486.

190. Lord, E. E. *Children handicapped by cerebral palsy.* New York: Commonwealth Fund, 1937.

191. Lowrey, L. G. Personality distortion and early institutional care. *American Journal of Orthopsychiatry*, 1940, *10*, 576–585.

192. Lurie, L. A., and Levy, S. Personality changes and behavior disorders of children following pertussis. *Journal of the American Medical Association*, 1942, *120*, 890–894.

193. Lurie, L. A., Levy, S., and Rosenthal, F. M. The defective delinquent. *American Journal of Orthopsychiatry* 1944, *14*, 95–103.

194. Masserman, J. H., and Balken, E. R. The clinical application of phantasy studies. *Journal of Psychology*, 1938, *6*, 81–88.

195. Maurer, K. M. *Intellectual status at maturity as a criterion for selecting*

items in preschool tests. Minneapolis: University of Minnesota Press, 1946.

196. Mautner, H. Spina bifida occulta and Spinal dysraphism in feebleminded. *American Journal of Mental Deficiency,* 1948, *53,* 239–246.

197. Mayman, M., and Rapaport, D. Diagnostic testing in convulsive disorders. In P. H. Hoch and R. P. Knight (eds.), *Epilepsy.* New York: Grune & Stratton, Inc., 1947.

198. McCoy, A. D., and Voris, H. C. Sturge-Weber syndrome. *Archives of Neurology and Psychiatry,* 1948, *59,* 504–510.

199. McFadden, J. H. Differential responses of normal and feebleminded subjects of equal mental age, on the Kent-Rosanoff free association test and the Stanford revision of the Binet-Simon intelligence test. *Mental Measurement Monographs,* 1931, No. 7.

200. McGovern, J., and Yannet, H. Asymmetric spastic infantile cerebral palsy. *American Journal of Diseases of Children,* 1947, *74,* 121–129.

201. McHugh, G. Changes in I.Q. at the public school kindergarten level. *Psychological Monographs,* 1943, *55,* No. 2.

202. McIntire, J. T. The incidence of feeblemindedness in the cerebral palsied. *Proceedings of the American Association on Mental Deficiency,* 1938, *43,* 44–50.

203. McIntire, J. T. A study of the distribution of physical handicap and mental diagnosis in cerebral palsied children. *American Journal of Mental Deficiency,* 1947, *51,* 624–626.

204. McNemar, Q. *The revision of the Stanford-Binet scale.* Boston: Houghton Mifflin Company, 1942.

205. McPherson, G. Preliminary consideration of the heredity of mental deficiency. *Proceedings of the American Association on Mental Deficiency,* 1936–1937, *42,* 124–131.

206. Mead, M. *Coming of age in Samoa.* New York: William Morrow & Company, Inc., 1928.

207. Mead, M. *Sex and temperament in three primitive societies.* New York: William Morrow & Company, Inc., 1935.

208. Mickelson, P. The feebleminded parent: a study of 90 cases. *American Journal of Mental Deficiency,* 1947, *51,* 644–653.

209. Miller, N. E., and Dollard, J. *Social learning and imitation.* New Haven: Yale University Press, 1941.

210. Mintz, A. Lateral preferences of a group of mentally subnormal boys. *Journal of Genetic Psychology,* 1947, *71,* 75–84.

211. Mowrer, O. II., and Kluckhohn, C. Dynamic theory of personality. In

J. McV. Hunt (ed.), *Personality and the behavior disorders,* chapter 3. New York: Ronald Press, 1944.

212. Muench, G. A. A follow-up of mental defectives after eighteen years. *Journal of Abnormal and Social Psychology,* 1944, *39,* 407–418.

213. Munn, N. L., and Stiening, B. R. The relative efficacy of form and background in a child's discrimination of visual patterns. *Journal of Genetic Psychology,* 1931, *39,* 73–90.

214. Munro, T. A. *The genetics of phenylketonuria.* London: Cambridge University Press, 1941.

215. Murphy, D. P. Ovarian irradiation; its effect on the health of subsequent children. *Surgery, Gynecology, and Obstetrics,* 1928, *47,* 201–215.

216. Murphy, D. P. *Congenital malformations.* Philadelphia: University of Pennsylvania Press, 1940.

217. Murphy, D. P., Shirlock, M. E., and Doll, E. A. Microcephaly following maternal pelvic irradiation for the interruption of pregnancy. *American Journal of Roentgenology and Radiation Therapy,* 1942, *48,* 356–359.

218. Murray, H. A. *Explorations in personality: a clinical and experimental study of fifty men of college age.* New York: Oxford University Press, 1938.

219. Murray, H. A. *Manual for the thematic apperception test.* Cambridge: Harvard University Press, 1945.

220. Neal, J. B. (ed.). *Encephalitis, a clinical study.* New York: Grune & Stratton, Inc., 1942.

221. Oberholzer, E. Zur differentialdiagnose psychischer folgezustaende nach Schaedeltraumen mittels des Rorschach'schem formdeuteversuchs. *Zeitschrift Gesamte Neurologie und Psychiatrie,* 1931, *136,* 596–629.

222. Odoroff, M. E. The occupational background of cerebral palsy. *American Journal of Mental Deficiency,* 1945, *49,* 369–372.

223. Orlansky, H. Infant care and personality. *Psychological Bulletin,* 1949, *46,* 1–48.

224. Parsons, L. G. Maternal rubella as a cause of congenital defects. *British Medical Bulletin,* 1946, *4,* 193–196.

225. Paster, S. Group psychotherapy for combat neuroses. *American Journal of Orthopsychiatry,* 1944, *14,* 53–68.

226. Paster, S. Group psychotherapy in an Army general hospital. *Mental Hygiene,* 1944, *28,* 529–537.

227. Patterson, H. A., and Fonner, D. Some observations on the intelligence quotient in epileptics. *Psychiatric Quarterly,* 1928, *2,* 542–548.

228. Patterson, M., and Magaw, D. C. An investigation of the validity of the Rorschach technique as applied to mentally defective problem children. *Proceedings of the American Association on Mental Deficiency,* 1938, *43,* No. 2, 179–185.

229. Patterson, R. M. Significance of practice effect on readministration of the Grace Arthur Performance Scale to high grade mentally deficient children. *American Journal of Mental Deficiency,* 1946, *50,* 393–401.

230. Patterson, R. M. Analysis of practice effect on readministration of the Grace Arthur Scale in relation to academic achievement of mentally deficient children. *American Journal of Mental Deficiency,* 1948, *52,* 337–341.

231. Penrose, L. S. *Mental defect.* New York: Farrar & Rinehart, Inc., 1934.

232. Penrose, L. S. Two cases of phenylpyruvic amentia. *The Lancet,* 1935, *228,* 23–24.

233. Penrose, L. S. *A clinical and genetic study of 1280 cases of mental defect.* Medical Research Council. London: His Majesty's Stationery Office, 1938. (No. 229.)

234. Pfister, O. Results of the Rorschach test with oligophrenics. *Allgemeine Zeitschrift für Psychiatrie,* 1925, *82,* 198–223.

235. Phelps, W. M. In *Hearings before the Committee on Labor (Subcommittee on Aid to Physically Handicapped), House of Representatives, Seventy-ninth Congress.* (October 11, 1945.) Washington: Government Printing Office, 1945.

236. Phelps, W. M. In *Conference on the cerebral palsied child.* Los Angeles: Crippled Children's Society of Los Angeles County, 1946.

237. Piotrowski, Z. A. The Rorschach ink-blot method in organic disturbances of the central nervous system. *Journal of Nervous and Mental Diseases,* 1937, *86,* 525–537.

238. Potter, H. W. Schizophrenia in children. *American Journal of Psychiatry,* 1933, *89,* 1253–1270.

239. Preiser, S. A., and Davenport, C. B. Multiple neurofibromatosis (Von Recklinghausen's disease) and its inheritance: with description of a case. *American Journal of the Medical Sciences,* 1918, *156,* 507–540.

240. Price, J. C., Waelsch, H., and Putnam, T. J. dl-glutamic acid hydrochloride in the treatment of petit mal and psychomotor seizures. *Journal of the American Medical Association,* 1943, *122,* 1153–1156.

241. Quinn, K. V., and Tagdell, H. A. A study of Little's disease. *Proceedings of the American Association on Mental Deficiency,* 1939, *44,* 64–71.

242. Ramsay, H. H. Treatment of epilepsy with tridione. *American Journal of Mental Deficiency*, 1946, *51*, 193–194.

243. Rank, B. Adaptation of the psychoanalytic technique for the treatment of young children with atypical development. *American Journal of Orthopsychiatry*, 1949, *19*, 130–139.

244. Rapaport, D. *Diagnostic psychological testing*. Chicago: Year Book Publishers, Inc., 1945, vols. i, ii.

245. Rau, M. M. Mental deficiency in relation to intermarriage. *Child Development*, 1935, *6*, 213–226.

246. Rautman, A. L. Relative difficulty of test items of the revised Stanford-Binet: an analysis of records. from a low intelligence group. *Journal of Experimental Education*, 1942, *10*, 183–194.

247. Read, G. D. *Childbirth without fear*. New York: Harper & Brothers, 1944.

248. Rheingold, H. L. Interpreting mental retardation to parents. *Journal of Consulting Psychology*, 1945, *9*, 142–148.

249. Ribble, M. A. *The rights of infants*. New York: Columbia University Press, 1943.

250. Rogers, C. R. Three surveys of treatment measures used with children. *American Journal of Orthopsychiatry*, 1937, 7, 48–57.

251. Rogers, C. R. *Counseling and psychotherapy*. New York: Houghton Mifflin Company, 1942.

252. Rorschach, H. *Psychodiagnostics*. New York: Grune & Stratton, Inc., 1942.

253. Rotter, J. B. Studies in the use and validity of the Thematic Apperception Test with mentally disordered patients. I. Method of analysis and clinical problems. *Character and Personality*, 1940, *9*, 18–34.

254. Sachs, B. On arrested cerebral development with special reference to its cortical pathology. *Journal of Nervous and Mental Disease*, 1887, *14*, 541–553.

255. Sachs, B. A family form of idiocy. *New York State Journal of Medicine*, 1896, *63*, 697–703.

256. Sarason, E. K., and Sarason, S. B. A problem in diagnosing feeblemindedness. *Journal of Abnormal and Social Psychology*, 1945, *40*, 323–329.

257. Sarason, S. B. The use of the Thematic Apperception Test with mentally deficient children. I. A study of high grade girls. II. A study of high grade boys. *American Journal of Mental Deficiency*, 1943, *47*, 414–421; 1943, *48*, 169–173.

258. Sarason, S. B. Projective techniques in mental deficiency. *Character and Personality*, 1945, *13*, 237–245.

259. Sarason, S. B., and Potter, E. H. Color in the Rorschach and Kohs block designs. *Journal of Consulting Psychology*, 1947, *11*, 202–206.

260. Sarason, S. B., and Sarason, E. K. The discriminatory value of a test pattern in the high grade familial defective. *Journal of Clinical Psychology*, 1946, *2*, 38–49.

261. Sarason, S. B., and Sarason, E. K. The discriminatory value of a test pattern with cerebral palsied, defective children. *Journal of Clinical Psychology*, 1947, *3*, 141–147.

262. Schaefer-Simmern, H. *The unfolding of artistic activity*. Berkeley: University of California Press, 1948.

263. Schaefer-Simmern, H., and Sarason, S. B. The therapeutic effects of artistic activity. *American Journal of Mental Deficiency*, 1944, *49*, 185–196.

264. Schmidt, B. G. Changes in personal, social, and intellectual behavior of children originally classified as feebleminded. *Psychological Monographs*, 1946, *60*, No. 5.

265. Schmidt, B. G. A reply. *Psychological Bulletin*, 1948, *45*, 334–343.

266. Schott, E. L. Superior intelligence in patients with Fröhlich's syndrome. *Journal of Applied Psychology*, 1938, *22*, 395–399.

267. Schreiber, F. Mental deficiency from paranatal asphyxia. *Proceedings of the American Association on Mental Deficiency*, 1939, *44*, No. 1, 95–106.

268. Schroeder, P. L. Behavior difficulties in children associated with the results of birth trauma. *Journal of the American Medical Association*, 1929, *92*, 100–104.

269. Seipt, I. S. (ed.) Psychotherapy for the exceptional child. *Proceedings of the Tenth Institute of the Child Research Clinic of the Woods Schools*, Langhorne, Pa. The Woods Schools, 1943.

270. Sherif, M. *An outline of social psychology*. New York: Harper & Brothers, 1948.

271. Sherif, M., and Cantril, H. *The psychology of ego-involvements*. New York: John Wiley & Sons, Inc., 1947.

272. Skeels, H. M., and Dye, H. B. A study of the effects of differential stimulation on mentally retarded children. *Proceedings of the American Association on Mental Deficiency*, 1939, *44*, No. 1, 114–136.

273. Skodak, M. Intellectual growth of children in foster homes. In R. G. Barker, J. Kounin, and H. Wright (eds.), *Child behavior and development*. New York: McGraw-Hill Book Company, Inc., 1943.

274. Sloan, W. Mental deficiency as a symptom of personality disturbance. *American Journal of Mental Deficiency*, 1947, *52*, 31–36.

275. Sloan, W. Prediction of extramural adjustment of mental defectives by use of the Rorschach test. *Journal of Consulting Psychology*, 1948, *12*, 303–309.

276. Sloan, W., and Guertin, W. H. A comparison of H-T-P and Wechsler-Bellevue I.Q.'s in mental defectives. *Journal of Clinical Psychology*, 1948, *4*, 424–426.

277. Smith, G. B. Cerebral accidents of childhood and their relationships to mental deficiency. *Welfare Magazine*, 1926, *17*, 18–33.

278. Snyder, L. H., Schonfeld, M. D., and Offerman, E. M. The Rh factor and feeble-mindedness. *Journal of Heredity*, 1945, *36*, 9–10.

279. Spitz, R. A. Hospitalism. In *The psychoanalytic study of the child*. New York: International Universities Press, 1945 and 1946, vols. i, ii.

280. Stewart, R. M. Observations on the pathology of cerebral diplegia. *Proceedings of the Royal Society of Medicine*, 1942, *36*, 25–32.

281. Stoddard, G. D. *The meaning of intelligence*. New York: The Macmillan Company, 1947.

282. Strauss, A. A. Typology in mental deficiency: its clinical, psychological and educational implications. *American Journal of Mental Deficiency*, 1939, *44*, 85–90.

283. Strauss, A. A. The incidence of central nervous system involvement in higher grade moron children. *American Journal of Mental Deficiency*, 1940–1941, *45*, 548–554.

284. Strauss, A. A., and Kephart, N. C. Behavior differences in mentally retarded children measured by a new behavior rating scale. *American Journal of Psychiatry*, 1940, *96*, 1117–1123.

285. Strauss, A. A., and Lehtinen, L. E. *Psychopathology and education of the brain-injured child*. New York: Grune & Stratton, Inc., 1947.

286. Strauss, A. A., and Werner, H. Disorders of conceptual thinking in the brain-injured child. *Journal of Nervous and Mental Diseases*, 1942, *96*, 153–172.

287. Strauss, A. A., and Werner, H. Comparative psychopathology of the brain-injured child and the traumatic brain-injured adult. *American Journal of Psychiatry*, 1943, *99*, 835–838.

288. Strother, C. R. Evaluating intelligence. *The Crippled Child*, 1945, *23*, 82–83.

289. Sullivan, E. B., and Gahagan, L. On intelligence of epileptic children. *Genetic Psychology Monographs*, 1935, *17*, 309–376.

290. Swan, C., Tostevin, A. L., Mayo, H. and Black, G. H. B. Congenital defects in infants following infectious diseases during pregnancy. *Medical Journal of Australia*, 1943, *2*, 201–210.

291. Swan, C., Tostevin, A. L., Mayo, H., and Black, G. H. B. Further observation on congenital defects in infants following infectious diseases during pregnancy, with especial reference to rubella. *Medical Journal of Australia*, 1944, *1*, 409–413.

292. Terman, L. M., and Merrill, M. A. *Measuring intelligence*. Boston: Houghton Mifflin Company, 1937.

293. Teska, P. T. The mentality of hydrocephalics and a description of an interesting case. *Journal of Psychology*, 1947, *23*, 197–206.

294. Thompson, C. W., and Magaret, A. Differential test responses of normals and mental defectives. *Journal of Abnormal and Social Psychology*, 1947, *42*, 285–293.

295. Thorne, F. C. Developmental studies of pyramidal spasticity. *American Journal of Mental Deficiency*, 1944, *49*, 43–51.

296. Thorne, F. C. The anticonvulsant action of tridione. *Psychiatric Quarterly*, 1945, 686–691.

297. Thorne, F. C. Counseling and psychotherapy with mental defectives. *American Journal of Mental Deficiency*, 1948, *52*, 263–271.

298. Thorne, F. C., and Andrews, J. S. Unworthy parental attitudes toward mental defectives. *American Journal of Mental Deficiency*, 1946, *50*, 411–418.

299. Town, C. H. *Familial feeblemindedness*. Buffalo: Foster & Stewart Pub. Corp., 1939.

300. Tredgold, A. F. *Mental deficiency*, 1st ed. New York: William Wood and Co., 1908.

301. Tredgold, A. F. *A text-book of mental deficiency*, 6th ed. Baltimore: William Wood and Co., 1937.

302. Tredgold, A. F. *A text-book of mental deficiency*, 7th ed. Baltimore: Williams & Wilkins Company, 1947.

303. Vernon, P. E. Recent work on the Rorschach test. *Journal of Mental Science*, 1935, *81*, 894–920.

304. Waelsch, H., and Price, J. C. Biochemical aspects of glutamic acid therapy for epilepsy. *Archives of Neurology and Psychiatry*, 1944, *51*, 393–396.

305. Waggoner, R. W., Scharenberg, K. L., and Schilling, M. E. Agenesis of the white matter with idiocy. *American Journal of Mental Deficiency*, 1942, *47*, 20–24.

306. Wallin, J. E. W. A statistical study of the individual tests in the Stanford-Binet scale. *Mental Measurement Monographs*, 1929, No. 6.

307. Wallin, J. E. W., and Hultsch, C. L. The pathognomonic significance of psychometric patterns. *American Journal of Mental Deficiency*, 1944, *48*, 269–277.

308. Warkany, J. Some factors in the etiology of congenital malformations. *American Journal of Mental Deficiency,* 1945, *50,* 231–241.

309. Warner, W. L., and Lunt, P. S. *The social life of the modern community.* New Haven: Yale University Press, 1942.

310. Warner, W. L., Havighurst, R. J., and Loeb, M. B. *Who shall be educated?* New York: Harper & Brothers, 1944.

311. Wechsler, D. *The measurement of adult intelligence.* Baltimore: Williams & Wilkins Company, 1941.

312. Wechsler, I. *A textbook of clinical neurology with an introduction to the history of neurology,* 6th ed. Philadelphia: W. B. Saunders Company, 1947.

313. Wegman, B. S. Intelligence as a factor in the treatment of problem children. *Smith College Studies in Social Work,* 1943, *14,* 244–245.

314. Werner, H. Perceptual behavior of brain-injured, mentally defective children: an experimental study by means of the Rorschach technique. *Genetic Psychology Monographs,* 1945, *31,* 51–110.

315. Werner, H. Abnormal and subnormal rigidity. *Journal of Abnormal and Social Psychology,* 1946, *41,* 15–24.

316. Werner, H. The concept of rigidity: a critical evaluation. *Psychological Review,* 1946, *53,* 43–52.

317. Werner, H., and Strauss, A. A. Types of visuo-motor activity in their relation to low and high performance ages. *American Journal of Mental Deficiency,* 1939, *44,* 163–168.

318. Werner, H., and Strauss, A. A. Causal factors in low performance. *American Journal of Mental Deficiency,* 1940–1941, *45,* 213–218.

319. Werner, H., and Strauss, A. A. Pathology of figure-background relation in the child. *Journal of Abnormal and Social Psychology,* 1941, *36,* 236–248.

320. Werner, H., and Thuma, B. D. A deficiency in the perception of apparent motion in children with brain injury. *American Journal of Psychology,* 1942, *55,* 58–67.

321. Werner, H., and Thuma, B. D. Critical flicker-frequency in children with brain injury. *American Journal of Psychology,* 1942, *55,* 394–399.

322. Whiting, J. W. M. *Becoming a Kwoma.* New Haven: Yale University Press, 1941.

323. Wiener, A. S., and Brody, M. The encephalopathy (Kernicterus) of erythroblastosis fetalis, its serologic diagnosis and pathogenesis. *American Journal of Mental Deficiency,* 1946, *51,* 1–14.

324. Witmer, H. L. *Psychiatric interviews with children.* New York: Commonwealth Fund, 1946.

325. Wittenborn, J. R., and Sarason, S. B. Exceptions to Rorschach criteria of pathology. *Journal of Consulting Psychology*. In press (1949).

326. Woodworth, R. S. Heredity and environment. *Bulletin 47*. New York: Social Science Research Council, 1941.

327. Yakolev, P. I., Weinberger, M., and Chipman, C. C. Heller's syndrome as a pattern of schizophrenic behavior disturbance in early childhood. *American Journal of Mental Deficiency*, 1948, *53*, 318–337.

328. Yannet, H. The etiology of congenital cerebral palsy. *Journal of Pediatrics*, 1944, *24*, 38–45.

329. Yannet, H. Diagnostic classification of patients with mental deficiency. *American Journal of Diseases of Children*, 1945, 70, 83–88.

330. Yannet, H. The care of the epileptic child in residential schools in America. *The Nervous Child*, 1947, *6*, 93–98.

331. Yannet, H. Mental Deficiency. In A. G. Mitchell and W. E. Nelson (eds.), *Textbook of pediatrics*, 5th ed. Philadelphia: W. B. Saunders (to be published).

332. Yannet, H., and Lieberman, R. The Rh factor in the etiology of mental deficiency. *American Journal of Mental Deficiency*, 1944, *49*, 133–137.

333. Yannet, H., and Lieberman, R. A and B iso-immunization as a possible factor in the etiology of mental deficiency. *American Journal of Mental Deficiency*, 1945, *50*, 242–244.

334. Yannet, H., and Lieberman, R. Further studies on ABO isoimmunization, secretor status and mental deficiency. *American Journal of Mental Deficiency*, 1948, *52*, 314–317.

335. Yepsen, L. N., and Cianci, V. Home training for mentally deficient children in New Jersey. *The Training School Bulletin* (Vineland, N. J.), 1946, *43*, 21–26.

336. Zimmerman, F. T., and Ross, S. Effect of glutamic acid and other amino acids on maze learning in the white rat. *Archives of Neurology and Psychiatry*, 1944, *51*, 446–451.

337. Zimmerman, F. T., Burgemeister, B. B., and Putnam, T. J. Effect of glutamic acid on mental functioning in children and in adolescents. *Archives of Neurology and Psychiatry*, 1946, *56*, 489–506.

338. Zimmerman, F. T., Burgemeister, B. B., and Putnam, T. J. A group study of the effect of glutamic acid upon mental functioning in children and adolescents. *Psychosomatic Medicine*, 1947, *9*, 175–183.

339. Zubin, J. *Manual of projective and cognate techniques*. Madison, Wis.: College Typing Co., 1948.

PART TWO

•

Psychological and Cultural Problems
in Mental Subnormality:
A Review of Research

SEYMOUR B. SARASON
THOMAS GLADWIN

ACKNOWLEDGMENTS

We wish to express our deep appreciation to Dr. Masland for setting up our end of the project in a manner such that we could function in what for us was an efficient manner. In addition to preparing his own report, and grappling with more than the usual budget gymnastics, he was always on the lookout in his travels, reading, and thinking for information which might be relevant to our report. For all of this we are indeed grateful. We also wish to express our gratitude to Mr. Roy J. Jones who in an early phase of the survey helped us greatly in a preliminary review of the literature.

It is a source of pleasure to us that we can publicly acknowledge our indebtedness to Mrs. Iris Keim who was of inestimable value to us in countless ways in the preparation of this report. It is difficult to see how without her help this report could have been finished in time.

During the past year we visited numerous places and people over the country in order to find out what research was being done and also to try out in a preliminary fashion some of the ideas which were developing as a result of our own work. To all of these we extend our thanks for their hospitality and stimulation.

I. INTRODUCTION

The report which follows was written by a psychologist and an anthropologist.[1] The participation of an anthropologist in this undertaking reflects a conviction on the part of both authors that real understanding of the nature and implications of subnormality can only be approached by paying more than lip service to the fact that this is a social and cultural as well as a biological and psychological problem. In our society the problem looms large, statistically, financially, and emotionally; in most non-European societies it is inconsequential, confined to cases of severe pathological defect who are cared for, as long as they live, with a minimum of distress or dislocation. The difference lies in culturally determined attitudes, behaviors, and criteria of social acceptability, as we shall endeavor to make clear. Therefore, although we shall be concerned primarily with the sources of retardation rooted in the individual and his environment, we must pay equal attention to the way in which society defines, perceives, reacts to, and attempts to cope with mental subnormality regardless of its origin. Even a child with severe mental defect must be viewed as deficient *relative to* cultural standards of acceptability; the cause of his deficiency may be organic, but its magnitude is dependent upon social criteria.

Viewed in a different light, the study of mental subnormality can make important theoretical and substantive contributions to our understanding of the nature and development of normal intellectual functioning, in much the same way that we have enriched our understanding of normal biological and psychological processes through the study of pathologies in those spheres of functioning. In this way, for example, we can relate deficits in childhood learning to failures and successes in later adjustment and thus obtain a clearer picture of those aspects of learning (the acquisition of culture) most essential for social living, and at the same time isolate cognitive or intellectual components from the totality of demands a society makes on its members. One of our primary objectives in writing this report is to present the problem in terms which we hope will encourage social scientists, who have thus far been almost totally uninterested, to view mental subnormality as an important research area. We also hope to lure more psychologists, psychiatrists, and others whose disciplines are already somewhat represented in the field, to join our ranks, and perhaps provide them with a few fresh perspectives. There are undoubtedly many reasons for the lack of interest

---

[1]Reprinted by permission of The Journal Press. Copyright, 1957, by The Journal Press.

by competent researchers in subnormal mental ability, but we believe few if any of these reasons have a realistic basis. We are convinced that the result of this disinterest has been a serious loss in the development of the science of human behavior as well as a failure by our society to come to grips with a problem it has itself largely created.

Our primary concern is necessarily with etiology. The fact that subnormality can only be meaningful with reference to some external criterion of normality is important, but from a practical point of view it would be unrealistic to hope for a change in the cultural standards of mental normality sufficient to resolve the problems with which we are here concerned. We must therefore take as our point of departure the realization that only a minority of the population falls into that end of the distribution we label "subnormal." In seeking the causes of the misfortunes of this minority we immediately discover the multiplicity of factors operative within individuals and within groups which culminate in a diagnosis of subnormality, and we find that this diagnosis itself is highly variable and dependent upon shifting criteria. Under these conditions it is not surprising that the field at present has some of the attributes of chaos, particularly from the research point of view. No matter how determined our intentions we cannot hope with two reports to bring all the issues into orderly focus, and will be satisfied if we can clarify the range of questions which must be answered before such order can be achieved.

We begin by attempting to indicate in a general way the major cultural and psychological research problems which mental retardation presents. Before taking up in detail the variety of factors subsumed under the term cultural, we consider it necessary to, discuss two problems. The first concerns the criteria, reviewed in Section III, by which one judges the significance of test results, more specifically, the failure to study systematically the relations between problem-solving behavior in test and non-test situations. The second problem concerns some recent contributions to conceptions of intelligence and their implications for the measurement or evaluation of intellectual functioning (Section IV). In Section V we discuss the implications of widespread belief in the heredity of mental subnormality; the lack of a demonstrable basis for this belief with respect to mental retardation leads us to a closer examination of environmental factors, particularly those which are culturally determined. Section VI therefore constitutes a critical review of existing research relevant to the cultural determinants of both normal and subnormal intellectual performance as this is expressed in intelligence test

results, while Section VII suggests the questions which must be explored
with reference to the broader implications of intellectual performance in social
living as a whole, including the later adequacy of persons who were judged
retarded while of school age or on the basis of test scores.

Sections VIII and IX primarily concern the severely defective child. Because misconceptions about these cases are fairly extensive—both in terms of
varieties of behavior which may be observed and the importance of the
research problems which such behavior presents—we have more than elsewhere in this report quoted rather extensively from the clinical literature.

In Section X our discussion concerns the so-called higher grades of
mental deficiency. The research we shall be discussing primarily is of two
kinds: it either concerns certain diagnostic groupings (e.g., minimal brain
injury) or characteristics (e.g., rigidity) which have almost exclusively been
studied within the high grade portion of an institutional population—a restriction to generalization which is not always recognized. There is no
doubt that the high grade segment of an institutional population is largely
made up of what is traditionally called the familial defective. As will be
indicated in different parts of this report, we think it to be a source of confusion to label such cases as mentally defective when they are institutionalized
and as mentally retarded when they remain in the community—as if the act
of commitment is a valid criterion in the consideration of etiology and diagnosis.

Finally in Section XI we attempt to pull together in summary form the
research implications and suggestions which have emerged from our survey
with the hope that many more researchers than at present will see and take
up the challenge offered by this rich but largely unexplored field of mental
subnormality.

II. THE UNEDUCATED

A. MILITARY REJECTION FOR MENTAL DEFICIENCY

In 1953 Ginzberg and Bray (87) published a book entitled "The Uneducated." This book contained a searching and illuminating analysis of men who were rejected on the ground of mental deficiency for military service in World War II. It also contained a study of a sample of men who had been accepted by the armed services but who were illiterate or semi-illiterate. The men in this sample had been through a special education training program set up by the military. We shall discuss this book not only for the data it contains but also because we feel that it can serve as a basis for raising some of the most important research problems in the area of mental retardation.

From the beginning of selective service until the end of the war, there were 716,000 individuals who were between 18 and 37 years of age and were rejected on the grounds of mental deficiency. Some of the problems associated with the interpretation of this figure may be seen from the following quotation (87, p. 41):

> Relatively little research has been devoted to ascertaining the number of individuals in the population who cannot meet a minimum performance criterion as workers and citizens. Some authorities estimate that approximately one per cent of the population can perform even unskilled work only under close supervision in a protective environment. It is believed that another one per cent of the population are able to work effectively only if they have some type of special supervision. According to these estimates the percentage of persons who would not meet a minimum performance standard because of intellectual deficiency would be 2 per cent. The more than 700,000 men rejected for military service under the general heading of "mental deficiency" amounted to about 4 per cent of the men examined. On the surface this might be taken to mean that the screening standards used were somewhat tight but approximately correct. Again, however, a national average obscures the truth, for nearly 14 per cent were rejected in some states and only one-half of one per cent in others. The fact that the national rejection rate was only a little higher than the theoretical rate of true mental deficiency cannot be taken as an indication that the screening validly assessed either mental deficiency or ability to give satisfactory performance. The regional patterning of the rejections indicates that the screening assessed primarily the individual's educational background.

TABLE 1
Rejection Rates Per Thousand Registrants, by Region and Race
[From Ginzberg and Bray (87)]

Region	Total	White	Negro
Total U. S.	40	25	152
New England	17	16	65
Middle Atlantic	15	11	67
Southeast	97	52	202
Southwest	60	54	107
Central	14	12	61
Northwest	14	13	40
Far West	10	9	50

The regional patterning of rejections is indeed striking as can be seen in Table 1. Ginzberg and Bray (87, p. 43) comment:

Several striking facts are revealed by this table. First, the rate of rejection in the Southeast is almost ten times as large as that in the Far West. All of the regions of the country except two have a total rejection rate between 10 and 17 per 1,000 examined; the Southeast and the Southwest have rates of 97 and 60, respectively. Although the range is less for the white population, it is still striking. The Far West has a rejection rate of 9 while the Southeast and the Southwest each have a rate of more than 50. The Negro rate is so much larger in every region that it might appear to be a different population; the over-all Negro rate is just over six times the white rate. However, there is evidence within the Negro distribution to suggest that the population is basically parallel. One finds, for instance, that the rate of rejection for Negroes in the Northwest and the Far West is actually below the white rate in the Southeast and the Southwest. Even in the other three regions—New England, Middle Atlantic, and Central, the Negro rate is only slightly above the white rate in the South. The sixfold difference in total rates between Negroes and whites results from the exceptionally high rejection rate for Negroes in the Southeast and the lower but still high rate in the Southwest. The most extreme regional and racial differences are between the rejection rate for whites in the Far West of 9 per 1,000, or less than one per cent, and the rate of 202 per 1,000, or more than 20 per cent, for Negroes in the Southeast. Unless there were evidence that there are gross differences in mental capacity among various racial and ethnic groups, here is an overwhelming demonstration that the results of the screening examination reflected primarily differences in the educational and environmental opportunities in different regions.

Although similar rejection rates have been tabulated and analyzed by various experts, all of the analyses to date have been limited either to national totals, regional comparisons, or state comparisons. These comparisons shed considerable light upon the problem of the illiterate and the poorly educated youth of the country, but a more thorough understanding of the problem awaits an analysis of smaller geographic units which might bring out the range of specific factors likely to contribute to high or low rejection rates.

On the basis of Selective Service sample data, we prepared two detailed maps. The first presents the rate of rejections for mental deficiency for white registrants in each of the more than 3,000 counties throughout the United States. The second map is necessarily less extensive; it shows the Negro rejection rates for Eastern counties having at least 100 Negroes in our sample. Nearly all other counties in the nation had too few Negroes examined to compute a rate. Exceptions were a few large urban counties.

The most general finding that emerges from the study of rejection rates on a county basis is the general gradation from low to high rates rather than abrupt changes. In a large number of cases this gradualness ignores state boundaries, suggesting that local factors play the predominant part in determining the differential rates. There is, however, contrary evidence which suggests that in some instances state policies are determining. Sharp differences are conspicuous between Mississippi and the bordering states, and between the western and northwestern counties of Texas and the much higher rates in the neighboring states. Much the same contrast is observed between the higher rates in West Virginia and those in the border counties of Ohio and Pennsylvania, and in the border counties of Kentucky and Virginia.

The map of county rejection rates for Negro registrants in the Southeast helps to bring certain generalizations to the surface. An outstanding fact is that every county in South Carolina, without exception, had a Negro rejection rate of 175 per 1,000 or more. The situation in Alabama was a little better. The counties in which the cities of Birmingham and Mobile are located show, however, relatively low rates. The other states show greater variation between high, medium, and low county rejection rates. There is no doubt that the degree of urbanization is a major factor related to lower rejection rates of Negroes, just as for whites. On the basis of sample studies, the other two factors which seem frequently to be connected with relatively low rejection rates for Negroes are the economic prosperity of the county and a relatively low proportion of Negroes in the total population. There are, however, a considerable number of counties where such specific factors as local white or Negro leadership, or special efforts by outside groups, such as foundations interested in Negro education, apparently are important. Such factors may be at work where the rejection rate for a particular county or group of counties is low in comparison to others which are broadly similar on an economic and demographic basis.

We have presented but a small fraction of Ginzberg and Bray's analysis and comments. From what we have presented above, in addition to the wealth of other data contained in the book, it seems justified to conclude that rates of rejection for mental deficiency were affected by at *least* three factors: regional-cultural differences, minority group membership, and rate of expenditure for educational facilities. Let us now turn to the interpretation and research problems which such a conclusion suggests.

B. The Diagnostic Criteria of Mental Deficiency

A cursory review of the literature in mental deficiency will quickly reveal that one cannot at all be sure that different researchers employ similar criteria in the diagnosis of mental deficiency (225). The criteria which probably have received most acceptance—if only a token acceptance—are as follows:

1. The mentally defective individual is one whose mental defect existed at or shortly after birth.

2. The mental defect manifests itself in intellectual and social deficiencies which prevent the individual from solving problems to the degree that other individuals of similar age are capable of doing.

3. Because of the social and intellectual deficiencies, manifestations of a basic central nervous system defect, the individual is and always will be in need to some degree of the guidance of others.

4. Mental deficiency is essentially an incurable condition.

The diagnosis of mental deficiency clearly requires the presence of central nervous system pathology. Within this group, however, there is tremendous variation in degree and site of pathology and, of great practical importance, in the degree to which normal intellectual and social development are possible. For purposes of this report we shall use the term mental deficiency or mental defect to refer to those individuals who have demonstrable central nervous system pathology of a kind and to a degree which probably rules out normal social and intellectual functioning. This, of course, involves in young children the prediction of status at maturity, which in some cases it is difficult to do. It should also be explicitly stated that although the diagnosis of mental deficiency implies irreversibility of the condition, it clearly does not rule out that in the future we will learn how to prevent entirely certain types of mental deficiency or bypass the drastic effects by early detection (e.g., galactosemia, phenylketonuria).

We feel it is important to differentiate between mental deficiency and mental retardation. Mentally retarded individuals—the majority of Ginzberg and Bray's "uneducated," the majority of those in special classes, and the majority of our "high grade" institutionalized cases—these individuals presumably do not have any central nervous system pathology.[2] They almost invariably come from the lowest social classes. In fact, the frequent practice of labelling these individuals "subcultural" reflects the fact that their functioning reflects cultural rather than constitutional variables.[3] The low test scores of these individuals cannot be considered a reflection of intellectual *potential*. The bulk of them are capable of leading an independent social existence, as many follow-up studies well indicate. The need to differentiate between what we have called mental deficiency and mental retardation has been recognized by many workers in the field. Kanner (146) has put it in the following way:

> 1. *Absolute feeblemindedness.* One variety consists of individuals so markedly deficient in their cognitive, affective, and constructively conative potentialities that they would stand out as defectives in any existing civilization. They are designated as idiots and imbeciles. They would be equally helpless and ill-adapted in a society of savants and in a society of savages. They are not only deficient intellectually but deficient in every sphere of mentation. They are the truly, absolutely, irreversibly feebleminded or mentally deficient in every sense of the word. The most carefully planned therapeutic and education efforts will not succeed in helping them to function self-dependently, without the need for protecting supervision. They continue throughout their

---

[2]The familial defective (variously called the Kallikak or garden-variety, or subcultural defective) represent the bulk of the "high grade" cases in our institutional population. They differ in no fundamental respect from the bulk of the mentally retarded in the community. We think it misleading to label, as is traditionally done, the institutionalized mentally retarded as mentally defective. This problem is discussed further in Section X.

[3]The use of the term "subcultural" in referring to the mentally retarded as a group is not strictly in accord with anthropological usage because these individuals, found as they are in places varying both geographically and culturally, do not and cannot share common cultural experiences. Reference to the mentally retarded as "subcultural" does at least direct attention to the most important aspect of the problem. However, one sometimes gets the impression that a value judgment is implied in the use of the term, i.e., the subculture is inferior to our own middle-class one. The danger in such a value judgment is that by branding the subculture as inferior, one is likely to misperceive or misinterpret the behavior of individuals in the subculture, that is, it becomes difficult to understand the subculture in its own terms (see Section VI).

lives in need of custodial care, the custody being carried on by relatives or in appropriate institutions. Even in this group, the assumption of irreversibility has recently been challenged. Disregarding the sensational claims made in newspaper reports and popular magazine articles, one must still await further and more conclusive results of experiments with glutamic acid. So far, sporadic additions of a few points to the intelligence quotient have not managed to lift even the most responsive patients out of the absoluteness of their defects. At least for the time being, the enthusiasm about glutamic acid is a little too reminiscent of the promises made not too long ago with regard to the "brightening" effects of cortin in mongolians.

2. *Relative feeblemindedness.* Another, larger variety is made up of individuals whose limitations are definitely related to the standards of the particular society which surrounds them. In less complex, less intellectually centered societies, they would have no trouble in attaining and retaining equality of realizable ambitions. Some might even be capable of gaining superiority by virtue of assets other than those measured by the intelligence tests. They could make successful peasants, hunters, fishermen, tribal dancers. They can, in our own society, achieve proficiency as farm hands, factory workers, miners, waitresses, charwomen. . . .

The members of this group are not truly and absolutely feebleminded or *mentally* deficient. Their principal shortcoming is a greater or lesser degree of inability to comply with the *intellectual* requirements of their society. In other respects, they may be as mature or immature, stable or unstable, secure or insecure, placid or moody, aggressive or submissive as any other member of the human species. Their "deficiency" is an *ethnologically determined phenomenon* relative to the local standards and, even within those standards, relative to educational postulates, vocational ambitions, and family expectations. They are "subcultural" in our society but may not be even that in a different, less sophisticated setting.

It is for this group that the suggested designation of intellectual inadequacy seems more appropriate than any other existing term.

From the standpoint of etiology, diagnostic clarity, prognosis, social implications, educational orientation, and research planning, it can only be a source of confusion if mentally defective and mentally retarded individuals are not differentiated from each other.

Stating the above criteria is far easier than describing the procedures, technical and interpretive, which would allow one to assess validly each of the criteria. Perhaps the most incisive (but too succinct) discussion of this problem is that by Jastak (38, 130, 132). He points out the limitations both of the social and conventional statistical criteria and presents a schema which, while not as yet substantiated by published research, has the definite virtue of focussing on and clinically illustrating the most significant problems: (*a*) the development of more pure measures of intellectual factors which are more numerous than conventional tests suggest; (*b*) similarly, the development of better measures of personality variables; (*c*) the absolute necessity of considering the relation between intellectual and personality factors. What is unique in Jastak's approach is the significance he attaches to the highest score an individual obtains on a particular factor *regardless of his scores on other tests*, i.e., even if the score on the particular factor is far above all other scores, it is regarded as an approximation of the individual's capacity. As Jastak puts it (130, p. 372):

> In agreement with most psychologists, we regard intellect as a capacity, potentiality, or latent power. Webster defines capacity as "the power of receiving, containing, or absorbing; extent of room or space, content, volume; maximum output." Concepts of capacity incorporate the idea of use to the fullest extent or maximum potential. This notion of capacity is as useful in psychology as it is elsewhere in science and in daily life. To determine the capacity of a water tank, its maximum volume is obtained. It would be senseless to take repeated measurements of water actually contained therein, average them, and regard the average as the capacity of the tank. The analogous procedure in psychometrics in the form of *IQ* is equally misleading as a measure of capacity.
>
> Fortunately, there is in every psychometric record an ability through which a person's latent intellectual power may be adequately approximated. It is the ability which yields the highest score. . . .
>
> Intellect is not what is, but what could or would be if everything else were normal. As everything else is rarely normal, intellectual power remains incompletely consummated in nearly all people. Some individuals function close to their capacities, others far below them because of abnormal character traits, personality disturbances, and environmental deprivations. We call this index of latent potential the altitude quotient. Even though it is a maximum score, the altitude quotient underestimates rather than overestimates the potentialities of a great many people suffering from severe personality abberations or from lack of educational opportunities.

In Jastak's approach the significance of an individual's pattern of intellectual abilities—in terms of present or future social, vocational, or educational functioning—depends on their relationship to personality variables. Once this relationship is understood, it will be possible to formulate an appropriate program for the individual. Jastak's approach, which is really an outline for research, deserves the strongest support. Jastak is rare in that he has taken seriously in his writing and research the lethal criticisms which over the years have been made against conventional tests and *IQ* scores—in addition, he has been bold enough to make suggestions about tests and diagnostic criteria which, if they are not correct in all respects, are of a most constructive nature.

It is probably entirely justified to assume that the above criteria were not employed in the large bulk of the 716,000 "uneducated" men who were diagnosed as mentally deficient. First, the evidence is rather compelling that many research workers in the field, who presumably should know better, base their diagnoses either on narrow criteria (e.g., test scores) or on a superficial evaluation of the several criteria (225). Second, the large majority of selective service physicians were undoubtedly not trained and experienced in making such diagnosis and the few who were undoubtedly did not have time to evaluate the above criteria. It is not surprising, therefore, that the number of rejectees was 100 per cent more than would be expected.

To the student of mental deficiency what we have thus far presented and discussed is neither terribly new nor surprising. In addition, the relevance of the Ginzberg and Bray study for an understanding of the rôle of psychological and cultural factors in the causation of subnormal functioning has, at this point at least, not been made clear. We have begun our report in the way we have in order to make the following point: since we are dealing with a problem which is defined and assessed differently by different people (i.e., between and within the different disciplines), it is not only extremely difficult to evaluate certain aspects of the problem but it forces one to be very pessimistic about the fruitfulness of future research. This condition is certainly not peculiar to the field of subnormal functioning, witness the diversity of opinion which existed, and to a somewhat lesser extent still exists, in psychiatry concerning the descriptive and etiological aspects of adult and childhood schizophrenia, hysteria, and various so-called borderline and latent psychotic and neurotic states. But whereas these problems in psychiatry occupy the interest both of the trainee and practitioner in the field, and have given rise to a good deal of research, the complexity of the problem of subnormal functioning nowhere receives such attention. It is our opinion that until the nature and standards of training in subnormal functioning are formulated, and implemented in our university and research centers, our basic knowledge about subnormal functioning will not increase perceptibly. It is also our opinion that until such a development takes place the importance of the field of subnormal functioning for such disciplines as anthropology, psychology, and psychiatry will not become apparent. It is our hope that by the end of this report the importance of such a rapprochement will be a little clearer.

C. The Cultural Factor

It will be remembered that on the basis of their detailed analysis, Ginzberg and Bray concluded that "The regional patterning of the rejections indicates that the screening assessed primarily the individual's educational background." It is, of course, impossible to determine for how many of the rejectees this generalization holds. It is probably justified to assume that a fair proportion of the 716,000 rejectees for mental deficiency would clearly meet comprehensive criteria for such a diagnosis. Our concern here is with that proportion where educational retardation was the important, if not the sole, factor in the diagnosis.

We might approach the problem by asking a deceptively simple question: What accounts for the somewhat fantastic differences in rejection rate between different sections of the country? Concretely, why should the rejection rate be 97 per thousand registrants in the Southeast and 10 per thousand in the Far West? Omitting the Negro registrants the figures are 52 for the Southeast and 9 for the Far West. The fact that these regions differ strikingly in expenditure for educational facilities tempts one to the conclusion that the rejection rates are *caused* by differences in educational opportunities. In a broad sociological frame of reference such a conclusion has meaning, although even in such a frame of reference it is dangerous to use correlational data as a basis for determining causation. As soon as one realizes that the two areas differ in many respects other than the quantity and quality of educational resources, the possibility arises that we are dealing, generally speaking, with people who differ culturally in some important respects. To be more concrete, we put the following questions:

1. How do these people differ in their view of the function of education? Are there differences in conception of the relationship between schooling and later adjustment in the society in which they live?

2. Are there differences in the kind and extent of personal rewards which are available through education? What are the differences in the punishments which go with the avoidance of or failure in schooling?

3. Are there differences in how these people conceive of "success" and "achievement"?

One could raise many more questions, and in connection with other problems where cultural differences exist we shall find it necessary to do so. On the basis of the few questions posed above, we wish to suggest that the relationship between educational opportunity and educational (and intellectual) attainment or level is a very complex one in which the quantity and quality of educational resources may be symptomatic of a cultural constellation which is primary in the sense that it gives rise both to the educational resources and to the attitudes toward education. One might pose the question in this way: Would educationally retarded individuals in the Southeast and Far West react to or conceive of their retardation in similar ways or would there be marked differences reflecting the different cultural contexts in which they have developed? One could, of course, ask the same question in terms of how educationally retarded are viewed and reacted to by the non-retarded individuals in each region.

We should reiterate at this point that we are concerned with that indeterminable group of rejectees who could not enter the armed forces because their degree of educational retardation was so extreme as to be labelled mentally deficient by people in their own regions. There is every reason to believe, as the data presented by Ginzberg and Bray suggest, that a large number of men with similar or somewhat less educational retardation were inducted into the armed forces. We are, obviously, dealing with a staggering national problem. How this problem is met and handled will, of course, depend in part on our scientific knowledge. On the assumption that we are dealing with a complex problem—one that cannot, for example, be explained simply in terms of genetics—we have to guard against our tendency to oversimplify. For example, we earlier raised questions concerning the relationship between regional differences in educational retardation and possible cultural differences in conceptions of education. (On the basis of Ginzberg and Bray's data one could pose the problem in terms of intra regional differences.) Let us assume that an anthropological study would reveal significant cultural differences in conceptions of education. We would then be faced with at least three problems: How does a distinctive cultural factor affect the psychological development, content, and motivational structure of the individual? What are the differences between individuals in the different subgroups of each area? In the sphere of educational achievement, how does one explain those who are atypical for their group?

It should be clear by now that we are dealing with the problem of the relationship between performance level and capacity, a problem of tremendous import in such fields as genetics, psychology, anthropology, psychiatry, and education. It seems also clear that the problem cannot be adequately handled by any one of these disciplines.

D. THE EFFECTS OF SCHOOLING

It is our opinion that one of the implications of the Ginzberg and Bray study—an implication which we have attempted to elaborate above—is that educational retardation is not likely to be significantly decreased by building new and more schools and hiring more teachers. If future· research should establish that educational retardation and quantity and quality of educational resources are in fact symptomatic of prevailing attitudes and experiences in a particular subculture, then sheer expenditure of money for buildings and personnel should not be expected to have a marked effect. Unless such expenditures reflect some kind of cultural change, and take into account the cultural setting in which changes are hoped for, a good deal of time and money may be wasted. We are not saying that better and more adequate educational facilities *per se* have no effect on the population concerned; there is no evidence that such an effect takes· place. For example, Wheeler (290) reported a study in which group intelligence tests were administered to over 3,000 children in 40 mountain schools of East Tennessee and the results compared with those obtained with children in the same areas and largely of the same families similarly studied 10 years earlier. Wheeler found that the children tested in the second study were superior at all ages and all grades to those tested 10 years earlier.[4] He pointed out that in the decade (1930-1940) between the two studies "there has been definite improvement in the economic, social and educational status of this mountain area." It is deserving of reiteration in light of our previous discussion that improvement in educational status seemed related to, if not a function of, more widespread cultural changes. Without knowledge of the details and dynamics of cultural change, it is difficult to assess the significances of a general increase in test scores in terms of psychological structure, varieties of problem-solving situations, and the range and explanation of individual differences. For example, in Wheeler's study we have little real understanding not only of the apparent increase in test scores but

---

[4]This increase in scores has been reported by others and Anastasi (5) presents an excellent discussion of some of the problems involved in explaining such increases.

of the finding that in 1940, as in the first study, there is a steady and dramatic decrease in *IQ* as one goes up the grades—a finding which is not completely explicable by the nature of the test, and which is similar to that found in other studies of educationally backward areas (5).

That the influence of schooling, even when viewed from a narrow psychometric approach, is not a simple one can be seen by a Swedish study reported by Husén (125) as well as in an earlier one by Lorge (172). In Husén's recent study, his subjects were a group of 613 boys in a Swedish town to whom a group intelligence test had been administered in school when they were approximately 9½ years of age. At the time of the first test all subjects had received the same amount of school training. Ten years later this sample was retested at induction to military service. Husén found (*a*) the mean *IQ* scores were found to be slightly lowered for those that had not gone beyond primary school while they were raised for others in proportion to four levels of additional academic training; (*b*) when the data were analyzed according to levels of ability (using test scores at CA 9½) it was found that those with the highest scores retained their level, even if the effect of schooling was excluded, while those with the lowst scores regressed downwards in the statistical sense. Husén points out that the calculated regression effect in the case of those with the lowest scores should have been upward. In analyzing the effect of secondary schooling, which automatically excluded those with initial below-average scores, Husén found positive gains in test score whereas the calculated regression effect was in the downward direction.

Although Husén's study suggests that amount of schooling has important effect, we do not know how a variable like "amount of schooling" is reflected in the psychological structure of individuals differing in intellectual status—nor do we know how amount of schooling and intellectual status interact with or are reflections of certain cultural factors. For example, it may be that the failure of low-scoring individuals to show expected gains is due to factors other than amount of schooling. It may also be that the problem-solving behavior of low-scoring individuals outside the testing situation is significantly better than in a testing situation. There is fair agreement in the research literature that the adult level of non-test problem-solving behavior of individuals who as children received "retarded" scores is frequently better than predicted (8, 14, 40, 70, 151, 173, 189).

When one views the problem of the relationship between capacity and functioning in terms of the interaction of psychological processes and cultural settings, one soon realizes the inadequacies and dangers of conclusions based on test scores. This, of course, is a banal conclusion. But when one reviews the literature on the nature and causes of mental and educational retardation, it becomes apparent that at least *four* assumptions are implicitly made about intelligence tests: (*a*) intelligence is *a* thing; (*b*) this thing can be measured by *a* test or tests; (*c*) the testing situation is a representative sample of all problem-solving situations; (*d*) that we know enough about psychological processes and development in relation to broader cultural variables to guard ourselves against the drawing of invalid conclusions concerning capacity and functioning. With the hope that we will not, at best, be considered rank pessimists and, at worst, nihilistic and destructive critics, it is our opinion that the first assumption is untrue, the third probably untrue, and the fourth likewise untrue. Insofar as the second assumption is concerned we do believe that a more comprehensive theoretical formulation of intellectual functioning than we now have will be capable of being evaluated by testing procedures, a problem which will be discussed in a later section. Suffice it to say at this point that recent studies on the nature and varieties of intellectual capacities strongly suggest that much of our present conceptions, and more of our practices, will have to be scrapped if our understanding is to be extended.

Two Dutch studies by de Groot (61, 62) are suggestive of the rôle of cultural disruption on educational and intellectual status. In one study his subjects were 13-14-year-old candidates of a boys' industrial school; one group from the pre-war years and the other from the years 1944 and 1945. He found a significant drop in mean intelligence test score from the pre- to post-war groups and attributed this to the disruption of educational facilities during the war. He also found that tests closely related to school training showed more decline from 1944 to 1947 than tests unrelated to schooling, supporting his contention that lack of training was responsible. In a second study de Groot found that the average *IQ* for classes of applicants for the years 1948, 1949, and 1950 had already achieved prewar level. We have presented de Groot's studies not only because they suggest that educational deprivation is related to discrepancy between potential and functioning but also because it is clear that the educational deprivation was one aspect of widespread cultural disruption in which many spheres of an individual's behavior were affected.

E. The Uneducated in the War

In order to amplify some of the points raised above, and to make concrete some of the directions that future research might take, we turn to Ginzberg and Bray's study of a group of men who had been accepted by the armed services but who were illiterate or semi-illiterate. These men had been through a special education training program set up by the military, a program that became increasingly larger as the standards for acceptance into the armed forces became progressively lower. The men sent to the Special Training Units were of two kinds: those who were formally classified as illiterate and those who scored low (Group V) on the Army General Classification Test. Re the latter Ginzberg and Bray state: "These men were considered 'slow learners' but in reality were mainly those who had had only a little more education than those called illiterate." The problem of illiteracy confronting the military can be seen from the following (87, p. 77):

> More than 400,000 illiterates served within the Armed Forces during World War II. The combined group of illiterates and poorly educated who saw active duty totaled almost 700,000. To this must be added more than 700,000 additional persons, the vast majority of whom were rejected outright for military service because of serious educational deficiencies. In short, the findings which emerge are directly relevant for appraising a group of almost one and one-half million persons out of a total of 18 million registrants who were screened. Clearly we are dealing with a significant sector of the nation's manpower resources.

In setting up the Special Training Program certain specific goals were sought (87, p. 69):

> 1. To teach the men to read at least at a fourth-grade level so that they would be able to comprehend bulletins, written orders and directives, and basic Army publications.
> 2. To give the men sufficient language skill so that they would be able to use and understand the everyday oral and written language necessary for getting along with officers and men.
> 3. To teach the men to do number work at a fourth-grade level, so they could understand their pay accounts and laundry bills, conduct their business in the PX, and perform in other situations requiring arithmetic skill.
> 4. To facilitate the adjustment of the men to military training and Army life.
> 5. To enable the men to understand in a general way why it was necessary for this country to fight a war against Germany, Japan, and Italy.

The maximum amount of time that an individual could remain in the course was 120 days. "Approximately 40 per cent of the men graduated in less than 30 days. Almost 80 per cent graduated in less than 60 days. Only a very few, less than 11,000 out of 255,000 graduates, remained in a Special Training Unit more than 90 days" (87, p. 70).

Let us make the following assumptions: (*a*) more than a few of those formally classified as illiterates were not intellectually retarded; (*b*) more than a few of the "slow learners" were diagnostic errors—their true *IQ* was above that indicated by Army test scores; (*c*) more than a few of the graduates did not reach the goals previously indicated and did not in fact pass the examination in reading and arithmetic required for graduation. Making the allowances indicated by these assumptions we think it not unreasonable to make the further assumption that the above figures suggest that the *rate of learning* of more than a few men was far beyond that which one would expect from their potential as inferred from test scores. Put in another way: the performance of more than a few was better than an evaluation of the potential or capacity had indicated. Here again one cannot avoid inquiring about the possible factors which can produce an apparent discrepancy between capacity and functioning. In order to do so it would be helpful if one described some of the background characteristics of the sub-sample of 400 men whose Army records were scrutinized by Ginzberg and Bray (87, p. 80):

> Our sample, it will be recalled, consisted of 400 men: 200 white and 200 Negro, half drawn from the deep South and half from the border states and the North, half inducted in the latter part of 1943, and the other half in the last six months of 1944.
>
> All but three of the 400 men were born in the United States. Since, at the time of the 1940 Census, almost three-fifths of the 1.5 million draft-age men with less than four years of schooling lived in small communities or on farms, it is not surprising to discover that most of our group also came from rural backgrounds. Almost three-fourths were born in communities of under 5,000 population. More than one-third, however, had migrated from their birth places. When inducted, 56 per cent lived in communities under 5,000 population; a little more than a fifth were inducted from cities of more than 100,000.
>
> Slightly under half, 179, were 20 years of age or less when inducted; 275 were 25 or less; and just under 85 per cent of the entire group were 30 or less. Thirty-nine were between the ages of 31 and 35, and 14 between 36 and 38. The median age for the entire group was 21.5 years. The median age of the Negroes, however, was 2.4 years higher than for the whites.

There were no conspicuous differences between the years of school completed by the whites and the Negroes, but the "northern" group (Camp Atterbury, Indiana) showed a higher average than the "southern" (Camp Shelby, Mississippi, and Fort Benning, Georgia) group. The men inducted in 1944 also had a higher average number of years of schooling than the group inducted in 1943. The most striking fact about the educational background of the group is that 55 per cent had completed more than four years of schooling. Only 3 per cent had never attended school. Almost 5 per cent had more than eight grades of schooling, and more than 25 per cent had reached at least the seventh grade. In light of these facts, it is surprising to find that of the men for whom information was available, 228 were designated as illiterate, while only 69 were classified as literate and sent to special training because of a low score on the Army General Classification Test.

More than half of the group, 226 men, had once been farmers, although less than half were farmers when inducted. Just more than two-thirds of the whites had farming backgrounds, but less than half of the Negroes. Only about a third of the Northern Negroes but almost 80 per cent of the Southern whites had been farmers at some time.

Not only is it clear from the above that these men came from rural areas where educational resources are generally inferior, but also that many of these men either learned nothing or little from their schooling, or that whatever they did absorb during school was of no significance in their later lives and consequently was "unlearned." That an individual can go through eight grades of school and then at the age of 20 appear to be illiterate may be explained in different ways; that the same individual at age 20 can in a very short period of time demonstrate a fair amount of educational progress increases the complexity of the problem. We feel that we do not have a basis for choosing among different explanations. We do feel, however, that it is justified to suggest that we are not dealing primarily with an educational problem in the narrow sense of the word but one of motivation and attitude both of which cannot be understood unless studied in the cultural matrix in which they arise.

Also deserving of discussion is the fact that a fair number of the men had migrated from smaller to larger communities. In terms of tested intelligence and educational status it would seem from this study that the larger urban centers tend to attract inferior individuals, but as will be discussed in Section VI, this generalization is not supported by all studies of the problem. In terms of the intellectual capacities of these migrants we feel such a conclusion to be premature. It may be that the capacities of these individuals are not essentially inferior.   It may also be, for example, that their capacities are inferior but that the discrepancy between performance level and capacity need not be as large as it is.   That the problem of selective migration is by no means a simple one can be seen when one realizes that we do not know either why the migration or the effects of it.   Further characteristics of the 400 men studied by Ginzberg and Bray (87, p. 81) follow:

> About 55 per cent of the group were single when inducted. Just under 40 per cent were married. Fourteen men were separated, seven were divorced, and three were widowers.
>
> In 94 per cent of the records there was no evidence that the men had ever run into any trouble with law-enforcement authorities.
>
> In summary, almost all were native-born, and the majority were in their early twenties and came from rural backgrounds. At least one man in four had migrated to a larger community before induction into the Army. Very few had failed to attend school at all, and the majority had gone at least to the fifth grade. One is forced to conclude that the education received was poor and that the men had retained only a small amount of what they had once been taught.
>
> Although more than half of the group were employed as farmers or common laborers at the time of induction, a considerable number were holding semi-skilled jobs, and a few were employed at skilled work. With very few exceptions, these men were self-supporting. Considering their background and education, their earnings were about what might be expected for the kinds of jobs they held.
>
> The fact that almost half were married or had been married reflects the tendency among the rural population of the Southeast toward early marriage. It also indicates, however, that the men earned enough to assume the responsibilities of the head of a household. It is particularly noteworthy as far as we could tell, that only 6 per cent had police records of any kind.
>
> It would appear, then, that the vast majority of these men had made a reasonable adjustment to civilian life. They were economically self-sufficient and socially responsible. This does not deny that the group might have contained a few "floaters." But if account is taken of the background from which they came, the type of education which they received, and the kinds of employment open to them, the civilian adjustment of most of the group must be considered adequate. At least there is no evidence to the contrary.

Table 2 contains information concerning the occupational status of the men at induction.   Since we know that these men were either illiterate or low scorers on an intelligence test, it is not surprising that they had the

TABLE 2

OCCUPATIONS AT INDUCTION OF MEN ASSIGNED TO SPECIAL TRAINING UNITS
[From Ginzberg and Bray (87)]

Occupation	Total	White		Negro	
		North	South	North	South
Farmer	173	43	60	22	48
Non-Farm:					
Laborer	90	22	13	29	26
Janitor, porter, busboy, etc.	36	3	4	21	8
Truck driver, chauffeur,					
auto mechanic, etc.	44	12	6	15	11
Factory operative	26	11	8	5	2
Coal miner	13	7	2	4	0
Craftsman	7	1	3	0	3
Other	11	1	4	4	2
Total non-farm	227	57	40	78	52
Grand total	400	100	100	100	100

kinds of jobs they did. However, it is one thing to say this is expected and another thing to provide an explanation. In one sense it is perfectly correct to say that these men held the jobs they did *because* of their intellectual and educational status—these are the kinds of jobs available to them. But this brings us back to the recurring question: What are the factors determining the intellectual and educational status of these men? Again leaving this question aside—primarily because our current knowledge only permits us to suggest, as indicated earlier, what some of these factors and their interaction might be—we would like to pose another question: How does one evaluate an individual's problem-solving behavior outside of a test situation? Throughout the course of the day in the life of any individual he is presented with problems the solutions to which vary in the complexity of response they require for resolution. Not only may we commonsensically assume variation through the course of a day but also among problem-solving activities in different spheres of functioning, e.g., educational, vocational, sexual, etc. Although more often than not there is a fair degree of variation or "scatter" within an individual's own test performance, it is surprising how frequently we assume that the level of problem-solving behavior outside the test situation is fairly even. When it is remembered that our discussion concerns those men whose performance in the Special Training Units suggests a capacity beyond that indicated by their test scores and educational status, we think it justified to raise the possibility that the previous non-test problem-solving behavior of these men was in some spheres or activities better than their test scores or educational status suggests. Unfortunately, there have been no systematic investigations of this problem. It is apparent that there are extremely thorny problems involved in the observing, sampling, and recording of non-test problem-solving behavior— aside from the problem of quantifying samples of behavior obtained in situations over which we have no control. But if problem-solving behavior in test situations cannot be assumed to be representative of all problem-solving, the lack of research in this problem can no longer be excused.

In the context of the present discussion it is important to report briefly the results of the analysis of the military records of the subsample of 400 men.

To check on the reasonableness of our evaluation of the military performance of the uneducated, the graduates of the Special Training Units were compared with a control group consisting of average soldiers whose education and mentality were sufficient to enable them to enter basic training immediately after induction into the Army. This control group was constructed by selecting the man of the same race whose serial number was next higher than that of each man in the Special Training Unit group. If the man with the next higher number had also been assigned to a Special Training Unit, the man with the nearest higher number was selected. The control sample was not representative of the Army as a whole, but permitted a comparison between men inducted from the same localities who differed primarily with respect to their level of education.

While 26 per cent of the 400 Special Training Unit men had less than four years of schooling, this was true of only one per cent of the control group. Only 2 per cent of the whites and 8 per cent of the Negroes in the Special Training Unit group, but 55 per cent of the control group had attended high school. Five per cent of the control group had attended college. Obviously, there was a significant difference in the educational background of the two groups. With respect to occupational background, the size of the communities in which they had been born, the extent to which they had migrated, and their place of residence at the time when they were inducted, however, the differences between the two groups were not substantial. . . .

In order to judge the relative over-all performance of the Special Training Unit and control groups, a summary card was prepared for each man. Care was taken that the cards would contain no hint whether the case was a Special Training Unit graduate or a control case, or whether the man was white or Negro. These cards were then shuffled and sorted into the five groups: very good, good, acceptable, not acceptable, and non-chargeable. . . .

This objective comparison showed that just under a quarter of the men of the control group were very good, a third were good, another third were acceptable. Only 7 per cent of this group were not acceptable, and 3 per cent were non-chargeable. Only 9 per cent of the men of the Special Training Unit group were very good, but slightly under a third were good, and almost half were acceptable. Twelve per cent were not acceptable, and 3 per cent were non-chargeable.

This comparison demonstrates conclusively that, granted our criteria, the control group contained many more very good soldiers than the Special Training Unit graduates. One of our criteria, however, was rank, and it is to be expected that those with more pre-service education would more often qualify for higher non-commissioned-officer assignments. It was, in any case, not expected that the Special Training Unit graduates would include a great many outstanding soldiers. The question was rather whether any appreciable number would perform adequately and represent a clear gain to the Army. This question is answered unequivocally. Eighty-five per cent of the graduates performed acceptably or better as compared to 90 per cent of the control group. Clearly, at a time when the Armed Forces needed men badly, they were able with a small investment to turn many illiterates and poorly educated men into acceptable soldiers.

It should be noted that Ginzberg and Bray were quite aware of the many problems involved in utilizing and categorizing military records. Even if one were to assume that the "true" picture of the records of the men from the Special Training Units was not as favorable as Ginzberg and Bray describe, it would still be reasonable to conclude that the problem-solving behavior of many of the men was better than objective educational and test data indicated. It would repay the reader to study the 22 case records which Ginzberg and Bray present in one of the chapters in the book. In more than a few of these cases the discrepancy between problem-solving behavior in and outside the test situation is marked.

We have previously noted that the rate of learning of many of the men in the Special Training Units was surprising. Unfortunately we do not have the data or observations with which to evaluate such a conclusion. However, the following partial description of the Training Unit has some important implications for future research on this problem (87, p. 71).

A "cadre" or staff of enlisted personnel form the basis for all instruction in the Special Training Unit. Each man has been selected for the position on the basis of his academic background as well as being a capable military instructor. With but few exceptions, all of the instructors are college graduates, many of them possess Master's degrees and a few holding various Doctor's degrees. Formerly they were connected with civilian school systems, ranging from the elementary through the college level. The unit is staffed by 26 officers qualified both academically and militarily.

Experience has shown that men of the calibre that are received in the Special Training Unit learn more and faster if they are allowed to absorb the training given with the same group of men for the entire period they are here. For that reason, men are assigned to barracks and remain there until they leave. One classroom is set up on each of the two floors of the building and provided with tables, chairs, blackboards, and other instructional aid pertaining to the type of work being covered. For a short period of time after entrance into the barracks, some men are prone to exhibit shyness due to the fact that they have never associated closely with other men.

Gradually the spirit of teamwork and coöperation are developed and within a few days the men have made an adjustment sufficient to enhance learning. Since changing from one group to another would tend to prolong the period of adjustment, that method is not employed. The military instructor, a Corporal or Sergeant, lives in the barracks with the men, eats with them and works with them and it is rare that he fails to gain the complete confidence of his men almost immediately. The instructor's job lasts 24 hours per day. During the off duty hours much of his time is taken up writing letters for the trainees or giving them advice on their personal problems. Also he will devote considerable time to additional instruction for men who are learning slower than others.

The implications of this excerpt might be put in a series of questions: What significance did these men attach to being sent to the Training Unit? Did they view the education they were now receiving differently than when they had previously been in school? What were the kinds and strengths of motivations engendered in these men by this experience? To what extent was their progress due to the fact that instruction was specifically geared to their needs? Were the attitudes of the instructors to the men different from those of the teachers they had in their previous school experiences? Was there a change of attitude on the part of these men toward education as a result of experiences after leaving school?

The above questions bring us back to a question raised earlier in the report: Both between regions which differ in cultural outlook and organization and within a particular cultural region, how are differences in attitude toward schooling related to kinds and strengths of motivations as well as quality of problem-solving behavior? Within recent years increasing recognition has been given to the rôle of middle-class values and aspirations in determining public school curricula and "climate." In addition there is now general acceptance of the conclusion that our achievement and intelligence tests contain types of items and information which unfairly penalize the lower-class child, giving us a distorted, or what may better be termed an unreliable, estimate of such a child's potentialities (55, 56, 58, 68, 106). While these broad generalizations are probably true we are far from an understanding of several aspects of the problem. For example, and as we have several times indicated, while it is important to know that certain groups differ culturally, the significance of such differences is not clear until we understand how they are reflected in such psychological variables as motivation, attitude, and problem-solving behavior. It is also important to bear in mind that any particular cultural group—however distinctive it may be from other groups—is made up of individuals who differ widely among themselves on important psychological variables—a conclusion rather well illustrated by the study of the Trukese (90). This conclusion is also supported by Lemkau in his discussion of the epidemiological aspects of mental deficiency (165):

> The social class structure of a society presents many epidemiological problems that are still far from solved. One of these that is now attracting a great deal of attention is the "nesting" of diseases of widely divergent types in a small group of families of a community. This has been illustrated most clearly, perhaps, by the St. Paul study which showed that social and health problems, including mental deficiency, were concentrated in that 6 per cent of the population which absorbed 50 per cent of the social, health, and recreational services available in the community. Similar "nesting" of diseases, including mental diseases, has been reported by Downes on the basis of sickness surveys, and by Plummer and Hinkle in surveys of industrial health problems among telephone operators, though in the last study mental deficiency does not appear to have been a factor.
>
> Although it remains clear that mental deficiency is distributed more heavily in the lower socio-economic group than in the higher, it is also clear that the defectives are not evenly distributed within the lower socio-economic group, but are concentrated, along with other diseases and social defects in particular groups of persons. More defined studies of local distribution are greatly needed and offer a challenge to epidemiologists.

From the standpoint of future research it would seem that greater attention should be given to individual differences in problem-solving behavior within distinctive cultural groups. To illustrate the direction of this suggestion: Let us take a geographical area which contributed a disproportionate number of mentally defective or mentally retarded individuals. This area may be either urban or rural. Within this area let us take a representative school where we shall focus on those children who will be entering school for the first time. Our first problem is to attempt to evaluate each child, before he begins school, in terms of those variables (psychological, familial, physical) and experiences which our current knowledge of child development indicates as important in determining the content and organization of personality. Our focus would be on the ways in which the child behaves in various spheres of his activities, the rôle of external factors in such behavior, and the developmental factors to which such behavior might be related. On the basis of such information it would be important to attempt to predict each child's response to schooling in terms of the kinds of problem-solving demands which the particular school will make and also in terms of the kinds of interpersonal relationships that are established with teacher and peers. Such a prediction would have to be based in part on intimate study of the kinds of values, restrictions, and adult personalities (e.g., teacher, principal) to which he will be exposed. The final steps in such a study would involve direct and sustained observations of the child in the school environment and the relationship of such data to the family's response to the child's new experiences.

The above is obviously not a research design in the technical sense. Each step in the above problem involves many thorny problems of a methodological and theoretical nature. We presented the illustrative problem in order to emphasize several things. First, within any distinctive cultural grouping there is much variation and our understanding of any particular form of behavior (e.g., problem-solving) will depend on our knowledge of the factors related to such individual differences. Not all children in such a study would show, for example, the same kind and level of test behavior even though as a group they would be rather different from other groups of children that could be studied. We are here asking a question which has been raised and studied with much profit in another problem area (91): Why does one child in a particular geographical area become a delinquent while another does not?

A second reason for presenting the above research problem is to reiterate a point which while obvious when stated seems not to be fully comprehended by researchers in the behavioral sciences: understanding the mentally retarded child presents problems no different than those involved in understanding other children, problem or so-called normal. The complete absence of intensive, longitudinal, psychological studies of the mentally retarded may well be a reflection of the inability of the behavioral scientist to identify himself with the problems of that large group of individuals from whom he differs so markedly intellectually and culturally. Interest in a human problem presupposes a personal identification with it. If these kinds of speculations have some degree of merit, they suggest the situation in which the cultural narrowness of the behavioral scientist prevents him not only from a proper understanding of a particular group but, as a result, of a better understanding of his own cultural background. We may be in a situation analogous to that which Davis (55) has described in his discussions of children from what he calls our "slum culture"—a culture which contributes a great number of mentally retarded individuals. He points out that the middle-class psychiatrist, working primarily with individuals in his own class and utilizing theories based on such a narrow clinical foundation, not only is prone to misinterpret the significances of the behavior of people from another class background (e.g., the slum child) but is also prevented from seeing in true perspective the ways in which his own class background has determined his theory and practice.[5]

It may well be that for many of the crucial problems in child development focusing on the mentally retarded child might be methodologically easier and ultimately more fruitful for theory than focusing either on the so-called normal or on other varieties of atypical children. For one thing such children can at least be very reliably diagnosed, even though our testing procedures can tell us little about etiological factors or the degree of discrepancy between functioning and capacity. Also, the fact that the mentally retarded are a very large group makes it likely that one can get respectable numbers of cases to fit most research designs. Finally, and perhaps most

---

[5]In this connection mention might be made of the series of studies by Redlich, Hollingshead, Myers, *et al.* (120, 121, 190, 210, 211, 215, 216, 234) of the relationships between social stratification and psychiatric disorders. In several of these studies there was found a significant relationship between social class of the patient and the type of therapy administered—psychotherapy definitely not being the treatment of choice for lower-class individuals. As these authors suggest, such findings require serious discussion because they suggest that decisions about type of therapy with lower-class individuals reflect more the cultural biases of the middle-class therapist than they do any empirical evidence concerning amenability of such people to the psychotherapeutic process. It might be added that similar biases long prevented the recognition that both the mentally retarded and defective individual could benefit from psychotherapy (225).

important, the fact that the mentally retarded come from a cultural milieu, probably rather different from that of most researchers and the experimental populations they tend to study raises the possibility that the rôle of cultural variations in producing between and within group differences will become a more integral part of theory and practice in the behavioral sciences. It is fashionable today to believe that cultural factors are important for understanding behavior and it is even fashionable to assume that our theories and practices are influenced by such factors. Unfortunately, however, since most behavioral scientists have an intimate knowledge of but one, their own, sub-culture, it is not surprising that when talking about other classes or groups we overgeneralize from our findings and never get to the point of testing conclusions which are, so to speak, class based.

In this chapter we have attempted to indicate in a general kind of way something of the extent and significance of the cultural aspects of mental retardation. We have done this not only to emphasize that the cultural factor is important but also to suggest that we are dealing with a too-long-neglected research area which should be central rather than peripheral to the social sciences. In Sections VI and VII we shall return to a more detailed consideration of the rôle of cultural factors in mental retardation.

III. PROBLEM-SOLVING BEHAVIOR IN NON-TEST SITUATIONS

In a real sense part of the previous discussion has begged a question which, while central to any analysis of the problem of subnormality, has received surprisingly little attention. We refer here to the question: What do our available intelligence tests measure? From the previous chapter one could conclude that these tests to a marked degree measure educational opportunity and achievement. While it is encouraging to know that these tests are significantly correlated with these variables, the implications of such correlations are both far reaching and disturbing. Since the contents and goals of our school curricula are extremely narrow in terms of the skills and contents encompassed, we are faced with the possibility that our intelligence tests measure a very restricted range of problem solving stimuli and intellectual activities.[6] Let us put the problem in cross-cultural terms: if one were to observe daily learning activities of an urban American 10-year-old and his counterparts among the Navaho or the Alorese, one would be struck by the differences in the kinds of problem-solving stimuli and intellectual activities which would be observed. Although the differences on the stimulus side would probably be greater than on the response side (i.e., the kinds of thinking sequences required for problem solution), the important point is that any conclusion about the "intellectual performances and capacities of 10-year-olds" would be limited and even misleading if based on the observation of any one of these cultural groups. In this connection it should be recalled that in the previous chapter it was pointed out that for many children in our culture, particularly those that have been labelled mentally retarded or slow-learners, there is reason for raising the possibility that the kinds of intellectual stimuli and activities which one observes in a test or school situation may be of a different level and/or kind than one would observe outside of such a situation. In other words, there is no *a priori* basis for rejecting the possibility that the range of differences we observe cross-culturally may be found, to a lesser degree, between and within certain groups in our own culture *if a representative sample of their problem-solving behavior was obtained*. It should perhaps be made explicit that we are not equating problem-solving with all intellectual activity or thinking

---

[6]Wertheimer (288) presents some observations of problem-solving behavior in the classroom which suggest how pedagogical technique can limit the kinds of intellectual processes which the child can employ and, perhaps more important, even interfere with the learning of more productive ways of thinking.

behavior. We stress the problem-solving situation, be it a standardized one as in a test or one observed in a free situation, not only because of what we learn about the adequacy, level, and varieties of problem-solving behavior but also because it allows us to make inferences about kinds and characteristics of thought processes. Equally important is the fact that the problem-solving situation, being a clear instance of goal-directed or motivated behavior, gives us the possibility of studying the relationships between intellectual and personality variables.

That intelligence tests may be excellent indicators of educational achievement and poor indicators of non-test or non-academic intellectual activity is something to which the practicing clinician, particularly the one who has worked in an institutional setting, will readily attest. Some examples follow:

Case 1

Ginzberg and Bray (87, p. 89) describe the case of a man who was either a low scorer on the Army General Classification Test or illiterate—or both. In any event, he was one of the many who after induction was sent to one of the Special Training Units. This man subsequently received the Silver Star, one of the infrequently given medals during war. This man's behavior during combat is given in the following citation:

> At this time PFC E.S.M. was a member of a squad whose mission was to clear an enemy position of a delaying force of Germans in order to permit the remainder of the platoon to advance. PFC E.S.M., by his intrepid action, quick thinking, and deliberate coolness under fire, killed three and wounded three of the enemy, led to the capture of 20 prisoners, and paved the way for the balance of his platoon to attain their immediate objective. Suddenly he came upon a group of three Germans and quickly fired three shots. The result was two enemy killed and one wounded. Although it was daylight and there was no cover whatsoever, and the Germans in the area had opened fire upon him from all directions, he deliberately exposed himself to those dangers and with determination and boldness moved forward. Three more Germans tried to stem this individual advance, but PFC E.S.M. fired three more well aimed shots and three enemy met the same fate as their comrades. Still under fire of enemy riflemen and machine guns, he surged forward never losing sight of the fact that he had a squad in back of him. PFC E.S.M. encouraged them to move forward as he personally removed each obstacle from their path. This unusual display of outstanding individual initiative and courage so startled the surprised Germans, that the 20 remaining enemy defending this particular terrain threw up their

hands and surrendered. PFC E.S.M.'s heroic and courageous action on this occasion reflect great credit on himself and become the highest traditions of the American soldier.

If one views the described instance as a sample of problem-solving behavior, it seems not unreasonable to conclude that this soldier was capable of a completely adequate degree of sustained problem-solving activity, his previous level of performance on intelligence or achievement tests not withstanding. That this soldier's behavior suggests that "personality" factors were probably not irrelevant to his problem-solving behavior, as indeed they never are, goes without saying.

Case 2

The second case is also from Ginzberg and Bray (87, p. 122):

E.H., a white soldier, born and still living in rural Kentucky when inducted, represents perhaps the clearest case of a man who should be classified as a very good soldier. He was inducted at the age of 19 in the summer of 1943. While being examined for registration a year previously, he fainted and fell and suffered a simple fracture and a lacerated wound, for which he was hospitalized at the local Air Force Station Hospital. Shortly after induction, he was sent to the Special Training Unit at Camp Atterbury, Indiana, where he spent two months. He had attended school for four years. The date is not given, but when E.H. took the Army General Classification Test, probably prior to his assignment to the Special Training Unit, he received the very low score of 42. After completing the special training, he was sent to the Infantry Replacement Training Center at Camp Blanding, Florida. Although many men received ratings of excellent for character and efficiency during basic training, E.H. was graded very good in character and only satisfactory in efficiency. He was trained as a rifleman. Immediately after "D Day" he was en route to the European Theater as a member of the 8th Infantry Division. He received the Combat Infantry Badge, which made him automatically eligible for the Bronze Star Medal. Moreover, he earned three Bronze Service Stars for the Campaigns in Northern France, the Rhineland, and Central Europe. But his most important achievement was the award of the Silver Star for gallantry in action, which carried the following citation:

Sgt. H., a squad leader, exposed himself to enemy small arms, mortar and artillery fire to work his way within 25 yards of an enemy machine gun position which was holding up their advance. He threw two hand grenades and then overran the positions, killing one of the enemy and wounding two others. Later, during the attack, his squad accounted for more than 30 Germans. Sgt. H.'s great courage, coolness under fire, and devotion to duty were an inspiration to his men.

Although we do not know the kinds of intellectual activities or problem-solving behaviors involved in being a squad leader, more particularly, a successful squad leader under conditions of stress, it again seems not unreasonable to conclude that this man's intellectual activity is not predictable either from his meager educational achievements or very low test score.

Case 3

Another case (224) describes a girl who had been institutionalized when she was 15 years of age. On a battery of tests several years later her mental age ranged between 10 and 11 years, and on achievement tests her grade placement in reading was 3-9, in spelling 3-0, and in arithmetic 4-9. At the time of psychological testing this girl had been working for some time in the hospital laboratory. After one year of such work she was able to perform the following tasks:

1. Sterilization and chemical cleansing of glassware used in bacteriology and quantitative chemistry.

2. Preparation of bacterial media, physiological and chemical solutions used in bacteriology, hematology, and qualitative chemistry.

3. Cleansing of volumetric, graduated, and hematological pipettes and special chemical filters.

4. Complete urinalysis, except for microscopic including qualitative and quantitative sugars, albumin, acetone tests, and specific gravity.

5. Streaking and plating of bacterial cultures with aseptic technique.

6. Assistance in quantitative blood and tissue chemistry as in total proteins, lipids, sodiums, and potassiums.

7. Staining of hematology and bacterial slides.

8. Taking stool culture and finger blood tests alone.

9. Keeping daily record of work performed.

10. All blood typing (all work is, of course, checked by the head of the laboratory).

We presented the above not because it unequivocally demonstrates a surprising degree of problem-solving behavior (although this is likely) but because it illustrates (a) that much more attention should be given to non-test behavior, and (b) that the problems involved in describing the intellectual processes at work in non-test behavior are probably far more difficult than in the formal test situation where we have more control over the presentation of the stimulus problem.

Case 4

The next example concerns an institutionalized woman of 30 who obtained an *IQ* of 49, her problem-solving behavior in any situation never seeming to be out of line with such a score. This case has been described by Schaefer-Simmern (232, 233) in great detail and the reader is urged to consult his full description. Selma was one of the "children" with whom Schaefer-Simmern worked in order to study the nature and development of artistic activity in the efforts of defective individuals. In choosing children for the study Schaefer-Simmern (232) did not select on the basis of ability to draw but rather on the basis that the child's drawing did *not* reveal a tendency to copy or imitate nature or to represent objects schematically, e.g., stick figures. The initial drawing of the children would be considered most primitive by conventional artistic criteria. Selma (as did the other participants) came to a workshop one day a week. When she was requested to show her first drawing:

> Her feelings of inferiority, her shyness, and even a certain anxiety gripped her. Turning her face away, she submitted her drawing with trembling hands. She obviously feared attention and criticism. Selma's first picture—according to her own statement, the only one she had ever done—indicates that even a mentally deficient person can create in a modest degree an ordered pictorial whole. It was astonishing that she was able to accomplish even so simple a pictorial result, and the writer praised her for her work. Her reserved attitude disappeared at once and a big smile spread over her face; apparently a word of encouragement was what she needed. Another fact was still more astonishing. While the writer was engaged in supervising the work of the other girls belonging to the same group, Selma took some drawing paper from the desk and started a new picture. She repeated almost the same subject. . . . Except for a little more careful execution of her drawing, there is no further development in the organization of form. But two essentials must be noted: the smaller trees show a different application of the stage of variability of direction of lines, a variation of form invented by herself; and furthermore, the fact that she drew this picture spontaneously indicated the possibility of an unfolding of energies that no one expected (232).

Language is an inadequate means for conveying to the reader what becomes evident from a study of Selma's artistic development—a development which can be labelled creative in that the content and structure of each of her drawings reflected her own decisions, her own way of solving the problems which such activity presents. Unfortunately, little interest in or research about the intellectual and problem-solving aspects of artistic activity is reflected in the psychological literature, although there can be no doubt that such activity is in large part of a problem-solving nature. The significance of Selma's case is not only that she was capable of a degree of sustained effort and achievement which was not predictable from her test or school behavior but also because it emphasizes how a particular kind of intellectual activity is not sampled by our tests. In addition, as a reading of Schaefer-Simmern's case description would clearly reveal, the problem of the content and structure of intellectual activity cannot be considered apart from that of motivation and the nature of the stimulus conditions (i.e., the pedagogical procedures and goals employed).[7] We have singled out the case of Selma only because of our focus on mental retardation. Schaefer-Simmern's book contains many instances of individuals of differing test-score status where the development of a high degree of problem-solving behavior is indeed dramatic. It is difficult to avoid the conclusion that conceptions of the nature of intelligence underlying the development and use of our conventional tests give one a rather limited sample of intellectual activity.

Thus far we have been discussing the possibility that our intelligence tests measure a restricted range of problem-solving stimuli and intellectual activities, and we have focused on the suggestion that these tests may be excellent indices of educational achievement and poor indicators of non-test intellectual activity. Support for the conclusions drawn has been largely observational, a fact which reflects not only the absence of systematic research but, more important, the tendency to view intelligence from the perspective of our current tests. The often heard statement that "intelligence is what intelligence tests measure" may have the virtue of being an operational definition but it may also have the vice of being scientifically nearsighted to a degree where one cannot see the forest for the trees.

At this point mention should be made of a large body of research, spear-

---

[7]When Schaefer-Simmern's procedures are contrasted with those ordinarily employed in the occupational therapy units in institutions for defectives— for that matter, in art classes in our ordinary schools as well—one has a rather clear example of how the content, procedures, and goals of our schools restrict the range of problem-solving behavior which one can observe. This conclusion is identical to that which may be drawn from Wertheimer's (288) observation of conventional procedures of teaching geometry. It is important to emphasize that both Schaefer-Simmern and Wertheimer discuss and describe intellectual processes (i.e., the creative, the productive) which are neither reinforced by pedagogical technique nor in any way reflected or measured in tests of intelligence. The implications of Schaefer-Simmern's work for recent studies of rigidity among subnormal individuals are discussed on page 253.

headed by Davis and Havighurst which rather clearly indicates that our conventional intelligence tests consist of materials and problems to which lower-class children are exposed in the course of their lives to a lesser degree than in the case of middle or upper class children.[8] In other words, our conventional tests tell us more about non-school problem-solving experiences of middle rather than lower-class children—perhaps a reflection of the fact that teachers and psychologists come largely from middle-class backgrounds.

Because of the findings in regard to cultural bias in intelligence tests, in addition to the fact that most intelligence test items present the child with problems which he infrequently meets in real life, Davis and Eells (56) standardized a test of problem-solving ability in which they attempted to reduce cultural bias and to include items more clearly reflecting problem-solving situations met in everyday life. The following quotation, which concerns why certain items were eliminated from the final form of the test, gives one a succinct but partial picture of Davis and Eell's approach (56, pp. 48-50):

> One item will illustrate the way in which several lines of evidence frequently contributed to the ultimate decision to eliminate an item. One Analogy item required the pupil to report that a horse bears the same relationship to a horse's hoof as does a boy to a boy's foot. The item was relatively easy, being answered correctly by 77 per cent of the six-year-old children, 88 per cent of the eight-year-old children, and 98 per cent of the 10-year-old children. This item also showed a very substantial socio-economic difference at the six-year-old level. Of children from high-status homes, 93 per cent of the six-year-old children answered correctly, while only 78 per cent of the low-status children answered correctly. This socio-economic difference was more than twice as great as the average for Analogy items at this age level. This socio-economic difference would not, of itself, have been grounds for eliminating the item, unless examination of the item led to the conclusion that the difference was due to bias in the nature of the item rather than to basic differences in the problem-solving ability of children in the two groups.

---

[8]It will be recalled that thus far in this report we have been discussing that large group of low test scoring individuals who conventionally have been regarded as representing the low end of the normal distribution curve of intelligence—individuals in whom there is no apparent central nervous system pathology. These individuals we have labelled for purposes of discussion as mentally retarded, in contrast to the mentally defective in whom there is some central nervous system pathology (e.g., mongolism, phenylketonuria, convulsive disorders, metabolic disfunction, etc.). The significance of the researches we are discussing above resides in the fact that the large bulk of the mentally retarded are of lower social class status.

In the case of this particular item, it seemed clear that in order to answer the item correctly, the child must be able to recognize that the drawing of the third term in the analogy was of a horse's hoof and not of a dog's or a cat's paw. Since the item was tried out in a large metropolitan city, it seemed unlikely that many of the six-year-old children had had much firsthand experience with horses. Recognition of the picture as that of a horse's hoof would probably be dependent, almost totally upon familiarity with children's books which contain pictures of horses. Books of this sort would, of course, be much more frequently found among high-status homes than among low-status homes. It appeared likely, therefore, that the higher proportion of correct answers from children of high socio-economic background reflected, not a basic superiority in problem-solving ability, but merely greater familiarity with the particular subject matter of this item. The reasoning involved here may be made clearer by thinking of this item as it might be answered by rural and urban children. If rural children should be found to do better on the item than urban children, as seems quite likely, this would probably be due to the greater opportunity which rural children have to be familiar with horses' hoofs and not to any genuine superiority in problem-solving ability on the part of the rural children. It was decided, therefore, that the item should be eliminated in favor of one dealing with materials more likely to be equally familiar to children from different cultural backgrounds.

Incidentally, the distribution of wrong responses on this item bears out the interpretation just suggested. Almost all the errors made by low-status children on the item involved checking the dog instead of the horse. For a child unfamiliar with the details of a horse's hoof, this seems an "intelligent" response, since the drawing more nearly resembles a dog's foot than that of a cat.

Because of the importance of this question for proper interpretation of the scores on the present test, it must be stressed that *no item was eliminated simply because it showed a large socio-economic difference.* Only if such difference served to call attention to a previously unnoticed bias in the content of the test item (as in the case just described) was the item eliminated. As a matter of fact, four other Analogy items which showed socio-economic differences larger than this one were not eliminated, and appear in the final test, since examination of the items did not reveal any obvious reason for believing the items to be biased.

It is important to point out that the test devised by Davis and Eells is the only one where an attempt was made to choose problems on the basis of observation (and interviewing) of children in such areas of activity as school, home, play, stories, and work. In addition, this is the first widely used test where the validity of the instrument is not evaluated by correlations with school grades or other standardized tests.

A general intelligence test is valid if it measures over-all capacity to solve mental problems. Since scientists have discovered no objective criterion of intelligence, previous test makers have tended to rely on the correlations of test scores with school grades, and upon the fact that their problems proved more difficult for lower-age groups than for higher-age groups, as evidence that their tests were actually valid measures of intelligence. But, as many, including Binet, have pointed out, school grades are greatly influenced by work habits, attentiveness, conscientiousness, home training, desire to compete, and many other aspects of the pupil's work. Therefore school grades are not satisfactory as a criterion of validity for a test of general mental capacity. Secondly, the fact that a problem shows an increase in the percentage of pupils passing it at increasing ages does not at all validate the problem as an index of intelligence. Large increments in percentage of pupils passing a problem at successively higher chronological ages may result simply from the fact that increasing instruction and practice are given pupils on similar problems, as the pupils advance through school and become older.

The fact is that there is no satisfactory objective criterion of true mental capacity, and therefore no possibility, at least at present, of constructing a satisfactory test of intelligence by purely objective means. It is necessary for the makers of intelligence tests to construct items which appear to require the main types of intellectual problem-solving behavior. The keenest insights of psychologists and students of culture are called for in this process.

It follows that the validity of the *Davis-Eells Test* necessarily must rest, as does that of any other intelligence test (as distinct from a "scholastic aptitude" test), on the reasonableness of the problems as indicators of general problem-solving ability (56, pp. 6-7).

A recent study by Zweibelson (302, 303) lends support and corroboration to Davis and Eell's rationale and findings. To 258 fourth-grade public school children, Zweibelson administered the Otis-Alpha, Otis-Beta, Davis-Eells, and Stanford Achievement tests. Previous to these tests the children were given the Test Anxiety questionnaire which concerns attitudes toward and experiences in test taking situations in school (226).

1. In Table 3 are given the correlations of the three standardized intelligence tests with the achievement test. As one would expect from Davis and Eell's rationale and findings, their test is least correlated with a criterion of academic achievement—although it is itself significantly correlated

TABLE 3

CORRELATION OF SCORE ON MENTAL ABILITY AND ACHIEVEMENT TESTS
[From Zweibelson (302), $N = 258$]

Stanford achievement	r with mental ability		
	Otis-Alpha	Otis-Beta	Davis-Eells
Paragraph meaning	.56	.77	.50
Word meaning	.53	.77	.43
Spelling	.50	.73	.44
Language	.59	.69	.49
Arithmetic reasoning	.57	.72	.48
Arithmetic computation	.48	.54	.38
Mean achievement	.62	.81	.52

with such a criterion.   If the three mental ability tests were placed on a continuum on the basis of content, format and similar factors, the Otis Alpha could easily be estimated to be in a position between the two other mental tests—an estimate congruent with the size of correlations found in Table 3.

2.   When scores on the three tests were correlated with teacher opinion about whether a child was or was not a reading or arithmetic problem, the Davis-Eells was least related to teacher opinion, the Otis Beta was most related, and the Otis Alpha again in between.   These results suggest that the problem-solving abilities measured by the Davis-Eells are less related to what may be called problem-solving in reading and arithmetic than is true of the other tests.   The above findings were most clear in the case of reading.

3.   Test Anxiety was significantly less related to Davis-Eells score (—.14) than in the case of the Otis Alpha (—.28) or Otis Beta (—.24). In other words it would seem that anxiety is less of an interfering factor in the Davis-Eells than in the other tests—a finding predictable from the rationale and administration of the Davis-Eells.

Because the Davis-Eells test reflects a different and refreshing approach to the problem of the measurement of intelligence, it is important that it be critically scrutinized.

1.   The final forms of the test consist of four types of problem-solving items.   As we shall see in the next section, it is extremely doubtful that four types of items are in any way representative of the range of human abilities, either of adults or children.   Consequently, it would seem unjustified to interpret scores on this test as reflecting intelligence or problem-solving ability *in general*—a limitation not peculiar to this test.   While the various criteria for inclusion or rejection of types of items could be justified in a clinical sense (e.g., mode of administration, de-emphasis of time limits, real-

ism of problem situations, etc.), they nevertheless resulted in a test with a very restricted range of problem-solving situations. There is nothing inherently wrong with a test of restricted range of items. But it would seem unwarranted to call such a test one of general intelligence or problem-solving ability.

2. Although Davis and Eells attempted to reduce the usually obtained differences between social classes in test score, such differences still obtain with their test. This finding is susceptible to a variety of interpretations, as discussed in Section VI. We wish only to point out that until the relationships between social class and motivation for achievement are studied and clarified, the differences in intellectual performance between individuals in different social classes cannot properly be evaluated, as the writings of Davis (55) and the work of Haggard (101) suggest. In comparing the test performance of a group of Americans and Australian Aborigines, one would hardly be justified in attributing the poorer performance of the Aborigines to poorer general intelligence or problem-solving ability, although ultimately this *may* be found to be the case. This, of course, is an extreme example but it does serve to illustrate that differences in test performance between groups of differing experiences (i.e., culture background) are associated with other kinds of differences (non-intellectual) which *a priori* cannot be considered effects rather than causes of the test differences. There are two limitations of the Davis-Eells as well as other more conventional tests. First, as already suggested, there is no evidence or justification for the assumption that the problem-solving tasks sampled by these tests are representative of problem-solving behavior in everyday life. Second, whatever theoretical rationale underlies these tests has not come directly to grips with the problem of the relation between motivation and abilities, a problem to which Bray (26) has recently called attention.

3. As we indicated earlier, Davis and Eells made a deliberate attempt to observe children in various spheres of life activities as a guide in selecting items for their test. Unfortunately, in terms of the point of view we have presented, these workers never seemed to consider the problem of the relation between problem-solving in and outside of the test-situation, although the importance of this problem is implied in much of Davis' writings. For example, when one finds, as Davis and Eells did with their test, that there are pervasive differences between certain social class groupings, are there similar differences when the everyday problem-solving behavior of these groups is studied? Put in another way: are the differences in level of problem-

solving behavior in the test situation observable in *all* problem-solving behavior outside of the test situation?　While it should be indispensable in
constructing a test to observe non-test behavior as a guide in selection of
items, it should also be essential that one demonstrate that the level of problem-solving which is elicited by these test items is highly correlated with behavior to these items when they are met with in everyday life.　In constructing a test to select certain machine operators, one selects items which
clearly reflect what these operators actually do or will be required to do,
and one endeavors to construct the test so that it will differentiate between
levels of actual performance.　Similarly with our intelligence tests: implicitly and explicitly they have been validated on the basis of scholastic
achievement and the content of these tests reflect such an aim.　If one's goal
is to construct a test which will predict problem-solving behavior outside of
school-like situations—then it would seem necessary to study and demonstrate the relationship between performance in such situations and in response to the test.　Although Davis and Eells correctly maintain that their
test cannot be validated by the usual criteria of academic achievement or
degree of correlation with other tests (which themselves employed the academic achievement criterion), it does seem that their own theoretical position requires that they employ, in part at least, the criterion of problem-
solving behavior observed in everyday life situations.

In this as well as in the previous section we have centered our attention
on some aspects of the logic of intelligence test construction, paying particular attention to the limitations of the criteria most frequently employed.　In
doing so we have attempted to indicate that these limitations are as much of
a problem with a test designed to reduce the effects of culture bias as with
the more conventional ones.　The specific ways in which cultural and social-
class factors may influence test performance are discussed in Section VI
which also contains an evaluation of culture-fair or culture-free tests in light
of existing studies.

IV. "THE STRUCTURE OF INTELLECT"

Although the recognition that cultural bias pervades our conventional tests of intelligence represents an important advance in our knowledge, it does not in any explicit way consider the problem of the nature, range, or organization of intellectual abilities. In the previous discussion, however, we have had occasion to raise this question: how adequate are our tests for describing or evaluating the various human abilities? The most succinct answer to this question has been given by Guilford (99) in his penetrating discussion of the "structure of intellect":

> The advent of multiple-factor analysis has done something to broaden and enrich our conception of human intelligence, but factor theory and the results of factor analysis have had little effect upon the practices of measurement of intelligence. We do have a great variety of tests in such intelligence scales as the Binet and its revisions and in the Wechsler scales, to be sure. Too commonly, however, a single score is the only information utilized, and this single score is usually dominated by variance in only one or two factors. There is some indication of more general use of part scores, as in connection with the Wechsler tests, but each of these scores is usually factorially complex and its psychological meaning is largely unknown as well as ambiguous. The list of factors that is to be presented in this article should clearly demonstrate the very limited information that a single score can give concerning an individual, and on the other hand, the rich possibilities that those factors offer for more complete and more meaningful assessments of the intellects of persons (99, p. 267).

It cannot be too strongly stated that most of our tests are woefully inadequate for the evaluation of the various human aptitudes, a point of which more than a few clinicians have long been aware. To give some idea of the complexity of the problem as well as an indication of the progress which has been made we present below a portion of Guilford's discussion of but one (the cognition or discovery factors) of the three groups of factors which seem to fall under the general heading of thinking:

> The cognition factors have to do with becoming aware of mental items or constructs of one kind or another. In the tests of these factors, something must be comprehended, recognized, or discovered by the examinee. They represent functions on the receiving side of behavior sequences.
> The cognition abilities can be differentiated along the lines of two major principles. For some time we have been aware that thinking factors tend to pair off according to the material or content used in the

tests. For each factor of a certain kind found in verbal tests there seemed to be a mate found in tests composed of figures or designs. We found, for example, a factor called *eduction of perceptual relations,* parallel with a factor called *education of conceptual relations*; a factor called *perceptual foresight,* parallel to one called *conceptual foresight*; and a factor of *perceptual classification,* parallel with one of *conceptual classification.* Only recently there has been increasing evidence for a third content category. Factors were found in tests whose contents are letters, or equivalent symbols, where neither perceived form or figure nor verbal meaning is the basis of operation. Factors based upon this type of material have been found, parallel to other factors where the test content is figural or verbal. Thus a third content category seems necessary.

A second major principle by which cognition factors may be differentiated psychologically depends upon the kind of things discovered; whether it is a relation, a class, or a pattern, and so on. Thus, for each combination of content and thing discovered, we have a potential factor. The cognition factors can therefore be arranged in a matrix as shown in Table 4. The third and fourth rows seem to be complete at the present time. There are vacancies in the other four rows. With each factor name are usually given two representative tests by name to help give the factor operational meaning. A word or two will be said in addition regarding the less familiar tests.

It should not be surprising to find the factor of *verbal* comprehension, the best known, and the dominant one in verbal-intelligence tests generally, in the first row of the cognition factors and in the conceptual column. The fact that the cognition factors sometimes come in threes leads us to look for parallel factors for the perceptual and structural columns. One candidate for the perceptual cell in this row would be the well-known factor of *perceptual speed.* This factor has to do with discriminations of small differences in form rather than in awareness of total figures, hence it does not quite fill the requirement of parallel properties with *verbal comprehension.* A better factor for this purpose is the one Thurstone called "speed and strength of closure," called *figural closure* (Table 4). For this factor, awareness of perceived objects from limited cues is the key property. The limitation of cues is necessary to make the test sufficiently difficult for testing purposes. . . .

Two factors involving ability to recognize classes are known, one in which the class if formed on the basis of figural properties and the other on the basis of meanings. It was interesting that the Picture Classification test had more relation to the *perceptual-classification* factor than to the *conceptual-classification* factor in spite of the fact that the things to be classified were common objects, the basis for whose classification was intended to be their meaning. This might mean that the

TABLE 4
COGNITION (DISCOVERY) FACTORS
(From Guilford, 99)

Type of thing known or discovered	Type of content		
	Figural	Structural	Conceptual
Fundamentals	*Figural closure* Street Gestalt Completion Mutilated Words		*Verbal comprehension* Vocabulary
Classes	*Perceptual classification* Figure Classification Picture Classification		*Verbal classification* Word Classification Verbal Classification
Relations	*Eduction of perceptual relations* Figure Analogies Figure Matrix	*Eduction of structural relations* Seeing Trends II Correlate Completion II	*Eduction of conceptual relations* Verbal Analogies Word Matrix
Patterns or systems	*Spatial orientation* Spatial Orientation Flags, Figures, Cards	*Eduction of patterns* Circle Reasoning Letter Triangle	*General reasoning* Arithmetic Reasoning Ship Destination
Problems			*Sensitivity to problems* Seeing Problems Seeing Deficiencies
Implications	*Perceptual foresight* Competitive Planning Route Planning		*Conceptual foresight* Pertinent Questions Alternate Methods *Penetration* Social Institutions Similarities

perceptual-conceptual distinction is a somewhat superficial matter, pertaining only to how the material is presented. It is possible, however, that in many of the items in this test the general shapes and sizes and other figural properties are an aid in classification. For example, there are cleaning implements, containers, etc. in some items, where similarities of appearance may serve as clues. . . . For the discovery of problems, there is only one factor—*sensitivity to problems,* which is in the conceptual column. The appearance of this factor parallel to *general reasoning* in the row preceding, emphasizes the well-known observation that it is one thing to be aware that a problem exists and another thing to be aware of the nature of the problem. The titles of the tests are quite descriptive. A sample item from the test Seeing Problems asks the examinee to list as many as five problems in connection with a common object like a candle. The test Seeing Deficiencies presents in each item the general plan for solving a given problem, but the plan raises some new problems. What are those problems?

Whether we shall ever find parallel factors for seeing problems or deficiencies of figural and structural types remains to be seen. Problems of a figural type are faced in aesthetic pursuits such as painting and architecture. Problems of a structural type might be faced in connection with spelling or the development of language. Tests pertaining to the seeing of problems have thus far provided no figural or structural bases for problems. It should be relatively easy to test the hypothesis that such factors exist. If they do exist, their possible implications for everyday performance need further study. . . .

Porteus has maintained that his series of maze tests measure foresight. He can well claim support from the factor-analysis results just mentioned. The type of foresight measured by maze tests, however, is of a concrete variety. This ability may be important for the architect, the engineer, and the industrial-lay-out planner. It may not be found related to the abstract type of planning that we find in the political strategist and the policy maker. So far as our results go, the maze test should by no means be offered as a test of general intelligence. This statement might need modification, however, after the maze test is factor analyzed in a population of lower general intellectual level (where general intelligence is defined operationally as an average of all intellectual abilities). In a population of "high-level personnel," we can say that a maze test measures most strongly the factor of *perceptual foresight* and, incidentally, to some degree the factors of *visualization* and *adaptive flexibility.*

The appearance of a factor called *penetration* . . . , along with *conceptual foresight,* calls for comment. A factor of penetration was hypothesized in the first analysis of creative abilities and was not found. An unidentified factor found there might well have been *penetration.* A factor has been so identified in a more recent analysis that emphasized creative ability tests. It is strongly loaded on a test called Social Institutions, which asks what is wrong with well-known institutions such as tipping. It was designed as a test of *sensitivity to problems,* and it has consistently had a loading on that factor. In the first creativity analysis, two scores were based upon this test; one being the total number of low-quality or obvious defects and the other was the total number of high-quality or "penetrating" defects—defects that can be seen only by the far-sighted person. As a matter of fact, the two scores had much to do with effecting a separation of the seeing-problems tests into two groups, one of which might have been identified as the *penetration* factor.

In his article Guilford also presents and discusses two other broad thinking factors: production and evaluation. Several things should be said or emphasized or concluded from his presentation.

1. The identification of a factor involves consideration of at least two things: (*a*) the kinds of thinking sequences that a problem presumably engenders in or requires of the individual and (*b*) the content of the stimulus task. The significance of Guilford's research in this connection is that he has demonstrated that the number of different intellectual factors is probably far greater than had been previously thought or is contained in existing tests of intelligence.

2. Guilford has described factors, the production and evaluation ones, which previously either had not been systematically studied or had not at all been considered as intellectual processes. Guilford describes these two groups of factors as follows:

> The second large group of thinking factors has to do with the production of some end result. After one has comprehended the situation, or the significant aspects of it at the moment, usually something needs to be done to it or about it. In the analogies test, for example, having seen the relation between the first pair of elements of an item we must then find a correlate to complete another pair. Having understood a problem, we must take further steps to solve it.
>
> Evaluation factors have to do with decisions concerning the goodness, suitability, or effectiveness of the results of thinking. After a discovery is made, after a product is achieved, is it correct, is it the best that we can do, will it work? This calls for a judgmental step of some kind. It was our hypothesis in the project that the ability to make such decisions will depend upon the area within which the thinking takes place and the criteria on which the decision is based.

Guilford's description and discussion of these factors represents a systematic attempt to observe in a test situation intellectual processes which heretofore had been noted as important in the non-test problem-solving behavior of people. It seems to us, in fact, that the discrepancies that too frequently are found between test and non-test problem-solving behavior (the latter being better than the former) would perhaps arise with less frequency if the tests had included what is in part subsumed under Guilford's production and evaluation factors.[9] In other words, what we observe outside of the test situation cannot be gleaned from test behavior because of a narrow conception and inadequate sampling of intellectual abilities.

3. Regarding the large number of factors reported we can do no better than again to quote Guilford:

> A theory or a method should be judged by its fruits. If the results that have been reported here contribute to psychological understanding and, through that, to useful psychological practice, factor analysis has passed this kind of test. The mathematical model that has been applied, which conceives of individual differences in intellectual performances as being represented by a coordinate system of n dimensions, has served certain purposes. While it may be shown at some future time that the model is not the best that could be applied, its power to generate new psychological ideas and to extend considerably the conception of the realm of intellect has been demonstrated.
>
> The average reader will no doubt be surprised by the large number of dimensions that seem to be required to encompass the range of intellectual aspects of human nature. Some 40 factors are reported as being known and a great many additional unknown factors are forecast. This would seem to go against the scientific urge for parsimony.
>
> The principle of parsimony has led us in the past to the extreme of one intellectual dimension, which everyone should now regard as going too far in that direction. There is actually no fixed criterion for the satisfaction of the principle of parsimony. In science we can satisfy the principle to some degree whenever the number of concepts is smaller than the number of phenomena observed. Forty, sixty, or even a hundred factors would certainly be a smaller number of concepts than the number of possible tests or the number of observable types of activities of an intellectual character. In this sense the principle of parsimony has been satisfied.

---

[9] We emphasize the situation where level of non-test problem-solving behavior is better than in the test situation because we think there is sufficient clinical and research evidence that among the mentally retarded such a discrepancy is by no means infrequent. The reverse situation—where level of problem-solving in the test situation is markedly above the individual's actual achievements—is certainly not a rare occurrence among the non-retarded, as the observant reader can attest. Here, too, the "discrepancy" and reaction of surprise are probably a function of the implicit but unwarranted assumption that the sample of behavior observed in the test situation is a representative sample of problem-solving behavior.

The number of the factors is less unattractive when we find that they can be subsumed within a system that is describable by a smaller number of categories or principles. Some readers will ask whether, since there are many probable intercorrelations among the factors, a small set of second-order factors will not suffice. Granting that we can make sufficiently accurate estimates of the intercorrelations among the factors, which the writer doubts that we can do at present, to use only second-order-factor concepts would lose information. This follows from the fact that where n linearly independent dimensions are necessary to describe a domain geometrically, no one dimension can be entirely accounted for by combinations of the others.

It may be asked whether some of the factors listed are not really specific factors rather than common factors. This is a legitimate question. It is not uncommon experience in factor analysis to find what was formerly regarded as a single common factor appears later to split up into two or more factors. The "splitting up" description is not completely accurate. It applies best to the fact that a group of tests having a "factor" in common later divide into two or more groups each defining its own common factor. In clear thinking about this phenomenon, we must keep in mind the distinction between "factor" as a mathematical concept and "factor" as a psychological concept. The immediate results of a factor analysis are in terms of mathematical factors. Whether each mathematical factor represents a single psychological factor or a combination of psychological factors has to be determined by interpretation and by further experimental work applied to the designing of new factor analyses. Eventually we reach the stage where further efforts to "split" a factor fail. Whether this has brought us to a specific factor in any particular case can be decided on the basis of a single criterion. Are the tests defining this factor essentially just different forms of the same test? This cannot always be decided with certainty, but there is usually little difficulty in doing so. If we suspect that any factor is a specific, a new analysis that includes more obviously different tests, but tests that should measure the same *common* factor, should be done.

4. Guilford's research is based on studies of the superior human adult. Although it is probably true, as Guilford indicates, that in studying such individuals one can "investigate intellectual qualities and functions in their greatest scope and variety," one can only hope that similar studies will be done with those in the lower end of the distribution curve. At this point mention might be made of Satter and McGee's (229, 230, 231) studies of a group of retarded adults who showed an unexpectedly good level of vocational behavior (i.e., unexpected in terms of initial testing on admission to the institution) and also showed test score increases beyond the age of fif-

teen or sixteen. "This group was then matched with one of equal size and composition on the basis of *IQ* earned on the 1916 Stanford-Binet at the time of admission, its length of residence, chronological age and its etiological background." A variety of tests was given to the subjects and a factor analysis was done with the 27 variables which had been found discriminating between the two groups. Three factors were extracted: a general one, a perceptual motor one, and a substitution one.[10] Although Satter and McGee's studies are worthy of note because they illustrate the fruitfulness of attending to non-test problem-solving behavior, they also exemplify an important limitation in a factor analytic approach. We refer here to the fact that the kinds of factors which will emerge in such a study depend in large part on the kinds of tests employed. For example, Satter and McGee used the more conventional psychological tests and because of this many of the factors described by Guilford could not appear. It is also obvious that to sample the varieties of intellectual processes would require many more tests than the relatively few used by Satter and McGee. Jastak (130, 131), who has thought most penetratingly about the usefulness of factor analysis in relation to mental subnormality, concluded on the basis of his research and clinical experience that "from 20 to 50 different mental functions will have to be tested before a truly scientific diagnosis of feeblemindedness can be made." In fact, both from a clinical and theoretical standpoint Jastak's approach—which unfortunately for the field has never been systematically and comprehensively presented by him— goes beyond Guilford's in that he emphasizes the absolute necessity of viewing the intellectual factors in terms of the personality ones. His illustrative presentation of individuals with an identical low *IQ*, differing psychometric patterns on 12 intellectual factors, and radically different "personality genotypes" effectively directs attention to what is perhaps the most important research in the field. Equally important is Jastak's emphasis (supported, we think, by his unpublished research) that it is only on the basis of this approach and the research to which it gives rise (*a*) that more sensible therapeutic and educational programs can be developed and (*b*) that the frequently found "discrepancies" between level of conventional test scores, on the one hand, and level of social and vocational performance, on the other hand, can be seen as artifacts of conventional test scores.

---

[10]In a non-factor analysis study of two retarded groups who also differed in level of problem-solving behavior outside the test situation, Sarason and Sarason (227) also obtained significant differences in the perceptual-motor sphere.

It could be argued that many of the factors that Guilford obtained with his superior group would not be applicable to or simply would not be found among the mentally retarded. This *may* be so but it would be a scientific mistake of no small proportion if such assumptions were considered as facts and prevented the kind of systematic research which is so desperately needed in this area. It would be our opinion that unless such research is done we not only may be kept from a better understanding of the retarded but we may also be misled in some of the conclusions drawn about the significance of and interrelationships among the various factors in the superior individual. One could point to several problems—such as amenability to psychotherapy or level of social and vocational competence—where unjustified and untested assumptions about what the retarded could do prevented the acquisition of new knowledge, to the detriment both of practice and theory.

5. One of the intriguing and important problems suggested by Guilford's research may be put as follows: What is the relation between variety and relationships of intellectual factors, on the one hand, and cultural differences, on the other? Put in cross-cultural terms: What would likely be obtained if we were to attempt to replicate Guilford's findings (on superior American males) with the Eskimo? Having posed the question we could predict at least two things: (*a*) we would probably not know how to begin such a study, and (*b*) many of the tests used by Guilford would clearly make no sense to the Eskimo (even taking the language barrier into account). To do such a study would require a most intimate knowledge of Eskimo culture in the hope that such knowledge would allow us to construct meaningful tests for the different factors. It may well be that such intimate knowledge would lead us to conclude that some of the intellectual factors we find in certain groups of our culture do not manifest themselves in Eskimo culture. Is it that the brains of Eskimos are different or is this a reflection of the fact that their culture is quite different from our own? If it turns out, as we think likely, that the great bulk of the mentally retarded in our own culture come from or constitute a different sub-culture, we would be faced with the same kinds of questions that arise when one compares drastically different cultures, e.g., Eskimos and Americans. The important result of such a study would be to illuminate the kinds of cultural settings which inhibit or facilitate the development of particular intellectual factors. It is difficult to see how without these kinds of studies a really comprehensive general theory of human intelligence—its nature, development, and relationships or interactions with motivation and life experiences—can be de-

veloped. At the present time we have knowledge of the nature of some of the intellectual processes. One can only hope that such knowledge, based as it is on a very restricted sample (culturally and intellectually), does not result in premature theory building about *all* people. The study of individual differences, between and within cultures, may well give us the kinds of data necessary for a general theory of human intelligence. We strongly feel that psychological theories built upon data obtained without explicit and systematic regard for the factor of cultural differences are likely to be either incomplete and/or misleading. In such instances much talent and time are wasted and not until the rôle of the cultural variable is demonstrated does one see the inadequacies of past practice and theory—a good example of this being the lack of recognition of the cultural bias in our conventional tests of intelligence (see previous section). Perhaps a better example of this is the status of social science research before and after the development of modern anthropology.

Thus far in this and previous sections we have discussed the problem of the measurement of intelligence in terms of a few propositions which might be summarized as follows:

1. Conventional tests sample a very limited number of intellectual processes, for the most part those kinds of processes which are required in scholastic achievements.

2. Conventional tests, by virtue primarily of their content and means of validation, contain a large element of social class or cultural bias.

3. There is no evidence that the level and kinds of problem-solving behavior signified by scores on conventional tests are highly correlated with non-test problem-solving behavior.

4. It appears that the bulk of the mentally retarded are found primarily in the lower social classes and that the cultural matrix in these classes is different in important respects from that of other groups. Because of the cultural bias in conventional tests, the intellectual potential of this group, as well as its level of functioning outside the test situation, cannot be assumed to have been adequately assessed.

5. It is becoming more and more apparent that the variety of intellectual processes is far greater than had been thought previously to be the case and that the continued use of conventional tests and test scores *in practice and research* is likely to be, at best, non-productive. Whatever new knowledge we have (or will obtain) in this respect is due less to a particular method (e.g., factor analysis) than to changes in conceptions about the

nature, organization, and variety of intellectual processes. This statement perhaps requires some elaboration. Although factor analysis has been around for some time and has long influenced or given rise to theories of intelligence, its fruitfulness has been reduced by the failure of many workers to realize that the conventional tests they used immediately and drastically reduced their sample of intellectual activities. Put in another way: one's conceptions (i.e., theory) about the variety of intellectual functions should dictate the tests devised and employed rather than one's conceptions being dictated by tests which happen to be available. It is difficult to avoid the conclusion that some workers have been uncritically dependent on tests because they have no theory concerning the structure of intellect. We have been impressed with Guilford's work less because he employs factor analysis than because he seems to have started out with a rather broad conception of the varieties of intellectual functioning. It is not surprising, therefore, that Guilford discusses and attempts to measure activities which are not found in our conventional tests. This is not because Guilford uses factor analysis but because of his conception about what is "intellectual." When the clinical psychologist has to evaluate an individual's intellectual capacity and performance, he almost always finds himself taking into account so-called qualitative factors which are either not at all or inadequately sampled by conventional tests, so that his final judgment reflects more than test scores. It is our impression that Guilford has come closer to recognizing these qualitative factors than previous factor analysts. The reader unfamiliar with the nature, usefulness and limitations of factor analysis might profitably read Anastasi and Foley (7) and Bray (26).

6. Unless research in this area explicitly takes account of cultural variations we will be robbing ourselves of an important source for the understanding of the factors which determine the nature and organization of different patterns of intellectual processes.

V. HEREDITY AND ENVIRONMENT

In 1912 Henry H. Goddard (92) published *The Kallikak Family, a Study in the Heredity of Feeblemindedness*. He was by no means the first to propose that feeblemindedness was an inheritable characteristic, but his study was accepted as confirmation so conclusive that it was scarcely questioned for at least 10 years after publication of the book. Although at the present time practically all responsible workers in the field recognize that conclusive proof of the heritability of mental ability (where no organic or metabolic pathology is involved) is still lacking, the assumption that subnormality has a genetic basis continues to crop up in scientific studies. This undoubtedly results in some degree from the general failure to observe a distinction between "simple" retardation on the one hand, resulting presumably from inadequate learning and stimulation, and true deficiency of probable organic origin on the other. But it must also be recognized that an assumption of inferior heredity can provide an appealingly simple explanation for a condition which to the average person is both very disturbing and quite incomprehensible. The most recent example which has come to our attention is an article by McGurk (181) in a national magazine, purporting to demonstrate the inherent inferiority of Negroes. This irresponsible product employed seductively plausible but scientifically spurious reasoning to fuel the fires of an explosive national issue. It need concern us here only insofar as it underlines the dangers inherent in giving any serious weight to genetic factors until—and unless—they can be demonstrated to be relevant.

As we review in this section a selected few studies bearing on the effects of heredity versus environment in the etiology of mental subnormality and as we discuss the research implications of these studies, it will be our thesis that a hereditary determinant of mental capacity must not be assumed to exist unless proven. Furthermore, proof should be sought in terms of our present knowledge of human genetics and of the nature of human intellect, rather than, as is commonly done, through the administration of routine intelligence tests to a variety of different "racial" and other groups. We do not propose to *deny* that heredity is a factor, particularly in mental deficiency, but rather that we should leave it out of our accounting until it is supported by more than speculation and bias. Although scientifically we must retain an open mind, we must also recognize that among laymen and among many physicians and other professionals the assumption of a genetic determinant is customarily accepted. A considerable educational effort will therefore be necessary before they can even share our state of open-mindedness. The belief is widespread that even moderate subnormality results from a defect in heredity and is therefore irreversible. This belief carries with it a sense of hopelessness which not only prevents doctors and others from encouraging people to look for means of rehabilitating the mentally handicapped, but also discourages most researchers from entering the field. In the broader context of our society it implies biological as well as social support for the concept of segregation, and helps keep alive the idea of sterilization as a means to reduce the numbers of retarded and problem children. These trends would at best not be healthy if they were founded on known facts, but resting as they do on an assumption which, despite repeated efforts, has as yet to receive scientifically acceptable proof we can only view them with distress.

Goddard's (92) study of the two Kallikak families, with its fairly obvious methodological weaknesses, is too well known to require review. Very few later researchers followed Goddard's lead in applying the genealogical method in large-scale studies of mental subnormality, except as applied to cases of clearly identifiable pathology. The method itself can be valuable and has been used to good effect by Kallmann (140), in conjunction with statistical prediction procedures, in the study of schizophrenia. It does not, however, appear applicable to research in mental retardation due to the virtual impossibility of obtaining reliable diagnoses or even adequate behavioral descriptions of people who are dead or cannot be located. This difficulty exists in addition to those we shall discuss later which apply to almost any type of research in the heredity of mental capacity, and virtually precludes genealogical research in this field.

Interest in the heritable factors in subnormality took a new turn with the availability after the first World War of the results of large-scale intelligence-testing of draftees. Among the first things to be observed in these data were the significantly lower test scores attained by Negroes than by whites. Although subsequent analyses of these same data revealed regional and other factors which were at work in determining test outcomes,[11] the fashion was established of applying intelligence and other types of performance tests uncritically to a wide range of ethnic groups. Typically in many studies the averaged IQ's and other indices of two or more groups

---

[11]For a review of these data, see Montagu (186).

were compared, with the explicit or implicit assumption that these comparisons were somehow descriptive of "racial" characteristics. Not infrequently the researcher, having watched the test subjects wrestle with language and other problems in the tests, would conclude with the hesitant suggestion that there were perhaps factors of environment, schooling, or the like which affected the results. However, these afterthoughts were not enough to discourage further research of the same order. Without any attempt to track down all studies of this sort we uncovered several dozen which fit this description during our survey of the literature. Although most of these date from the 1920's and 1930's, they continue to appear in diminishing numbers to the present time. In later studies various attempts were made to use tests which the researcher believed would hold constant the cultural and environmental factors; in the next section we discuss some of these tests and point out that none we have discovered control environmental factors in the hoped for manner.

We shall not attempt to review these studies in any detail, although a number of them are discussed elsewhere in this report as they have bearing on particular problems. It is, however, important to note the persistence of this research approach over time, in spite of the doubts which it so often engendered in the minds of the researchers and in the face of other research and theoretical criticism which demonstrated in a variety of ways the invalidity of any "racial" or ethnic IQ. With the problems attendant upon the gradual rise in the social and economic status of the Negro as a background, it was probably not merely the availability of subjects which led so many researchers to focus particularly upon Negro-white comparisons. Nor is it surprising that, in spite of evidence to the contrary, we find Henry E. Garrett (80), having reviewed some studies, writing in 1947 that "the regularity of this result [i.e., lower Negro IQ] from babyhood to adulthood makes it extremely unlikely, in the present writer's opinion, that environmental opportunities can possibly explain all the differences found" (p. 333). Although Garrett does admit that these are not true "racial" comparisons, it is disturbing to observe a person in his professional position making the bland assumption that he has in fact explored all possible explanations other than that of constitutional inferiority. It is also significant to note that in the 14 studies which we culled from our review in which Italian IQ's or mental retardation rates are compared with those of a variety of other ethnic groups, the Italians consistently fall near or at the low end of the continuum (sometimes below the Negro groups selected for comparison), yet nowhere did we find a claim that Italians are constitutionally inferior to other persons of European origin.

As early as 1921 Artlitt (13) published a study in which she determined Stanford-Binet *IQ*'s and ranking on the Taussig Socio-economic Scale of 191 native-born white, 87 Italian, and 71 Negro primary school children. She concluded that "the difference in median *IQ* which is due to race alone is in this case at, most only 8.6 whereas the difference between children of the same race but of Inferior and Very Superior social status may amount to 33.9 points" (p. 182). Because of the early date at which this research was conducted it is only to be expected that the assumption of a racial factor remained, but she appropriately titled her paper "On the Need for Caution in Establishing Race Norms," a warning which was unfortunately widely disregarded. Had she taken into account other factors such as language handicaps, length of residence in the United States, or educational level of the parents she would undoubtedly have found even less of a residual difference to be accounted for on "racial" grounds.

Only three years later Bere (17) conducted an even more sophisticated study which is relevant even today. She administered the Stanford-Binet and the Pintner-Paterson Performance Tests to boys of immigrant Hebrew, Bohemian, and Italian parents, 100 of each ethnic group, and all having been at least two years in the New York City public schools. Through comparisons between the various tests and subtests she attempted to identify the types of thinking process associated with the differing cultural backgrounds and experiences of the boys, concluding that the Hebrew boys did best in problems involving abstraction whereas the Italians thought in more concrete terms, with the Bohemians falling between. This attention to qualitative differences in problem-solving thought processes learned in different cultural settings was true pioneering. It is only in quite recent years that additional serious work had been undertaken in this area, yet it is increasingly clear that this is the direction in which we must travel if we are truly to understand the mechanisms which produce cultural and ethnic differences in problem-solving behavior, to say nothing of quantitative *IQ*'s.

In the years following, along with the continued outpouring of naïve comparisons of "racial" *IQ*'s, a variety of increasingly sophisticated critiques and critical research was undertaken. In 1927 Mead (184) compared a group of 160 American children with 276 children of the same grade in whose homes Italian was spoken, utilizing *IQ*, social status measures, amount of English spoken in the home, and length of parental residence in the

United States, concluding among other things that "classification of foreign children in schools where they have to compete with American children, on the basis of group intelligence test findings alone, is not a just evaluation of the child's innate capacity" (p. 468). In separate articles published in 1928 Thompson (269) and Viteles (279) reviewed a number of comparative studies of Negro and white IQ's and concluded that existing tests appeared to measure only acquired, not innate, ability and were therefore worthless for interracial comparisons. In 1932 Daniel (51) compiled a checklist of factors which must be taken into consideration in attempting interracial comparisons of mental ability, including statistical considerations, sampling, norms, test artifacts, educational opportunities, and the like. Subsequent work would suggest a further expansion of his list, but acceptance even of his criteria would be sufficient to invalidate virtually all extant comparisons of racial intelligence. Franzblau (73) in 1935, rather ingeniously administered the nonverbal National Intelligence Test to groups of girls in Copenhagen and in Rome, and then to Danish-American and Italian-American girls of similar age in the United States. Confirming the results of other studies, it was found that in the United States the Danish girls scored higher than the Italians, but the differences between the Danish and Italians girls tested in their home countries were not statistically significant. Because of the possibility of selective migration or other intervening factors one cannot accept this study as proof that native Danes and Italians are in fact identical in intelligence, but it does place the burden of proof on those who would contend that cultural background has no effect on the ability to adapt to and profit from the American educational system.

Also in 1935, Nissen, Machover, and Kinder (195) attacked the problem somewhat differently. They compared, on the basis of performance tests, groups of Negro children in West Virginia, St. Helena Island, and West Africa, the last from an area from which the slavers drew most of the slaves who were the ancestors of the present Negro population of the New World. As might be expected the West African Negroes scored lowest, while the New World Negroes were higher but below the white standardization norms. The differences, as might also be expected, were greatest on those subtests which the authors considered to have the greatest amount of Western cultural content. More important here than their research results are the conclusions they drew from their research experience, which are worth citing at some length.

In most reports of psychometric test findings with "racial" groups, whether civilized or primitive, the purpose, either expressed or implied, is that of affording an objective basis for the determination of "racial" differences. If test results are interpreted as reflecting differences only in specific, immediately present abilities which are closely related to those involved in the tests, there is little room for disagreement. If, however, differences in test results are generalized and considered as indicative of differences in *general* ability or adaptability, we encounter difficulties. Leaving aside the question of the significance of various traits and abilities for diverse cultures and environments, we cannot even be sure that the correlates of a given test performance are the same for all "racial" groups. Interpretations become even more speculative when the attempt is made to adduce from observed differences in test results evidence of inherent "racial" differences in specific or general native potentiality, potentiality for differential development being maximum at birth and never the same thereafter. Even assuming perfect analysis of the test, it would be virtually impossible to trace, not to say measure and make proper allowance for, all the subtle and elusive factors which contribute to the development of the associative abilities.

The difficulty of determining the degree of racial homogeneity of any given group, consideration of the mobility of races, which raises the issue of the fairness of temporal sampling, and the necessity of securing adequate geographic samplings for experimental purposes, complicate the problem immeasurably.

The sheer accumulation of test scores, then, whether or not they consistently point in the same direction, must leave us with the essentially inseparable variables, viz.: race and environment. The test which will eliminate or measure the effect of either element alone has not yet been devised, nor can we accept speculation as a substitute for the scientific differentiation of these two factors (pp. 309-310).

Starting in the late 1920's Otto Klineberg of Columbia University, both through his own research and through reviews of the work of others, has been one of the most continuous critics of comparative studies of "racial" intelligence. He has considerably extended the number of factors which must be considered as affecting test performance, including such matters as culturally determined attitudes toward speed of performance in any context or toward excelling in a test. In 1941 (158) he summarized "some of the factors in the social environment which may be responsible for the observed ethnic differences in test scores, and which should be controlled before any direct comparison between two different ethnic groups can legitimately be made. These include the factors of motivation, rapport, schooling, socioeconomic status, and language, as well as the background of interest, attitudes, and point-of-view which collectively we may call 'culture'" (p. 293).

Various aspects of Klineberg's work are discussed in more detail at several points in this report. He is one of the few psychologists concerned with this problem who has had anthropological research training.

An extensive research program at the University of Chicago, conducted by Allison W. Davis and Robert J. Havighurst and their colleagues, also handled social and cultural factors with sophistication. Because their primary focus was on the influence of social class factors in urban areas of the United States, rather than on ethnic factors, the results of this research are more appropriately discussed elsewhere. Davis and Havighurst (59) succinctly summarize their basic orientation as follows: "The crucial problem raised by the attempt to compare scientifically the capacity of any two individuals to learn is that of finding situations with which the two individuals have had equal experience" (p. 301).

Although ethnic comparisons undoubtedly form quantitatively the largest bulk of research relevant to heredity factors in mental ability, there have been other more direct approaches to the problem. One of the more obvious lines of attack is to administer intelligence tests to the children of persons who, in their earlier years, were adjudged retarded. Recent examples of such studies are those of Reed, Reed, and Palm (212) and of Charles (40). In the former, 37 people institutionalized as children at the Faribault (Minnesota) State School and Colony during the period 1910-1918, with an average IQ of 48, had 80 children who could be located and tested in the 1950's. These children had a mean IQ of 71. Charles, as part of a larger study, tested 73 children of parents adjudged in an earlier survey to be retarded on the basis of IQ and poor performance in the Lincoln, Nebraska, school system. He found their IQ's to average 95.4, with only one-sixth of the group below 80. This rise in the IQ of children compared to their retarded parents, which is confirmed in other studies, is not capable of clear-cut interpretation. In the first place, the parents themselves when retested after living in the community for some years generally show higher IQ's than they did as children (cf. Fairbank, 70; Muench, 189) ; this was true in Charles' sample and immediately raises the question whether we are viewing the parents' genes as having been determinants of their earlier or their later IQ's. Furthermore, it is rarely possible to test the other parents, that is, the spouses of the persons originally judged retarded, and patently impossible to determine what their IQ's would have been had they been tested at the earlier time, so at best we knew only half the genetic picture. Finally, we have ample evidence (e.g., Skeels and Harms, 246) of the effect of a more or a less stimulating environment on the development of intelligence of the sort measured by tests. Unless we have detailed data on the environments in which both the parents and the children were reared we can say nothing about the effects, if any, of heredity as the determinant of the children's higher *IQ*'s.

Herndon (114) addressed himself to a particular aspect of the folklore of the genetics of retardation, to wit, the belief that inbreeding, presumably by "weakening the strain," produces an increase in retardation. It is of course well known that inbreeding is more likely to permit expression of pathological and other characteristics determined by recessive genes, but the popular belief appears more general in nature and implies that inbreeding of itself has a weakening effect on intelligence as well as other characteristics. It was this belief which Herndon undertook to test. He administered the Wechsler-Bellevue to 223 persons in 86 inter-marrying families who lived in isolated pockets in the Blue Ridge Mountains of North Carolina, comparing these results with those obtained on other rural, but not isolated, North Carolina populations. He found "a range of *IQ* scores within normal limits for a rural population, occurring in a population with an unusually high cousin marriage rate and with presumably small size of mating isolates" (p. 57). The mean *IQ* was 94.5. This result is the more notable when viewed in relation to an earlier study by Sherman and Key (240). These authors administered a battery of tests to people in four of these "hollows" in the Blue Ridge Mountains somewhat north of the locale of Herndon's study, as well as to a group of people who had left the mountains to work in a sawmill in a Virginia town. The environment was similar but there was no evidence of a high rate of inbreeding. They found that, by ranking the communities on degree of isolation from day-to-day contact with the outside world, greater isolation appeared to correlate with a lower *IQ*. However, with more isolation there was also a lower socio-economic status, this latter having been shown in many studies to correlate with *IQ* also. Thus we cannot with assurance blame the environmental effects of isolation alone in the Sherman and Key study, but we *can* say that Herndon's inbred group lived in an environment at least no more conducive to developing a high *IQ* than their unisolated rural neighbors. Similarly, the study by Eaton and Weil (65) discussed more fully in Section VII of the inbred Hutterite population showed the morbidity rates of mental deficiency to fall within a normal range, while in the non-defective population at large there was no evidence of depressed intelligence.

Researchers concerned with separation of the effects of the seemingly inseparable factors of heredity and environment in humans have long been intrigued with the possibilities inherent in studies of identical twins. It requires more than mere superficial similarities in appearance to determine with certainty that such twins actually originated with a single fertilized ovum, but once such a determination has been made it is safe to assume that the two twins have identical hereditary endowments. From this it follows that any differences which appear between them are due to environment alone. It is then deceptively easy to slip into the next step of the argument, that if a pair of twins are reared apart all the differences between them can be ascribed to identifiable differences in their respective environments, and conversely any similarities which exceed those shared by other persons respectively in these two environments can be attributed to heredity. This line of reasoning has caused a great deal of interest to be focused on studies of identical twins reared apart, but alas, few firm answers have emerged from such studies.

There are a number of reasons for this, one being that relatively few cases are available for study. In 1941 Woodworth (300) reviewed the literature on the subject and was able to report only 22 seemingly valid cases of identical twins who were raised separately. More have come to light since, but when one considers that some attempt must be made to match at least approximately the respective environments of the twin pairs it is evident that the number of subjects available for valid comparison is very small. It would not be very meaningful to compare one pair of twins placed in middle class and lower class rural homes with another pair placed in middle class and lower class urban homes. If one further takes into account educational factors in both foster parents and children, number of foster siblings, language factors, regional characteristics, and the host of other things known to have bearing on the development of mental ability, each twin pair becomes practically unique.

Another problem arises in identifying the environmental factors responsible for the differences observed. We know that their respective foetal positions in the womb, birth order, and probably other factors create differences in genetically identical twins even by the time of their birth, so we cannot say their relevantly different environments are in their foster homes only, nor that they were born identical. Assuming they are not separated on the day of their birth, we have also to take into account the effects of coexistence with each other, for the immediate presence of another identical infant creates an environment significantly different from that of the single baby (cf. Burlingham, 33). This environment probably even differs, particularly with respect to adult responses to the baby, in important ways from that experienced by fraternal twins, but on this point we have no data. Furthermore, once they have grown up and we wish to make statements as to the relative effects of heredity and environment in determining their similarities and differences, we have to have some idea of how similar they would have been had they not been twins. Here again we run into the great multiplicity of factors which affect the development of intellect, personality, etc. A valid basis for estimating environmental differences calls for comparison groups comprising for each twin persons of the same age and sex, from the same or a very similar neighborhood, who are also adopted into foster homes with a similar number of children in them, where the same language and ethnic backgrounds obtain, of the same social class, and so on. It is obvious that it would be extremely difficult if not impossible to locate such comparison groups of sufficient size to average out the individual genetic factors in each group. We cannot just go out and find such groups, but rather have to look for them in the area where we happen to have located one of a pair of twins. It is perhaps by now clear why precise answers to questions as to the relative effectiveness of heredity and environment are not likely to be found in twin studies. Unless we can define the environmental forces we cannot say how much effect heredity really has, nor in what ways it is effective. Conversely, even though we know heredity is identical in a pair of twins, we must pinpoint just which environmental factors produced the observed differences in each twin. Otherwise we know no more than we did before about environmental influences except to say with assurance what we have said before, that genes alone do not determine intelligence or behavior. We cannot say, however, that we have proven that they have no effect.

Similar conclusions can be reached from studies of children placed in foster homes or actually adopted. Probably the most conclusive among these are the follow-up studies done at the Iowa Child Welfare Station (cf. Skeels and Harms, 246; Skodak and Skeels, 248) of children born to occupationally and intellectually inferior families and adopted into average or superior homes. The *IQ*'s of these children conformed quite consistently to the norms of their adoptive parents, with averages substantially higher than those of their own parents. This confirmed the findings of earlier but less well controlled studies (e.g., Wells and Arthur, 284, and Speer, 257.)

However, Skeels and Harms did find in one of their groups that despite the higher level of performance of the children (mean IQ 105.5 vs. 62.7), their IQ's correlated (.23, significant at the five per cent level) with the IQ's of their mothers, implying strongly that the foster home environment was not the only determinant of intellectual ability. This correlation is higher than that found in any earlier studies (cf. Snygg, 255). This relationship might be explained in a number of ways, including the possibility of selective placement of children from better true parents in the better foster homes, but in the absence of a positive causal explanation it forces us again to leave open the question of how much or little influence heredity has in determining mental ability.

The uniformly negative conclusions we have reached in this synoptic review of research on the effects of heredity versus environment in mental retardation might lead to the presumption that we feel no research at all in this area should be undertaken. Rather, however, we would say that the moral to be drawn from the vast amount of relatively futile effort which has gone into the subject is that research should only be contemplated if it can proceed without the help of unjustified theoretical assumptions, building only upon the foundation of known facts and relationships. Unfortunately, this second statement, although more optimistically phrased, at present says virtually the same thing as the first. It is our conviction, which we shall try to document below, that the scientific tools to work with are simply not yet available, and that the undeniable pressures from society to do something will not justify the substitution of conceptual tools derived from folklore.

An instructive analogy can be drawn from the field of physical anthropology. One of the earliest and most enduring orientations in this field was toward race, starting with the three major divisions of Caucasian, Negroid, and Mongoloid, followed by the gradual definition of a variety of subtypes within each. These distinctions were refined on the basis of a large number of reassuringly objective and quantitative scales of observation and measurement of external morphological features—head form, skin color, body build, and the like. (We might note in passing that all of these were more constant and more verifiable than the IQ.) The validity of these racial criteria, and of the research in race mixture, etc., which utilized them, rested of course upon the assumption that they were determined by genetic factors which ultimately would be identified. Over a period of many years literally millions of painstaking measurements and observations were made on both skeletal material and living subjects, many anthropologists devoting their entire professional lives to this line of endeavor. Washburn (281) has described the situation in words which might provide food for sober thought by many psychometricians: "The efforts of physical anthropologists have been to get agreements on how to take measurements and observations. Introductions to physical anthropology are largely instructions on how to take measurements, with little or no indication of what it is that the measurements are supposed to mean. International congresses have ended with pleas for uniformity, so that the classification might continue" (p. 717).

Finally, questions began to be raised as to the actual genetic and developmental significance of the measures selected as racial criteria. A series of investigations led to increasingly discouraging conclusions. Then, after the war, a group of younger physical anthropologists who had taken the time to obtain a thorough training in embryology, developmental anatomy, serology, genetics, and other relevant fields, began the serious study of the concepts so long in vogue, each from the standpoint of his own additional specialty. Within a very few years the work of lifetimes was discarded (except as the data were useable by anatomists, human engineers, and the like) and a completely new start was made, based upon a few characteristics (especially blood groups) whose genetic determinants were known, and upon the growing understanding of population genetics. It is interesting to note, parenthetically, that the breeding populations tentatively defined on a world-wide basis through serology bore practically no resemblance to the classical groupings of racial types so long assumed to be real entities.

Research in the genetics of mental subnormality and we must emphasize again that we are *not* talking about identifiable pathologies—appears to be following a similar path, although the effort expended thus far is not nearly as great. There are two differences which should be noted, neither of them encouraging. First is the fact that the IQ and other measures of mental ability are far more unstable and indeterminate than any used by traditional physical anthropology. Second is the far greater social significance of any research results in this field, particularly in the context of racial issues in the United States and elsewhere in the world, a significance approximated by physical anthropological research only during the Nazi era. In this situation science bears a moral as well as a professional responsibility to be highly critical of the validity of the assumptions it uses.

The most crucial assumption in any genetic investigation lies in the identification of a true genotype, that is, a characteristic which can be observed and which reflects the influence of genes. No possibility exists at present of being able, through microscopic or other means, to determine by observation of reproductive cells the characteristics they will help to create in the organism.   Studies in genetics therefore must depend upon the observation of characteristics of the organism known or presumed to have certain determinants in the genes, followed by deductions concerning the manner in which such genes are transmitted and reach expression.   It is not necessary that we be certain that a characteristic is genotypic—that is, that it represents the result of genetic rather than environmental forces—in order that we examine its distribution.   Kallmann, for example, in the study of schizophrenia cited earlier, simply assumed that a tendency toward schizophrenia was inherited in certain ways, calculated predicted frequencies of distribution of the disorder among twins, siblings, and other classes of relatives, and then successfully compared his predictions with actual frequencies of occurrence.   His research has been criticized on several grounds, but there appears to be little argument as to the soundness of this type of genetic research as such.

However, although we do not have to *know* that we have an observable genotype, we do have to have a basis for making such a presumption.   The first requirement for establishing a presumption of genetic determinism is that the characteristic in question be relatively constant over time and be reliably observable by independent observers with similar results.   Mental retardation without detectable pathology does not even approach these requirements.   The recent survey of persons under 18 referred as mentally retarded in Onondaga County, New York (New York State Department of Mental Hygiene (193)), provides eloquent refutation of both points. With regard to constancy, the age-specific curve rises to a peak at age 15, and thereafter drops off sharply.   Unless one wishes to make the preposterous assumption that the majority of retarded children do not live beyond 16 or 17 one is forced to conclude that retardation means different things to different people, and that the criterion changes at about 16 (which happens to be the upper limit of compulsory education in New York State). Furthermore, it did not prove possible to isolate any one diagnostic criterion which was applicable to all cases; for example, although it is often customary to set the cut-off point for mental deficiency at *IQ* 70, almost 25 per cent of all referred cases in Onondaga County had reported *IQ*'s of 90 or over.

It is equally unsatisfactory to presume that the *IQ* alone is a genotypic characteristic.   There is in the first place abundant evidence that the *IQ* as determined by intelligence tests is not constant in the individual over time, and that its variation does not follow a uniformly predictable pattern such as one would expect of a hereditary characteristic which changed along with the biological maturation process. In different individuals the *IQ* may increase or decrease over time. Also, *IQ*'s are derived from a variety of different tests and most psychologists now require knowledge of the test used before attaching any real significance to an *IQ*. This of course means that the *IQ* is not a reliable and absolute measure of over-all intelligence. Finally, much of this report is devoted to documenting the various ways in which environmental experiences determine mental ability and therefore *IQ* level. Most psychologists recoil in alarm over the implication that the *IQ* be taken as a measure of inherent—as against learned—mental capacity, yet this presumption must be made if the *IQ* is to be considered genotypic.

This assumption, when accepted, can lead to remarkably devious reasoning when an attempt is made to account for the known environmental variables. It is for example well known that retardation and a low *IQ* are more common in lower socio-economic levels of society, whereas so-called idiots and imbeciles are randomly distributed through all social classes. It is customarily concluded that most of the retardation in the lower classes results from lack of stimulation, poor schooling, and various motivational factors, while idiots and imbeciles represent pathologies (some probably genetic in origin) which occur fortuitously. Yet one finds persons with a genetic point to prove (e.g., Moore, 187, or Halperin, 103) stating that the idiots and imbeciles are indeed pathological, but that the morons are of genetically inferior stock which cannot compete successfully in the framework of *laissez faire* capitalism and therefore sinks down the social scale. This oversimplified application of the principle of natural selection and survival of the fittest would fit more appropriately into the intellectual climate of the 19th Century than of today, for students of biological evolution have come to realize that in altering the characteristics of large populations natural selection operates in highly complicated ways and only over long periods of time (Snyder, 254). Even if one were to assume that the *IQ* reflects true genetically determined mental capacity, the concentration of a pool of inferior genes in the lower classes would require many generations of breeding, coupled with a relatively complete lack of intermixture between social classes. These conditions obviously do not exist in our society. The opportunity, and actuality, of vertical social mobility is almost a byword, with many persons in each generation marrying outside of the social class into which they were born, assuring a flow of genes up and down the social scale. Furthermore, in the United States at least, very few generations have elapsed since the population reached approximately its present size, not nearly enough time to stabilize even an isolated breeding population.

Even if it were possible to determine the actual inherent mental capacity of various ethnic and socio-economic groups, the differences observed would not lead necessarily to a genetic explanation. Pasamanick (202) has demonstrated that, in addition to gross defects, more minor brain damage sufficient to affect intellectual functioning can result from both complications during the mother's pregnancy and premature birth of the child. In his study of these factors in Baltimore, Pasamanick found that Negro infants run a 50 per cent greater risk of prematurity than white, presumably because of dietary and other cultural influences. Similarly, he compared the incidence of complications of pregnancy in upper class whites with that found in lower class whites (on the basis of a five-class scale) and in Negroes. They showed an incidence respectively three times and 10 times greater than the upper class whites. From the standpoint of the heredity versus environment controversy, these findings simply point up yet another environmental influence on intelligence which must be controlled before it can be maintained that a purely genetic component has been isolated.

If one examines further the requirements of genetic research it becomes apparent that most research approaches require not merely the presumption of a genotype, but also the presumed identification of a single gene or a specific combination of genes which determines the genotype. This applies to the genealogical method, to most twin studies, and to the determination of gene frequencies in population genetics. Again it should be emphasized that it is not necessary to *know* such a relationship exists, but it must be possible to provide at least an a priori justification for an assumption of this order, if only as a basis for predictive hypotheses to be tested. Yet if we look to researchers in the field for an indication of where to look for aspects of intelligence which might have such unitary determinants, we find Lawrence H. Snyder in genetics and J. P. Guilford in psychology, each outstanding in his field, agreeing that intelligence is multifactorial. After reviewing some sorts of human pathology whose genetic bases are isolable, Snyder (254, p. 397) concludes that intelligence and indeed most of "those genetic differences which are involved in [the] non-pathological range of human variability are most probably contingent upon multifactorial inheritance." Approaching the problem from a different angle, Guilford undertook to determine by factor analysis the components of intellect. His research is discussed in detail in Section IV and we may simply note here that, having identified 40 factors and believing that his list was not yet complete, Guilford stated (99, p. 287): "The question 'Is intelligence inherited or is it acquired' makes less sense than it ever did. Such a question must be asked regarding each and every factor."

We must therefore conclude that the *IQ* is unstable over time, cannot be reliably measured by any agreed-upon single instrument and has strong environmental determinants, and that its genetic determinants are sufficiently multifactorial that they do not lend themselves to existing techniques of genetic research. Therefore, genetic studies based on the test *IQ*, or upon the even vaguer concepts of mental deficiency or retardation, do not present a very promising avenue for research.

If, however, we turn to mental defectives with identifiable pathologies or to variations in blood chemistry or physiology which appear to be related to mental functioning we can undertake valid and fruitful genetic studies. Recent research in phenylpyruvic oligophrenia, galactosemia, and cerebral palsy are cases in point. Twin studies are particularly useful in determining whether a hereditary factor is involved and, often in combination with other techniques, can reveal much of the nature of the genetic process involved. With this knowledge one can predict the likelihood of occurrence, and furthermore be fairly explicit as to the certainty with which such predictions are made. On the other hand, these genetic studies may conclude with some assurance that heredity is not involved and thus point research more positively in other directions. Either outcome is productive and will fully justify the genetic approach, provided only that a sufficiently determinate factor is fed into the genetic equation in the first instance. Rather than continuing to devote money and talent to genetic studies based on the elusive *IQ*, it would appear sensible to wait upon the biochemists, physiologists, and others who are increasingly turning up suggestive leads based on factors which experience has taught us are likely to have identifiable genetic determinants. There may be a single enzyme, determined by a single gene, which has an important effect on mental capacity, but this enzyme appears more likely to be discovered in the laboratory than through the administration of intelligence tests to persons of differing ethnic origins or social classes, or to various relatives of institutionalized subnormal children or adults. The wide range of possibilities for research in the biological determinants of intelligence—both normal and subnormal—is reviewed in the companion report prepared by Dr. Richard L. Masland, also under the auspices of the National Association for Retarded Children.

VI. CULTURAL BACKGROUND FACTORS AFFECTING TEST PERFORMANCE

A. School Performance

In our discussion of the hereditary versus the environmental factors in the etiology of mental retardation we concluded that, except for certain identifiable pathological conditions, a hereditary determinant of intelligence has yet to be isolated and demonstrated. Even if, however, it should ultimately prove possible validly to estimate the effects of heredity in a given case this will not eliminate mental retardation. This knowledge will make possible some preventive measures but it will do little or nothing to resolve the problems of defective or retarded persons already born. It will, furthermore, contribute only very indirectly to improving the lot of those whose environment, as children and adults, limits their opportunity to develop the full use of their inherent intellectual capacity. It is this latter group with which this report is primarily concerned.

A vast amount of research has gone into the effort to elicit the social and cultural factors which affect intellectual functioning. Almost all of the research in this area has accepted an intelligence test of one kind or another as the primary criterion of level of intellect, with the derived intelligence quotient providing a measure of advancement or retardation. In this section we shall therefore be summarizing the major findings of research on the environmental antecedents of test performance as such, working backwards from the test situation in search of explanations for differences in performance. In the next section we will reverse the order of our inquiry and widen its scope, focusing upon the kinds of thinking processes to which children in various social and cultural groups are exposed and attempting to relate this to the intellectual demands made by society upon its members through life, recognizing intelligence tests only as an incidental factor important in a few cultures.

We cannot, however, defer consideration of one kind of intellectual demand which our own society imposes upon practically all of its members, the school situation. Two facts force us immediately and constantly to be aware of the intellectual problems presented by school. First is the fact that school is the principal, and often the only, context in which many children of borderline intelligence are labelled and treated as mentally retarded. Reference has already been made to the survey of Onondaga County, New York (N.Y. State Department of Mental Hygiene, 193), which shows the prevalence of identified retardation rising with age until, with the years of compulsory schooling behind, from age 16 onward the age-specific rates drop off dramatically. Earlier studies have demonstrated the same thing elsewhere (e.g., for England and Wales, Mental Deficiency Committee, 185, and Baltimore, Md., Lemkau, Tietze, and Cooper 166, p. 280). In other words, many children who through their final year of schooling are still labelled "retarded" immediately thereafter merge into the "normal" population with at least sufficient completeness no longer to be reported statistically. The compulsory school experience may therefore be viewed for many people as in effect the most difficult intellectual hurdle which will confront them throughout their entire lives, although later in other settings they may perform tasks of substantial complexity.

The second fact which forces our interest in intelligence tests to focus also on the schools is that school performance is the criterion to which the great majority of intelligence tests predict and against which they are validated. Furthermore, as Davis and Havighurst (59, p. 307) have pointed out, the problems presented in intelligence tests are essentially academic problems. Yet they will probably be with us for a long time. Budd (32), commenting on the efforts of Davis, Eells and others to develop culture-fair tests, observes:

> Teachers and administrators feel they know the "good" students in their schools and present day intelligence tests largely corroborate their judgment. It is therefore difficult to envisage the time when the present tests will be replaced in a very practical way by such newer and theoretically more valid instruments (p. 334).

Stenquist (263) expresses the same dilemma in a slightly different way:

> If in this study the purpose is merely to discover new techniques . . . to try to salvage individuals who have already shown that they cannot compete with the scholastically minded, I fear that the harvest will be meager. Through efforts to recognize and respect status differences we may establish that a few more individuals actually possess the type of ability that is reflected in the traditional I.Q. concept if we extend these crutches to them and thus help them a little up the ramp. But I fear this is meeting only a part of the problem. It seems clear to me that if we are to guage our measuring stick to the whole range of mental ability we must have a broader criterion than success in present-day schools (p. 187).

Although it is our purpose in this report to consider some ways in which the broader criterion of which Stenquist speaks may be established, in this chapter we limit ourselves to existing research and are thus largely bound to the conception of school as the proving ground of intellect, and therefore of intelligence tests.

Often in the pages which follow our discussion will focus on the factors affecting test performance in a wide variety of "normal" groups and in the population as a whole rather than being confined to the problems only of retarded persons. The reason for this is simple. Within any social or cultural grouping there is a distribution of intelligence, and of test scores if the people are tested. There are high scorers and low scorers and all grades in between but the majority of people usually have scores near the mean or median for the particular group in question. These average scores, we will see, differ quite markedly from one social class or subculture to another, even in our own society. But at the same time in this culture of ours, as represented by the school systems, occupational placement policies, etc., there is defined through the *IQ* or other criteria a level below which a person, whatever his origin, will be considered inadequate. It is therefore apparent that if the distribution of test scores around a mean is for any reason pushed downward within a given group, more of its members will fall below the level of socially-determined adequacy and be considered retarded. Consequently, the more we know about the factors which produce high or low average scores in groups as wholes the more we will know about the sources of retardation in those who fall below the line defined for our society at large. We cannot say that every retarded child from a subcultural group is retarded solely because of his group membership and experience, for there are others who perform adequately among his fellows, but we can say that the handicap which affects them all has contributed also to his misfortune. If this particular handicap can be alleviated he can very possibly improve to a point of social adequacy. For this reason, then, we must examine the factors affecting the test performance of all members of a given segment of society, not merely of those who are retarded.

Although, as we have seen, researchers who are concerned with demonstrating a hereditary component in intelligence occasionally make fairly naïve assumptions about the *IQ* as a measure of inherent capacity, the great majority of psychologists recognize that there are both cultural and individual differences in experience which predispose a person toward a good or a poor test performance. This realization in fact goes back practically to the inception of intelligence tests themselves. As Allison Davis (55) pointed out so effectively, Alfred Binet himself explicitly recognized as early as 1908 that cultural and social class differences existed, but he was unable to resolve the difficulty.

For some years thereafter little attention was given to the problem. As in the case of investigations of heredity of intellect, the first real stimulus to environmental studies came from the results of testing World War I recruits with the Army Alpha and Beta. Soon after it was determined that Negroes had lower average scores than whites, it was further discovered that the average scores of Negroes from several Northern states were higher than those of rural white persons in some Southern states. From this initial finding of broad regional differences the focus sharpened down during the 1920's to isolate for study most of the areas which have concerned researchers ever since—socio-economic and social class factors, ethnic differences, language handicaps and bilingualism, rural-urban differences, sex differences, and cultural and subcultural factors. We shall review the major findings in each of these areas. It may be well, however, first to anticipate in general terms a criticism which will be levelled repeatedly at studies in all of these categories. With a few notable exceptions far more effort has been expended on establishing that the *IQ varies with,* for example, social class than has been devoted to finding out *why* lower class people test lower. Even where reasons have been sought, the focus has commonly been upon the test situation—motivation, speed, competitiveness, comprehension, and the like—rather than upon the kinds of thinking which on the one hand are necessary to solve test problems and on the other are likely to be learned in various environmental contexts. We thus find available for both retarded and standard populations a wide array of correlations between *IQ* and almost any other factor imaginable, but in these studies one finds very few hints as to specific causal relationships.

If we are to have the understanding of subcultural mental retardation necessary for training, rehabilitation, and prevention we must know the "why" of the correlations. The early research which established that *IQ* varied with social class was of great value, but we cannot stop there and wait for the problem of subcultural retardation to be solved on the utopian day when over-all class differences cease to exist. Nor, as Stenquist observes, will the construction of special tests judged *a priori* to be more "fair," but of uncertain predictive value, erase the fact that the school performance to which standard tests predict is no longer merely preparation for adult life but has become a crucial end in itself. Failure to surmount the hurdle of school and intelligence tests brands the child as subnormal, implying, at least, that he is unfit not only for school but also society at large. Kanner (146) comments with some bitterness on the stigma of retardation to which a child is vulnerable when "scholastic curricula demand competition in spelling, history, geography, long division, and other preparations deemed essential for the tasks of feeding chickens, collecting garbage, and wrapping bundles in a department store" (p. 10).

The introduction of special classes in school systems provides ever increasing opportunity for the training and education of retarded children, but helps little with the stigma. Since we cannot reasonably expect, nor indeed desire, that over-all scholastic standards be overhauled to fit the limitations of marginal students, it would appear more fruitful to seek out the particular aspects of the social or cultural experience of these students which were inadequate or detrimental to the development of the intellectual skills required to do well in school (or on intelligence tests). With these more specific relationships established correction and prevention can have more clearly defined targets.

Consider for example arithmetic and sentence diagramming. These certainly involve abstraction and symbolic logic. But are the intellectual processes in both essentially the same, so that a child who is equipped for one is also equipped for the other? And how does this skill relate to the skill required for example on the digit-symbol subtest of the Wechsler-Bellevue? And again, how severely handicapped in this regard is the lower-class Italian child who is expected to do his daily tasks around the house in response to concrete instructions, without bothering his elders with abstract questions about the how and why of things?[12] If we knew the answers to these questions we could perhaps plan to give Italian children certain kinds of special training when they first enter school, training designed to correct their particular deficits. In this way they could cope from the beginning with the gradually rising level of abstraction in the curriculum in later years, rather than fumbling and bluffing in the lower grades and failing outright later on.

The most ambitious effort to explore the environmental determinants of school and test performance in this country thus far has been that conducted by Allison Davis and his associates at the University of Chicago. Although they have concentrated their research primarily on social class differences their interests have ranged more widely to embrace almost all aspects of the prob-

---

[12]This statement, as well as others concerning the living patterns of lower-class Italian children to be discussed in Section VII, is based only upon impressions and conversations with a (middle class) Italian acquaintance of one of the authors. It is an unhappy commentary on research in this area that despite the consistently low test scores obtained by Italian children over the years no one has, to our knowledge, undertaken any systematic study of the reasons for this deficit.

lem. Some of their more general conclusions will serve as an introduction to a more detailed review of the field. Haggard (101) has this to say of the intelligence tests themselves:

In terms of our present knowledge, the standard-type intelligence tests are inadequate on several counts. Among other things, (a) they have measured only a very narrow range of mental abilities, namely those related to verbal or academic success, and have ignored other abilities and problem-solving skills which are perhaps more important for adjustment and success—even in middle-class society; (b) they have failed to provide measures of the wide variety of qualitative differences in the modes or processes of solving mental problems; (c) they have ignored the influences of differences in cultural training and socialization on the repertoire of experience and the attitude, motivation, and personality patterns of sub-groups in our society, and the effect of such factors on mental test performance; and (d) they have considered mental functioning in isolation, thus ignoring the interdependence of the individual's motivational and personality structure on the characteristics of his mental functioning, as seen, for example, in the differences between rote learning and the ability to use previous experiences creatively in new contexts.

A re-evaluation of the purposes and problems involved in the appraisal and description of mental abilities is necessary before adequate mental tests can be developed. But before this can be done, it will first be necessary to conduct anthropological, sociological, and psychological studies to learn how representative children in our society live. For lower-class and ethnic children, for example, information is needed concerning their value, attitude, and motivational systems, the nature of their daily experiences, and the range of mental behaviors and modes of thinking used in finding solutions to their life problems. It will also be necessary to consider the growing body of evidence that mental functioning does not exist in a vacuum, but that the individual's motivational and personality structure, his attitudes, interests, needs, and goals are intimately related to, and in a large measure determine, his mental processes (pp. 180-181).

Allison Davis, in his Inglis Lecture (55), stresses repeatedly the way in which both intelligence tests and school curricula are rooted in middle class values and standards:

Fundamentally, the cultural bias of the standard tests of intelligence consists in their having fixed upon only those types of mental behaviors in which the higher and middle socio-economic groups are superior. . . . They do not use problems which are equally familiar and motivating to all . . . groups. . . . By choosing a limited range of mental problems, notably scholastic problems, the present tests very likely bias our mental ratings of even the middle-class child (pp. 47-48).

Davis points out that 95 per cent of all teachers are middle class, and discusses the values they therefore share:[13]

> From his middle-class culture, learned from his parents, teachers, and friends both the teacher and the professor of education have learned to regard certain mental interests and skills, certain moral values, as the "best," or "most cultured," or "most intelligent." Granted that, for this society, the basic *moral* values of middle class people may be the most adaptive for survival, it does not follow that present-day middle-class academic skills and goals are most effective in developing the intellectual, imaginative, and problem-solving activities of human beings (pp. 89-90).
>
> The present curricula are stereotyped and arbitrary selections from a narrow area of middle-class culture. Academic culture is one of the most conservative and ritualized aspects of human culture. Its formalization, its lack of functional connection with the daily problems of life, has given a bloodless, fossilized character to the classroom which all of us recognize. For over a generation, no basically new types of mental problems have been added to intelligence tests. . . . What proportion of the *basic mental problems* met by children (and by adults for that matter) in their daily life can be solved by having a large standard vocabulary, or skill in reading, or skill in arithmetical process? (pp. 97-98).

To these comments of the University of Chicago group we should add only the observation of McCandless (177, p. 675) that "many authors have failed to see that the construction of an intelligence test is actually a definition of 'intelligence.'" At present there is really no other available way operationally to define intelligence than through the *IQ* or its equivalent. This is readily seen if one observes persons who work regularly with retarded children. They will watch or work with a child and then, even though they may never have seen his test results or records, will often phrase their estimate of his capability as "probably *IQ* so-and-so" or the like. This tendency to define the level of retardation in terms of the *IQ* is, of course, reflected also in many of the attempts to arrive at a legal definition for purposes of institutionalization, sterilization, etc. Therefore, however great our dissatisfaction with the *IQ* measure, we must recognize the importance of finding out all we can about the factors which contribute to intelligence test performance.

At the same time we must not err in the other direction and conclude that

---

[13]Warner (280) cites the proportion of teachers who are middle class or higher as 97 per cent in "Yankee City," 100 per cent in "Midwest," and 97 per cent in "Deep South." All of these are cities studied under the auspices of the Committee on Human Development of the University of Chicago.

an examination of test performance will tell us all we need to know about the etiology of subcultural mental retardation. The Onondaga County, N. Y., survey found that one out of every four children referred for suspected mental retardation had *IQ*'s of 90 or above. The label of mental retardation spreads wide, and is applied for many reasons. We can agree that everyone who bears the label has a problem, but scientifically we cannot be satisfied with the criteria established by either the *IQ* or community referral.

With these words of caution in mind, we may proceed to the examination of factors which have been explored in the search for the social and cultural determinants of intelligence test performance.

B. Socioeconomic Class

Studies demonstrating the correlation between social class status and *IQ* vie with research on ethnic and racial factors for first place both in the early date of their beginnings and in the number of replications. Clear-cut and significant relationships between *IQ* of children and the social and occupational level of their parents were obtained in separate studies by Mead (184) and Stoke (266) as early as 1927. By 1938 Neff (191) was able to survey the numerous studies by then available and, in connection with a reanalysis of data collected by Terman and Merrill, conclude that:

> (1) the standardized tests are far from constant, particularly when the retest interval is large; (2) continued residence in a very poor environment brings about a considerable loss in *IQ*, often from the "normal" level to that of "dull" or even "borderline;" (3) translation from a poor to a good environment brings about large increases in *IQ*, which, at the extremes, may amount to 30 or 40 points; (4) there is a strong possibility that the positive relation between age and social status does not exist below a certain age level; (5) some evidence from identical twin studies indicates that there is a correlation of about .50 between social status and intelligence even where heredity is held constant; (6) the inequality of social and economic opportunity renders suspect one of the major assumptions basic to the construction of the test; namely, that knowledge and information are a direct function of native ability and that the former may be used to measure the latter (p. 754).

Although the bulk of studies in this area are concerned with white groups in the United States, there is ample evidence that the relationship between socioeconomic status and *IQ* is not confined to this population.[14] We may in

---

[14]Similar results have been obtained for Negroes in the United States by Canady (36), Tomlinson (273), Edmiston and McBain (66), Jenkins and Randall (137),

fact safely endorse the statement of Eells (in Eells, Davis, Havighurst, Herrick, and Tyler, 68):

> In view of the large number of research studies which have shown the existence of sizeable and statistically significant IQ differences between pupils from different social-status backgrounds and in view of the almost total lack of any contrary indications from any of the research to date, it seems abundantly clear that there is no need for further research aimed merely at establishing the existence or nonexistence of such differences (p. 4).

Granted that such a relationship exists there is, as pointed out above, little that we can do with the information. A number of different approaches have therefore been tried in an effort to come closer to identifying more specifically the relevant aspects of middle class versus lower class experience. One line of attack has been to seek other factors which correlate more closely with IQ than does the father's occupation or the other commonly accepted measures of socioeconomic status (family income, size of house, etc.). One reason for adopting this approach has been the realization that the correlations usually employed are, although statistically significant, not nearly high enough to permit of prediction in the individual case—that is, there are still a lot of high-IQ lower class children, and vice versa (cf. Wellman, 282). Loevinger (169) reviewed several studies and concluded that average income was the poorest predictor of intelligence available, and father's occupation little better; the IQ and educational level of the parents (which are also a function of social class status, of course) showed substantially higher correlations. A rather careful study by Honzik (122) of California school children produced similar conclusions, except that she found that the IQ of the mother was a substantially better predictor than the educational level of either parent. She also found that these correlations (including that with social status) became higher with advancing age (up to 8 years in her study). It will be remembered that Neff reached a similar conclusion in the study cited earlier; we shall return later to a fuller discussion of these and similar findings regarding age effects. Focusing on a population heavily weighted toward the lower end of the occupational scale, District of Columbia Negroes, Robinson and Meenes (217)

---

and undoubtedly others. Robbins (214) reported the same trend on the basis of a 10-year study of 9956 fourth grade children in the public schools of Ottawa, Canada. A sampling of studies from Europe follows a similar pattern: Kuiper (161) on Holland and Germany; Sandels (223) on Sweden; Forbes (71) on Northern Ireland; and Heuyer, Piéron, and Sauvy (116) on France are examples. Also consistent are the findings of Ginnsberg (86) in Brazil, and Kirahara (153) in Japan.

found very little relationship between *IQ* and father's occupation, but a substantially higher correlation than other studies have shown with economic factors, particularly the average rent in the area and the ownership of radios. In interpreting this outcome it should be borne in mind that, as the University of Chicago and other studies have pointed out, the relationships between lower class parents and children tend to be less close than in the middle class and therefore involve less transfer of intellectual stimulation between generations within the immediate family. Furthermore, lower class Negro fathers tend to drift in and out of the family relationship more casually and frequently than other groups. We may therefore speculate that whatever stimulus value (or lack thereof) the father's occupation may have in the general case is more diluted in this population of District of Columbia Negroes. Concomitant with this, we would expect the children to receive a greater proportion of their stimulation from the neighborhood around them, and that therefore measures of the socioeconomic status of the neighborhood would be more relevant than father's occupation as correlates of *I.Q.*

In the studies just described a relationship has been sought between certain aspects of the social and cultural background of individuals and the *IQ*'s of the same individuals. Another way to approach this problem consists in seeking relationships between, on the one hand, the average test scores of groups of people in a large number of communities and, on the other, characteristics of these communities as wholes derived from census data. Thorndike (271) utilized in this manner Pintner *IQ*'s and Metropolitan Achievement scores[15] available on half a million children in 300 communities. Correlating average test scores for each community with a variety of other measures, he found the following correlations with *IQ* to be significant (in decreasing order of significance): educational level of the adult population, proportion of persons owning their own homes, quality and cost of housing, proportion of native-born white persons, rate of employment of women (a negative correlation), and the proportion of professional workers in the population. Correlations with achievement scores were significant only for the proportion of professional workers and educational level of adults. The tests were administered exclusively in public schools and, where schools were segregated, only in white schools. Utilizing a similar approach, Davenport and Remmers (53) utilized mean test scores by states of young men who were candidates for officer training under the wartime A-12 and V-12 programs and found sig-

---

[15]The testing was done in connection with the standardization of a revision of the Metropolitan Achievement Test.

nificant correlations with number of telephones per 1000 population, per capita income, and the value of school property in each state. These officer candidates of course represented a selected population of college graduates. In both these studies it is immediately apparent that the items which correlate with intelligence are either actual indices of or closely related to the general socioeconomic level of the community or state, and as such serve only to verify what we already know. However, it is of importance to note in Thorndike's findings that the most significant correlate of IQ was the educational level of adults—i.e., with the parents of the children being tested. This provides additional support for the identical finding in Loevinger's research on individuals. It would be interesting to know whether, if adult $IQ's$ were available from these communities, they would support Honzig's further conclusion that the mother's IQ is an even more crucial determinant of children's intelligence than parental education. Since adults are seldom tested routinely once they are old enough to have school-age children this would probably be very difficult to test on a mass basis.

The closeness of a child's relationship with his parents as well as the intellectual content of the relationship is probably a factor in determining the degree to which the child can find intellectual stimulation in the home. Skeels and his associates at the Iowa Child Welfare Research Station conducted a number of studies exploring the effects of intellectual stimulation. Most relevant here are those concerned with the adoption of children born into lower class families (cf. Skeels and Harms, 246; and Skodak and Skeels, 248). They found that these children, whose mothers often had borderline IQ's, themselves developed IQ's averaging well in the normal range in middle class homes, while those adopted into superior homes had correspondingly superior IQ's. Haggard and others at the University of Chicago attempted to produce similar effects experimentally. In a carefully controlled study, over 600 11-year-olds divided into high and low social status groups and matched for school grade, age, and IQ, were given a variety of standard and special intelligence tests and then retested with various combinations of these tests four days later. One group, comprising both high and low status children, received three days of concentrated training on the tests between test and retest, whereas a similar control group did not. Although a preliminary analysis of these data (Haggard, Davis, and Havighurst, 102) appeared to indicate that the low status children had profited more from the training than the high status ones, and some class differences did emerge under some of the controlled conditions, Haggard (101) concluded after full analysis, "When the effects of all such treatments and conditions were thrown together, there was no significant difference between the two groups of children in their ability to learn to solve intelligence test problems" (p. 184). This outcome suggests that the intellectual void created by the lower class environment is not one which can be filled through intensive but brief training. Skeels' children had years in which to build their intellectual foundations; lacking such foundations Haggard's children did not score major gains even when the training was very specific to the tasks at hand. Haggard's findings, incidentally, make it appear unlikely that the improvement in Skeels' children could have been attributable to the practice effect of retesting after a period of years.

In an effort to explore some of the causes of differences in personality as well as intellectual functioning associated with social class differences, Davis and Havighurst (57) conducted interviews with 200 mothers in Chicago, largely on the South Side. They interviewed 50 each from the middle and lower classes, Negro and white. The found, among other things, that the lower class parents, both Negro and white, tended to permit their children more freedom earlier, in effect often turning them loose to find their own entertainment and activities as soon as they were able to take care of their basic physical needs through the day. In contrast the middle class parents were more protective and more strict in training, but at the same time were more likely to assign the children definite responsibilities at home and outside at earlier ages than in the lower class. It is clear that, aside from the consequences for personality and emotional development, this difference is important for intellectual development. Both groups of children are presented with problems for solution, but whereas the lower class children can seek solutions only on a trial and error basis, with their equally inexperienced peers as mentors, the middle class children are supervised in the discharge of their responsibilities and are guided in their selection and execution of solutions along lines of known effectiveness, solutions which also fit into the accepted patterns of middle class culture. Not only is this training and responsibility well adapted to preparing the child to cope with the problems presented by middle class teachers, but by virtue of its early inception it begins to equip the child for the school experience before he starts school. The responsibilities assigned to a lower class child come later in his development, often after he has started off his school career at a disadvantage from which he will never fully recover.[16]

---

[16]The findings of this study, although probably in the main valid, must be viewed with caution because the data are derived only from mothers. Fathers might have

The impoverishment of a lower class child's opportunity for intellectual development is by no means confined to his lack of early assigned and supervised responsibility; we must recognize, although we have very little firm knowledge in this area, that there are many other facets of the intellectual climate of the home environment of a child in the lower class (or other disadvantaged subculture) which leaves him ill-prepared to cope with school and its associated intelligence testing. We are forced to this conclusion by the consistency of the relationship found in a variety of cultural settings between social class and *IQ*. However, if it is true that home environment operates across the board to stimulate or depress intellectual development, we should then expect the inadequately *prepared* lower class child to *perform* inadequately from the time he first enters school. This turns out not to be so, at least if we accept the intelligence test as a measure of the ability of a child to do school work—and if it does not measure this it measures nothing.

a different perception, and both might differ from the perceptions of an independent observer, as Havighurst and Davis (107) themselves later pointed out. Sears, Maccoby, and Levin (238) conducted a study in the Boston area which in part paralleled the Chicago interviews, again confining their attention to mothers, and arriving at somewhat different conclusions. We cannot attempt here to judge the soundness of the over-all findings of either study, but inasmuch as both were concerned primarily with aspects of the emotional development of children, and only secondarily with intellectual factors, most of the differences are irrelevant here. The important findings of Davis and Havighurst that middle class children were assigned tasks and responsibilities under parental supervision earlier than lower class is largely confirmed in the Boston study. With respect to the second conclusion of Davis and Havighurst we have stressed, that lower class children have more unsupervised freedom than middle class, Sears and his colleagues believe their data point in the opposite direction. However, it appears that whereas Sears is referring to the amount of restriction to which the child is subjected as long as he remains in the house or near his mother, Davis and Havighurst are concerned with the amount of time spent away from this supervised environment. For example, in our opinion one cannot equate in terms of parental guidance the middle class mother permitting her child to go down the block to visit with a child of well known neighbors on the one hand, with the lower class mother letting her child go off with his friends unescorted to the movies on the other. Furthermore, whereas the children studied in Boston were all five years old, the median age of the lower class children in Chicago was six, an important factor in determining the amount of freedom they might be allowed. Finally, Sears and his coworkers attempted to obtain a balanced sample of mothers of children in various ordinal positions—only children, and first, middle, and youngest children. Inasmuch as the number and spacing of children varies significantly with social class (as shown in the sample, random with regard to this factor, studied by Davis and Havighurst) the sample used in the Boston study *must* be unrepresentative of at least one if not both of the social classes, since the middle class families in their study averaged 2.7 children, as against 2.5 in the working class—an insignificant difference, and opposite to the expected direction. (In the Chicago study the figures were 2.2 and 3.2 for whites, 2.2 and 3.7 for Negroes.) In view of these considerations we do not consider the studies comparable, and because of the sampling bias introduced into the Boston study we do not at present see any basis for questioning the validity of those findings of the Chicago study with which we are concerned in this report.

It will be remembered that the mental age equivalents of intelligence test performance are so standardized upon a "normal" population that they will coincide on the average with chronological age, with the intention that the average IQ of groups of "normal" children will fall fairly close to 100 at any given age level, and thus hopefully remain essentially constant. Turning to children of lower class or culturally marginal groups, however, we find quite consistently that during the first two or three school years, although they obtain scores somewhat lower than those of middle class white children, they deviate far less from the normal IQ than they do later. Often the early differences do not even reach statistical significance. This phenomenon has been demonstrated in testing of Negroes of various ages enrolled in the schools of Atlanta, Georgia, by Graham (96) and in Oklahoma and Texas by Garth, Lovelady, and Smith (83). Tomlinson (273) obtained better control of the home environment by testing only siblings. He administered Forms L and M of the 1937 Stanford-Binet to 75 pairs of Negro siblings from age 4 to 9 and found that whereas their over-all average fell 10.4 below the white norm, most of this difference was contributed by the older siblings. Furthermore, the correlation of IQ with the Sims index of socioeconomic status increased with increasing age, thus showing rather clearly that despite the presumed continuity of home environment its depressing effects are delayed for several years, at least in their expression in test performance.

A similar decline of IQ with age of children in marginal groups was found by Sherman and Key (240) in the isolated "hollows" of Virginia, by Skeels and Fillmore (245) in orphanage children, by Garth and Johnson (82) among the Mexican population of Texas and New Mexico, by Haught (105) in Indians of the Southwestern United States, and by Nissen, Machover, and Kinder (195) among the Sousou tribe of West Africa. Finally, it will be recalled that Neff and Honzig, in separate studies referred to earlier in this section, also found their correlations of IQ and socioeconomic status increased (negatively) with age among lower class American white children. Eells, Davis, Havighurst, Herrick, and Tyler (68), in an extensive study of almost 5000 white children in the age groups 9-10 and 13-14, reached similar conclusions, although with an interesting additional point of difference. In the 9-10 year group, which it should be remembered had already had a few years of schooling, test performance did correlate with socioeconomic status up through lower middle class, but thereafter there was no correlation. In the 13-14 year group the correlation of test performance and socioeconomic status was maintained throughout the social class range. This means in effect that in the lower age group the lowest class children were already suffering from their inadequate preparation for schooling, but the tests were not discriminating differences among the children of more privileged background. After a few more years of schooling, differential environments were showing their effects at all social class levels.

A very different, but equally interesting, outcome was reported by Estes (69). She administered the Wechsler Intelligence Scale for Children (*WISC*) to 80 children, half of high socioeconomic status and the other half low (using, as in the study of Eells, *et al.,* above the Warner Index). Each status group was further divided by age and grade into two groups; one group was clustered closely around age 7½ and in the second grade, while the other was 10½ years and in the fifth grade. (The subgroups were further divided equally into boys and girls, but this does not concern us here.) What should be noted about this sample is that it is not defined on the basis of age *or* grade, but age *and* grade. In other words, the children tested included only those who were keeping up with their grade and therefore were, by this definition at least, not retarded. If we bear in mind this difference in sampling from other studies, it is perhaps not surprising that whereas she found a significant difference in average test scores of the two socioeconomic groups at the younger age, this difference was not significant in the older group. It is encouraging to find that the *WISC* can discriminate in at least one study as early in school as the second grade, although this may be accounted for by the fact that the socioeconomic groups were selected from near the two extremes of the Warner scale. But it is far more interesting to find that it does not discriminate later. One is forced to conclude that in the particular community studied the great majority of children who were not equipped to cope with schooling on a par with their fellows had already dropped back a grade or more before reaching the fifth grade. One immediately wonders what it was in the background of the lower class children who did stay in grade (and who performed adequately on the test used in this study) that permitted them to do this whereas their fellows fell by the wayside (cf. p. 22). On the basis of the massive contrary evidence we cannot assume that this particular school system was able to build up the intellectual skills of all its deprived students to a par with the higher class children, so there must have been many children 10½ years old who did not get into the fifth grade on schedule and therefore were not tested. Unfortunately, Estes did not investigate the special characteristics of her lower class fifth graders in this way, but perhaps the greatest value of her study lies in pointing up this possible avenue for future research. Due to the highly selective nature of her sampling, the study is not comparable to the others we have reported and cannot of itself provide much insight into the mechanisms whereby lower class children become scholastically handicapped, and upper or middle class children aided, by their cultural backgrounds.

If we accept the assumption, as indeed we must, that the intellectually deprived child is ill-prepared for schoolwork from the time he enters the first grade, it appears that we can only explain the paradoxically late manifestation of his disability by making the further assumption that the intelligence tests themselves present different *kinds* of problems at higher age levels, problems progressively less appropriate to the nature of intellectual preparation the subculturally handicapped child has had. All intelligence tests, of course, become more difficult as they reach each mental age criterion level, but the evidence presented here suggests strongly that along with increasing difficulty, the tests begin to move into new sorts of intellectual processes at higher levels. This discontinuity in what the tests are testing is not apparent in the performance of the middle class child who is doing adequately in school, but shows up in the deprived child who can "get by" at first and then stumbles more and more as new intellectual dimensions assume increasing importance. Evidently the child who is well equipped to profit from schooling derives from his first years of study the skills necessary to handle the later hurdles, but the lower class or culturally marginal child, although seemingly performing fairly adequately on the basis of test results, actually lacks the intellectual and doubtless also verbal foundation upon which his schoolwork should be building in order that he can handle the different kinds of tasks which will come during the following years. Viewed from a different standpoint, the intelligence tests fail in the lower school grades to measure the capabilities which will later become of critical importance, and thus do not detect intellectual deficits at the very time most appropriate for remedying them. They also cannot be expected to take into account the progressively increasing discouragement experienced by many marginal children through the school years.

It is interesting to note that the failure of intelligence tests to identify potentially retarded children in the lower grades of school extends also into preschool years. Kirk (154) attempted for a research project in Urbana, Illinois, to find a group of children three, four, and five years old who would have Stanford-Binet *IQ*'s between 45 and 80. He had great difficulty in finding any children who were not either grossly deficient with an organic diagnosis or else had *IQ*'s over 90. His conclusions follow:

> Apparently, children with low intelligence are not detected at the preschool ages by social workers, doctors, or other agencies dealing with children. This, coupled with the small number of cases located, suggests that many children later placed in special classes or institutions are not mentally retarded in terms of intelligence test scores at the ages of three, four, or five. Some children, whose older brothers and sisters were in special classes, tested approximately normal at the preschool ages. This raises the question as to whether children from low cultural levels who are approximately normal at an early age may later become mentally retarded because of their cultural environment or other unknown variables (p. 698).

We still lack the careful research necessary to determine the precise nature of the thinking processes the growing importance of which progressively handicaps the deprived child, and sooner or later often results in his being labelled "retarded." Some efforts have been made to analyze the performance of lower class children on various subtests of the standard intelligence tests in order to see which subtests are relatively more difficult for them than others. The research of Haggard, Havighurst, and their associates referred to above is probably the most exhaustive in this area. Although a scattering of statistically significant differences have been discovered, the results are very difficult of interpretation. One reason for this is that in the process of standardizing these tests on a "normal" population it is customary to eliminate or modify those items and subtests which do not intercorrelate fairly well with the overall test scores; this means that the subtests generate variables which depend not only upon social class (or some other independent variable chosen) but also upon the indeterminate weighting created by the original statistical screening of items in the subtests. Another, and more crucial, difficulty arises from the fact that the subtests are not designed and validated to measure some particular and explicit type of intellectual process as such, but are rather justified for inclusion because of their intercorrelation with total test score. The test as a whole is in turn justified on the basis of its correlation in a standardization population with performance on the Stanford-Binet or some other well established instrument. This interlocking mesh of correlations avoids examination of just what the various tests and subtests measure, and thus makes it almost impossible to reach more than inferential *post hoc* conclusions as to the real meaning of consistent variations in subtest scores in various subcultural groups. Guilford's (99) factorial studies of the components of intellectual process discussed in Section IV hold great promise for the future, but his findings are as yet far from being applicable to studies of subcultural differences in thinking patterns.

Some clues to the nature of various subculturally determined differences may perhaps be found in the following formulation of the levels of intelligence proposed by Sir Cyril Burt (34, p. 71): "(i) the level of simple sensory and simple motor processes; (ii) the level of complex perceptual and complex motor processes; (iii) the associative or reproductive level (imagery, mechanical memory, and habit formation); and finally (iv) the relational level, including generalization by concepts (abstraction), generalization by propositions (judgment), and rational inference (reasoning)." It would appear reasonable to assume that it is in the last, or highest, of these levels that we should look for significant differences in the thinking of various social class groups when faced with academic-type problems.

Although the evidence to be considered later in this chapter with respect to the effects on intellectual process of ethnic and cultural differences is perhaps a little more conclusive than that for socioeconomic status, some suggestive studies do exist in the latter area. However, in order to arrive at conclusions of the order with which we are here concerned, additional inferential interpretation is necessary. Thus we find in two related studies by the Chicago group (Havighurst and Janke, 109, and Janke and Havighurst, 129) a large array of tests administered to all the available 10-year-olds and 16-year-olds respectively in a Midwestern community. Among other things they reported at age 10 a high intercorrelation between all tests, and a consistent correlation of test performance with socioeconomic status, including the results of the Minnesota Mechanical Assembly Test. At age 16, however, although the other tests (Stanford-Binet, Wechsler Performance Scale, Iowa Silent Reading, and Minnesota Paper Form Board) correlated significantly with socioeconomic status, the Minnesota Mechanical Assembly Test did not. If we make the not unreasonable assumption that mechanical ability is learned as a part of living in the American culture irrespective of school experience, whereas the other tests (with the possible exception of the Paper Form Board) are increasingly drawing upon the abstraction, judgment, reasoning, and vocabulary learned in school, we can then say that the results reported support the view that lower class children are handicapped primarily in Burt's fourth level of intelligence.

Even more tenuous inference is necessary to reach this conclusion with regard to the 13-year-olds in this community (Havighurst and Breese, 106) who were given the Thurstone Primary Mental Abilities Test; all abilities correlated with socioeconomic status, but the highest correlations were attained with numbers, verbal comprehension, and word fluency, whereas space ability, reasoning, and memory showed a lesser relationship to social class. Even if we assume that the subtests measure what they purport to measure, we would be hard pressed to demonstrate that the highly correlated abilities involved a consistently higher level of abstraction than the lower. Similarly, Britton (27) administered several intelligence tests to 232 children aged 9 to 11, and one year later administered the Goodenough Draw-a-Man Test to the same children; whereas the intelligence tests correlated significantly with social status, the Goodenough did not. Again, we are forced to make assumptions about the level of abstraction and the kinds of intellectual skills required for performance on the Goodenough; the kinds of assumptions made will determine whether or not the results of this study will support our hypothesis. This is at best dubious scientific procedure, and serves well to point up the complete inadequacy of studies into the "why" of the progressive failure of lower class children in school and on tests as they grow older.

The most direct and the most ambitious attack on this problem to date was made, again at Chicago, by Allison Davis and Kenneth Eells. Their premise, stated in the manual for the Davis-Eells Games (56), is as follows:

> The fact is that there is no satisfactory objective criterion of true mental capacity, and therefore no possibility, at least at present, of constructing a satisfactory test of intelligence by purely objective means. It is necessary for the makers of intelligence tests to construct items which appear to require the main types of intellectual problem-solving behavior (p. 7).

Furthermore, in the course of the numerous studies of intelligence test performance undertaken by the Chicago group it was established that, to a degree not previously realized, children tended to give correct answers to analogies, and to other questions involving reasoning, on a basis different from that which the test constructor had in mind. By thus producing the right answers for the wrong reasons they made test scores even more unreliable and difficult of interpretation.

In an attempt to remedy the difficulties they perceived, Davis and Eells devised a group test, the Davis-Eells Games, administered with verbal instructions, which presents the child with a series of problems presumably familiar to anyone living in an urban environment in the United States. Three alternative solutions to each problem are presented in a comic-book format with verbal instructions and questions, the child being asked to select the one most effective or appropriate. The authors feel that the problems are typically encountered by children of all social classes, but warn that, although the test is applicable to American children in any city or small town, "scores for children from homes where a foreign language is spoken, and scores for children from strictly rural areas, should be interpreted with caution" (56, p. 1). They did not expect that the Index of Problem Solving Ability derived from the test would correlate highly with standard achievement tests because of the lack in the Davis-Eells of emphasis on memory and efficient work habits. They actually found the mean coefficients of correlation with various achievement tests administered in urban schools to be: reading, .43; language, .40; arithmetic, .41; and spelling, .24.[17]

Davis and Eells characterize their test as "culture-fair" in order to distinguish it from the so-called "culture-free" tests we will be considering later. This designation gives recognition to the fact that no test can avoid favoring certain kinds of cultural experience over others; the authors feel that their test does avoid social class bias within the limits of English-speaking urban children in the United States. Since this presumption rests upon a priori considerations it cannot be proven to be true, but at the same time there are no immediately apparent grounds for disputing it. However, a serious question must be raised as to the utility of the test, as applied to children in general and to retarded children in particular. Put more directly, if we have an Index of Problem Solving Ability (IPSA) on a child, what can we predict about the child from this index?

Earlier in this chapter we cited the comments of Stenquist (263) on the research which led up to the Davis-Eells Games, to the effect that until teachers, the public, and others cease the practice of effectively equating "intelligence" with the ability of a child to handle schoolwork there is little purpose in devising a test which will measure intelligence in any way other than the recognized IQ. Davis and Eells state explicitly that the IPSA is not the same thing as the IQ, but are not prepared to say exactly what relationship obtains between the two. Geist (84) attempted to explore this point by administering the Davis-Eells and the Stanford-Binet Form L to 50 children, 10 each from Grades 2 to 6, divided into upper, middle, and lower class. He found the two tests correlated within the three class groups with Pearson r's of .00, .67, and .78 respectively. Even if one disregards the

---

[17]Compare the similar correlations found by Zweibelson (Table 3).

small size of the sample, these results are inconclusive and can be interpreted in several ways. One conclusion might be that children with educational advantages can bring different specialized skills to each kind of test, whereas deprived children respond in the same way to all tests, thus explaining the lack of an upper class correlation and a high lower class correlation. This does not, however, permit any conclusions as to what the *IPSA* actually measures even in the lower class. Another kind of observation we might make is that if the Davis-Eells is designed to correct the unreliability and undue difficulty of standard intelligence tests for lower class children, why should it be in this class group that the *IQ* and *IPSA* correlate most closely? Viewed in this way, the Davis-Eells appears to perpetuate the disadvantages of the Stanford-Binet without improving on its predictive value in the higher social levels. However, all we can really say is that the Geist study tells us nothing positive about the predictive value of the Davis-Eells and perhaps increases our doubts as to its utility.

A similar ambiguity exists with regard to the findings of a study by Rosenblum, Keller, and Papania (222). They administered the Davis-Eells Games, Stanford-Binet Form *L*, Wechsler Intelligence Scale for Children, and California Mental Maturity Test to 30 lower class, non-organic, retarded children at the Wayne County Training School; these children were equally divided between white and Negro, and averaged 12 years of age and 2.6 years in the school. The mean *IPSA* score of 64.6 was lower than that attained by these children on any other of the tests, the highest being on the Wechsler Performance Scale (72.7). Since all of these tests are standardized to yield a median score at 100 on a "normal" population, it is clear that the Davis-Eells offered the children no better opportunity to show what they could do than any other test. The authors felt that this might perhaps be due to the fact that the tests were administered by middle class people and hence mobilized the hostility of the children to all the tests; this would not, however, account for the probably significant difference between the highest and lowest results. They also noted, more significantly, that these retarded children appeared very concrete in their approach to the Davis-Eells problems with little ability in abstraction, and that they were exceedingly poor in providing correct or appropriate reasons for the selection of particular problem solutions, whether these were correct or not. This, of course, is the very criticism levelled at the standard tests of intelligence by the Chicago group, and suggests that at least for these retarded children (who had a mean *IQ* of 67.6 on admission, range 55-75) the Davis-Eells comes no closer than standard tests to providing a true measure of mental ability. Finally, although this point is not mentioned by the authors, it should be borne in mind that many of the neighborhood activities of play, shopping, etc., portrayed in the Davis-Eells Games are not likely to fall within the experience of children institutionalized in a training school, making the test not "culture-fair" for children who have resided for some time in an institution.

Angelino and Shedd (9) undertook to evaluate the culture-fairness of the Davis-Eells Games by administering the test to two groups of children in Oklahoma City, 152 of lower class and 155 of upper class, utilizing the class criteria employed by the Chicago group. Approximately equal numbers were taken from each of the first six grades of two elementary schools. With the exception of the second grade, the differences in mean scores exceeded 15 points, and all the differences were significant at the one per cent level. Surprisingly enough, however, whereas the differences favored the upper class in Grades 2 through 6, in the first grade the lower class children were markedly superior to the upper class. This first grade result reflected a very low score (78.0) for the upper class rather than unusually high performance by the lower class children. Although it is impossible to determine the meaning of the first grade reversal, one is forced to agree with the authors that this study strongly suggests that the Davis-Eells is probably still contaminated with cultural factors. It should, however, be noted that no mention is made of the language spoken in the home of the children tested. Although the care taken by the authors to conform in other respects to the requirements established by Davis and Eells presumably was extended also to language, in the absence of a specific statement the possibility exists that some children speaking Spanish or some other language—presumably in the lower class groups— may have affected the results.

A similar comparison of children divided into upper and lower class groups was made by Altus (4) in the elementary schools of Santa Barbara County, California. She confined herself, however, to drawing only on fourth grade children, and also had some reservations as to the accuracy of placement of some children with respect to social class on the Warner Index. As did Angelino and Shedd, she found the Davis-Eells *IPSA* favored the upper class children, who averaged 106.4 as against the lower class mean of 97.9. Altus also administered the California Test of Mental Maturity to the same children; the *IQ* derived from the *CTMM* closely paralleled their *IPSA*'s, the means falling at 113.1 and 95.6 respectively. Of the total of 168 children, 46 showed differences between *IQ* and *IPSA* of 20 points or more. Of those with a higher *IPSA* than *IQ*, the great majority as might be expected came from the lower half of the socioeconomic scale, 14 as against two. However, there were also 10 lower class as against only four upper class who had *IQ*'s 20 points or more higher than their *IPSA*'s. The culture-fairness of the Davis-Eells Games is thus again in question—the findings of this study seem to suggest the Games are almost as biased by social class as a standard intelligence test. However, the criterion of upbringing in an urban environment is not well met in Santa Barbara County; most of the county is rural agricultural and Santa Barbara, the only real city, is of medium size (about 50,000 population) and spread out over a considerable area.

We have engaged in a rather extended discussion of the Davis-Eells Games here as well as in Section III because this test represents the first systematic effort to control the social class factor in the measurement of intelligence, and thus has raised real hopes of providing a basis for more realistic estimates of the ability of children to cope with their over-all environment. Thus far, unhappily, we do not have evidence which would suggest that this hope has been realized. It is clear that for the test to be "culture-fair" the children tested must have shared in reasonable degree in the "typical" urban American culture. This means, among other things, that it is likely to be less fair for the more retarded children whose restricted life does not necessarily include as many opportunities to go shopping, ride street cars, participate in free play groups, work with tools, handle money, and so forth. This does not mean that the test is inappropriate for all retarded children, but it does mean that for any child, retarded or not, some knowledge is necessary of the range of social experience to which the child has previously been exposed. Without this information on each child who takes the test we become to an indeterminate degree more uncertain in any predictions we may make on the basis of *IPSA* scores.

But even if we are concerned with an urban American child from an English-speaking home who we know has had the experiences typical for his background, what can we actually predict from the Index of Problem Solving Ability? We know that the standard *IQ* is the best available single predictor of the usual sorts of school performance, being in effect validated against this criterion, and that the *IPSA* is not intended to measure the same thing as the *IQ*. Therefore it is to be presumed that the Davis-Eells is not the most useful instrument to employ in determining fitness in the classroom. It may help to identify the child who is sufficiently "bright" but who for some other reason cannot adjust to school, but unless we can identify and deal with the other impediment we have gained little, and the Davis-Eells is not designed to identify extraneous emotional or cultural factors.

Nevertheless, there is value in having a means of being more certain that we are dealing with a potentially adequate child whether or not he does well in school. Even if he never overcomes his school difficulties, there is good reason to suppose he will be in the vanguard of those many adolescents who proceed from a school career of consistent retardation to an adult life of adequate and sometimes superior social and occupational performance. Intelligence, when not tied to a circular definition in terms of the *IQ*, is usually considered to involve the ability to solve problems, and in particular those problems relevant to the successful performance of the individual in all the normally expectable cultural settings. Clearly this is the ability which the Davis-Eells Games undertakes to test and, despite the questions raised by the studies discussed above and in Section III, it has yet to be demonstrated that it is not a fair test of this ability provided it is used on the population for which it was designed. When we say that we do not know what sorts of real-life performance the *IPSA* predicts we are in effect saying that we are not equipped to capitalize on intelligence unless it is adapted to the school situation. Viewed in this way the "uselessness" of the Davis-Eells reflects not so much a failure of the test constructors as a lack of flexibility in our culture— the inability to develop alternative ways of preparing those children for adult life who are not able to profit from conventional schooling. This is a point of view to which we will return in the next section.

C. ETHNICITY

Here we are concerned with the relationship between test performance and what used to be referred to loosely as "racial" origin, embracing nationality, cultural-religious entities such as Jews or Arabs, and more properly racial groups such as American Indians or Negroes. As we observed in the chapter on heredity and environment, studies in this area have employed the premise, implicit or explicit, that differences in intelligence are somehow inherently associated with ethnic origins. This genetic premise appears firmly rooted in our folklore although, as we saw, it as yet lacks any scientific basis. However, despite the inconclusiveness of research on the influence of ethnic origin on intelligence, there have been a sufficient number of studies with this particular focus to warrant separate attention to at least a selected few. The majority of these are early, concentrated particularly in the early 1930's.

As we have mentioned before, a rather large number of studies have demonstrated that children, particularly of school age, of different ethnic groups perform differently on intelligence tests even when age, social class, and the like are held constant. Correspondingly, of course, there are differences in the incidence of mental retardation. There is furthermore some consistency to these findings, which suggests that Jews come near the top of the list in average test scores, Negroes and Italians near the bottom, and others fall in between although with less consistency in rank order. The difficulty of course arises when we try to discover what factors are operative to produce these gross differences. Some studies, therefore, have been undertaken to break the problem down into more manageable components.

One approach has been to test children of mixed Indian-white or 'Negro-white blood to determine whether more white blood regularly raises the *IQ*. In 1933 Garth (81) published the most careful of the several studies done on children of Indian-white parentage. He administered the Otis Classification Test to 1022 children in Grades 4 to 9 of government schools in Oklahoma and South Dakota, classifying each in accordance with the proportion of white blood in his ancestry. On purely sociocultural grounds one would expect the degree of white blood to show some relationship with intelligence and school achievement, because a white parent would be more likely to draw a child away from traditional Indian culture and therefore more into the white environment where he would be exposed to the kinds of stimuli and experience necessary for successful test performance. (As we shall see later, a closer tie to Indian culture does in fact appear to hold down the *IQ*.) Even this expectation was only slightly realized; the degree of Indian blood correlated with intelligence score and achievement score respectively only .19 and .11. In contrast intelligence, achievement, and school grade intercorrelate .67, .68, and .81, with little change in coefficients when degree of Indian blood is partialled out. In other words, intelligence and achievement are much more intimately related to the amount of schooling received than to the amount of white blood. Of course it could then be argued that only the children with more white blood were capable of handling higher grades of school, but here we find that degree of white blood and school grade correlate only .12—i.e., there is only a slightly greater amount of white blood in the ancestry of children in higher grades than lower.

There are several facts to be borne in mind in assessing the significance of Garth's study. First is the size of his sample, large enough to assure statistically reliable results. Second, the majority of Indian-white mixtures are of sufficiently recent date to provide reasonably confident genealogical determinations. Third, the European and Indian populations which met in North America comprised breeding populations kept genetically, geographically, and culturally separate over many centuries if not millenia. And fourth, there is ample evidence that in most American Indian groups white admixture carries with it a strong implication of acculturation toward a white way of life and abandonment of Indian values and patterns of thought and action, leading us to expect that with more white blood Indian children would be likely to be more acculturated and thus to perform better on tests devised for white populations. In view of these facts the relationships found by Garth between school-related factors and degree of white admixture are if anything surprising in being so low. As with so many other approaches to the nature-nurture problem in intelligence, this study cannot disprove the existence of inherent ethnic differences but it puts the burden of proof very heavily on those who would claim such genetic differentials are real.

In 1936 Witty and Jenkins (298) undertook a critical survey of the more numerous studies dealing with the relationship between proportions of Negro and white blood and the *IQ*. They found that the preponderance of evidence pointed toward a lack of relationship. This result was probably to be expected if for no other reason than the variety of factors which make the study of persons of Negro-white ancestry considerably less clear cut than is the case with Indian-white admixture. Intermixture of Negroes and whites on a large scale has been going on for much longer than with Indians, and generally more covertly, so that genealogical records are vague in the extreme and degree of mixture is often estimated on the very unreliable basis of appearance. Genetically, the separation of the populations of Europe and of Africa has not been nearly as complete as in the case of Europeans and American Indians. Within the mixed group a selection process has taken place through the "passing" of individuals who combine lighter skin and, perhaps, a superior ability to adapt to different behavior patterns. On the other side, however, the likelihood of a cultural correlate of admixture is less for Negroes, thus providing greater a priori credence to a genetic basis for any correlation which might be found with degree of white blood. One reason for the lesser cultural difference is that, although there are subcultural differences relevant to intelligence test performance between general Negro culture in the United States and white culture, this difference is not nearly as dramatic as that obtaining between Indian culture and European culture. Furthermore, whereas a "halfbreed" Indian is in somewhat different social status than a pure Indian, a Negro of mixed ancestry is still socially all Negro. The cultural factor in ethnic mixture of Negroes is thus less strongly weighted in favor of showing a correlation between IQ and amount of white blood, but it is by no means eliminated and simply makes it even more difficult to determine which differences, if any, shall be considered genetically significant. This, combined with the difficulty in obtaining genealogical data, makes the study of Negro-white mixtures a singularly unpromising line to pursue in the study of ethnic differences in IQ.

The remaining studies to be considered in this section may be discussed more briefly. Several point up various possible pitfalls of research in ethnic correlates of IQ. In 1928 Klineberg (156), after administering the Pintner-Patterson Performance Tests to a number of Indian and Negro groups, concluded that they scored lower than the white norms primarily because they could not meet the time criteria, but when given adequate time to complete the test they could reach the norm level of accuracy. This finding raises the question of whether time-limited tests, of which there are many in use, are appropriate for use with any subcultural groups who do not place a premium on speed. Put another way, if members of ethnic subgroups are able to solve problems correctly and live in a setting which does not require that problems be solved with great rapidity, is it justified to view test results which are lowered by a speed factor as indicators of inferiority, whether inherent or learned?

Smith (253) administered some special tests, one of them non-verbal and the others intended to test comprehension of written and spoken English, to children of representative ethnic groups, aged 10 to 15, in Honolulu in 1924, and then readministered the same tests to comparable groups 14 years later in 1938. He found that although the rank order of the various ethnic groups had not changed over the years, mean scores for each group had risen substantially. This outcome is probably to be expected in view of the gradual Americanization of the polyglot population of the Hawaiian Islands. It of course indicates the need for caution in interpreting results of testing of ethnic groups at different points in time, or of separate groups in differing stages of acculturation. But, more importantly, it shows such test results to be at least as dependent upon the historical flux of opportunity as upon any inherent capability of different groups. A similar outcome, for example, was reported by Wheeler in isolated Tennessee communities in a study discussed in Section II.

We discussed in the section on heredity and environment Pasamanick's (202) findings that subcultural influences affecting intelligence should be traced back to conception and even earlier, particularly as these affect diet. He has criticized the work of others who make ethnic comparisons (e.g., his 1951 critique of Carlson and Henderson's (37) study of Mexican children, 201) without due regard for these early environmental differences. However, he also found (200) that if it is possible to control the prenatal and perinatal environment, at least approximately, the effects of postnatal influences are not apparent until early childhood. He made a careful study of 53 Negro and 99 white infants born after full term pregnancies in New Haven, Connecticut, and found that with prematurity ruled out the differences known to exist later do not appear before the third year of life. This implies that whatever the postnatal influences are that later become effective in depressing test performance, they do not have any detectable influence on motor ability or other developing capabilities at least until the child of a minority ethnic group has reached an age of talking and otherwise interacting socially.

Jenkins studied several groups of highly superior Negro children, drawn primarily from the public schools of Chicago (Witty and Jenkins, 298; Jenkins, 134, 135, 136). He found that gifted Negro children, including some of apparently pure Negro ancestry, cover the range of intelligence all the way up to the highest levels reached by white persons and that their backgrounds are in general comparable to those of gifted white children, including a large proportion of middle class and professional parents. However, Jenkins found that the proportion of Negro children who are gifted, with high *IQ*'s and school grade advancement, is considerably smaller than among white children. As he observes (136, p. 401): "The abstract mental tests that contribute to psychometric intelligence do not measure the factors of personality and motivation that largely determine success in life."

Turning now to the influence of ethnicity in children definitely adjudged retarded, two studies are of particular interest. In one of these Gibson and Butler (85) selected from the files of their institution for retarded children in Ontario, Canada, 200 cases admitted over a 10-year period. These were selected to include only cases in two groups, one in which a hereditary etiology was diagnosed and the other comprising cases in which no medical basis for retardation could be found. These cases were then determined to have been either of foreign parentage or from homes in which the parents were native born to the United States or Canada (French Canadians were excluded entirely). An estimate of adequate or poor home environment was also made. They found that in the group with identifiable hereditary etiology the distribution of nationality and home environment corresponded approximately with that of the surrounding community at large. This was largely true also of the group of undetermined etiology whose *IQ* was under 50. However, those admissions with an *IQ* over 50, a level at which neurological complications are generally considered to be less likely, showed a far higher proportion both of foreign parentage and of poor home environment than in the other groups or the general population. In the undetermined etiology group, for example, the *IQ*-over-50 group of 33 had 70 per cent foreign parents, whereas in the 59 cases with *IQ* below 50 only 30 per cent of the parents were of foreign origin, a difference significant at the .001 level. Comparable differences were found with respect to home environment within the undetermined group. These findings strongly suggest that at the borderline level where pathology, hereditary or otherwise, is less likely to be operative, ethnic handicaps as well as socioeconomic deprivation can depress a child's performance sufficiently to push him over the line into an institutional status.

A different approach to ethnicity in institutionalized children was taken by Shotwell (242) with results closely congruent with those of Gibson and Butler. She selected 80 Mexican and 80 American children of comparable ages from the Pacific State Hospital in California. Their Binet *IQ*'s ranged from 50 to 79. She administered to each of these children the Arthur Performance Scale tests and compared their Arthur scores with their Binet *IQ*'s. The American children averaged five points higher on the Arthur than on the Binet, but the Mexicans averaged 22 points higher. In no case did a Mexican subject have an Arthur score more than five points below the Binet score, whereas 22½ per cent of the American children had Arthur scores more than five points below. Of the Mexicans, 27½ per cent had Arthur scores 30 or more points *above* Binet. Thus members of the ethnic minority were institutionalized with low *IQ*'s based on a verbal intelligence test, but when these same children were given a non-verbal performance-type test which presumably was less handicapping they obtained scores in or near the normal range. Although a low *IQ* does not automatically lead to institutionalization, it can often play a crucial rôle in such a decision. Taken together these studies in Ontario and California cast strong doubts on the validity of the customary intelligence test results as criteria for placing a child of a minority ethnic group in an institution, and lead one to wonder how many of the ethnic children in our schools for the retarded may not have a potential for fairly immediate return to the community. Of course one could raise a similar question regarding many non-ethnic children also, but Gibson, Butler, and Shotwell force us to realize that it is a question particularly appropriate to ask regarding members of at least some ethnic minority group members.

To sum up, the studies reviewed here which are concerned with the influence of ethnicity on *IQ* return us to the conclusion implied at the outset, that is, that differentials in intelligence test performance by members of various ethnic groups are, as far as the evidence we have available goes, primarily cultural in origin, compounded doubtless of motivation, thought, and habit patterns, and differences in language. Because language appears to loom so large in this whole problem, we shall turn to this next.

D. Language

The relationship between language facility and intelligence, particularly intelligence measured by a test score, has been a major focus of interest for many years and has attracted some excellent researchers. Two aspects of the problem have received primary emphasis. First, both historically and in amount of study devoted to it, is the assessment of language skills or handicaps as they affect performance on the verbal types of intelligence tests which comprise the bulk of the standard tests—the Stanford-Binet, Wechsler-Bellevue, etc.—which, among other things, provide one of the primary diagnostic criteria of mental retardation. Since the groups most conspicuously handicapped in this regard are those of foreign ethnic origin, the majority of studies in this area have been concerned with bilingualism. Regardless of the direction from which this problem is attacked, one is constantly confronted with the close association of the three phenomena of ethnicity, bilingualism, and retardation, each interlinked with the other in a vicious circle of cause and effect. We see this in the French Catholics of the Northeastern United States, the Spanish-Americans of the Southwest, Italians and Puerto Ricans in New York and other big cities, and in American Indians scattered throughout the country.

The second and more recent focus of interest reflects the intimate relationship between language and culture, language being the primary medium of cultural learning and itself reflecting the categories of experience stressed within the culture. The presumption here is that a person retarded in language development will therefore be handicapped also in learning the other aspects of culture which are important to his over-all functioning in the society and to his performance on any sort of intelligence, performance, or aptitude test. For example Nisbet (194), in a study discussed in some detail in Section X, reaches the conclusion that differential language facility is a major factor in determining the inverse correlation of *IQ* and family size.

Among the several "firsts" which can be claimed for the study by May

Bere (17) in 1924 of Italian, Bohemian, and Jewish school children in New York City is the systematic examination of the effects of bilingualism on test performance. She pioneered many of the procedures used repeatedly by later researchers, including assessing the effects on test scores of differing degrees of bilingualism (in this case based on the amount of the foreign language spoken in the home), comparing the performance of bilinguals on verbal versus non-verbal tests (using the Stanford-Binet and the Pintner-Patterson Performance Tests), and evaluating the relationships between all of these factors. Her findings also anticipated much of the ambiguity of results which has characterized research in this area. She found, for example, in partialling out such factors as father's occupation, length of residence in the United States, and the like that some correlations showed significant relationships, including amount of foreign language spoken in the home, but none of these correlations were consistently significant for all groups. Similarly, she divided her subjects into those whose Stanford-Binet score was higher than their Pinter-Patterson score, and those for whom the reverse was true. She found significant differences between the ethnic groups on this basis, but the differences one might then expect between these subgroups in regard to the amount of foreign language spoken in the home failed to materialize.

Similar inconsistencies, and failures to find statistically significant relationships between variables in some populations where other studies would lead one to expect them, have characterized research in bilingualism ever since. Conveniently, this is a field which has been subject to periodic and exhaustive reviews of the literature, including those by Arsenian (11, 12) in 1937 and 1945, Spoerl (258) in 1942, and Darcy (52) in 1953. Arsenian's 1945 review is probably the most penetrating of these and is therefore worth citing at some length:

> In general the pattern of these investigations has been to administer tests of intelligence to bilingual and monoglot children and to compare the results. Some of the investigators have used only verbal tests of intelligence, others only non-verbal or non-language tests, and still others have administered both verbal and non-verbal tests to the same groups of children. These investigations have been conducted on from nursery school and kindergarten to the college and university levels, with most of the studies covering the elementary school period. Both individual as well as group tests of intelligence have been used, and in a few instances the verbal intelligence test has been administered in the two languages of the bilingual child. The determination and the measurement of the degree of bilingualism of the child has been variable: in some instances the performance of the bilingual child has been compared with

that of his monoglot contemporaries of his own natio-racial group, at other times with a different or a mixed group.

A few of the studies are longitudinal—the observations and the testing having been made on the same child at different periods of growth, most of the studies are cross-sectional—the observations and testing having been made at one point in the child's development. A few investigators have used the correlational technique in seeking the relationship between degrees of bilingualism and intellectual ability, most researchers have satisfied themselves with a comparison of averages and variabilities and the statistical significance of differences between bilingual and monoglot groups.

Because of these circumstances the results of these studies are not uniform, however, after examining nearly 100 investigations in this country and abroad the following summary of the findings can be made:

1. Bilingual children as compared with monoglot children of the same age and environment are neither retarded nor accelerated in their mental development. This conclusion is especially evident when the two groups are compared on non-language tests of intelligence.

2. When verbal tests of intelligence are used for comparison in the majority of cases, the bilingual children fall short of their monoglot contemporaries, this disparity being greater the more verbal the content of the test is. This generalization must however be limited by two observations:

a. On the whole, the older the bilingual child and the higher the level of his educational attainment, the smaller is the discrepancy between his verbal intelligence test performance and the performance of a monoglot of the same age or educational attainment.

b. The verbal intelligence tests show that the apparent retardation of bilingual children varies from place to place and from group to group. Bilingual children in urban areas, like the Welsh children in the cities and the Jewish children in London or New York, show either no retardation or a slight superiority to the norms of monoglot children, while in rural Wales the Welsh children, and in the southwest of the United States the Spanish-speaking children according to these verbal intelligence tests show a serious handicap.

This summary points to the conclusion that bilingualism neither retards nor accelerates mental development, and that language handicap is most likely the factor responsible for the discrepancy between the performances of bilingual and monoglot children on verbal tests of intelligence.

Bilingualism and Language Development

Several individual studies of language development of bilingual children have been made by parents. The classical study in this field, and the most careful, is that of Jules Ronjat. In 1913 Dr. Ronjat (220) reported in great detail on the linguistic development of his bilingual son, Louis. From the time of Louis' birth, his father spoke French and his mother spoke German invariably in the presence of the child or in speaking to him after he was able to talk. According to Ronjat, Louis' accent, pronounciation, and knowledge of the two languages were not retarded in any way because of his bilingualism. In 1923, 10 years after the publication of his monograph, Dr. Ronjat in a private communication to Dr. Michael West was able to confirm his earlier statement regarding the normal development in the two languages of his son, Louis.

Several other developmental studies of this type summarized by Spoerl (258) seem to indicate that whenever the sources of the two languages were kept distinct and the manner of presentation remained consistent during the early developmental period the situation was normal. However, when the process was interfered with, as when the mother spoke sometimes German and at other times English, or when the child was moved from a bilingual to a unilingual environment, or vice versa, difficulties arose, such as refusal to talk in one of the two languages learned, or some confusion and retardation in language development, at least temporarily. In this connection one should bear in mind the situation in numerous second generation immigrant homes in the United States, where the parents speak English to the child while the grandparents consistently use the language of the old country, with no permanent illl effects on the child's language development.

Two studies of the language development of preschool children give somewhat divergent results. McCarthy (178), studying children from foreign language homes in the United States, concludes: ". . . the hearing of a foreign language in the home does not seem to be a handicap in linguistic development as it is measured by the mean length of response, which when applied to larger groups has proved a very reliable index."

Smith (251), studying an extensive sampling of children in Hawaii from Chinese, Filipino, Hawaiian, Japanese, Korean, and Portuguese-speaking homes, finds serious language handicap in children from two to six years of age. Two of her conclusions are pertinent:

"The children in Hawaii were compared with a monolingual white American group previously studied. They are found to use more exclamatory and slightly fewer interrogative sentences, and to make much less frequent use of complex and compound sentences. Sentences that serve merely to name an object or person continue to a later age than with monoglot children. However, age trends are found to be similar, for exclamatory and naming sentences decrease; questions, answers, and complex and compound sentences increase with age.

"The evidence, although insufficient, suggests that pidgin English is more responsible for incorrect English and bilingualism for the overuse of interjections, short sentences, immature type of questions when classed as to meaning, and lack of complex sentences."

While the difficulties encountered by the bilingual child in his early period of language development are of interest, and must be provided for in an educational program, it is of greater interest to know whether or not these difficulties are permanent. . . .

It is necessary, therefore, to canvass the studies of the language development of bilingual children on successively higher educational levels. Most of such studies cover the elementary school period. There are a few on high-school level, and very few indeed on the college or more adult levels. The usual method in these studies has been to compare the vocabulary size of the bilingual child with that of his monoglot contemporary. . . .

The results of these studies are not uniform. Certain of the studies, notably those in Puerto Rico, in the southwest of the United States, and in rural Wales show rather serious vocabulary handicap for the bilingual child in both languages. Other studies, notably those in urban centers of the eastern part of the United States, show equality with monoglots, or in a few instances even a larger size of vocabulary in the English language by bilinguals as compared with monoglots. The explanation of these apparently contradictory findings is to be sought in the following:

1. The higher we go on the educational level the more opportunity does the bilingual child have to catch up with the monoglot in his knowledge of the vocabulary of the dominant language. Terman's finding is of great interest in this connection. He discovered that for the bilingual student, vocabulary is lower than mental age up to the third or fourth grade, but that after 12 years of age vocabulary is equal to mental age. This result receives some corroboration in the findings of Decroly in Belgium, and Saer in Wales.

2. The higher we go on the educational level the greater the selection of bilingual students, since, as the New York Regents inquiry shows, a larger percentage of bilingual children leave school than of monoglots. Intelligence and language facility are probably two of the factors in this selective process.

3. There is truth also in the statement of the Canadian committee appointed to inquire into the conditions of the schools attended by French-speaking pupils, namely, that proficiency in the use of one language is assuredly no barrier to securing equal proficiency in the other if proper methods of organization and instruction are followed.

On the whole, these studies show a language deficiency for the bilingual child. However, the extent and period of such deficiency seem to depend on certain factors, such as the extent of educational opportunities, the intelligence of the bilingual children, and the methods of organization and instruction in schools.

Bilingualism and School Achievement

The bilingual's deficiency in language reflects in his school performance, especially on the elementary school level. Studies reported from Belgium, Czechoslovakia, Canada, the Philippine Islands, Puerto Rico, and a number from this country are almost unanimous in showing lower performance by the bilingual child. This deficiency of the bilingual is most apparent in verbal subjects, such as reading, history, and geography; and is much less apparent in non-verbal subjects, such as arithmetic and science. On the high school level—there are few satisfactory studies—the differences seem very slight, and on the college level they apparently disappear. The most satisfactory investigation on the college level is that of Spoerl, who equated two groups of Freshmen—bilingual and monoglot—as to age, sex, socio-economic status and intelligence, and compared their performances on the Nelson-Denny Reading and the Purdue English Placement tests, in addition to examining their school grades and progress. Dr. Spoerl (260) concludes her study with the following statement:

"Summarizing the conclusions based on the various tests which were administered, it becomes clear that at least at the college level, there are no continuing effects which stem from a bilingual childhood and which show themselves in the academic records, vocational choices or English ability of bilingual students. Neither does bilinguality seem to have a significant effect on the performance of college age students on a verbal test of intelligence. If there were a bilingual handicap in their childhood, it has certainly become stabilized by the first year of college."

It must be borne in mind that in the studies regarding school achievement, especially those made in the United States, the language situation is such that the student is in the process of losing one language—his vernacular, and of learning another—the dominant language. A truly bilingual situation where the two languages are on equal footing is not encountered. Fortunately one study exists, that reported by Professor Bovet (23), where the latter situation obtains. M. E. T. Logie, the director of a school in the Union of South Africa, by special permission from his government, conducted an experiment in his school as follows. The pupils in his school were given bilingual instruction, the same lesson being taught in Afrikaans, and then recited in English, or vice-versa; the same teacher taught the subject in both languages without favoring either one or the other. It was also seen to that the children in playing games were mixed rather than divided into linguistic groups. The affective as well as the purely language learning factors were therefore constant for the two language groups. After four years of this experience the children were tested as to their knowledge of the mother tongue and of the second language, both, also in arithmetic (this subject being selected as a test for logical thinking), and in geography. The results of these tests were compared with the results of the same tests taken by pupils in unilingual English and Afrikaans schools. On none of the tests were the bilinguals shown to be inferior to their unilingual contemporaries. This experiment, more crucial than any others, shows that bilingualism per se need not be a cause for school retardation even in the elementary school. . . .

Bilingualism in Relation to Personal and Social Adjustment

In most bilingual situations the two languages involved do not carry equal social prestige; one of the languages is usually more dominant, carries greater social approval, is the representative of the "superior" culture. This situation obtains especially in countries of immigration and colonization. The question arises whether in such situations the bilingual person does not suffer from a sense of inferiority or inadequacy, whether or not he is socially frustrated, how well he is able to accept himself and his social group, how securely anchored he is in the two cultures represented by the two languages.

There are many speculative claims but little experimental evidence. A study by Darsie using teachers' ratings as measures of pupil adjustment finds the Japanese children more stable emotionally than the American children in the same schools. Pintner and Arsenian report zero correlation between degree of bilingualism as measured by the Hoffman Scale and school adjustment as measured by the Pupil Portraits Test. The population in this study consisted of 469 native-born Jewish bilingual pupils of the 6th and 7th grades in a New York City public school.

The most noteworthy study in this field is that of Dr. Spoerl (259). She equated two groups of college freshmen on mental ability, age, sex and socio-economic status and then studied intensively the personal and social adjustments of the bilingual and the monoglot groups using a number of good measuring and analytical devices of adjustment. These were: the Allport-Vernon Study of Values, the Bogardus Test of Social Distance (modified), the Kent-Rosanoff Association Test (modified), the Bell Adjustment Inventory, and the Morgan-Murray Thematic Apperception Test. Her conclusion of this study is worth quoting at length:

"Our conclusion, then, is that the emotional maladjustment of the bilingual student, insofar as it expresses itself in terms of reactions to social frustration, and particularly in terms of family disharmony, is the result of the culture conflict to which the native-born children of immigrants are subjected. But this culture conflict is complicated by the bilingual environment. Thus it is that bilingualism enters into the situation, not in its intra-personal aspects, but rather as a symbol of one of the environmental factors converging upon the second generation. Most of the emotional maladjustment of the bilingual student is environmentally determined, and is not the result of mental conflict engendered by the complexities of thinking or speaking in two languages. This is true of the social mal-adjustment, the lack of harmony in the home situation, and the lack of identification with the present environment (coupled with a rejection of the cultural background of the parents), all of which tend to characterize college students who are bilingual.

"One finding remains, however, which does not fit into this culture-conflict complex. That is the finding, primarily from the Association Test, of a significantly larger number of reactions on the part of bilingual students in terms of the act of speech to the word language; and in terms of the act of understanding to the word understand. These suggest that, although at the college level bilingualism, as such, is not affecting the student's expressive power (as evidenced by his control of English, his almost equal vocabulary, and his academic performance) there is in his mental organization a residual effect of the emotional turmoil and mental effort which must have been present in the early days of his school career when English was not, for him, a facile medium of expression."

The social psychology of bilingualism is most interesting as well as most important because of the following facts. Language is the medium of culture; in addition to being a code it is also a tradition; it embodies in itself the sufferings as well as the aspirations of a nation. As language represents one of the most potent forces of national existence, its encounter and struggle with another language calls forth an interplay of emotional forces which result in the pathos and drama of human life. Here we are dealing not merely with the acquisition of two languages in place of one, but with the complex psychological and sociological phenomena of a culture conflict. . . . (pp. 73-80).

It is clear from the above discussion that although for the otherwise well-advantaged child bilingualism need not be a handicap, in the majority of cases it does result in retardation in school and inferior performance on the verbal tests which are the mainstays in assessment of school-age children. Inasmuch as most bilingual children come from ethnic minority families, the conflict in cultural rôle identification discussed by Spoerl is undoubtedly a strong contributing factor to the poor school performance and adjustment of bilinguals revealed in statistical surveys, although this point is seldom explicitly recognized. It would, however, be almost impossible reliably to estimate the amount of deficit introduced by emotional as against intellectual obstacles in the development of ethnic bilingual children.

The necessity of learning two languages simultaneously must create additional obstacles to learning for a child, however effortless or successful the process may appear. The maintenance of a normal developmental curve, at least during the first years of school and before, is almost certainly accomplished in spite of, rather than because of, the additional language. In the first place, the sheer number of words and grammatical rules which must be learned to reach a certain level of proficiency in two languages is obviously nearly double that required to reach this level in only one. Smith (252), for example, tested the vocabularies of 30 Chinese children aged 3 to 6½ years born and raised in Hawaii, and found that whereas two-fifths of her sample exceeded the norms of monolingual children, when words of identical meaning were counted only once instead of twice only one-sixth exceeded the norm.

More important than the quantity of learning required is the complexity. In discussing the results of his study of monolingual and bilingual children in Belgium, Toussaint (274) pointed out that during the early years when children learn primarily in terms of concrete one-to-one associations between words and perceptual stimuli, the necessity for learning two words for each stimulus and remembering which word to use in a given context can present a very substantial obstacle. As Arsenian pointed out above, if there is consistency of persons or contexts for the use of each language, the choice and ambiguity are reduced, although not eliminated. However, the restriction of one language or the other to use only in certain contexts can result in poor performance when the child is forced to use one of his languages in a situation in which he usually uses the other. Keston and Jiminez (152) administered the Stanford-Binet to 50 bilingual Spanish-American fourth graders in Albuquerque, each being tested with both the regular English version and a Spanish translation, half receiving the English first and half the Spanish first. They found a correlation with school grades of .62 for the English test, but of only .11 for the Spanish. The authors concluded that, although Spanish was the mother tongue of these students, all their schooling had been in English and it was in school that they learned the kinds of skills required for performance on this test. This conclusion forces one to question the usually-heard opinion that bilinguals should not be tested in their second language lest they be unfairly handicapped. Unfortunately, however, the Spanish translation of the Stanford-Binet used in this study was one which had been prepared in Madrid and therefore employed Castillian Spanish, which differs substantially from the idiom spoken in the American Southwest. It is impossible to determine how much of the variability in the Spanish test scores bears on the conclusions reached by the authors and how much is a result of the use of an unfamiliar form of Spanish. This ingeniously designed study should be replicated using a more appropriate translation.

Two interesting but not immediately explicable findings emerged as a by-product of the study by Altus (4) of Santa Barbara County fourth graders referred to earlier in the discussion of ethnicity. Her sample included 31 bilingual children, primarily Spanish-American and lower class. Although their scores on the California Test of Mental Maturity were lower than those of their monolingual lower class schoolmates (language IQ 86.7, non-language IQ 93.8, versus 95.6 full-scale IQ for all lower class) their $IPSA$'s on the Davis-Eells Games were almost identical with the lower class mean (bilingual 97.7, lower class as a whole 97.9). Although this finding is not statistically significant, should it be duplicated in larger studies of more typically urban children it might lead to the suggestion that the Davis-Eells, whether or not it is "culture-fair" for children of all social classes, is "language-fair" for bilingual children. Should this prove to be true it would provide an unexpected but valuable addition to the tests useable for bilinguals; we say "unexpected" because the authors of the test specifically exclude its use on children in whose homes English is not the primary language. Secondly, it is interesting to note in this study that whereas the bilinguals averaged only a seven-point difference in their language and non-language scores, the total sample had a 10-point difference (97.2 versus 107.4), quite the reverse of what one would expect of a putatively linguistically handicapped subsample. Altus apparently overlooked this comparison (in fact suggesting that the 10-point difference might be due to the inclusion of the bilinguals) so we do not have information as to possible reasons for this paradox, nor can we determine whether it is statistically significant.

Bilingualism is of interest to us here because it is one of the important factors contributing to subcultural mental retardation. Studies of bilinguals are also important to us for the light they shed on general learning and use of language as this affects test and school performance of all retarded children, whether they know one language or several. The bilingual child is primarily handicapped because of his inadequate facility in one or both of his languages, and his problem therefore probably has much in common with that of any child whose language development is below the norm. This larger group would include children with a variety of speech and hearing defects, and probably also a large proportion of lower class children. Schulman and Havighurst (237), in one of the few studies of this aspect of language abilities, found in their research on 9th and 10th graders in a Midwestern community that vocabulary size correlated .46 with socioeconomic status, although there was considerable overlap between the status groups. Also, some of the children may themselves have been bilingual, but were tested only for English vocabulary.

In considering the significance of this correlation between vocabulary and social status it is important to bear in mind that the IQ also correlates with social status. This is of course true of IQ's based on verbal tests, and we have just noted that such tests are considered unfair for children with language handicaps, but it is also true of non-verbal test IQ's, albeit in somewhat less degree, as the University of Chicago studies cited earlier in this section have shown. Although there is no obvious and direct relationship between language handicaps and performance on non-verbal tests, there is increasing recognition that a child with retarded language development lacks the ability properly "to incorporate his environment, and increase progressively in the power to handle it" (McCandless, 177, p. 679). In other words, intellectual development is an important part of general learning of one's culture, and since language is the primary modality of such cultural learning, it readily follows that an impairment in language can be expected to affect all areas of intelligence.

Perhaps because this relationship between language and intelligence is so obvious very little research has been done to explore in more detail how the process operates. One early study by Robson (218) in 1931 is worth mentioning. He administered a word-association test to three different groups of children within the age range of 7 to 13: 16 children from a poor industrial district in England, selected by their teachers for backwardness, 18 English-speaking children from South Africa, similarly selected, and 20 institutionalized retarded children, selected for high intelligence. Sixty per cent of all these children failed to respond to the meanings of the words given at all, offering words which rhymed or sounded alike, or merely repeating the word or staying silent instead of producing a semantically related word. We do not know the degree to which the subjects were inhibited by the test situation itself or were otherwise prevented from best utilizing their abilities, but we can probably agree with Robson that at least some of the children reflected in their inadequacy in using words a "relative inability to interpret other people's behavior and consequently to share their experience" (p. 135).

A more recent study by Wellman and McCandless (283) makes quite clear the importance of language in developing the skills necessary for test performance. They administered the Stanford-Binet Form L and the Smith-Williams Vocabulary Test to 34 preschool children aged three to five in the fall and spring of one school year. They found that whereas those children who in the fall had a higher vocabulary age than mental age gained an average of 7.6 *IQ* points through the year, those whose vocabulary age was lower than their mental age gained an average of only 0.6 *IQ* points. We may conclude from these results that those children best equipped to profit from the stimulation and learning opportunities of preschool were those with the greatest language facility, although we must also bear in mind the possibility that in some cases the teachers may have been talking "over the heads" of all but the most linguistically adept children and thus not giving the others a fair learning opportunity.

These studies, although useful in supporting the commonly assumed relationship between language facility and intelligence, provide little insight into the more detailed mechanisms whereby the relationship is implemented. Much more research is needed in exploring the verbal tools necessary for the development of rational and abstract thinking, particularly in order that we may be better prepared to give the retarded child the essentials he may need to develop his intellectual skills in closer conformance with his true capacity.

E. RURAL-URBAN AND REGIONAL DIFFERENCES

A large number of studies are available which consistently show that persons, both children and adults, who live in cities are more "intelligent" than those who live in rural areas. These findings are based in general on three kinds of data: test results on school children, entrance tests for college students, and rejection rates for draftees.[18] Equally consistent results have been reported with respect to regional differences, particularly the analyses of intelligence test performance and rejection rates for mental deficiency of draftees in both World Wars. The outstanding work in this area is that of Ginzberg and Bray (87) on World War II and Korean War data; their book is discussed at some length in Section II and needs no additional consideration here. It may simply be observed that, in the United States at least, regional differences in intelligence correspond rather closely to regional differences in urbanization, and most of the conclusions we may reach regarding rural-urban differences can therefore be generalized to the regional level. It should be noted that in the South and Southwest, which showed the highest

---

[18]Typical studies are those of Hauch (104) on Silesian 12-year-olds from rural and industrial districts; Wheeler (289) on Tennessee mountain school children; Smith, (249, 250) on University of Kansas freshmen; Nelson (192) on State College of Washington freshmen; and Hyde and Kingsley (126) on draftees from the Boston area. Armstrong (10) compared the test performance of "rural" children from Bedford, N.Y., with children from New York City, matched for school grade and father's occupation, and found no difference; this unexpected outcome probably results from the fact that Bedford is an upper middle class suburban community, not rural in the usual sense of the word.

draftee rejection rates for mental deficiency, not only is a larger proportion of the population rural, but also there are proportionately fewer large cities, and those studies of rural-urban differences which have also taken into account the size of cities have shown a consistent correlation of this factor with test scores.[19]

Obviously the mere concentration of people in a limited area is not in itself enough to account for the increase in measured intelligence with urbanization. The explanations for this phenomenon which are generally advanced fall into three major categories: (1) the ability of cities, with a more concentrated tax base and more children available as students, to build better schools, attract better teachers, and assign students to classes all of whose members have approximately equal levels of performance; (2) "selective migration," by which is meant that the more capable people in a rural area or small town will be the ones most likely to have the resources, initiative, and motivation to improve further their status by moving to the city, leaving their duller fellows behind; and (3) the city, through the stimulation and competition induced by a larger number of interpersonal relationships, and through the wider range of experiences available, provides a better opportunity to develop the skills important for an intelligence test or in school—intellectually, emotionally, and in specific knowledge. Looked at in one way it might be said that the first of these explanations—better schools—is but one aspect of the generally superior intellectual opportunities of the city; however, schools reach only those who are brought up in the cities, whereas the other urban effects are at least theoretically operative at any age. Another reason for maintaining a distinction between school age children and adults in this context is well stated in the words of caution with which Lemkau, Tietze, and Cooper (166) introduce their data on mental deficiency in the Eastern Health District of Baltimore:

> The definition of mental deficiency was originally based upon social competency, but with the development of applied psychology, diagnosis has become more and more dependent upon the results of tests designed to evaluate the so-called intellectual functions of the personality. The rapid popularization of intelligence tests, based on the demonstration of their usefulness, especially in the field of education, has tended to make

---

[19]As was pointed out in Section II, the great majority of draftees rejected for "mental deficiency" would actually come under our designation of mentally retarded, many undoubtedly because of membership in a subcultural group, because those with identifiable neurological or other pathologies resulting in mental deficit are likely to be screened out on medical grounds before they come up for testing.

mental deficiency an inability to perform certain set tasks, rather than an inability to discharge the responsibilities of living in society.

This change in definition, from terms of social competency to terms of *IQ* or its equivalent, has extended beyond the instrument that made it possible. The tests of intelligence generally used in this country are not properly standardized for use with adults. Nevertheless, they are so used, and the results are directly compared with those secured from children of the age groups for which proper standardization has been made.

Persons who are now in school, or who have recently been in school, in large centers of population have almost all been tested, and mental deficiency, as the term is applied to this group, means, all too frequently, failure in tests. Social competency continues to be the basis of definition for most older adults, those who were out of school before the widespread use of testing. However, in the case of these older persons also, tests are often used to substantiate observation and to reduce the estimate to quantitative terms. This situation must be kept in mind constantly in evaluating statistics on mental deficiency (p. 278).

To this we need only add that their observations regarding older people apply in only slightly lesser degree to persons taught in small country schools, where there is little need for classifying large numbers of students by levels of ability and psychological services are often not available for this purpose even if the need were felt.

Many educators feel that more favorable opportunities exist for developing an effective curriculum in an urban as against a rural setting. The argument for this point of view runs as follows. Large schools with large numbers of students close at hand permit not merely separate classrooms and teachers for each grade, but often a division of the grades on the basis of the capability of the various students. The "four-track" system recently introduced in the Washington, D. C., public schools was accomplished essentially by reassignment of the available children and teachers; were it attempted in a country school with at best only one teacher available for the basic curriculum at each grade level such a system would require a substantial increase in staff. Experience in the District of Columbia and elsewhere has shown that this specialization of curriculum permits not only the gifted children to advance more rapidly, but also the slow ones. It also helps reduce the stigma often associated with special classes with their implication of a separation of the "subnormal" from the "normal" children. Another advantage lies in the opportunity to employ more teachers of specialized subjects such as music, shop, foreign languages, and the like. Extra-curricular activities can be organized and directed by persons trained in a variety of fields, and pupil personnel services are provided to help students with remediable handicaps. Furthermore, although the rapid growth in urban population has unquestionably created serious problems of overcrowding, it should be borne in mind that it has also resulted in the building of large numbers of new school buildings whose architecture and facilities are generally superior to the older country schools. All of these factors combine to afford the child better educational opportunities and at the same time to provide a more satisfying environment for teaching, thus helping to attract more and better teachers irrespective of salary differentials.

Rural schools also have more attendance problems. Bringing children in from a distance can be seriously impeded by weather and other factors which have little effect on city schools. In agricultural areas, particularly in the South, children are often taken out of school, even to the point of closing the schools, to help in the fields at certain seasons. Davis (60) found that in a state-accredited Negro school in the South, whereas children completing the eighth grade were supposed to have had 72 months of schooling, the children in this school averaged only 53.5 months. Their IQ's were generally low (range 55 to 105, median 78) and showed a significant positive correlation with the number of months of actual school attended.

The arguments favoring specialization and differentiation in the organization of necessarily large school systems are certainly persuasive. However, the small—even one-room—country schools also have their champions. Large schools can only judge success in the education of large numbers of students on an essentially statistical basis. This means in effect that they must rely primarily upon quantifiable measures closely related to the immediate curriculum objectives: school grades, promotions, and test results. As the data to be presented in the next section will attest, academic performance is not necessarily a reliable predictor of the ability to cope with the social, occupational, and other problems of life in our society. Through the more individualized teacher-student relationship of the small school, this broader preparation can often be realized more effectively. Furthermore, even a "platoon" system such as that mentioned above in the District of Columbia depends for its initial assignment of pupils largely on test results. Yet we know that even when predicting academic performance intelligence and achievement tests are far from being 100 per cent valid. Although a readiness to watch for and reassign students who appear to have been misplaced can compensate somewhat for these deficiencies, it can well be argued that the teacher in a small school, working continuously with her students as individuals, is better able to recognize their latent abilities and to perceive the steps necessary to bring these abilities to fuller expression. This individual work with children can be more rewarding to at least some of the kinds of people who enter the teaching profession, so that the superior qualifications of the teachers attracted by the inducements of city schools may be partially offset by the limitations imposed upon them through the standardization of curriculum and teaching techniques required in operating a large-scale educational facility. We do not know how many students benefit from this more intimate relationship with the teacher to the degree that they obtain a higher *IQ* than would otherwise have been the case, nor whether their numbers are sufficient to invalidate the explanation of rural-urban *IQ* differences in terms of the richer educational facilities in cities. We will discuss more fully in the next section the matter of preparation for broader life problems outside of the school and have mentioned the subject here only to indicate that even this seemingly certain explanation of rural-urban differences can be questioned.

The concept of selective migration, which accounts for rural-urban differences in intelligence by assuming that the brighter people leave the country and go to the cities, has also acquired a somewhat controversial flavor. This apparently results from a tendency to phrase the concept as a general law, applying to all situations. Actually, there is quite conclusive evidence that in some instances selective migration does take place, whereas in others it perhaps does not. Schmidt (236) followed up the graduates of a rural school near Berlin, and found that the people who had had the higher grades in school were the ones who generally gravitated toward the metropolis, while those ranking lower in grades stayed in the country. Brugger (31) found a similar tendency in four districts in Switzerland, but less pronounced due apparently to the smaller contrast in way of life between villages and cities in Switzerland; however, there was a marked preponderance of more gifted men (although not women) who emigrated out of the country. Husén (124) analysed the results of large-scale administration of a Swedish Army group intelligence test and found that migration from lower to higher population density areas was significantly more frequent among those with high test scores, and that the migrants generally had scores comparable to the average for the higher density area into which they moved. These tests were, however, administered at indeterminate periods after migration, and the new environments may have altered the subjects' test capabilities. Similarly Fairbank (70) compared a "normal" and a "subnormal" group 17 years after they were first studied in Baltimore and found that the normals, more frequently than the subnormals, had the initiative and resources to move to other parts of the city in search of more varied employment opportunities. Gist and Clark (89) conducted a carefully controlled follow-up of 2544 high school students from rural communities in Kansas. These people were tested at the time of their graduation from high school in 1922-23, and then in 1935 their places of residence were compared with their IQ's at graduation. There was a progressive increment in average intelligence among those resident in 1935 in each of four categories of cities graded by increasing size, the highest scorers living in metropolitan centers or emigrating out of the state entirely.

Evidence of this sort, pointing clearly to the operation of selective migration among some groups, was readily coupled with regional differences in Negro scores found on the Army Alpha and Beta tests of World War I and led to the conclusion that the urban centers of the North were draining off all the capable Negroes from the South. Klineberg (157) tested this hypothesis among Negro children who, with their parents, had moved to New York City from the Southern cities of Nashville, Birmingham, and Charleston during their school years. He compared their school records before moving with those of other children whose parents had not moved and found no significant differences, demonstrating that whatever the reasons which prompted some people to go North while others remained behind, these were not reflected in the school performance (and therefore presumably IQ) of their children. From these findings he concluded "that the Negro who leaves the South for the North is not on the average superior to the Negro who remains behind, and that the present superiority of the Northern over the Southern Negro may be explained by the more favorable environment, rather than selective migration" (p. 62). This conclusion, although very possibly correct, does not appear necessarily to follow from his data. The parents, not the children, were the ones who took the initiative in moving, and we do not have IQ's or any other measures of intelligence for them. To conclude that the movers were not superior to the non-movers we have to assume (a) that the children's school records reflected accurately what their IQ's would have been had they been tested, and (b) that the parents' IQ's are close correlates of those of their children. Both of these assumptions have some a priori validity, but taken together they introduce a sufficient number of unknowns to make Klineberg's rather sweeping conclusions appear somewhat tenuous. In addition, it should be noted that he studied only children who had come North from some of the largest of Southern cities; this was probably necessary in order to prevent the cost of data-collection from rising to prohibitive levels, but his sample was by the same token in no way representative of the total influx of Southern Negroes into New York City, for many come from rural areas in the South. The possibility therefore remains that among Southern Negroes the same trend obtains as demonstrated elsewhere—i.e., that migration is selective for higher intelligence from rural areas both to Nashville, Birmingham, etc., and to the North. We cannot say that this is so, but Klineberg's data do not demonstrate that it is not. To prove this point conclusively either way would probably require a very large scale survey and follow-up, whose cost would have to be weighed against the possible gain to be derived from having such knowledge. Whether or not the North is skimming the cream of Southern Negro society there is little or nothing anyone can or necessarily should do about it.

The important fact is that the Negroes, and particularly the Negro children, who arrive in the cities of the North are intellectually inferior to those born or long resident there, but with the passage of time, and in particular with continued attendance in Northern schools, this deficit is largely made up. In connection with the study discussed above, Klineberg also tested a number of children who had moved from the South into New York City schools and found that *IQ* showed a fairly high correlation with years of residence in New York. Before this McAlpin (176) and Long (170) had conducted similar studies with identical findings in the District of Columbia; Long also concluded that the *IQ* increase of his immigrants as compared to that of his controls who were born in Washington stabilized after about 8½ years of residence in the District of Columbia. Lee (163) replicated these studies in Philadelphia and reached comparable conclusions; his findings were more conclusive because he had available not only the length of residence in Philadelphia for each child, but also the results of tests administered at the time of first admission to the local schools. In this way he was able to appraise the actual improvement in the children rather than just knowing that the ones who had lived there longer tested higher. He had available, as did the earlier researchers, a control group of Philadelphia-born Negro children.

The rise in *IQ* of these Negro children who moved into Northern cities can fairly readily be explained on the basis of the schools available to them in the North, which were superior to those they had previously attended. The greater possibility for job advancement in return for good school grades undoubtedly also increased the motivation toward schooling for some. But it is probable also that living in these cities, particularly for those children who came from rural areas, provided specific experiences which increased their ability to cope with the sorts of problems posed by intelligence tests. Shephard (239) for example administered a battery of tests to two groups of children, matched for parental occupation, age, sex, and United States citizenship, from rural communities in Kansas and from New York City. He found the rural Kansas children significantly superior in mechanical ability and the urban New York children in verbal ability and speed. These differences doubtless reflect motivation as well as content of experience, but would appear to support his general conclusion that: "From the results of this study there is an indication that the common assumption that one regional group is intellectually superior or inferior to another is unjustified. Rather, the performance of the different groups should be evaluated in terms of the degree to which they possess specific traits and abilities" (p. 462). In connection with a larger study of social class and intelligence Havighurst and Janke (109) administered a similar battery of tests to 110 ten-year-olds in a Midwestern community with closely comparable results. Even though this was a relatively small community (10,000 population) those children classified as urban did better in all the tests than the rural children, with the exception that the rural boys were superior in mechanical ability. The mechanical skills (measured by the Minnesota Mechanical Assembly Test) displayed by the rural children in both these studies undoubtedly were acquired through experience with farm equipment.

In a somewhat similar earlier study, Jones, Conrad, and Blanchard (138) found that a group of rural New England children, although performing much lower on the Stanford-Binet than a comparison group of gifted urban children, surpassed the urban group when given a special formboard test which involved deliberately rural content. Although it can justifiably be said that the special test was biased in favor of the rural children in this case, it should be borne in mind that the majority of the children in the standardization populations for most intelligence tests are drawn from urban areas. Since we know that urban and rural children perform differently, establishing test norms in this way constitutes a bias in favor of the urban child. We must constantly bear in mind that the Stanford-Binet and other standard tests of intelligence measure only one special set of skills. As with the mechanically gifted farm boys, we are seeing here children who, even though the commonly accepted criterion of the Stanford-Binet would classify them as *below* average in "intelligence," can sit down in a testing situation and use their minds with *above* average effectiveness with respect to a different, but for them highly relevant, set of skills.

The study of rural-urban differences, and particularly of children and adults who leave the country and arrive in cities with an apparent intellectual deficit, has great research promise for the exploration of subcultural mental retardation. We now know that many of these people are, in terms of the usual test criteria, retarded on their arrival, even though seldom very severely, and that they appear rather consistently to improve intellectually to a level of parity with their new neighbors. Careful longitudinal studies, starting with a precise evaluation of the areas in which their deficits lie—knowledge, mental skills, and motivations—and following on with study of the processes whereby these deficits are remedied, could tell us much we do not know about techniques and emphases to use in corrective education. Not only is this a readily available population for study, but it is one in which many of the variables which normally plague designers of research in subcultural groups are already controlled. Whether we are dealing with Southern Negroes who move to Harlem or the children of white farmers who move to the Bronx, we are studying people who blend with their neighbors in appearance and language—even though at first they may differ a little in dress or accent. They also share the values and knowledge of a single basic culture and are handicapped only in certain segments of experience. For the very reason that their problems are not so all-encompassing, we cannot apply our findings directly to the education of, for example, Puerto Ricans. But we can chart out some facts and generate hypotheses in an area which has thus far scarcely been touched. We are able to identify a large array of subcultural groups whose members are handicapped on intelligence tests and in other ways often to the point of being considered mentally retarded, but we can say very little about the actual processes whereby these handicaps are either created or corrected. The migrants who constantly flow into the cities appear to provide one excellent and relatively simple group upon which to begin.

F. Sex Differences

There is little that can be said regarding differential performance of boys and girls on present day intelligence tests, for it is customary in developing and standardizing these tests to eliminate those items upon which the two sexes consistently perform differently. Although statistically significant sex differences have from time to time been reported within normal populations, particularly when the analysis gets down to subtests or individual items, the findings do not conform to a consistent pattern. If enough groups are tested it can be expected by chance alone that in some cases differences will be found which appear significant within the data for a single group. Insofar as chance is not operative, we can only conclude that the test-makers have failed in their intention to eliminate items to which boys and girls respond differently.

The effort to avoid discrimination between the performance of the two sexes can be understood historically, particularly in the United States, by recollecting the era of uncritical enthusiasm for intelligence tests when they were felt to tap in each individual his inherent and unchanging mental capacity. It was at this time that Terman undertook his revision of the tests devised by Binet and Simon, with little evident concern over the doubts which plagued the original authors as to what they were really measuring. Within Terman's premises, a test which differentiated consistently between the sexes would thereby be demonstrating the inherent inferiority of one sex to the other, a wholly unacceptable proposition. Since that time it has become widely recognized that the *IQ* is not constant over time and therefore cannot be measuring purely inborn characteristics, that it is affected among other things by a host of cultural and emotional factors, that it is intimately related to academic experience, and that people can therefore perform differently on intelligence tests without necessarily being better or worse in the absolute sense envisaged by Terman. However, despite this sweeping reorientation to the meaning of intelligence tests psychologists continue to adhere closely to the precepts of test construction laid down in the original Stanford revision of the Binet test.

Thus there is still not available any test of over-all "intelligence" which will permit except accidentally of differential performance by the two sexes, although it is readily apparent that boys and girls of normal upbringing in our society have different sorts of experiences and we have different expectations of them, even in the schools. It is not likely that an item would be dropped from a mechanical assembly test because girls performed less well on it than boys, yet the intelligence test-constructors will not permit us to discover whether there are important differences we should know about in the intellectual functioning of the two sexes. No rationale has been offered for this ever since Terman simply stated that he eliminated tests which would be "relatively less fair to one sex than the other," seeing no need for further justification at the time. As Pastore (203) observed, would it not have been equally appropriate to eliminate items on which there was differential performance by Negro and white children? Davis and Havighurst (59) show some exasperation over Terman's procedure:

> How can a mental test be "less fair" to boys than to girls? It involves

no organic sexual differences, so far as we know. There is here no question, apparently, of different cortical structure, or glandular secretion. Clearly, then, if a question is unfair to boys, as compared to girls, it must be that their social experience is different, on the average. Their training as males or females in the family, school, and play group differs, and therefore the amount of experience they have had with various types of mental problems differs. Their social motivation, as boys or girls, to learn how to solve such problems must also differ. Terman certainly did not believe that girls were genetically superior to boys in mentality, or vice versa.

Thus, upon what must have been a purely social and cultural basis, that is, upon the conviction that any problem was "less fair" if either sex proved "superior" to the other sex in solving it, Terman eliminated all such problems from his test.

Upon exactly the same principle as Terman used to control sex bias in tests, one might throw out all problems in which any socio-economic group proves superior. . . .

The continuing attempt of test makers to obscure differences in performance by boys and girls runs counter to the constant and conscious effort of parents, teachers, and society at large to instill in growing children the very different attitudes, motivations, and behaviors expected of each sex. It is of course clear that the philosophy of test construction, tied as it now is to the criterion of school performance, reflects little sophistication in the realities of our culture as a whole; but even if one were willing to accept a limitation on the applicability of intelligence tests strictly to school use this would not justify the obliteration of sex differences. Certainly by high school, and in reality well before, the curricula and educational expectations of boys and girls are differentiated. It follows that if they are to learn different things they will need to draw upon different kinds of intellectual skills in order to do so, and a test which fails deliberately to discriminate between these skills must necessarily suffer a concomitant reduction in predictive accuracy. Furthermore, educational achievement as represented for example by a high school diploma is viewed by most teachers as more crucial for a boy than for a girl, since every boy must be prepared to get a job—preferably, in the teachers' value system, a white-collar job—whereas this is a matter of individual choice for girls. Thus, whether it is explicitly recognized or not, the standards of performance and the expectations a boy must meet tend to be higher than those applied to girls.

If the elimination of sex difference discrimination from intelligence tests makes little sense with respect to "normal" children, it represents a grave shortcoming when the tests are applied to retarded boys and girls. Here the sex differences are striking, important, and little understood. The Onondaga County survey (193) found, as have earlier studies, that roughly twice as many boys are referred for mental subnormality as girls.[20] Lemkau (165) has suggested that this may be "due primarily to two characteristics of the male that are well recognized: first, his retardation in comparison with the female as regards communication skills and second, his greater aggressiveness that tends to lead to lower grades in deportment, reflecting his greater capacity to 'make trouble' and thus have his defect discovered in the course of a fundamentally unrelated investigation. These two factors are not themselves uncorrelated, as any remedial reading teacher can testify."

Other explanations than those offered by Lemkau are equally plausible. The higher expectation of boys discussed above is probably at least partially

---

[20] The effect of possible differences in the incidence of organic disorders leading to mental deficiency is not clear. In the Onondaga survey, the sex ratio in referrals below the age of five with a clear organic diagnosis showed a marked preponderance of boys, but the prevalence of organic cases over five years was about equal for both sexes. One can speculate as to the significance of these differences, but for the purposes of this report it is probably sufficient to note that organic cases contributed only about one-seventh of the total referrals in Onondaga County. Their numbers would thus not be enough materially to affect the striking two-to-one ratio found in the total sample. Our discussion here is therefore concerned essentially with sex differences in referrals for nonorganic mental retardation.

(We feel it important to point out parenthetically that this particular problem of sex differences is but one aspect of the larger problem of sex differences in the prevalence of psychopathological or problem conditions. In the course of our survey we have come across numerous conditions and problems in which the prevalence among boys is significantly greater than among girls. As we shall see in Section IX, the prevalence of infantile autism and idiot savant among boys is clearly larger than among girls. Reading problems, stuttering, behavior problems, and childhood schizophrenia are other instances where the prevalence among boys is greater than among girls. In fact, it is our impression that up until puberty it is extremely difficult to find a pathological or problem condition in which the incidence among girls is greater than among boys. It would appear to us to be too simple to interpret all of these findings as reflecting a single factor or variable. Among the different variables operating to produce these sex differences we would suggest that special emphasis be given to the cultural one, i.e., boys and girls are born into a culture in which there are marked differences in the kinds of expectations and roles associated with the two sexes. One has only to spend a little time in the school culture, for example, to realize that there are boys' and girls' subcultures which are differentially responded to by the "adult culture." What is of great importance is the effect on the boy and girl of participating in their subculture and the degree to which such participation prepares them for certain important situations, e.g., school performance. The subculture of boys does not emphasize good school performance, while that of girls seems to attach more value both to grades and behavior.)

responsible, for more concern is likely to be shown toward the possible academic failure of a boy than a girl, and he will therefore probably be referred for attention—and tested—more consistently than in the case of girls. Also, as we shall see in the next chapter, in some lower class groups a boy who does well in school is considered to be trying to curry favor with the teacher and is therefore rejected by his group, whereas this stricture does not appear to apply to girls. Two important things are to be observed about these and other possible explanations for the greater number of boys than girls who are found in the higher categories of subnormality. One is that they are speculative. We do not know, and given the present nature of intelligence tests it is hard to see how we can know, what significance we should attribute to the kinds of test performance characteristic of retarded boys as against retarded girls.

The other is that we also do not really know whether the true incidence of mental retardation of boys and girls is different—i.e., whether screening methods and agreed-upon psychometric or other criteria would reveal the differences discussed above. The data we have, of which those derived from the Onondaga County survey are the latest and best, are concerned with cases reported or referred by a variety of agencies. We thus do not have data on how many children are actually retarded, but rather upon those about whose retardation someone saw fit to take action of one sort or another, thus bringing cases to attention.[21] This is an unfortunate situation from several viewpoints, but at the same time may not be as serious as it would appear. Mental retardation is a social and cultural phenomenon as well as a medical and psychological diagnosis. Children are identified as retarded in terms of culturally defined criteria, and it is equally as important to know about the characteristics of this total group which has been rejected by society as it is to isolate those who fail to meet a given single criterion such as obtaining an IQ over 80. We might find that there are no significant sex differences in the distribution of IQ throughout the lower end of the range and we would still be concerned with knowing what factors differentiate the larger group of boys who are socially designated as retarded from the smaller group of

---

[21]Jastak, whose contributions to the theory of intelligence are discussed in Section IV, undertook such a survey of the population of the State of Delaware with the objective of determining not only the prevalence but the nature and significance of retardation; unfortunately the analysis and publication of his material appears to be in abeyance, thus depriving us of a very rich source of factual information as well as the exploration of a series of highly challenging hypotheses. A preliminary report (Jastak and Whiteman, 133) does not deal with sex differences.

girls. The *IQ* simply does not provide a sufficient basis for guaging the numerical extent or nature of the retarded population as it presently exists, but a test of adequate sensitivity *should* be able to discriminate between various possible forms of intellectual deficit which have contributed to the retarded designation.

If the items on tests which differentiate between the sexes were not so systematically discarded, patterns would emerge from the intelligence test performance of normal children which we could say were characteristic of the respective sex rôles. We would then have some standard against which to compare the test profiles of retarded boys and girls and thus perhaps obtain some idea whether we should look first at intellectual, emotional, or cultural aspects of the problem in search of a cause and therefore correction and prevention. However, the existing tests will not permit of this, nor can they provide a test of any hypotheses our speculations might generate.

G. CULTURE

Everything we have said thus far in this chapter could readily be subsumed under the heading "Culture" in its usually accepted meaning. Intelligence tests measure—and attempt to predict—learning, yet learning and culture are but two sides of a single coin: culture provides the content and technique of learning, and learning is the medium for both continuity and change in culture. With respect to intelligence testing and measurement Davis and Havighurst (59, p. 301) have said: "The crucial problem raised by the attempt to compare scientifically the capacity of any two individuals to learn is that of finding situations with which the two individuals have had equal experience"—whether these two individuals are identical twins or live on different continents. And again (p. 303): "The sociologist and social anthropologist have been convinced, through studies of a great many human societies, that cultural learning runs through nearly all the 'mental' behavior of human beings. Social anthropologists therefore strongly doubt that cultural behavior can be eliminated from any intelligence-test response."

Despite our obvious agreement with this point of view we have elected thus far to treat social class, language, and so forth separately for two reasons. One is that it has been traditional to do so and one finds the literature naturally falling into one category or another. The failure thus implied to perceive that each of these factors is but part of a total cultural context, whose effects are interrelated and often cumulative, has been responsible, we feel, for much of the futile repetitiveness and sterility of research in this area.

Nevertheless by confining ourselves here to a review of existing research we have had little choice. The second reason is that by attempting to carry each line of attack as far as we can toward an adequate conclusion we have, we hope, demonstrated the necessity—even the inevitability—of taking into account the total cultural context of even such a specialized form of activity as performance on an intelligence test. The effects of bilingualism, for example, cannot be assessed merely in terms of the psychological problem of learning two languages, but must also take into account conflicts in cultural identification, values associated with the two cultures and languages, and often also minority group membership. Similarly social class has its correlates in level and kind of aspiration, in kinds of thinking which are encouraged or discouraged, in ethnicity, in language facility and in a host of other factors in addition to the primary fact of differing levels of economic resource.

We have until now been concerned principally with the results of testing done within our own cultural setting. Therefore the differences we have discovered should properly be called subcultural, because the people who have been sorted out for study into various kinds of groupings share in common much of our total cultural system. Viewed against the shared totality of their cultural experience, the differences between them appear minor when compared with, for example, the difference between any one of them and an Eskimo north of the Arctic Circle or a Bushman on the Kalahari Desert of Southwest Africa. Nevertheless these relatively minor differences are enough to affect test scores significantly and therefore are of importance to us.

As we now turn to examine studies done in cultures strikingly different from our own we find researchers sharing, explicitly or implicitly, the common goal of determining the degree to which various sorts of tests really measure intelligence in the abstract as against the more circumscribed array of skills considered important in our own culture. Even this, however, is an objective culturally bound by our own value systems. As we shall see in the next section not all peoples place a high valuation on intelligence, and certainly not on the "intelligence" we measure with tests, nor are persons mentally subnormal even by local standards necessarily ostracized or otherwise penalized. However, even though other peoples may not be concerned with the minor variations in IQ which cause so much distress in our own society, their test performance, in light of their radically different cultural backgrounds, may be able to give us some additional perspective on our own smaller subcultural differences.

But here again a word of caution is in order. Motivation is an important factor in any sort of performance, and it has been given substantial—although even then probably not adequate—attention in the literature of psychometric testing of retarded as well as normal children. But this attention has been focused primarily on motivation as it is specific to the testing situation: competitiveness and the desire to excel, anxieties over failure, the valuation of speed, etc. There has been little consideration of the broader implications of the label of retardation in our society. McCandless (177, p. 684) makes a useful distinction in discussing the development of subcultural mental retardation:

> First, the environment from which the subcultural mentally defective person comes is one providing minimal opportunity for the learning of the skills which are subsumed under the term intelligence.
>
> Second, the environment from which the subcultural mentally defective person comes is one in which he has maximum opportunity to learn "self-defeating" techniques—e.g., loosely defined, expectancies of failure, absolute as opposed to relative thinking, concrete as opposed to abstract thinking, belief in his essential worthlessness, etc.

Although we might argue that the kinds of thinking referred to under the second heading more properly belong with the skills referred to under the first, we find here clearly stated the separate aspects of the problem: on the one hand the different strictly intellectual learning processes characteristic of various subcultures, and on the other the more pervasive personality disorganization felt by retarded persons generally in our society. We can compare people who obtain low test scores in our society with those in another culture on the first dimension, but not necessarily on the second.

Most testing of non-European peoples has been done with performance tests of one sort or another. Although, as we have seen, many researchers have failed to perceive the handicap introduced by verbal intelligence tests when administered to subcultural groups in our own society, the language barrier is so obvious among less civilized peoples that few attempts have been made to utilize tests which require any language skills outside of the oral instructions. Two studies can be mentioned briefly to document the fairly self-evident implications of the use of verbal tests. Sparling (256) administered the Stanford-Binet and the Porteus Maze to 32 Indian children aged 8 to 17 institutionalized in Canada; their mean Binet IQ was 75 (range 54-101) while the Porteus Maze mean was 108 (82-142), suggesting that if a non-verbal test had been used initially none of them might have been institutionalized. Rohrer (219) in contrast administered the Goodenough Draw-a-

Man Test and the Otis Test of Mental Abilities to Osage Indians in Oklahoma and found their scores at or above the norms for the tests; many Osage, through oil revenues, have fared very well economically and enjoy equal opportunities with their white neighbors. Thus we see that American Indians are not necessarily handicapped at all in test performance if they are fully acculturated, but seriously handicapped on verbal tests if they have been living the life of Indians.

Turning to performance tests, one of the most searching and thoughtful studies on record, and also one of the few wherein the subjects had had practically no experience with Western schooling, was completed over 20 years ago by Nissen, Machover, and Kinder (195). They administered a variety of performance tests to 50 children of the Sousou tribe in French Guinea, a part of French West Africa from which many of the slaves were taken who contributed to the Negro population of the United States and the Caribbean. There were 42 boys and 8 girls, aged 5 to 14. As might be expected the Sousou performed consistently below the norms, but this was more evident on some tests than on others.

> Without attempting a thorough-going analysis of the functions underlying the tests, we may say broadly that tests which have pictorially representative content, which involve symbolic material, and which require combinative activity based on the perception of part-whole relationships, produced the poorest results when applied to our subjects; these tests include the Digit Symbol, the Ship Test, the Manikin and Feature Profile and the Healy 'A.' At the other extreme, tests which involve imitative functions, immediate memory, perception and retention of visuo-kinaesthetic cues and which, besides, are practically without representative content, yielded the best results; these tests were the Cube Imitation, Adaptation Board, Pyramid, and Paper Folding. . . .
>
> When the results on the separate tests are compared with each other . . . it is noted that as the content and activities involved in each correspond more to specialized experience in a civilized environment, they provide greater difficulties for our culturally primitive subjects. Conversely, as the content and activities involved in each correspond more to the common matrix of universal experience they provide less difficulty for our subjects. Without implying that the elements of native capacity underlying any of the tests have received optimal developmental stimulation in our subjects, we may therefore suggest that in general the higher the median score achieved on a test and the greater the variability of the scores, the less have the capacities underlying that test been restricted by the absence, in the environment of our subjects, of the features present in the environment of the standardization groups. The order of the tests

in the list, in addition to revealing any unevenness of native capacity, would be indicative to a considerable extent of the relative degree to which the development of the capacities underlying each of the tests has been specifically affected by the differences between the West African and American environments. The tests would naturally follow the same order as to appropriateness for measuring primitive capacities.

The marked differences among the separate tests with respect to the effectiveness with which they were handled by our group of subjects as a whole appears to us to have implications of fundamental importance for the use and interpretation of tests in clinical practice. In the application of the tests of this series to mental defectives we do not find the consistent discrepancies which are a part of the results of this study. It is particularly impressive, therefore, that a series of tests, co-extensive in normative range as standardized and clinically regarded as being comparable, should have yielded such disparate results when applied to our culturally primitive subjects whose environmental homogeneity is probably not exceeded anywhere. This is not a result of special abilities or disabilities for individual subjects; the unevenness which the results show is distinctly a group phenomenon. While from a practical clinical standpoint, where the disposition of individual cases is an ever-present preoccupation, tests may be regarded as being normatively comparable, our results suggest that for more fundamental interpretations a more analytical approach is required. Rather than the multiplication of statistical data, we feel the need of investigations directed toward the phenomenological aspects of tests and their relation to training, culture, environment and race (pp. 338-339).

In the interpretation of any data in the field of racial psychology, it is essential to recognize the limitations inherent in the standards of comparison which are used. Even though proficiency in the tests used may be a significant measure of the abilities required by the highly specialized culture and environment of the standardization groups, we are not warranted in assuming that it would be equally a measure of abilities encouraged by or suited to the quite different culture and environment of our subjects. The selection of features of our own civilization as a basis for measuring the inferiority of individuals of other cultures is obviously arbitrary and artificial. Our particular culture may, and probably does, emphasize certain aspects of "intelligence" to the neglect of other aspects. Furthermore, we have, as yet, no adequate measures of intensity of feeling or of the capacity for experiencing and expressing emotion; we have no standards for study of individual or social integrity. The tests which we have used take no account of these matters, and the civilization out of which the tests have developed seems to consider them relatively unimportant. It is conceivable that under a culture which would place greater emphasis upon affective experience, there might be

> correspondingly less concern with matters which seem to us of major importance (p. 352).

Particularly significant in this analysis is the realization that tests can be biased not merely by their content, but also by the perceptual and rational tasks required, some of which may involve processes of a kind not familiar within the culture—in this case those requiring "combinative activity based on the perception of part-whole relationships." The present writers found a very similar difficulty in their study of the natives of Truk, an island group in the Western Pacific (Gladwin and Sarason, 90). This study will be discussed more fully in the next section, for it attempted among other things to set "intelligence" within the broader framework of affect and personality in the manner urged by Nissen, Machover, and Kinder, but our experience with a performance test is worth noting here:

> The Kohs Block Designs, normally administered as part of the Arthur Point Scale battery, were selected for use on Truk with the hope that this test which requires no explicit verbalization might provide some measure of intelligence comparable to American standards. The test consists in arranging a number of identical colored blocks in patterns to conform to a series of increasingly difficult designs printed on small cards; the designs are geometric and linear and thus conformed in general to the types of design found in published works on Trukese material culture prior to leaving for the field. Unfortunately, it soon became evident that performance on this test correlated fairly closely with the amount of schooling to which each subject had been exposed. As the ability to see the content of photographs and other pictures appeared also to be a function of experience gained in school, it was concluded that the indigenous training of the Trukese leaves them poorly prepared to discern the field and ground relationships upon which successful performance in this test rests. Scoring of the test results along conventional lines, which would give data comparable to those for which the test was standardized in the United States, would in the case of the Trukese present a picture of doubtful significance. For this reason although the test was administered to all subjects in the interests of conformity no attempt will be made here to present an analysis of the results (p. 213).

Although not directly relevant to intelligence testing, it is interesting to note that in interpreting the protocols of the Bender-Gestalt (a psychodiagnostic test dependent upon the perception of spatial and field-and-ground relationships) Dr. Bender (in Joseph and Murray, 139, p. 142) found that among the natives of Saipan to the north of Truk, "Gestalt patterns corresponding to those found in confusional states appear to represent norms."

She apparently did not realize that the diagnostic norms of the test were vitiated by the different perceptual modes of the Saipanese. Living in our own culture, with virtually universal and constant exposure to pictures—three-dimensional forms projected on a two-dimensional surface—it is difficult to comprehend the difficulty experienced by some people in reversing this projection to separate subject from background.

Klineberg (156), Steggerda (261), and others have attempted to set down systematically all the factors their experience in intercultural testing led them to believe need be controlled in order to assure a valid measure. These included the obvious variables of language and cultural content, and particularly the attitude toward speed of performance. Many researchers have found to their frustration that "beating the clock" is not necessarily rewarding to peoples in cultures other than our own. Klineberg, after administering the Pintner-Paterson performance tests to several groups of Indian and Negro children in the United States, concluded that "there is evidence that the superiority of white over Indian and Negro children in performance tests is largely, if not entirely, a superiority in scores for *time*. There is no superiority, and in some cases an inferiority, in the scores [of white children] for *accuracy* of performance." One can either disregard the time limitations on the ground that a person who is not trying for speed is not having his ability in this regard validly tested, or else take the position that all of the performance criteria of the test are essentially those valued in our own culture and the time criterion should therefore remain in force as a logical part of the whole.

Other factors mentioned are the ethnic identity and relative status of the test administrator, whether the testing is done in a native or foreign setting, whether chronological age (denominator in the IQ) can be determined with any accuracy, group versus individual performance as a function of cultural attitudes (Clements, 48), and the amount of exposure of the natives to Western culture and in particular schooling. A surprising number of researchers, presumably preoccupied with determining the intelligence correlates of "race," have failed to record or take into account the amount of schooling their subjects have had. When this variable is included, as for example in the extensive study of Arthur Point Scale performance by Havighurst and Hilkevitch (108) of 670 children from six different American Indian tribes, it appears that schooling materially affects test scores. The effects of schooling are not, however, confined merely to the content of test questions. Leighton and Kluckhohn (164) found that 23 Navaho children who had some schooling achieved a mean IQ on the Arthur Point Scale (a combination of several separate performance tests) of 102.5, whereas 41 completely un-schooled children averaged only 79.8. The authors concluded from this testing experience that "it would be incorrect to claim that schooling makes the children more intelligent: rather it helps them to mobilize their own ability so that they can do well on the Arthur test." Only in school do they have real experience with pencils and toys and "familiarity with being told by a strange white person to do an apparently senseless task" (p. 153).

Numerous efforts have been made to produce tests more appropriate for cross-cultural applications. These range from such minimal modifications as the direct translation of a standard test into a foreign language to the construction of completely new tests. The two best known instruments to emerge from the latter activity are the Porteus Maze Test and the Cattell Culture-Free Test. The Porteus Maze, as its name implies, consists in a series of mazes the subject is asked to trace through. Although this would appear to be a rather esoteric form of activity the test has actually been administered to a very large range of peoples with little apparent difficulty or misunderstanding of instructions. It was included in the Arthur Point Scale battery until its 1947 revision, and Porteus himself (208) has used the test widely among tribes in Africa, Australia, and Southern Asia, as well as in Hawaii and other less remote regions. Porteus, as well as others, administered a variety of other performance tests along with the mazes, with variable results.

The fact that some people score higher and others lower on the mazes than on other tests does not, however, of itself prove anything about the validity of the test. Each test presumably measures a particular aspect of mental ability which will be favored by the cultural milieu of one group and in-hibited by another. Thus we come back to the essential dilemma of cross-cultural testing: lacking any constant criterion of intelligence, or even in many cultures a high valuation of intellectual skill, there is nothing against which to validate any test, nor any means to assure that any given test "makes sense" to the people taking it within a particular culture. This is the same dilemma we saw with the Davis-Eells Games, but greatly magnified. If exposure to Western schooling improves performance on a test, we can probably conclude at least that experience exclusively in the native culture does not equip the individual to do the best he could with the tasks presented—the point made above by Leighton and Kluckhohn. Porteus is in effect saying the same thing when he remarks that "the effect of schooling on performance tests is not related to the test content but rather to the whole test situation" (p. 215). Nevertheless, the Porteus Maze Test appears to be one of the "easiest", perhaps for some reason the least strange, for people of other cultures to work with. Havighurst and Hilkevitch found this to be true in their study of American Indian children cited above, and its wide use in cross-cultural testing would suggest that others have had the same experience.

But this does not mean that the mazes provide the magic key to comparisons of the innate mental capacity of different cultural groups. Porteus was the first to admit this: "A warning should be given, and emphasized, that the Maze is by itself far from being a satisfactory measure of intelligence. All we can say of it is that the complex of qualities needed for its performance seem to be valuable in making adjustments to our kind of society" (p. 257). Elsewhere he suggests that these qualities may include "prudence, foresight, and mental alertness" (p. 234). Its virtue, then, lies in the fact that many sorts of people can feel comfortable working with it, rather than in freedom from cultural bias.

The Cattell Culture-Free Test has not been utilized nearly as widely as the Porteus Maze and we cannot therefore judge as readily the degree to which it presents a comprehensible format to people of widely different cultural backgrounds. The premise implied by its name that it is free of cultural bias, its results reflecting individual capabilities but not differences in cultural experience, appears completely insupportable. The test comprises combinations of geometric figures, devised and arranged in various ways for the following subtests: series relationships, classification (identifying odd items), first and second order relational matrices, sequence matrices, and mirror images. The designation of these tasks as "culture-free" rests upon a series of a priori assumptions or rationalizations which would strike any anthropologist as naïve, employing as they do a stereotype of "primitive" culture seemingly derived more from Longfellow's *Hiawatha* than from any adequate sampling of the ethnographic literature on the diversity of cultures of the world. We may comment on a few examples of such reasoning contained in Cattell's (39) description of the test. Working with series relationships "has natural interest and connects with natural happenings, e.g., growth" (p. 169). In the test series the geometric figures are of a constant size and develop through the addition of component parts, precisely the opposite of animal growth, and scarcely comparable to plant growth. Even if this were arranged in a fashion comparable to actual growth, the transition from a three-dimensional living being to black lines printed on a white two-dimensional sheet of paper would be difficult indeed for many "primitives." With regard to classification, Cattell says: "Picking out the odd item . . . has a certain intrinsic fascination, and resembles operations known to primitives (e.g., picking out the odd animal from the herd)" (p. 171). Only a very small fraction of the peoples of the world are herdsmen, and they generally know each animal individually rather than identifying them by color or other general class characteristics. Furthermore, anthropologists are often frustratingly aware that the bases for classification in other cultures—the determination of what kind of a difference makes a difference—can be very different from our own. To some people it may simply not make sense, for example, that a series of figures of the same size, shape, and blackness are to be considered "different" simply because of a few little lines within their borders are differently arranged. On mirror images: "The images are mirrored about a horizontal axis, in order that the universal experience of seeing reflections in a pool may be utilized in the instructions" (p. 175-176). Mirror-imaging in a pool requires that (a) the countryside have pools, (b) the body of water be small and protected enough to be completely calm, and (c) there be sufficient backdrop to provide subject for reflection. These conditions are far from universal. Aside from people who live by the constantly moving ocean, by swift rivers, or on the desert, one wonders how many children reared in our own cities have the opportunity to become familiar with this phenomenon.

The experience of psychologists does not encourage one to consider the Cattell test culture-free either. Eells (67) observes that:

> If by a "culture-free" intelligence test is meant one in which the "intelligence" of a child is somehow measured entirely apart from the impact of any cultural experiences on the child, the term is practically a nonsense term. . . . The very fact of requesting the children to work with material that looks meaningless to them introduces problems of culturally-determined work habits and attitudes (p. 292).

Similarly Anastasi and Cordova (6) administered the test to Puerto Rican children in Harlem (finding they performed consistently below the norms) and concluded:

> No test can be completely "culture free," or even "culture constant," since the content of any test will tend to favor one or another culture. The elimination of specific culturally limited information from a test is only a partial and superficial solution. Each culture stimulates the development of certain abilities and interests, and inhibits others. The resulting psychological differences will inevitably be reflected in test performance, as in any other behavior of individuals reared in diverse cultural settings. In the Cattell test, for example, the items consist almost exclusively of abstract geometric forms and patterns; and the test is, of course, of the paper-and-pencil variety (p. 6).

The Cattell test, then, is simply not culture free. It has been standardized against other widely-used intelligence tests in our own culture and could therefore presumably be used as a substitute for them, in our culture, but this would have to be viewed as a convenience, not an improvement. We have no basis whatever for believing that this test is any more fair for a subculturally retarded child than is any other.

In concluding this discussion we must seek to answer two questions: First, What validity, if any, is there in the administration of tests across cultural lines? And, more importantly, What have we learned from this survey of cross-cultural testing that is relevant to the problems of subcultural mental retardation?, since it is clear that in many of the non-European peoples where testing has been done they do not view retardation as a serious problem, or indeed a problem at all. With respect to validity, it is safe to say at present that no test exists which can approximate to a measure of inherent mental capacity irrespective of cultural experience, or which can measure differences of intelligence between individuals of a different culture than our own along dimensions they themselves consider most important. It is also extremely likely that such a test or tests will never be successfully constructed, if for no other reason than that the very concept of testing is itself at home in only a few cultures, principally our own.

Presumably one could design a test for a given culture which would be a measure of intelligence as it is viewed by the participants in the culture, and thus differentiate between individuals, but this would be unique to that particular culture. Furthermore, since many peoples do not have an abstract concept of intelligence as such, one would find that one person is considered very intelligent because of his knowledge of folktales, another because of his knowledge of animal trails, and yet another because he can stalk or paddle a canoe silently. It would be hard to test for all of these at once, and if one did so it would be likely that one would then find that the people who told the best folktales did so because they were related to the teacher of folktales and he would not pass them on to others, and so on. The more specific a test becomes the more likely it is that day-to-day performance will reveal as accurately as the test whether a person possesses the skill in question.

On the other hand if one is concerned with identifying in a native population those individuals who would be the best prospects for schooling or for administrative or commercial jobs, that is for rôles in which our cultural values become important, tests appropriate for our culture are appropriate for them also. But in testing for this purpose we still do not wish to have the test itself create any more artificial stumbling blocks than necessary, which leads us to consider which tests are intrinsically most easily handled by non-European peoples. As we have seen, performance tests are more readily comprehended than verbal tests by non-European people, and among these there is some reason to feel that the Porteus Maze is the least threatening of all. Whether it would be adequate to predict, for example, school success among persons who had had no schooling at all remains to be demonstrated, but the evidence would suggest that this test would be a good one to try first.

The parallel between testing of non-Europeans and of subculturally retarded children in our own society is obvious, and thus brings us to consideration of the second question above. Let us take lower class ethnic children as an example. We already know that many consistently do poorly on standard intelligence tests, and also frequently in school. This failure on tests probably results from a combination of specific test content which is unfamiliar, of the demand for kinds of thinking for which they are ill-prepared, and of their motivation and attitude toward tests and school. If we wish simply to reconfirm this finding any standard intelligence test will do. But if we wish to correct their deficiencies, and particularly to concentrate on those with the most promising prospects, we are facing the same problem suggested above with respect to the selection of likely candidates for schooling or jobs among a native population. Granted we want to discover their potential for performance along lines *we* value, whether they do or not, but in testing them we wish the test itself to present a minimum of obstacles. In other words we wish that as far as possible the child taking the test will not find it strange, anxiety-producing, or intellectually formidable and hence hopeless. We also want to reduce to a minimum the specific content which we already know he has not mastered because of his subcultural upbringing. For this reason, with retarded children as with non-Europeans, performance tests should be viewed as superior to verbal tests. This is already recognized by many psychologists.

But practically no research has been devoted to discovering which of the many available performance tests *appear* least threatening to such retarded children. Surely there must be a difference, as there seems to be among tests administered to non-European peoples, and it is of real importance to discover the causes of this difference. Many of us can still remember the chill of despair which descended when the first question on the final exam turned out to be on a topic we had failed to review. How then must a child, who realizes a test may make a major difference in his future, feel when he is faced with an array of tasks many of which appear impossible? If he sees and at once understands a task he believes he can tackle he will undoubtedly perform more nearly at his best level. This may be the greatest virtue of the Porteus Maze Test for non-Europeans, and this virtue could well prove equally lustrous in the field of subcultural mental retardation. The whole question of how much anxiety is generated in the perception by a retarded child of one test as against another, to which a review of cross-cultural testing has directed us, has been almost completely neglected. Attention has instead been devoted to the appropriateness of content (e.g., verbal versus performance tests) and to comparison of scores on tests and subtests as though each of these scores reflected capability irrespective of differential anxiety and attitudes.

In sum, then, if we accept the fact that we cannot at present materially change the culturally determined standards of adequate performance, and that most intelligence tests will do little more for the retarded child than to confirm existing suspicions of inadequacy, we must turn our attention to determining which test or tests best differentiate among retarded children between those who have more promise and those who have less, and in what directions the assets or liabilities of all of them lie. To do this we must find which tests interfere least with the expression of those abilities which the child does possess. Reverting to the Davis-Eells Games described earlier in this chapter, we might wonder in terms of our present discussion whether the reason why even this test appears to penalize some lower class children is not because of unfamiliar content but rather that the choices between alternate solutions are perhaps sufficiently close or ambiguous that they seem hopeless and induce despair in the child who is intellectually unprepared for this kind of problem. This is pure speculation, but represents a line of research which should hold great promise of reward. It is certainly clear that in its present state of development psychological testing of retarded children contributes little either to our theoretical knowledge of the problem or to their personal dilemmas. Perhaps if we explore the emotional impact of various tests as such on retarded children this situation will improve.

VII. INTELLIGENCE AND CULTURE

A. PROBLEM SOLVING ABILITY IN SUBCULTURAL GROUPS

In the preceding chapter we have considered at some length the cultural implications of performance on intelligence tests for persons at both normal and subnormal levels of mental functioning. Intelligence tests, however, are but one of several criteria usually employed in assessing the capabilities and prospects of both normal and subnormal persons in our own Western society, and are of minimal or no consequence in this regard in many other cultures. So in this chapter we will look at intellectual processes in a broader cultural framework, seeking to determine what factors influence the development of various modes of attacking problems, and what kinds and levels of problem-solving ability are acceptable and approved in different sorts of cultures. For this purpose we have to pay attention not merely to the mechanics of the thinking process and how it is learned, but also motivations and attitudes toward intellectual achievement as these affect both children and adults. With respect to problem-solving, we will be concerned with the levels of ability (both high and low) the culture can accept, and in addition with the question of what kinds of problems are considered worth solving at all, and in what ways it is allowable to seek solutions. In other words, whereas in the preceding section our focus on tests forced us to remain largely within the limits accepted in our middle class culture for definitions of intelligence, here we may take a broader view of what intelligence and normality mean to people living in other cultures and within subcultural groups in our own society. In attempting to apply the results of existing cross-cultural research—or of that which we might suggest should be done— to the problem of subnormality in our society, we must bear in mind that the solutions found in other cultures are not necessarily applicable to our own. The fact that in another society physical ability is more highly valued than mental, and that all but the most severely mentally deficient persons are therefore not particularly penalized or even noticeable, will not help us to find a place for similarly handicapped persons within the framework of rigid intellectual demands characteristic of our social environment. Nevertheless cross-cultural research can provide us with valuable insights and perspectives on our own problems, can illuminate the causes and perhaps some solutions for retardation within subcultural groups in our society, and can make an important contribution to our understanding of the etiology of identifiable pathological conditions the occurrence of which follows different patterns in other cultural settings.

Unfortunately there are practically no systematic studies of subnormal functioning in non-European cultures, so this chapter necessarily must offer more hunches and hypotheses than facts. This meager prospect is relieved by one outstanding exception, the study of the Hutterites by Eaton and Weil (65). Because it is virtually unique in its field and because it will provide a setting against which a number of problems may be raised in the remainder of this chapter, a fairly extensive review of those aspects of Eaton and Weil's study which bear on mental subnormality will provide an appropriate starting point.

The Hutterites form an autonomous cultural group with a theocratic social system residing in the north central United States and southern Canada. The following is a partial description of Hutterite culture:

> Hutterites believe in the communal ownership and control of all property. Like the Catholic orders, they live under economic communism in the classical and nonpolitical sense. Christ and the Bible are their ideological guides. Hutterites expect the community to assume a great deal of responsibility for each member. It is the community which buys clothing, doles out pocket money to each person, and pays a traffic ticket. No wages are paid. Each person is expected to work to the best of his ability. He eats his meals in the community dining room; the meals prepared by different women in rotation. If he is sick, the colony pays for all necessary care. In case of male death, widows and dependents have no financial worries; the loss of a breadwinner never means the loss of bread. The Hutterite way of life provides social security from the womb to the tomb. The religious creed of the group gives the members a further guarantee of security beyond the tomb. It promises absolute salvation to all who follow its precepts.
>
> The average Hutterite baby is delivered at home with a midwife in attendance and by "natural childbirth." Ultimately he will have between ten and eleven siblings. Children are generally wanted. Birth control practices are considered sinful; violations of this taboo are extremely rare. There is much communal co-operation in the care and education of the children. Infants are looked after by the mother for the first two months after birth. Then the mother must work part of each day in the community kitchen or garden, and an older girl, not necessarily a relative, helps out. After the age of two and a half, all healthy youngsters attend a communal kindergarten, where they stay most of the day. When they reach school age, they continue to spend many of their waking hours as a group, often under the supervision of a Hutterite religious teacher. He is responsible for much of the discipline outside of the hours when the children attend public school. Since both mother and father work for the colony at least part of each day, older siblings assume much of the care of their younger brothers and sisters.

In general, young people do a great deal of their growing up within a stable and closely-knit group of peers. The process of socialization and development depends greatly on "horizontal" identification with their peer group. Imagination and expectations are influenced considerably by other children of similar physical and mental development. The Hutterite nuclear family performs fewer functions than is general in American society, but there is strong emphasis on kinship ties in all social relations. The cultural pattern of growing up to become a Hutterite adult varies little from colony to colony, but as in every human group, there are important variations in the emotional relationships between parents and children. Two mothers may be equally determined to teach an eight-year-old daughter to be an efficient caretaker of the baby and resist the temptation to run off in the yard to play with boys of her age (who have no such similar work expectations to live up to); but where one mother may teach and discipline with patience, humor, and love, another may be vindictive and infantile, almost forgetful of the fact that an eight-year-old girl is still a child.

Virtually all Hutterites leave school on their fifteenth birthday, the day which marks their assignment to an adult job. Full membership status is acquired after baptism, between the ages of 18 and 25. Very few people remain single. Several decades ago parents and community leaders exerted some influence on the choice of marriage partners; at present, however, this is rare. After marriage men tend to acquire more prestige and are given more responsible work assignments. They are put in charge of the carpentry, welding shop, horses, pigs, or some other department of the large-scale community farm enterprise. Women begin to raise a family. They also acquire more prestige in the informal discussions which precede all formal community decisions. Women can retire from regular community chores at the age of 45; retirement for men takes place later. No one is pushed to exert himself much beyond what he himself regards to be his capacity. "Do the best you can" rather than a competitive slogan, is characteristic of the entire life cycle.

All Hutterites live in small and nearly self-sufficient settlements in which social relationships are generally informal or primary. They have an average of 92 members, with 16 family units. There is virtually no movement from one to another, except for women at marriage when, with few exceptions, they move to the husband's community. Most members of the sect spend their entire life within the same group. When a community grows too large through natural increase, new land is purchased and another village is built. Half the membership, chosen by lot, "swarm" to form a new "hive," as Hutterites like to refer to this process of binary fission. In each of the 93 settlements there are individual differences in prestige, which are largely a function of age, sex, and work. However, this society comes as close to being classless as any we know (pp. 27-30).

In the study the fields of sociology, anthropology, psychology, and psychiatry were represented. What is unusual in this study is that a serious attempt was made to screen the entire Hutterite population. "There was no sampling; the entire population of 8,542 persons living in a large geographical area, including parts of South Dakota, North Dakota, Manitoba, Alberta, and Montana, was screened for cases of mental disorders. The staff visited 84 of the 93 colonies in existence at the time the field work was completed; the remaining nine colonies were screened through a variety of informants" (p. 230). Before presenting the findings of this study it should be pointed out that Hutterites are "quick to recognize severe or moderate forms of mental deficiency" (p. 149).

Of the 51 cases diagnosed as mentally defective, 15 were severely defective, being unable to talk or walk normally and frequently unable to feed themselves. Four of these were mongoloid, two of basal ganglion disease, two of Little's disease, two of hydrocephalus, one of dwarfism, and four of epilepsy (cases of epilepsy not associated with mental deficiency were considered separately).[22]

Twenty of the 51 cases diagnosed as mentally defective were considered as moderately defective. "They could dress themselves . . . and could do simple work under supervision. . . . They could all qualify for admission to an institution for mental defectives" (p. 151). The remaining 16 patients were diagnosed as mildly defective. "They generally had some schooling and

---

[22]The data on mongolism presented by Eaton and Weil raise some intriguing questions. Although these were not explored by the authors, they illustrate the kinds of opportunities cross-cultural research in mental deficiency—i.e., in organic disorders which result in mental subnormality—can provide. The cases of mongolism reported for the Hutterites yield a prevalence rate not notably different from that found in our own culture, but the mothers of these children averaged 29 years of age at the time of delivery whereas in our culture the average age is 41. Investigators of this disorder have frequently emphasized both the advanced age of mothers and so-called reproductive exhaustion; in the case of the Hutterites the first of these explanations does not appear applicable. Should we then conclude that reproductive exhaustion is the more crucial etiological factor? Or are there perhaps differences in diet, care of mothers during pregnancy, protection against heat or cold, or any one of a multitude of other possible cultural factors we should investigate? We would not venture an answer. The point rather is that we have here a population similar (as far as we know) to ourselves in a biological sense yet differing with respect to a frequently cited aspect of mongolism and at the same time experiencing—much more uniformly than we—significantly different culturally determined relationships with their environment. The investigator with a hunch or hypothesis regarding external factors in the etiology of mongolism would do well to inquire whether it fits the situation of the Hutterites—or of any one of the hundreds of non-European cultures available for study—before accepting a proof or disproof based only on evidence from our own society.

knew the rudiments of reading and writing. They participated in the work of their colony and as adults had a regular work assignment which required little initiative or skill" (p. 151).

Although Eaton and Weil felt they had located virtually all the moderate and severe cases, they recognized that they had probably failed to enumerate many cases which should have been diagnosed as mildly defective. There were several lines of evidence pointing in this direction. In the first place, in those settlements personally visited by the staff in which all members were examined the rates were 10 per cent higher than in the population as a whole. Secondly, on a rating sheet filled out by the Hutterite religious teachers and also by the non-Hutterite public school teachers, the public school teachers rated more children as "dull" than did the Hutterite teachers—a finding which did not become known until the field work was over so that these children could not be diagnosed by the research staff. Finally, 70 per cent of all cases diagnosed were of severe and moderate degree—i.e., presumably reflecting pathology rather than learning deficits—whereas other populations studied have shown a much higher proportion of mild degree. We may therefore conclude that if intelligence tests or other diagnostic criteria utilized within our culture were applied to the Hutterite population more cases of mild deficit would probably be found, although we cannot predict with confidence what the prevalence rates would be. The explanation for this discrepancy is almost certain to be found in the observation by Eaton and Weil discussed below that the Hutterites show a high level of social acceptance of mentally deficient persons, and thus might be able to absorb into the normal population without special attention persons who could not meet the sharply drawn levels of tolerance characteristic of our culture. This point deserves some emphasis, not because we wish to raise doubts as to the prevalence rates cited by the authors of this study, although these have been criticized, but because it makes clear the hazards involved in attempting to determine epidemiological statistics in other cultures with regard to mental subnormality. A diagnosis of mental deficiency or retardation is compounded in our culture of medical, psychological, social, and cultural considerations (implicit or explicit), and a setting in which the relevance of any one of these is different will produce a different distribution of individuals identified as subnormal by the members of the society under study.

There is an unusual amount of in-group marrying among the Hutterites, a fact which led Eaton and Weil to ask: "Is there evidence to support the widely held assumption that inbreeding in a population necessarily leads to deterioration in the germ plasm of a population, which shows up in a high frequency of mental deficiency?" (p. 152). The apparently moderate rate of mental deficiency among the Hutterites is sufficient basis for answering this question in the negative. However, Eaton and Weil did not report geneologies for the diagnosed cases of mental deficiency. In addition, we do not have clinical descriptions which would allow for a possible etiological classification. Consequently, we cannot evaluate the specific rôle of genetic factors in those cases which are reported. Neither can we ascertain whether certain types of mental deficiency (e.g., phenylketonuria) occur at all among the Hutterites. At one point Eaton and Weil (p. 152) state: "None of the defective adult women could find a husband, but four men married and had families. They had a total of 22 children in 1951, two of whom were moderately defective." Since we do not know the clinical picture either of the fathers or the two defective offspring, we cannot evaluate whether two defective offspring (which could be only from one or two of the four fathers) is an inordinately low or an expected number. In a community that can be as comprehensively studied as the Hutterites much valuable data on genetic factors in mental deficiency could be obtained—perhaps obtained more quickly than through similar studies in our own culture.

An important finding of the study is that none of the defectives has ever been institutionalized, although the Hutterites are not opposed to commitment.[23]

There is considerable social acceptance of mentally defective persons among the Hutterites. Once a child's retardation is recognized, he is usually taken to a doctor to determine if there is any medical remedy for the condition. If there is none, the child and his limitations are accepted fatalistically. The community provides the family with additional help, if needed, to give optimum physical care to the youngster. In some families the mother will turn the child over to a sister or her mother, who may have more time and patience. Feelings of rejection by the parents exist, but they are usually well repressed. Other children are punished if they ridicule or take advantage of the afflicted child. Defectives who reach adult life are encouraged to work.

Defectives are not thought to be morally responsible for what they do. Those who engage in antisocial activities are punished only if they show sufficient insight to be affected by punishment. The community keeps them in line by watching them carefully. In two cases where mildly defective individuals violated a number of religious rules, the community "cancelled their baptism" rather than excommunicate them. By can-

---

[23]Even in the case of the psychoses institutionalization among the Hutterites is rare.

cellation of their baptism they were reduced to the status of children, who are thought to be incapable of sinning and therefore can attain salvation automatically (p. 157).

One cannot find a greater contrast between Hutterite and American culture than in regard to institutionalization: in our own culture available institutional facilities are overtaxed, more facilities are in the planning stage, and the end is not in sight.   More important than the staggering financial burden of the situation is the unhappy fact that institutionalization frequently raises as many psychological problems as it resolves (225).   These are problems which the Hutterites, as well as people of many other cultures, do not have to resolve.

Granting that Eaton and Weil, focusing primarily on the neuroses and psychoses rather than on mental deficiency, did not provide us with clinical descriptions, genealogical charts, or other appurtenances of an ideal study of subnormality, yet they have documented some of the most important of the cultural implications of mental retardation.   Particularly, it is clear that among the Hutterites—however they may appear to outsiders—the intellectual preparation provided within the culture is adequate to meet the needs of adult life within that setting.   Furthermore, the standards of adequacy set by the culture appear to be wide enough to embrace most people who function at anything but a pathologically deficient level, a fact strikingly reflected in the very small proportion (compared to our culture) of the population identified as subnormal which falls in the "slight deficiency" category.   Finally, the Hutterite society is so organized that it can take care of *all* persons, whatever their level of functioning, within itself without resort to special institutional or other devices.   In all these respects the Hutterites conform much more closely to the patterns characteristic of the non-European cultures of the world than they do to the standards of our own society which surrounds them.

A more concrete comparison is perhaps in order.   On the one hand we may cite the Trukese, studied by the present authors (Gladwin and Sarason, 90).   In this island society in the Pacific inadequacy in intellectual functioning is simply not viewed as a problem except for a scattering of obvious pathological cases; people of both sexes appear to fall readily into productive activities they are fully competent to perform.   Younger men, however, often seek employment at the American administrative center, sometimes at the garage where trucks and other vehicles are maintained under the supervision of Americans.

These jobs were eagerly sought after, under the impression that one could thus quickly learn the facility in working with machinery which the Trukese greatly admire in Americans. These youths were anxious to learn and within the limits of their understanding of English followed carefully the instructions they were given. But if what they had been taught did not work they were helpless. An American boy interested in mechanics is soon inculcated with the idea that every new piece of equipment is a challenge; if he does not know how it works, much less what may be wrong with it, he should take it apart, find out how it works, and then fix it. This approach was incomprehensible to the Trukese; even when given an old engine to practice on, their only solution to a problem was to ask someone who knew (p. 142).

Compare this with the following description:

She is cheerful, inclined to be quarrelsome, very active and restless, very affectionate, willing, and tries; is quick and excitable, fairly good-tempered. Learns a new occupation quickly, but requires a half-hour or twenty-four repetitions to learn four lines. Retains well what she has once learned. Needs close supervision. Is bold towards strangers, kind towards animals. Can run an electric sewing machine, cook, and do practically everything about the house. Has no noticeable defect. She is quick and observing, has a good memory, writes fairly, does excellent work in wood-carving and kindergarten, is excellent in imitation. Is a poor reader and poor at numbers. Does fine basketry and gardening. Spelling is poor; music is excellent; sewing excellent; excellent in entertainment work. Very fond of children and good in helping care for them. Has a good sense of order and cleanliness. Is sometimes very stubborn and obstinate. Is not always truthful and has been known to steal, although does not have a reputation for this. Is proud of her clothes. Likes pretty dresses and likes to help in other cottages, even to temporarily taking charge of a group (pp. 7-8).

This is Goddard's (92) description of Deborah Kallikak, a girl of 22 who had spent the last 14 years of her life in an institution, presented by him as a classic example of mental deficiency. It is clear that the Trukese, completely adequate intellectually when operating within their own culture, perform no better than Deborah when faced with a problem from our culture which calls for rational thinking and logical induction. It should also be borne in mind that a garage mechanic in our society is viewed as a laborer—albeit skilled—and not an intellectual or professional.

Why do the Trukese develop such a concrete and limited approach to problem-solving? The answer must, as in our own society, be sought in childhood, the period when a person learns from the preceding generation the multiple facets of the cultural heritage to which he is born. Childhood for a Trukese is a period of freedom with almost complete lack of supervision by adults except for occasional, and inconsistent, reprimands and punishments.   Children play in groups together and are given practically no systematic positive instruction.   They are viewed by adults as irresponsible and, being unable to do responsible and useful work, not worth instructing. The word for "child" in the Trukese language in fact means "does not comprehend."

This freedom and lack of supervision or direction, although it might be looked upon as utopian by a middle-class American child, provides a very poor climate in which to learn effectively and efficiently to cope with problems or to profit from the wisdom of past experience contained in the culturally defined solutions to such problems.   In this connection we can recall the differences in amount of freedom noted by Davis and Havighurst (57) between lower and middle class children, with associated differences in intelligence test scores.   This freedom can also leave an individual drifting, uncertain, and without emotional support, a thesis developed at length for our own European society by Erich Fromm (77). The Trukese child suffers under these handicaps until he is close to adolescence, when he begins to be perceived as having a potential for usefulness and receives practically his first positive and systematic instruction of any kind.

> Having at first been told practically nothing, and later what not to do, now, finally, he is told what he should do. At long last he is given a guide by his parents for behavior, at least of certain kinds, and a more positive status in the household. He begins to learn that there are "right" ways as well as wrong ways of doing things for his parents. Set against the background of ambiguity which has surrounded his attempts to determine what his parents expected of him thus far in his life, these rather specific instructions take on more importance than one would otherwise anticipate. They are, in effect, likely to be overevaluated, not in the sense that the child would throw himself with overenthusiasm into his work, but rather that he would tend to take very literally and concretely his instructions, attempting to perform his tasks exactly as he had been told. Concreteness in following directions and a tendency to accept situations in their most literal sense is a characteristic of children even in our own society, and appears to be a means of responding to new situations for which past experience and immediate guidance is barely adequate. It is the "safest" way to react when one is unsure of the full significance of the total situation. If children in our society who are given consistent positive as well as negative guidance and instruction practically from the time they say their first words tend to respond concretely, it is small

wonder that the Trukese child takes literally these directions which he finally receives for the first time in the latter part of his childhood. He has been left largely incapable of dealing with new situations both by the generalized anxiety he has learned to feel toward any interpersonal situation as a result of his unpredictable childhood relationships and by his failure to distill out of his inadequate attempts to identify with his parents any over-all guide for behavior which would permit him to respond to his problems in any more generalized sort of way. Just as his relations with people are inherently superficial, so he looks in a new situation for the most superficial and obvious aspect which bears any resemblance to what he has encountered in his past experience, and interprets the situation in these terms.

Unlike Americans, however, the Trukese in general never lose this concreteness of response. It is a by-word among Americans that the spirit of the law is more important than the letter, and the ability to recognize this distinction in dealing with his problems is a measure of an American child's growing maturity. The Trukese, on the other hand, tend always to see the letter of the law and even as adults are seldom able to approach a situation with the more abstract view implied in seeing the spirit of it. Thinking in abstract terms involves a measure of ambiguity, a weighing of alternatives in terms of personal value judgments, which is an inherently more hazardous approach than simply to be literal and concrete, taking the situation at its face value and using its most obvious external signs as cues for behavior and response. By hazardous we mean that there is implicit in the abstract approach the possibility that one's opinions and reactions will not coincide with the interpretation of the situation made by one's fellows. If all situations are interpreted in the simplest and most literal terms the possibility of disagreement is reduced to a minimum, although the flexibility and creativity of the individual who habitually responds in this fashion is of course reduced. We see, then, why any child will tend to approach his problems literally and concretely: being faced by a constant succession of new problems with which he is more or less inadequately prepared to deal, he plays it safe and responds in a minimum fashion to all of them. The Trukese, however, lives out many of his formative years without really beginning to acquire the knowledge or experience which will equip him to approach his life situations in a well-rounded sort of way. When he finally does begin to learn, he responds in a fashion which American children at a corresponding age are beginning to grow out of, and for the rest of his life is seldom able to improve upon this type of performance.

This does not mean that because after all these years the Trukese finally receives in late childhood some actual positive instructions, he takes them literally and adopts this approach to problems for the rest of

his life out of sheer relief. Undoubtedly there is a measure of truth in
this statement, for the security he feels in finding a mode of behavior
which is indubitably "right" after a childhood spend in doubt and confusion is not likely soon to be forgotten. More important than the relief
he now feels, however, are the years which have gone by, years during
which he might have been learning how to deal with his parents and
other people in a confident and effective manner, and how to express
his opinions freely without fear of making some small misstatement and
with it bringing down about him what little security he has been able to
find in a generally hostile and unpredictable social environment. By
the time the Trukese child has, at an age of perhaps nine or ten, begun
to learn how he really should behave he has acquired a fundamental mis-
trust of his fellows and a lack of confidence in the adequacy of his own
resources as a means of coping with his social problems; as we have discussed in some detail in the preceding pages, his response to this sense
of social inadequacy is to attempt not to offend anyone, particularly his
relatives. It is for this reason that he seeks the "safest," the least pro-
vocative, and therefore the most conventional and literal response he can
find to every problem he faces. This conservatism and concreteness,
rooted in the uncertainty and inconsistency of his childhood, he carries
with him throughout his life. As long as he can structure a situation so
that there is but one correct solution he feels secure; but if the situation
demands of him initiative, responsibility, or assuming a position of emi-
nence and authority, he feels anxious and withdraws (pp. 269-271).

Hogbin (118), in one of the very few available descriptions of children's
learning experiences in non-European cultures, describes a similar outcome
of intellectual concreteness and rigidity resulting from a very different kind
of learning process among the Wogeo of New Guinea. They are a people
geographically in the same corner of the world as Truk, but culturally
quite different. The Wogeo believe that everything valuable in their culture
was handed down from mythical hero-ancestors and, being a traditionally oriented people, they are conservative and opposed to latter-day innovation
and initiative. In keeping with this they provide children, much earlier in
their lives than do the Trukese, with instructions and explanations "so detailed that the need for seeking additional information seldom arises, and
'why' questions, the everlasting bane of parents in our community, are
rarely heard" (p. 285). The implications of these two very different sorts
of learning process for the development of adult personality and for individual and cultural adjustment in the face of changing conditions are of
major consequence, but the important aspect of both for our present discussion is that they each produce by different means an intellectual set toward

the solution of problems characterized by concreteness and a severe limitation in the ability to contemplate an array of alternatives before reaching a solution. It would be safe to predict that a normal and adequate native of Truk or Wogeo, even though equipped with the necessary knowledge of language and formal cultural content, would do very badly indeed on the Stanford-Binet or in the fourth grade of school.

B. CULTURAL LEARNING AND INTELLECT

The fact that so similar and—by our standards—meager intellectual development can be produced in such divergent ways in two cultures immediately raises the question whether the consistent intellectual inadequacies found in children of our lower class groups, ethnic minorities, etc., may not actually have very different origins in one group as against another. This is a question for which we do not have an answer, and even a guess would probably not be justified. We have been aware of subcultural mental retardation ever since regional differences in intelligence test scores were established on the basis of World War I data, yet the 30-odd years which have intervened have been devoted almost entirely to determining the nature and extent of subcultural differences, not to seeking their causes, outside perhaps of identifying broad differences in the quality of school systems. We know, especially through the work of the Chicago group discussed in Section VI, some of the ways in which lower class children, for example, fare in school and the handicaps under which they suffer, but we do not know what it is in their preschool and extracurricular experience which has equipped them so poorly for this task. This is a—perhaps *the*—crucial question to answer with respect to retarded children of all sorts who do not show pathologies, but we have scarcely scratched the surface of exploring the group characteristics which must provide the background and basis for comparison in individual cases.

Cross-cultural studies can be helpful in suggesting the range of variables which should be examined, but much needs to be done within our own society right now. Studies of non-European societies have the disadvantage that often their members perceive no need for superior intellectual skills and can therefore afford to inhibit, as the Trukese and Wogeo do, the development of mental ability even in those individuals who for some reason tend in this direction. In our society, however, the rewards for intelligence combine with opportunities for mobility to assure that most persons can capitalize at least in some degree upon those intellectual tendencies which their inherent nature and their experience bring forth. Furthermore, few people in our society will deny the advantages of being intelligent and resourceful, even though they may vary widely in the amount of effort they are willing to devote to developing these qualities in themselves or in their children. In other words, the kinds of intellectual development valued in our society as a whole (the lack of which comprises mental retardation) can be assumed to be viewed as at least somewhat worth while by members of any subcultural group within it, something we cannot assume for many non-European peoples, and the values of his own subculture will not be likely severely to penalize an individual whose development is above average, thus assuring a full range of mental ability within the limits set by the opportunities offered within the given group. There will be exceptions, of course, such as adolescents who consider any boy who does well in school to be a teacher's pet (Margolin, Roman, and Harari, 183), but limitations are far less likely to stifle possibly superior children when they know or believe that society at large will offer rewards for their efforts. There is a truly urgent need for this kind of research. We have a surfeit of testing and the derivation of ethnic and social class *IQ*'s. What is needed now is a more exploratory anthropological type of approach to the values and processes governing the learning situation for children.

In view of the long-standing concern of anthropologists with culture and cultural transmission, it is difficult to explain the small amount of attention they have paid to the mechanics of this transmission. How early, and particularly how consistent, is instruction? Who assumes responsibility for instruction, not merely of formal skills, but also in the subtler aspects of values and social relationships? Who is available and recommended for emulation? Of great importance, what happens when a child asks, "Why?"— is he rewarded or punished, answered or not, answered in terms of logic or of tradition or is he told he is too young, is he encouraged or discouraged to think about it himself, etc.? What kinds of skills are presented as valuable? If these include mental skills, are they rational, memory, or what? What means are used to foster their acquisition? These, and a host of others, are the questions which must be answered if we are to understand how learning takes place, and how the intellectual tools for further learning are acquired. Persons studying non-European peoples should seek answers to them, and they are equally at the core of the problem of mental retardation in our own society.

In the absence of any detectable pathology there is at present available no valid explanation of a child's retardation except a deficit in learning. Furthermore, since all or most children in a given group are exposed at least formally to the same classroom environment, yet some do well and some do not, we must assume that the deficit results from the foundation of skills, attitudes, emotional sets, and social and intellectual habits the child brings to that environment. This foundation is built in the cultural and individual milieu of his home and peer group. Until we can identify those factors which are relevant to the building of a foundation for learning, and establish some norms with respect to these, we have nothing against which to evaluate individual experience and opportunity. For this purpose we have available in our society not only the "average" middle-class children of old American ancestry, but a variety of subcultural groups in which we know the children are less well prepared to learn the intellectual skills demanded by the larger culture and within which research should be able to isolate significant and important differences in the process of learning and preparation for further learning. Once some of these are identified and assessed more systematic means of observing and perhaps measuring them can be devised, and individual studies as well as surveys can have more meaning. We know that neither present intelligence scales nor any other single instrument can be expected reliably to predict subsequent failures when administered to preschool children, and therefore certainly cannot be used to identify those aspects of a child's experience which are helping or hindering his learning at the time. The study of learning in children from subcultural groups, whose later performance our present knowledge permits us to predict will in many cases be below average, can reveal at least some of the factors necessary to fill this large gap in our knowledge of mental retardation.

As we suggested in the preceding section, we may find that lower class Italian children—who consistently average low in *IQ* and often do poorly in school—are expected to do many tasks around the home strictly in the manner they are told, without inquiring as to the reason for doing these tasks in a certain way or as to why the tasks need be done at all. This might be expected to produce some rigidity in their approach to problem-solving, and hence a low intelligence test score. If this is so are German children—who usually score higher and do better in school—assigned their tasks differently, and if so, in what way is the process different? Or if not, both being treated inflexibly in this regard, what makes the later difference? We may then find that the Italians tend more toward the common non-European thesis that manual skills are more important than mental, thus lowering the motivation of children toward school. Or perhaps Italian children during school years are expected to do some of their household jobs in the morning, and thus arrive at school (where most testing is also done) tired whereas German children do not—not a profound difference, but if it exists, important to know. These examples are speculative, but suggest the kinds of avenues which need exploring. They also reflect variations which can be expected to appear on an individual basis in middle class families; the findings of such research would by no means be applicable only to the particular groups studied.

Some beginnings have been made in exploring the subcultural differences in learning experience of the sort discussed here. The work of Davis and Havighurst (57) and of Sears, Maccoby, and Levin (238) on social class differences in child rearing discussed in Section VI is of course highly relevant, although the primary focus of both studies is on emotional development and any conclusions we may reach about the effect of the differences found on intellectual development are largely inferential. The exploratory nature of their approach, guided by theory in the kinds of questions asked but otherwise taking little for granted, is however precisely what is needed at this stage in the study of learning processes.

McClelland and his associates have done considerable work in the study of motivation, using as a starting point an achievement score derived from stories told by the people tested (McClelland, Atkinson, Clark, and Lowell, 179) ; the procedure is similar to that used in the Thematic Apperception Test except that the stimulus material is verbal rather than pictorial and the test situation is structured to be variously relaxed, neutral, and achievement-oriented. The stories are then scored for achievement motivation in accordance with a special set of criteria. Winterbottom (179), in connection with this study, established a series of 13 aspects of independence training of children, determining that those mothers who sought to have their children reach these goals of independence at an early age were those who also had high achievement scores. In other words, the mothers appeared to project their own achievement motivation, be it high or low, upon their children in terms of seeking early or later independence training. McClelland, Rindlisbacher, and deCharms (180) administered questionnaires regarding the desired age of independence training to a series of parents aged 30 to 50 who had at least one child, utilizing those items found by Winterbottom to correlate highly with achievement score in mothers only. Dividing the parents on a religious basis, the means for all items and both parents were as follows, each figure representing the age at which they hoped their children would become independent in the 13 types of activity: Protestant, 6.64; Jewish, 6.59; Irish Catholic, 7.66; and Italian Catholic, 8.42. On the basis of these findings the Catholics could be expected to push their children's development less hard than the others; at the same time the difference between Italian and Irish Catholics makes it clear that religious affiliation is but one aspect of broader subcultural differences which are at work. With respect to education of the parents, parents who did not graduate from high school hoped for an average independence age of 7.81, those graduated from high school but not college, 7.43, and college graduates 6.75. We cannot of course tell here whether educational level itself creates a desire to push the children along, or whether both reflect social class or perhaps ethnic differences. Finally, they found that mothers were more eager than fathers, the means being 6.88 and 7.77 respectively. We do not know what this means, but the plausible explanation comes to mind that independent children give more independence to their mothers than to their fathers. This ingeniously contrived series of studies can provide, in themselves and in the further exploration of this method, many fruitful hypotheses. Unfortunately for our purposes, however, they fail to examine the crucial variable: the intellectual and motivational development of the young children of these parents, and how it is affected by the aspirations of their parents for them.

Other studies in intellectual motivation, although dealing with the children themselves, do not focus on the preschool years. However, insofar as motivation during school is subculturally determined it is affecting the performance of children in these groups at the time when differences between subcultural groups become most apparent. A number of studies have demonstrated that motivation for academic achievement is less in lower social classes (Hollingshead, 119; Girard, 88). Rosen (221) found this reflected in the projective achievement score described in the preceding paragraph. He established scores for 427 boys, aged 8-14, in New England, identified by ethnicity, religion, and social class. Although the ranking of motivation (from high to low) in the total sample followed the expected order—Greek Orthodox, Jews, white Protestants, Catholics (French-Canadian and Italian), and Negroes—when middle class groups only were compared the white Protestants were highest and the Negroes not significantly different from them, higher than any other group. An analysis of variance indicated that social class was a stronger over-all determinant of motivation than ethnicity.

A questionnaire survey of the mothers of these boys ranked them on their vocational and educational aspirations for their sons in slightly different order, the Jews being highest, closely followed by the Greeks, and the French-Canadians lowest.

There is some agreement that the social class impact on intellectual motivation results at least in part from the lesser rewards, tangible and intangible, received by lower class boys from middle class teachers who find children of their own class more acceptable (Davis, 54; Abrahamson, 1). This probably provides some realistic basis for the already noted opinion of some lower class boys, particularly with behavior problems, who attribute school success of their companions to currying favor with the teacher (Margolin, Roman, and Harari, 183; Glueck and Glueck, 91). We do not know to what degree these attitudes are derived from parents, and how much they are based on the perceptions and resentments generated within the peer group of children themselves. Some indication of this is, however, found in a study by Stendler (262) in which she interviewed 250 mothers of first graders. She found that whereas the mothers' aspirations for (and preparation of) their children increased with higher social class, criticism of the school's handling of their children showed no relationship to class position. If these findings were found to be generally true they would suggest that the level of aspiration is determined at least partially by parental attitude, but that the resentments or satisfactions are derived from the children's own experience.

Another aspect of motivation emerges from studies of the disparity between level of aspiration and level of performance. A greater disparity between aspiration for occupational and social achievement on the one hand and test or academic performance on the other seems to be characteristic of minority groups. Beckham (15) and Boyd (25) found this to be true in testing Negroes as compared to whites. We do not know to what degree these findings are affected by the social class differences in Negro motivation noted by Rosen. Gould (95) concluded from a study of Columbia College students that those in which the discrepancy between present and expected future achievement was greatest belonged in more cases to minority groups: lower class, foreign parentage, and/or minority religions. All three of these studies, however, applied to urban populations who were presumably maximally exposed to the philosophy of personal success which permeates our culture. In contrast to this Lewis (168) found white children in the Cumberland Mountains of Tennessee attending poor schools with no encouragement from their parents and with no personal aspirations, in most cases, other than to remain as they were and where they were.

It is clear from this brief review of the motivational aspects of learning that important differences in both parents and children exist within the sub-cultural groups of our society, and that the origins of these differences are complex and probably often multiple. The examples of Truk and Wogeo, as well as other cultures for which intellectual motivation is more sketchily described, suggest that the differences are even greater when we look at non-European peoples. Undoubtedly motivational factors, subcultural and in-dividual, play a major rôle in precipitating mental retardation and deserve careful attention in assessing individual cases. Outside of fairly crude value judgments, however, we do not have any basis for determining how much and what kinds of motivation are really beneficial for learning. Low mo-tivation will undoubtedly in most cases lower achievement, but it may also lower frustration if a discrepancy between aspiration and attainment might otherwise exist, and through better emotional balance lead ultimately to more effective social and even occupational performance. Too much pressure from parents may lead to withdrawal, and, as Kanner (147) suggests, even to autism. At present we really know very little of the manner in which motivation is dynamically related to learning, or which aspects of motivation deserve most attention.[24] Yet motivation is the one factor in the learning process on which we have any information which is at all adequate regarding subcultural or cultural differences.

If we turn from research in the motivation for learning to seek subcultural differences in the intellectual processes of learning—ways of thinking and attacking problems—we find virtually no studies available. We do know from the many studies referred to in the preceding section and in Section II that highly significant and consistent differences do exist between the school and test performance of children in various subcultural groups. But we cannot tell where the determinants of these differences lie. The effects of social class, ethnic subcultures, language, etc., are confounded together. We do not even know as a starting point how much should be attributed to different ways of thinking as against different motivations for thinking. The data cited from non-European cultures suggest that we should look for differences between groups in our own society in the mode of attacking

---

[24]Although not concerned directly with retarded children, a ten year longitudinal study of school children conducted by the Committee on Human Development of the University of Chicago in coöperation with community of Quincy, Illinois (Bowman, DeHaan, Kough, and Liddle, 24) may provide a large body of controlled data rele-vant to the problems under discussion here. However, the study is only at its mid-point now, so several years will elapse before any extensive findings will become available.

problems, a conclusion supported by the very few studies of American children in which subcultural differences in subtest profiles have been analyzed. Haggard's (101) analysis of test results of high and low social status Midwestern school children pointed in this direction. Brown (29) reported a study of second generation Jewish and Scandinavian kindergarten children in Minneapolis which suggests that even identical over-all *IQ* averages may mask differences in problem-solving approach; this study is of particular interest due to the young, essentially preschool, age of the subjects. There were 324 Jewish children and 323 of Scandinavian extraction. Although the *IQ* varied in both groups with social class, ethnicity alone created no significant difference in average total scores. However, when performance on subtests (of the Stanford-Binet) was compared for both sexes the Scandinavian children excelled on tests involving motor coördination (draw a square, copying diamond, and ball-and-field) and patience, whereas the Jewish children excelled in counting pennies, distinguishing right from left, comprehension, naming coins, giving the date, and repeating four digits backwards. These findings are reminiscent of the rural-urban differences discussed in the last chapter, in which rural boys somewhat older than Brown's subjects do better on mechanical assembly tests and urban boys better on intelligence tests.

Paradoxically, although we have been pressing our contention that research should be devoted to cultural and subcultural differences in intellectual development in order to shed light on the causes of mental retardation, studies of the intellectual environment of severely retarded children, regardless of cultural affiliation, provide our most graphic picture of the importance of differences in the context of and stimulus for learning—in these cases characterized by extreme impoverishment. One of the present writers has already reviewed this subject (Sarason, 225, Chapter 6) so it will be necessary here only to cite material illustrative of the kinds of factors involved. Skeels, Updegraff, Wellman, and Williams (247) have provided us with a striking description of the effects of an orphanage environment (coupled with generally bleak earlier experiences) on the intellectual functioning of a group of 21 children, aged 18 months to five and a half years, who were enrolled in a special preschool training project in an otherwise typically understaffed and poorly equipped orphanage in Iowa:

> Language and speech were greatly retarded. Not only was the vocabulary meager and based upon very limited experience but the sentence structure was far below that ordinarily expected. Coupled to these two

serious handicaps were such faulty enunciation and poor speech habits that the language of the children was in the great majority of cases either entirely or practically unintelligible. Although children who were already acquainted were able to make each other understand some few simple interchanges, any constructive conversation seemed out of the question. Voices were unpleasantly monotonous, mumbling was common. With little provocation, talking voices would become loudly demanding. Finally, and of great significance in the teaching situation, was the fact that these children were not accustomed to listening to the words of adults or of other children in order to acquire ideas. Words as a medium of communication were poor commodities in this environment. In fact, the urgency for communication seemed to confine itself to situations of extreme discomfort (anything looked upon as discomfort by the child seemed to him extreme) and in such situations a loud crying was the favorite resort. On the other hand, there was a considerable amount of what might be called "verbalization," which consisted of imitation of the sounds of words of others, more with the idea of filling space than with definite communicative purpose. A phrase or word said by one child would be repeated by several not as a game, not in hilarity, but more as an activity arising from nothing and resulting in nothing.

The attitude toward adults was a strange mixture of defiance, wish for affection, and desire for attention. It was rather startling to find that there was little desire for the teachers' approval; the children seemed to crave attention but whether that attention was due to disapproval or approval mattered little. There seemed to exist what might be termed a feeling of the individual against the world, expecting no quarter and giving none. That a promise or consequence would follow simply because its prospect was stated seemed not so much to be disbelieved as to be ignored. There were few reactions which indicated a recognition of individual differences in adults. Strangers and visitors were objects of curiosity and overwhelming attention but the children's reaction would probably have been the same to wax figures. In other words, interest in clothing and appearances was uppermost and conversations were limited to a few stereotyped questions such as "What's that?" and "Who are you?" with little attention to or understanding of replies (pp. 23-24).

It might be added that the efforts of the staff to communicate with and help these children were heroic, and in many cases notably successful, as was a different experiment reported by Skeels and Dye (244) in which one- and two-year-olds from the same orphanage were placed under the supervised care of adolescent retarded girls in a training school. In both cases, of course, the children were suffering from severe emotional deprivation as well as from a lack of educational opportunity, but they provide us with some understanding of the nature of at least one kind of intellectual deficit as such, and the means whereby it can be remedied once a child has become emotionally accessible.

The unsatisfactory characteristics of the institutional environment will not necessarily be improved upon if a child is left at home with a mother who is herself retarded. Town (275) has forcefully described the environmental factors which can readily produce generations of Kallikaks.

> Without any assumption concerning why certain families are apparently foci for feeblemindedness, the simple, unelaborated fact that they are has far-reaching social implications. It means that in these families there are "blind leaders of the blind"; it means that feebleminded mothers, mere children in common sense, are rearing and caring for children, many of whom present problems that might well daunt the wisest of mothers; it means that children sicken and starve because their mothers are incapable of preparing their food and serving it at regular intervals; it means that babies die because their feebleminded mothers see not that they are ill; it means suffering, squalor and starvation of body and spirit (p. 1).

There can be little question as to the validity of this characterization; it would be seconded by any caseworker who has visited severely retarded mothers with children in their homes. It is even confirmed in a series of descriptions by Goddard of visits to the homes of Kallakaks (92, pp. 70-100) although he failed to perceive that he was thereby describing an environment in itself sufficient to explain the deficiencies of the Kallikaks without recourse to the hereditary deficit whose existence he believed he was documenting.

But if the effects of being reared by a retarded mother are so devastating, how can we account for the outcome of the Skeels and Dye experiment mentioned above? Here we have the example of 13 retarded orphanage children who were placed on the wards of a home for feebleminded girls, usually one to a ward, where their *IQ*'s increased an average of 27.5 points over a two-year period while their companions left in the orphanage were dropping an average of 26.2 points. Granted that the physical needs of the experimental children were better met than in the homes Town describes (although this was also true of the orphanage control group) and that the institutional girls were perhaps not quite as severely handicapped as Town's (or Goddard's) mothers, but these factors alone would not account adequately for the completely opposite outcomes. Skeels and Dye concluded that their substitute parents, although performing well below the norms for their ages, were nevertheless sufficiently ahead of their young charges to be able to provide them with an apparently rich (for babies) dose of intellectual stimulation. It is only reasonable to assume a similar capability is also present in the mother who keeps her child at home. Aside from matters of physical care, the important difference appears to lie in the fact that the institutional girls were living a life devoid of excitement or any particular focus of emotional interest; they were able and delighted to shower upon the babies in their care endless affection and attention along with the minimal but adequate intellectual stimulation which created the increase in IQ. At home on her own, however, the feebleminded mother is already overwhelmed by problems and activities with which she cannot cope and has nothing left over to give her child. What we are saying in effect is that whereas subcultural differences which result in higher rates of slight retardation are compounded of motivation and of patterned differences in approaches to problem-solving, in severely retarded families motivational deficits appear to be primary and result in reduced *amounts* of problem-solving activity rather than necessarily in different *ways* of solving problems.

Nevertheless if we take as our objective the determination of the full range of relationships between kinds of learning situation and kinds of thinking and problem-solving which result from this learning, the plight of the child of severely retarded parents or in an institution can be illuminating and is worthy of more research. At present this is the only group, distinctively different in intellectual development from the "typical" middle class child, on which we have any real information with regard to thinking processes as distinct from motivation for thinking. Furthermore, in the severely retarded group we know about both intellect and motivation and can see the relationship between them. The only systematic studies of subcultural differences in intellectual motivation—those discussed above based on McClelland's work—do not have corresponding data from their subjects on intellectual achievement, so that we cannot assess the effects of one on the other. This seriously limits the applicability of this body of research to the problems with which we are here concerned.

We do of course know a good deal about the adverse effects of some sorts of emotional maladjustment which block intellectual development. This, however, is a different problem from that of motivation for learning; its resolution is to be sought in personality theory and in psychotherapy and counselling. We recognize that it may often be difficult in the individual case to determine immediately whether we are dealing with a child who has never developed any real motivation to learn or whether his motivation has been blocked by other factors. This difficulty probably has played a large part in the failure of all the behavior sciences to give adequate attention to the positive aspects of intellectual motivation and their effect on cultural learning. If, however, we are concerned as we are here in determining the bases for research in the etiology of mental retardation we must make such a distinction very clearly in our research thinking. Differences in intellectual motivation and in intellectual process appear to affect large groups of people fairly uniformly, although they are at present little understood; emotional blocks, on the other hand, are more idiosyncratic in origin and have been and are being fairly extensively studied. Both contribute heavily to our population of retarded children and both equally deserve extended study. Intelligence is an integral aspect of personality, and there is no reason why, for example, anthropologists studying the relationship between personality and culture should not devote as much attention to the learning process as they do to weaning. In fact, since as we have already pointed out learning is the mechanism of cultural transmission, perhaps they should place learning near the head of their list of research priorities.

Before leaving the problem of learning to turn to the life situations for which this learning is the preparation it may be well to summarize what little we do know about subcultural aspects of the learning process. Because our data are thus far very fragmentary, we can express only impressions rather than conclusions. We can at least be fairly sure that the learning process, both in mechanics and in motivation, differs between subcultural groups whether these are defined on the basis of social class, ethnic origin, rural-urban, or other criteria. Of these various groupings we will hazard the opinion that, taking Western Europe and North America as a whole, social class probably exerts the most decisive effect—in other words that a lower class Frenchman is more like a lower class American along the dimensions with which we have been concerned than he is like a middle class Frenchman (88). There are of course differences, even if of a lesser order, between the two lower class groups also, with the result that when lower class Europeans emigrate to the United States they are doubly disadvantaged and thus contribute more than their share to the retarded population.

As to the nature of the differences we are still quite uncertain. We hope that this problem will become more manageable when research employing factor analysis and related approaches tells us more about the organization of intellect, and these findings have been applied to diverse segments of the population. It is here that we feel particularly acutely the interruption in the work of Jastak on the verge of his analysis of data from the state of Delaware, for his theoretical position is very close to that which we urge repeatedly in our report, and his is the first study of subnormality in our society to be based on a probability sample which can be expected to yield true prevalence data rather than merely rates of referral. The work of Guilford (99) and of Hebb (112) is promising, but has yet to be applied to subcultural differences. Meanwhile, we do know that there are some subcultural differences with respect to the motivation for intellectual achievement, although we cannot define the effects of these differences other than inferentially, and we also know that level of motivation correlates generally with higher social class.

With respect to kinds of thinking process, the continuum from concreteness to abstraction in thinking appears the most fruitful to explore until our tools become more refined. We know this dimension is important with respect to school and test performance, and it seems reasonable to assume that it is relevant also to total life experience. However, the fact that many school failures do not lead to lifelong failures requires that this projection be made with caution. Again, there is evidence that concreteness is particularly limiting to the intellectual ability of lower class children and probably adults, and perhaps also rural residents, but we cannot locate any ethnic differences along this continuum unless we wish to do so entirely by inference from IQ's. This about sums up the extent of our knowledge. Yet every time we refer to a limitation we are speaking also of a disproportionate contribution to the population of retarded children; viewed in this light it becomes urgent that we add to the very meager store of knowledge on subcultural intellectual differences we have summarized here.

C. INTELLIGENCE AND SOCIAL FUNCTIONING

We have repeatedly stressed the fact that mental retardation or mental deficiency (in other than severe cases), regardless of cause become problems only insofar as they interfere with the ability of an individual to function as a member of his society. We have had in Section II the example of our society rejecting as unfit vast numbers of its "uneducated" members, and in contrast to this we saw the Hutterites finding no difficulty in utilizing fully the energies of people often referred to by non-Hutterite teachers as "dull." The contrast becomes even more dramatic when we turn to non-European cultures, of which Wogeo and Truk have already been cited as examples. These comprise total populations all of whose members would probably be classified by our standards as markedly subnormal in intellectual functioning and, if we may accept the findings of cross-cultural intelligence testing reviewed in Section VI as a valid indicator, this outcome would probably be true also for many other non-European peoples.

One should not conclude from this that all these "primitive" cultures are characterized by extreme simplicity and a rather vegetative sort of existence. The Trukese, for example, have a complex social organization and an often intricate technology. To cite but one aspect of the latter, they build sailing canoes which are as notable for their hydrodynamic efficiency as they are for craftsmanship, and possess skills in open-ocean dead-reckoning navigation without the use of either compass or chronometer greater than any other people in the world. The Australian aborigines, who lack clothing and use only the crudest of tools, are all able to regulate their social relationships within a system of kinship so complex that it required the efforts of two generations of anthropologists to unravel its subtleties. These people have intelligence and use it very well; it is simply that they do not use it in the same ways we do, or perhaps we should say more properly that they do not define intelligence in our terms—if indeed they treat it as a separate conceptual entity at all. It is for this reason that we remarked earlier that knowledge concerning the intellectual requirements for functioning in cultures other than our own can be of little practical utility in the solution of our problems. It is the demands of our own society which are critical in determining who shall be rejected from our midst, and we must therefore have knowledge primarily of our own culture in order properly to define our task.

Cross-cultural comparisons do, however, provide us with some perspective for this task. We have noted in the non-European societies mentioned thus far that mental retardation appears generally to be no serious problem, and even the comparatively few mentally defective persons who may be found have to be fairly severe in degree or defect before they require special attention; these observations could be extended to most of the other cultures upon which we have any information at all. Yet we have also noted that the members of these societies have to possess considerable mental ability, even if this does not coincide with our definition of intelligence, in order to fulfill their culturally defined rôles. Furthermore, such societies seldom offer anything approaching the bewildering array of occupational and social choices we find in our own highly diversified culture, which means that within limits a person in a non-European society has to fit a certain set of requirements or else be unable to function—a plight an American college graduate would undoubtedly find himself in for a long time if he tried to become a member of Australian aboriginal society. Why, then, are there so few intellectual misfits, and most of these a result of organic disorders? The answer appears to be that practically all non-European children learn ways of thinking and behaving which are consistently appropriate to the requirements which will be placed upon them by their culture as adults. The conclusion is then inescapable that this is true in far fewer cases in our own culture.

We have already considered the first half of the equation, the learning of intellectual skills, and were forced to conclude that we are at present able to isolate for study only a very few of the doubtless many variables in the learning situation which affect a child's preparation for later life, and that we know very little about the effects of even those few factors we have identified as relevant, particularly as these factors affect groups rather than just individuals. If we look at the other side of the equation, the functional intellectual requirements of our society, the harvest is equally sparse.

One fact does stand out prominently, however, and that is that the criteria customarily used to define mental retardation are not adequate to predict social and occupational success or failure except at the extremes. We are fairly safe in predicting that even a borderline case will never reach the higher categories of professional-intellectual status, and we can be reasonably certain that a severely retarded individual will never be able to function fully independently in society. But between these extremes prediction becomes very doubtful. Several lines of evidence support this conclusion.

One of these is the age-specific prevalence of referred mental retardation, best and most recently exemplified in the Onondaga County survey (193) mentioned in earlier sections. At each age level we see the reported prevalence of retardation rising steadily, until at the age at which compulsory school attendance is no longer required an abrupt decrease is evident to a reported rate lower than for any of the school-age years. This means that children who have actually been considered retarded and intellectually inadequate in almost two out of three cases cease to be so identified as soon as their school obligations are outgrown, and can therefore be presumed to have made some sort of satisfactory adjustment.

The nature of this adjustment is suggested by a number of follow-up studies which have been done in various parts of the United States on persons who some years before had been judged as children, largely on the basis of IQ, to be morons, subnormal, defective, or the like (40, 70, 151, 189). With relatively few exceptions, the individuals in all of these studies were found to have made a social adjustment which would have to be considered at least adequate, the great majority of them being self-supporting, and when retested showed a consistent rise in IQ, often to dull normal levels or higher. Compared to individuals earlier judged "normal" who were used as controls, the formerly retarded persons have slightly higher divorce and minor civil offense rates and somewhat lower grades of occupations with lower standards of living. They are therefore not spectacularly successful, but can scarcely be called failures, inadequate to cope with the requirements of social living.

Further support comes from studies of occupational placement with respect to IQ. Hegge (113) examined the employment records of 177 boys who were paroled from the Wayne County Training School to meet war manpower shortages in 1941-42; they averaged 17 years of age with a mean IQ of 71.8. Eighty per cent of these obtained jobs, but the striking finding is that although these jobs covered a wide range of activities, including many in skilled categories, there was no significant correlation between the IQ at time of parole and the wage level obtained. A more extensive study by Himmelweit and Whitfield (117) points in the same direction. They related the scores of 10,000 British Army recruits on a 10-minute paper-and-pencil test which gave a rough approximation of IQ to placement of these recruits in 39 selected occupations. Although there was a tendency for persons of higher intelligence to enter into the higher grade positions, in all but the highest grades of work the full range of intelligence scores was found. In other words, persons of the lowest intelligence levels were able to perform successfully in all but the highest level jobs. Also in England, O'Connor (196) examined the ability of a group of 47 "feebleminded" (IQ mean 70, range 65-79) adolescents to obtain employment in the two years preceding Army service and found it no different than that of a control group who had normal IQ's (mean 99.5, range 94-106) although the normal group generally obtained more skilled jobs.

The most systematic research on this problem has been undertaken by Jastak. Although, as previously noted, the analysis of his data has unfortunately been interrupted, he has published with Whiteman (133) some preliminary findings on the social adjustment of the individuals in his sample who were classified as retarded. They comprised approximately five per cent of a random probability sample which included slightly over one per cent of the population of the State of Delaware. The criteria used for a definition of retardation were as follows: (a) an *IQ*, based on the combined results of 15 different tests, (b) an altitude score, representing the highest standard score attained on any of the subtests, (c) a schooling achievement index (number of grades achieved divided by the average number of grades achieved by his age group), and (d) an occupational achievement index based on the intercorrelated variables of skill level, salary, increase in salary from preceding job, whether or not he supervised others, mobility from his father's occupation, and mobility from his own first job. A person was considered retarded if he fell into the lowest 25 per cent of the distribution for each of the four criteria—in other words, although 25 per cent of the sample was for example considered low in *IQ*, only about one in five of these was also low enough on all of the other three criteria to be classified retarded. After examining the social and occupational adjustment of this retarded group Jastak and Whiteman concluded:

> One cannot help but be struck by the many similarities between the retarded and non-retarded in many areas of adjustment. The lower degree of intelligence of the retarded group does not prevent a sizable number of them from working gainfully, with a good deal of stability and satisfaction. Marital adjustment reveals no gross signs of disharmony. The retarded do not impose a disproportionate load upon community resources either in the form of legal infractions or excessive demands for social service. They are distinguishable from the non-retarded mainly by their dissatisfaction with educational experiences, by their absence from formal social participation, and by their dependence in choosing leisure time activities.
>
> Mental subnormality, it appears, need not connote an inability to fill an acceptable social rôle (pp. 66-67).

If one does not have to be mentally "normal" in order to fill an acceptable social rôle, what significance does the line dividing "subnormality" from "normality" really have? Certainly we would reject the suggestion that the jobs requiring lesser skills which these people (along with many "normals") fill are somehow fit only for outcasts of our society. It is in fact clear from the evidence presented that there is no criterion of culturally acceptable performance which most retarded individuals cannot meet, even if minimally, with one glaring exception. Were it not for this exception our society would probably have a problem of retardation little greater than that of the Hutterites or the Trukese. The exception is of course school performance, and the IQ concept which is a part of the same complex of standards and values.

Because of the hurdle of school, when we think of retardation we think of retarded *children*, and rightly so because it is only at school age that prevalence rates reach alarming proportions. We have already discussed in sufficient detail in this and the preceding section the various experiences and handicaps which a retarded child encounters in school under the screening of middle class criteria of behavior and performance. We do not need to repeat the discussion, and for our purposes here will only draw attention again to the emotional impact upon a child in his formative years of being segregated because of mental subnormality. Although we know very little about the nature and magnitude of this impact, it must be substantial, particularly in the areas of motivation for initiative and ambition which are so vital to occupational and social success in our society. No amount of intelligent dedication on the part of teachers of special classes can erase the fact that their pupils have been declared unfit to participate with their peers in an activity which society inflexibly demands of all its members of a certain age.

Worse off than those who are merely emotionally damaged by school failure are those who are institutionalized needlessly as a result of this failure. Happily the proportion of subcultural or "garden variety" retarded children in institutions is constantly decreasing, for the great majority of these can be expected on the basis of our present knowledge to be able with some help to make an acceptable social adjustment if they are not kept too long in the institutional environment described earlier in this section. Quite probably some of the children with milder degrees of organic defect who now go to institutions could also make an acceptable adjustment if they were pointed in this direction throughout their developmental years without regard to school standards. This is of course the objective of many special classes, but it is often implemented only after the child has tried and failed to cope with a normal curriculum, with all the damaged hopes and disillusionment of parents and child which this implies.

What is needed is a battery of scales which will predict to some degree at least the ability to develop social and occupational skills adequate for social living, scales which will be divorced as far as possible from the IQ concept. There are of course available tests of motor coördination, mechanical aptitude, social maturity, and the like which can be used with fairly young children, but their relationship to adult adjustment has been little explored, so we do not really know whether they will predict this or not. Here again we must return to Jastak's research. His data include the results of administering a large number and variety of tests and scales to persons of a wide range of ages and levels of social and occupational achievement. Although he cannot perforce supply longitudinal information leading from childhood tests to adult performance in a single individual, his research otherwise comes closer than anything undertaken thus far to determining the relationships between test variables of all sorts and the intellectual functioning required by our culture for adult non-school social adequacy in a broad range of activities. If we had the results of this study, and of others which it would undoubtedly stimulate, we would be much better prepared to advise parents on courses of action they should take, to help teachers of special classes for retarded children in establishing curricula, and to evaluate the importance of subcultural differences in learning with respect to social living as a whole rather than just school performance. We might even be able to make some suggestions to school administrators—who are after all trying to do the best job they can—as to what the elements of a realistic curriculum might be instead of just criticising them for being unrealistic. Although it is quite correct to say that teachers belong to the middle class and therefore teach in terms of the values and standards they have learned, it is scarcely just to hurl the middle class label at them as an epithet without even being able validly to propose other ways of teaching which might be more valuable for certain purposes and certain pupils.

In speaking of social adequacy we must not assume that this is an absolute standard or level of performance, common to all situations, or we will fall into many of the same fallacies which plague us when we try to interpret the meaning of the IQ. At the same time we must not so particularize the concept that we fail to take into account the variety of day-to-day activities in all of which an "adequate" individual must be competent within a given social setting. What we are referring to rather is the presumption that the different intellectual habits which we know are learned in different subcultural environments must reflect in some degree the criteria of normal mental ability demanded in these various settings. This is comparable to saying that the thinking patterns learned by the Trukese, although different from our own, are appropriate, adequate, and normal for functioning in Trukese society. The lower IQ's characteristic of the rural South doubtless reflect different ways of thinking and levels of adequacy for those who live in that part of the country, as compared to the Northeast for example. It is important that we should know what these differences are. But at the same time we should not assume that these standards are permanent, or even adequate for all the individuals who are members of a given group at one time. Both individual mobility and over-all social change can alter requirements. People move up and down the social scale between classes, children of immigrants move out of their ethnic enclaves, people move from the rural South to the urban North, and even the South itself is becoming industrialized and more like the North. A person who is adequate at one time and place may later prove inadequate, or the reverse, but we can neither predict nor advise in these matters until we know much more than we now do about the intellectual requirements for social adequacy. This is another area in which we know much more about emotional factors, and particularly emotional impediments, than we do about the equally crucial cognitive factors.

D. CULTURAL STEREOTYPES OF RETARDATION

We should mention briefly the usually negative reactions conjured up in many people in our society by the idea of mental retardation and particularly mental deficiency. These range perhaps from the gamut of "happy moron" jokes to real anxiety over the kind of social blight envisioned in Goddard's Kallikak study. The Kallikaks had their share of criminals, and they are often linked with the Jukes, who had even more. The presence of such unfounded stereotypes greatly aggravates the entire problem. It can be very damaging to the self-perceptions of retarded children and of their parents, and is likely to launch the child into any new social stiuation with two strikes against him. It generates unwarranted pressures within our society to get rid of the problem through the self-defeating device of institutionalization (in remote places) and through sterilization. And it undoubtedly has much to do with the lack we have so repeatedly noted of interest on the part of competent researchers to work in the field.

As we have already noted, many non-European peoples are, like the Hutterites, very accepting of even severely defective persons, caring for them patiently, often affectionately, and even sometimes striving to discover even one skill or attribute they can admire (cf. Bogaras, 21, p. 43; Hawes, 110, p. 250; Joseph and Murray, 139, p. 285; League of Nations, 162, p. 126). This information does not, however, help us to deal with the problem in our own society. It is essentially an educational problem, and there is little doubt that the virulent stereotypes are already gradually weakening. But a systematic social psychological study of the origins and strengths and distributions of these attitudes in our culture could provide a valuable educational tool for accelerating the present scattered progress in growth of understanding. The techniques and personnel for this kind of study are readily available and the price would be small compared to living longer in a climate of damaging public stereotypes.

E. Cross-Cultural Research in Organic Disorders

Although we have concluded that there are serious limitations to the practical application of cross-cultural research on either learning processes or criteria of social adequacy, just the reverse is true of the possibilities for research into the etiology of organic disorders resulting in mental deficiency. We know that diet, blood chemistry, heredity, and a variety of environmental factors play a part in at least some of these entities. Yet in our society we find extreme genetic heterogeneity coupled with usually very inadequate genealogical information, diets which vary widely between individuals and places and even from day to day, and extensive artificial manipulation of the environment from drinking water to air temperature.

Many of these factors are far more constant and determinate in non-European cultures, even those which have been subject to considerable foreign impact. Many of these peoples pay much more attention to preserving genealogies than do we; although in many cases the system of reckoning kinship may leave some of the geneticist's questions unanswered, the available data are still far superior to those provided by our sloppy practices. At the same time breeding populations are likely to be more stable, even though never completely isolated; this is particularly true of islands widely separated from each other. The research currently being conducted on Guam in amyotropic lateral sclerosis (*ALS*) is an example of the possibilities offered by such a population showing comparative genetic homogeneity.

Dietary patterns are often nearly uniform throughout large areas, particularly if regular supplies of imported foods are not available, and variations occur predictably with the seasons. This applies not only to the kinds and quantities of food eaten, but to methods of preparation. At the same time adjacent tribes may often be found who eat the same kinds of foods but prepare them differently, thus permitting controlled comparisons.

Although all cultures have means for controlling the external environment, this control is usually much less complete than it is in ours. The introduction of foreign clothing and housing, of public health services, and a variety of other factors are closing the gap slowly, but it remains wide, leaving non-

Europeans more directly exposed to environmental effects. It should be remembered that the major theoretical frontier established by the study of sickle-cell anemia had its beginning in observations made in the malarial regions of Africa, among non-European peoples.

If for example societies could be discovered in which mongolism did not occur and others in which it did, and it is our impression that both exist, hypotheses which involved blood chemistry or diet or environmental factors could readily be tested by a study of conditions obtaining in these societies and their members. There is also the possibility that a genetic hypothesis, if one were developed along some new line with respect to mongolism, could receive a more definitive test in a non-European culture where the disorder occurs. Furthermore, if it is possible to survey the entire population as Eaton and Weil attempted with the Hutterites we need not confine ourselves merely to presence or absence of a disorder, but can perhaps determine changes in incidence under measurable changes in external conditions.

The opportunities of cross-cultural research into the etiology and epidemiology of a variety of metabolic and other disorders, not merely those affecting mental capacity, are almost limitless and have been little utilized. Yet we know enough about a sufficient number of cultures to provide a basis for planning carefully controlled studies. Furthermore, anthropologists and other scientists often go out to study other cultures and conditions; with a little additional training they might well be prepared to undertake exploratory investigations before a major investment was made. This is one research area in which we feel cross-cultural research, as against studies of the cultural variations within our own society, can pay off handsomely.

VIII. THE SEVERELY DEFECTIVE INDIVIDUAL

A. PSYCHOSIS AND MENTAL DEFICIENCY

The relationship between psychosis and subnormal functioning is a research problem about which a fair amount has been written over the years. At different times comprehensive reviews of the literature and critical discussions of the problem have appeared (18, 28, 35, 97, 98, 111, 115, 128, 141, 198, 204, 206, 207, 209, 278, 291) which, with almost no exception, have made a plea for a systematic study of the problem. Unfortunately, as with so many other research problems in subnormal functioning, this theoretically and socially important problem has not attracted the attention of more than a few researchers. It would seem appropriate, therefore, to summarize briefly some of the things that seem to be known about the relationships between psychosis and subnormal functioning.

1. Psychosis is found at all levels of subnormal functioning. Even in the case of idiots marked and dramatic psychotic-like changes in behavior have been noted—in some cases, apparently, the behavior is episodic while in others it is followed by deterioration.

2. Psychosis occurs in cases with no discernible organic pathology as well as in those with marked pathology.

3. Practically every major psychotic symptom which has been described in the non-defective patient has also been noted in many of the defective cases. There appears to be little justification for the generalization that when psychosis occurs in a mentally defective individual it is necessarily less "complex" than when found in the non-defective individual. There is also little support for the equally sweeping generalization that psychosis or psychotic-like behavior in the defective individual tends to be of short duration.

4. As a result of work in the last 20 years on childhood schizophrenia, there is little doubt that many children who were committed to an institution for the mentally defective were in fact misdiagnosed and misplaced. Kanner's (142, 143, 144, 147, 148, 149, 241) now classic descriptions of the autistic child provided further evidence that our institutions contained cases in which personality or affective rather than intellectual maldevelopment was the primary factor. While one would like to believe that our institutions are admitting far fewer of these cases, there is no evidence that this is the case.

5. The schizophrenic type of reaction is the most frequently found psychosis among the mentally defective.[25]

6. The incidence of mental illness among the mentally deficient appears to be much higher than in the general population.

The theoretical and research implications of the above summary statements—which undoubtedly are not of equal status in terms of scientific validity—cannot, in our opinion, be discussed without serious consideration of the problems to which we now turn.

B. THE PROBLEMS OF DIAGNOSIS AND INCIDENCE

When we are confronted with the possibility of the diagnosis of psychosis in a non-defective individual, several questions are routinely asked:

How does the individual view and experience his environment and how deviant is this from the way in which we (or others in his particular cultural group) describe that environment? What is his conception of himself (e.g., ability, powers, attractiveness, usefulness, worthfulness) and how is this related to his conceptions of others in his environment? In asking these questions one is interested not only in the contents of an individual's views and experiences but in the kinds of thought processes which they indicate: the bases of his conceptualization, the nature of his associative processes, the degree and nature of fantasy, the rôle of language in communication, etc. Put most briefly, these questions are directed to answer the question of the nature and adequacy of the individual's interpretation of reality.

What is the nature and rôle of emotions and feelings in the individual's adjustment and thinking? How are these factors related to the questions raised above? What may be inferred about the rôle and adequacy of the defensive reactions associated with strong feeling and emotion?

What light is shed on the above questions from an examination or recon-

---

[25]In Pollock's (206, 207) study of mental disorders among mentally defective first admissions to the state hospitals of New York, approximately 40 per cent of the cases were of the episodic variety. The cases in this study probably are made up of individuals who resided in the community and those who were transferred from institutions for the mentally defective. It seems reasonable to assume that the chronically psychotic, mentally defective individual who has made some kind of adjustment in the community or institution would not be sent to a state hospital. The episodic variety—which may be characterized by excitement with depression, paranoid trends or hallucinatory attacks—usually present such supervisory problems to the community or institution that they are likely to be sent to the state hospital. If a more representative sample of the mentally defective population were studied, it would not be surprising if the proportion of chronic cases would be more than 20-25 per cent reported by Pollock.

struction of the life-history? What are the experiences (e.g., separation, trauma, failure) or types of relationships (e.g., social class, ethnic) which influenced the development of the individual and are reflected in his current life adjustment?

The above are certainly not all the questions that are asked when one is faced with the diagnostic problem of psychosis or, for that matter, understanding the personality of *any* individual. But we think we have listed enough of the questions to substantiate the conclusion that the diagnostic process is a searching comprehensive investigation which has the understandably ambitious aim of attaining understanding of another person's "psychology"—*that* individual's way of thinking, feeling, and acting. *Rarely, if ever, is the mentally defective individual studied or viewed in this way.* We think it would indeed be an interesting research project to obtain and evaluate diagnostic folders in the files of institutions for the mentally ill and the mentally defective. The important point for our present discussion is that since the mentally defective individual is rarely studied in the way indicated above, we cannot at all be secure in accepting available statistics on the incidence of psychosis in the mentally defective population. The absence of adequate and appropriate diagnostic procedures suggests that available statistics are probably largely based on the obviously psychotic individual and that the less flagrant case goes unnoticed or his "peculiar" behavior is blamed on his *IQ*. (When an individual with an *IQ* of 180 behaves peculiarly we do not assign cause to his *IQ*, but should an individual with an *IQ* of 50 behave similarly we usually point to the *IQ* as the etiological agent.)

It should not be thought that if one could carry out adequate diagnostic procedures with a representative sample of the mentally defective population, the true incidence of psychosis would be easily established. One of the most thorny diagnostic problems involves the lower grades (i.e., idiot and imbecile) of mental deficiency. In many of these cases language is either nonexistent or inadequate for communication, the establishment of rapport difficult, and a wide variety of organic pathologies present. In short, the conditions which ordinarily allow us to understand the covert reactions and experiences of another person are present minimally with many of these cases. It is usually when marked and dramatic changes in the overt behavior of such individuals are observed, that we can deduce that some kind of corresponding change has taken place in the covert aspects of behavior. The following cases from Greene (97) are examples of this:

In regard to the symptomatology of psychoses occurring in even the Low Grade Mental Defectives, it is a very common expression heard among the laity and I frequently hear it from the medical profession, including psychiatrists, that such and such an individual is an "insane idiot." Just what is meant by this term, I do not comprehend fully or fully understand what they comprehend by making such a diagnosis and think it a rather loose terminology, for certainly all idiots are not insane, neither all insane, idiots. It is my belief, however, that we do have actual psychosis appearing in the very low-grade mental defective and they do deteriorate. The following is an example of psychosis in an individual who might be definitely classified from the standpoint of mental defect as an idiot.

S.M., Chronological Age, 37 years; Mental Age, 2.6; IQ 16. This individual is the youngest of seven children, two of whom have been patients at this institution, both feebleminded. Other than sibling's history of mental defect, there is no other family history of note. Physically, she is under-height but generally well-nourished, with rough coarse skin, dissimilar ears of simple pattern and with adherent lobules. She has a high-narrow palate, facial asymmetry rather marked, otherwise no marked stigmata. Developmental history indicates that she began to walk at the age of one year and to talk at three years, but uses only phrases at the present time. According to developmental history, in childhood, she was obedient, apparently good-tempered and able to learn to do simple errands. Admitted to this school at the age of 14, she immediately began to show marked emotional instability in laughing one moment and crying the next, apparently without external stimulus; always exhibited a tendency to collect bits of rubbish and articles of clothing which she secreted about her person and this habit has continued to increase. Had long periods of crying at the age of 27 without apparent causative factors and at this age had to be excluded from the physical training classes because of her noisy and erratic behavior. She shows increasingly frequent periods of restlessness, sleeplessness, wandering and running about the house in an aimless manner between periods of sitting motionless under a piano or lying under a bed. During these excited periods she refuses to go to the dining room for meals and will tear her clothes in order to avoid it. She continues to cry without reason almost continually and must be coaxed and wheedled to do those things which she formerly performed without question. She has lost the ability to do tasks which she used to accomplish well, such as bed-making.

These episodes of excitement are usually accompanied by loss of weight. Between attacks, she seems to be in good physical condition, eats well and is generally quiet. The attacks of excitement are becoming more frequent and lasting for longer periods. In this case, the individual presents the differential diagnosis from the usual idiot in that she has episodic psychotic attacks, loss of weight, emotional instability, excitement and depressions, refusal of food, collecting of purposeless and useless rubbish, sleeplessness, and furthermore, she has deteriorated.

The following is an example of a low-grade imbecile with psychosis.

J.B., Chronological Age, 42 years; Mental Age, 4.6; IQ 28. This boy is a sturdy imbecile with the cyanotic hands, dissimilar ears, and facial asymmetry so often associated with mental defect. In addition, it is recorded that his eyes are dissimilar in size and shape; his speech is clear, and there is a peculiar twitching of head and extremities. He is somewhat under average height, with a very good muscular development.

The family background is very poor,—the mother mentally deficient and a patient in the department for the insane at the Tewksbury State Infirmary, and the father a chronic alcoholic. The patient is the last of six pregnancies, five having died,—four of hydrocephalus and one of phthisis.

There is very little definite information concerning early development, but the history states that the peculiarity was evident from birth. He has never learned to dress or undress completely, and though indolent, has always been obedient and amenable to discipline. When admitted to the institution he knew neither colors nor numerical combinations, could not be trusted to do the simplest errand or any sort of useful work.

Since his admission, most of the time has been spent at the farm colony, where he has learned some of the rudimentary tasks in connection with farming, but his work is not entirely satisfactory, for he is clumsy, erratic and undependable. His customary good nature has been increasingly interrupted by periods of violent excitement. During these episodes he exhibits the stereotyped attitudes and jerky, monotonous speech characteristic of Dementia Praecox. In 1926 these traits became more bizarre in character; he began to talk to himself and developed a rather elaborate ritual in regard to eating. The matron reports that at times he would remove his clothing and rush out of doors, irrespective of the weather; again, would pour hot liquid food over his head, and several times deliberately leaned against hot steam pipes.

There is a regular periodicity about these attacks,—the patient being quiet and well behaved for two weeks and disturbed and violent for the succeeding two.

These episodes became so increasingly severe that it was necessary to remove him from our farm colony and care for him in the infirmary of the institution proper and at the present time, he has changed from a pleasant, agreeable, rather talkative imbecile to one who wanders around by himself, rolls his head from side to side, has an anxious, apprehensive expression, talks to himself, has had an entire change of disposition. He exhibits erratic behavior, and instead of being able to help in the usual routine, requires constant supervision in order that he may be even clothed. He is very untidy in his habits, profane and obscene in his language, queer in his mannerisms about eating, each spoonful of food that he takes from his plate has to be passed under his knee and into the other hand before being put in his mouth. He is now a muttering, suspicious, erratic and depressed individual, with deterioration, and was committed April 23rd to a mental hospital.

Perhaps the most extensive clinical investigation of psychosis in the lowest grades of mental defect was that by Earl (64) who described what he called the "primitive catatonic psychosis of idiocy." From a study of 135 male idiots he differentiated a group of 38 cases whom he thought fitted this category. The following behavioral descriptions are from Earl:

Signs of deterioration

A general deterioration of behavior and of adaptation is constantly present. Speech fades out, toilet habits are lost, and the patient becomes apathetic, inaccessible, degraded, and destructive. Reliques of former abilities can often be demonstrated in grossly deteriorated patients. Thus several cases in this series show an understanding of speech quite out of keeping with their apparent mental level. Others can dress or undress or perform some simple task: two of the cases can play simple ball games well, though they are quite untrainable and require every nursing care and attention. Even on the purely neurological level these people often show a degree of co-ordination and control complexity of movement quite beyond the pure profound idiot.

Many of the symptoms of deterioration of behaviour can be analysed into catatonic manifestations or signs of emotional dissociation, and will be discussed under these headings. It seems probable, however, that a certain degree of permanent loss of potential ability is always present.

Signs of catatonia

Catatonia is a marked feature. The cases may be roughly divided into two groups—the stuporose or cataleptic, and the excited or hyperkinetic. There is no sharp line of demarcation between the groups; it would be more accurate to speak of a series, with the completely apathetic and the completely excited cases at either end. Twenty cases were mainly cataleptic and 18 mainly excited in type.

Catalepsy. That loss of motor initiative described by De Jong and Baruk in their experimental animals is well seen in the cataleptic group. These patients stand about in the typical posture of schizophrenic stupor, with bent head and semiflexed knees—hands hanging idly by the sides. The patients take little or no notice of threatened danger, but they will move when ordered to do so and, having once started, they will continue at a familiar simple movement. Thus they may be herded round a ward, or even engaged in very simple tasks such as cleaning spoons.

Automatic obedience. Echolalia is not uncommon but is rarely marked. Occasional echopraxia is also seen, and the understanding of words can sometimes be demonstrated in a patient who is allegedly "incapable of speech or of understanding speech"—for a sharp command, unaccompanied by gesture or facial expression, may be at once obeyed.

Muscular catatonia. The actual muscular catatonia varies. It could be demonstrated in 23 patients. It is commonest in the simple cataleptic group. In the hyperkinetics negativism is the rule, and muscular rigidity difficult to demonstrate.

The irregular type of stretching reactions described by Claude, Baruk, and Nouel was very well demonstrable in many cases. During passive extension of the flexed arm, the biceps tendon can be felt to resist, to contract, to move easily, even to anticipate movement; each for a moment in turn and quite irregularly. In some of the cases the anticipation of passive movement was obvious and the flexed arm extended itself in advance of the movement of the examiner. Lastly, in five cases after passive flexion and extension of the forearm, rhythmic repetition of the movements was set up which lasted for several minutes.

The degree of muscular catatonia present does not correlate exactly with the degree of psychosis present. This was well seen in one case in which the rhythmic repetition was continued for some minutes during which time it was possible to persuade the patient to attend to and even to reply to questions.

Autism is seen in all the cases, and is sometimes marked. The patients are not interested in their surroundings; and are often solitary, sometimes morose, refuse to mix with others and tend to conceal themselves under tables or in corners. The head is often bowed, or the coat pulled over the face; or the boy may sit in the 'intra-uterine' position.

Mutism. Some degree of mutism is always found. It varies from one patient to another and sometimes from day to day in the individual patient. Some patients will answer questions; some have a few stereotyped words and phrases; some remain quite mute. This mutism seems to be largely an autistic or negativistic feature rather than a true loss of ability. And here we have evidence that, in some cases at any rate, the mutism cloaks the degree of knowledge of, and contact with, reality. Thus one boy of 12 years who had been grossly psychotic since his second year, who had been partially mute for years, and who had spoken no word during the three months he had been under observation, managed to exasperate an attendant into threatening to smack him; to which he replied with great emphasis "No! you bloody well won't" . . .

Signs of emotional dissociation

Variability. The emotional abnormality shows itself in various forms, some of which have already been described under other headings. A rather wide variation in the general reaction to life frequently occurs;

a matter of months or even years at a time. More obvious is the occurrence of so-called 'episodes' or 'mental turns' lasting for a day or a week. These episodes may take the form of excited periods or states of depression, weeping or apathy, or vague anxiety. One of the hyperkinetic cases will weep steadily for two days at a stretch; another has days on which he is almost somnolent; whilst some of the mildest of the cataleptic group have their days of excitement and activity.

These episodes may be very early signs and may occur as the only emotional abnormality seen in otherwise fairly 'normal' idiots. They are possibly analogues of the psychotic episodes which occur in some highgrade aments, and which, when frequently recurring, sometimes presage the permanent installation of a psychosis.

Impulsiveness. Sudden outbursts of general excitement sometimes occur, lasting a few minutes or more, often accompanied by hyperkinesis and occasionally by manifestations of fear, rage or pleasure.

These outbursts are closely related to the hyperkinesiae, as are also the sudden flashes of impulsive violence which occur in these patients, who will suddenly scratch, bite or strike out at a nurse or a fellow-patient, sometimes in response to some trivial annoyance, more often without visible cause. Outbursts of excitement occur in nearly all the cases, being more dramatically striking in the cataleptics: violence is almost confined to the hyperkinetic group . . .

Mannerisms and attitudes. These are found almost only in the hyperkinetic group, just as in the experimental animal they occur in the stage of hyperkinesis. Some of these patients tend to assume the 'intra-uterine' position, and other strange postures. Thus one boy will sit for hours with his neck fully hyperextended; another assumes the 'crucifixion' attitude; another throws back his head and extends one arm and hand in a gesture of imperious command. One patient insisted on keeping all his fingers rigidly outstretched at times, even when concentrating quite well on a Wallin's peg board during a mental test.

Self-injury. Self-injury is frequent, occurring in 13 of the cases. Its usual forms are striking the head, tearing the skin with the nails, or biting the hand. One boy bit a large hole in his lower lip. Self-injury is, of course, not uncommon in simple profound idiocy, but there it is usually either the result of long-continued slow movements of auto-erotic type or else a part of a rage reaction. In the catatonics the action is sharp and energetic, is not a response to an external stimulus, and is accompanied by varying emotional expressions; sometimes weeping, occasionally pleasure, and in two cases no emotion of any kind.

Causeless weeping. A most important sign of emotional abnormality is the occurrence of weeping or laughter without cause. This occurred in 16 cases, and the writer has never seen it in a case which did not at the time or subsequently develop signs of psychosis. The periods vary in length and frequence, and the causeless weeping is sometimes accompanied by self-injury . . .

Depth. The depth of the psychosis is not easy to estimate; the clinical picture is confused by the profound intellectual deficiency. Generally speaking, the stuporose cases are surprisingly accessible to external stimuli, and though they quickly sink back, one cannot easily distinguish between the withdrawal of stupor and the mere apathy of idiocy. The writer has only seen one case of profound stupor—the case is not included in the present series. The hyperkinetic cases are less accessible, or respond only by exhibiting further abnormal psychomotor phenomena. In both groups, and particularly in the cataleptics, there is a definite day-to-day variation which is rarely seen in the stupor reactions of the intellectually normal.

A variety of clinical types were represented in Earl's series of cases:

'Simple' primary oligophrenia .... 10 cases

Mongolism .... 2 cases

Epiloia .... 5 cases

Acquired organic cerebral lesion .... 8 cases

Dementia infantilis .... 2 cases

Unknown .... 11 cases

Earl points out that because of inadequate case history data the exact age of onset of the psychosis could not reliably be determined. In the large majority of cases, however, the psychosis was already "definitely established" before the age of 10 years. It is worthy of note that Earl states that in this series "no case of congenital profound idiocy occurred." In each of these cases, apparently, the original level or potential was above the level of idiocy Earl found at the time of his study.

It has been argued by some that the undisputed fact that psychotic-like, particularly schizophrenic-like, symptomatology is frequently observed in the lower grades of mental defect is no basis for assuming that psychologically we are dealing with the same condition as when these symptoms are observed in the intellectually normal person or even the high grade type of mental defect. According to this argument the schizophrenic symptomatology—particularly some of the bizarre and repetitive motor phenomena—is a more or less direct reflection of the organic pathologies which so many of these cases have. Although organic pathology certainly cannot be considered a fortuitous factor, there has been no convincing demonstration of the nature of the relation between organic pathology and the behavioral symptoms—nor does the organic pathology seem capable of explaining either the episodic or the chronic nature of the motor and emotional symptomatology.[26] It is our opinion, which we will more fully discuss later, that the state of our present knowledge is such that we cannot rule out the possibility that psychological factors play a rôle in the psychotic-like behavior of many severely defective individuals. Until the kind of clinical investigation exemplified by Earl's work is combined with adequate life-history material—the kind of material which Earl recognized he did not have in his (institutional) cases—the question of the rôle of psychological factors in the psychotic-like behavior of the severest grades of mental defect must remain an open one.

---

[26]Dementia infantilis, originally described by Heller (100, 123), is a specific example of the problem, even though it is traditionally not included among the mental deficiencies. These are cases in which the child is apparently normal up until three or four years of age at which time a variety of behavioral changes are observed, the child deteriorating to a point whence he is frequently indistinguishable from many "conventional" defectives of the idiot or imbecile level. Some workers reported that they found the pathological anatomical basis of this condition and therefore excluded them from the schizophrenias. Others could not corroborate these pathological findings and considered it a variety of schizophrenia. As with the severe grades of mental deficiency, the inaccessibility of these cases makes the usual psychological and psychiatric diagnostic modes of study almost impossible. It is our opinion that it is unlikely that a specific pathological brain condition will explain the complex behavioral changes described in these cases. This is not to say that brain pathology may not be an etiological factor but rather that it interacts with psychological factors which also play a determining rôle in the course of the condition. We would agree with Earl's (64) conclusion about the etiology of psychosis in idiots: "The etiology of the condition is a subject for further study. The present evidence would appear to indicate the causal importance of physical rather than of experiential factors. The final decision cannot be reached until much more is known, both of the behaviour patterns of idiocy and of their physical correlates."

IX. THE SEVERELY DEFECTIVE INDIVIDUAL (continued)

A. PERFORMANCE AND POTENTIAL

In previous sections of this report we emphasized the importance of observing the non-test as well as test behavior of the individual. It was our opinion that if we could observe the individual in other life situations, we would be better able to understand discrepancies in level of functioning between test and non-test situations and, perhaps more important, to evaluate more validly the potentialities of the individual. In those sections we were primarily concerned with problems of the nature and measurement of intellectual processes. We feel that the same point of view may be of help here in indicating some direction in which research on personality organization and functioning of the mentally defective might take. It is our opinion that such research would be of relevance to the problem of psychosis among the mentally defective population.

The tendency to view the defective individual from the standpoint of a test score is probably most true in the case of those labelled as idiot or imbecile. With such individuals the intelligence or developmental quotient has not only exempted them as subjects of psychological research but it has also served as an effective barrier against innovations in training and treatment. This situation is all the more surprising in view of the findings of some of the psychological research that has been done. For example, in 1931 Aldrich (3) described a study of the problem solving behavior of idiots:

> The first problems of this series involved box-stacking as a means of obtaining a lure. The child was brought to the room by the experimenter, who then remained outside, observing the child's behavior through a one-way vision screen. The lure was suspended from the ceiling, at a height proportionate to the number of boxes to be used and the height of the child. The problems increased in difficulty until they were beyond the range of the child's ability to solve them. The circumstances which accompanied success or failure were carefully recorded.
>
> The second group of problems of this series involved the use of implements. These problems were likewise arranged in order of complexity. The lure was placed in a pen six feet square, made of palings four feet high. The implements were sticks which could be used either singly or combined, according to the problem.
>
> The solutions of the problems both with boxes and sticks depended upon self-initiated activity. There were no verbal directions and no adults or other children to depend upon for cues or encouragement. The child was in the room alone, and success in the problem could only be

573

expected when there was sufficient incentive value in the lure to bring about a spontaneous response in the child's behavior. This fact led to experimentation with the lure itself as a means of studying the effect of incentive on the individual performances.

The first lure was a ball, which in no case failed to attract the child's attention and bring about at least a reaching response, the most primitive form of adaptive behavior in such situations. Then a ball and a cookie were presented, and finally a banana.

As judged by the amount of activity induced in the subjects and the number of successful responses, the ball, although an eagerly accepted toy held less incentive value than the cookie, while the banana surpassed either of these. Tommy, for example, piled two boxes together for the ball and cookie, but absolutely ignored the third box. However, when a banana was substituted as the lure he immediately stacked three boxes together. Such an observation leads to the speculation that ability cannot be determined until stimulation is maximal.

Billy was obviously afraid of standing on three boxes after he had stacked them together. He attempted it several times when the ball was suspended above his head, and each time gave up. When the banana was used, however, he immediately stood on the same three-box structure, displaying no overt fear reactions. Incentive in this observation seemed definitely associated with the elimination of an emotional obstacle to success.

Many responses in the situations revealed personality differences of much importance. For example, when the child was taken to the room and the door shut between him and the experimenter, there were many kinds of reactions. One child cried at being left alone, and he continued to do so until it was necessary to take him from the room. Others whimpered when their attempts failed, and still others showed evidence of discontent and anger under such circumstances by stamping or banging on the door with their fists. However, the latter displays accompanied failure and not mere discontent at being alone.

The reactions of the children during the momentary presence of the experimenter at the beginning and end of the trial also suggested personality differences.

For example, Sammy began his solution of the problem the minute the door was open for him. Carl waited until the door was closed, with the experimenter outside, while Jimmy waited until the end of the trial period, when the experimenter had re-entered the room, before beginning any activity toward the ball, and then looked constantly for approval and assurance.

These personality differences displayed according to the presence or absence of the observer, suggest important considerations with respect to adult presence and attention in a training program. Obviously we must treat every child individually, encouraging those who respond best to encouragement and isolating those who develop best in self-initiated activities.

Distractibility was sometimes prevalent and in some cases associated with failure. George, who has very low intelligence and meagre adaptability, was hyperactive upon seeing the ball, and reached for it repeatedly. But he did not use the boxes at all until the experimenter placed them directly under the ball. George then became engrossed in climbing up and down, and completely ignored the ball. In this case the solution iself was a distraction in obtaining the end result.

Binet mental age within the limits of the group was not a good measure of a child's ability to solve these problems. The three who failed the simplest problems were of the lowest mental ages. However, the seven subjects who ranged in mental age from two to three years did not seem to be sufficiently differentiated by the tests to account for their varied ability in these situations.

These and similar observations of the idiot's activity in problem situations at the borderline of his ability suggested incentive, emotional makeup, and individual personality reactions as well as mental age as influential factors in idiot behavior and trainability.

Although Aldrich employed a "test" situation, it obviously differed in important respects from the formal testing situation—in fact, level of performance between the two situations was not highly correlated. Although the following statements are contained in the above quotation, we think they are deserving of restatement:

1. Under conditions of strong motivation, some severely defective individuals are capable of directing and sustaining their attention to the external environment, their level of problem solving in the process being surprisingly good. If we knew more about the everyday behavior of these individuals, this conclusion might take on added significance.

2. From Aldrich's description it would seem that some of these individuals were responding in more than a concrete fashion. One hesitates to ascribe to these individuals the capacity to reflect and organize but it seems to us difficult to square the descriptions with the assumption that these cases could respond *only* in a concrete, passive, unreflective way.

3. There are marked personality differences among severely defective individuals—suggesting that the kinds of interpersonal relationships which they have experienced were not identical. Put in another way: the factors to which we ordinarily attribute importance as a source of individual differences may be operative even when dealing with severely defective organisms.

There are a number of grounds on which one might question these conclusions. One might say, especially in regard to the second conclusion, that
these cases were not "true" idiots but individuals who had in effect regressed
from a higher level of functioning. But what are the personality dynamics
and external conditions associated with such regression? If one invokes some
organic pathology, how is one to understand the resulting individual differences? One need not resort to a construct of regression, embedded as it is
in a theory of personality, and simply state that some of these cases were
just not given an opportunity to develop what capacities they had—they were
given a label and then handled in a manner considered appropriate to it.
This is in effect saying that some of these individuals suffered from *understimulation*, an argument rarely advanced with the severest grades of mental
deficiency. Firm conclusions from Aldrich's study cannot be drawn, although
similar findings have been reported by Gardner (79).[27] The point that
seems least questionable is that even in the severe grades of mental deficiency
individual differences *in behavior and personality* exist. This is but another
way of saying that we are dealing with individuals whose behavior is not
due to static factors but to a dynamic interaction between internal and external forces which reflect previous experiences—in short, these dynamic
interactions have a history. From this viewpoint it should not be surprising,
therefore, that personality changes over time should be noted in some of
these individuals, even some of the marked and dramatic changes noted in the
previous chapter. The research problem is not so much what we label some
of these changes (e.g., psychosis) but understanding their psychological basis
and implications for training and treatment.

---

[27]In 1948 McPherson (182) presented a comprehensive review of experimental
studies of learning in subnormal individuals, several of the studies being concerned
with the severely defective cases. It is not surprising that McPherson concluded:
"The outstanding impression gained from this review of learning in the subnormal
is one of lack of information. The actual experiments have been few, the number
of subjects small, the tasks to be learned heterogeneous within a narrow range, and
the motivational factors inadequately controlled. The results of this review serve
not so much as an aid to the technician in meeting clinical problems but as a reminder
to the experimentalist." However, the following conclusions did seem to be supported
by findings of more than one investigator: (*a*) changes in incentives or motivation
resulted in increased learning and (*b*) there is a lack of relationship between
learning behavior and intelligence test score.

Recent studies in England by Clarke and Hermelin (47), Gordon, O'Connor, and
Tizard (93, 94), Loos and Tizard (171), and Tizard and Loos (272) certainly are
in line with the conclusions and findings given above. Clarke and Hermelin concluded: "It seems that the limits to the trainability of imbeciles are very much
higher than have been accepted traditionally either in theory or in practice." A
recent book by O'Connor and Tizard (197) has summarized most of the English
studies.

B. Significance of Itard's Study

It is something of a commentary on our contemporary knowledge that the best description yet made of the behavior of a severely defective individual is that by Itard (127) on the *Wild Boy of Aveyron*. For the purposes of our present discussion the following should be said of this classic:

1. At the time that Itard took Victor, the Wild Boy, under his wing there was no reason to believe that the boy had ever functioned at a higher level. Itard was viewed as something of a fool for attempting to work with the boy. We make this point because we think it not unlikely that were someone today to give as much time to an idiot or imbecile child as Itard gave to Victor, he probably would be viewed not as a fool but as someone with a curious penchant for wasting time.

2. Although Itard was disappointed that he could not make Victor into a normal youngster, what he did accomplish with the boy can be appropriately labelled as phenomenal. Over the long period of training one could see the development of various ego functions, the capacity to delay responsiveness—in short, one saw the development of a surprisingly complex personality.

3. Perhaps the most important conclusion that could be drawn from Itard's work is that even in severely defective individuals the quantity and quality of interpersonal relationships is an important variable in determining the level of complexity and efficiency of psychological functioning. Put in another way: even in the severely defective child the measurement of intellectual performance and potential cannot be meaningfully done without consideration of environmental opportunity and stimulation.

C. Significance of Research With the Severely Defective Individual

Thus far in our discussion we have concentrated on the severely defective individuals because, in addition to the research implications already noted, there are other considerations which make psychological research with these cases important. For example, it has been noted by Lemkau (165) and others that the distribution of intelligence may not be a normal one because the number of idiots and imbeciles is apparently significantly greater than one would expect from the normal probability curve. On the basis of our above discussion we think it not unlikely that such a conclusion may be a function of the practice of using test scores which reflect performance rather than potential.[28]   If in some of these cases we are dealing with personality regression, in others organic deterioration, while in others inadequate training and stimulation have not allowed for full development of potential— if these conditions occur among severely defective individuals, statistics about the incidence of idiots and imbeciles (as identified by test scores) cannot be considered as being very meaningful.

As soon as one seriously considers the possibility that even in severely defective individuals the quantity and quality of interpersonal relationships are important variables in development, the rôle of parent-child relationships must be evaluated.   In recent years we have become aware of how the severely defective child affects the lives of parents and siblings but little or no attention has been given to the influence of parent upon child.   In fact, when one considers the psychological disruption which frequently occurs in families with a severely defective child, it is difficult to avoid the conclusion that the child in some way is affected by it.   That this possibility has been little discussed, let alone studied, is probably due to the implicit assumption held by most professional workers that the severely defective organism has no personality or intellectual potential to speak of and therefore one need not be concerned about psychological consequences.   We have no doubt that in some cases such an assumption is warranted, but we also have no doubt that in some cases the assumption is without foundation.

The following question may have occurred to some readers of this report: assuming that what has been said so far has some merit, how can one justify the expenditure of time, money, and personnel for research with individuals who will always be in need of the closest supervision, even in the institutional setting?   This question can be answered in several ways.   On the most practical level one could say that to the extent that such research increases our psychological understanding of these individuals the problems of care and training would be correspondingly decreased.   If such research would serve to enable us better to help parents in the handling of these children, it would represent an important social contribution.   Again on a practical level: although the knowledge we may gain from such research may never enable us to help the severely defective individual as much as one would like, it may be of great value when applied to the less severely defective individual.   If by our increased understanding of the severely defective individual we can

---

[28]It is interesting to note in this connection that Earl (64) concluded that none of his psychotic cases of the idiot level were "congenitally profound idiots" as their behavior at the time of the study might have suggested.

learn how to modify his behavior and increase his range of adequate responsiveness, however small such modifications and increases might be, then we would have reason to expect that similar endeavors with the less severely defective individual would be more productive.

D. The Problem and Need of Theory

Perhaps the greatest significance of research with the severely defective individual is the challenge it presents to psychological theory and practice. How adequate are our psychological theories for understanding the problems we have thus far discussed in this and the previous chapter? The fact that most psychological theorists have never been concerned with problems of subnormal functioning is less important than the fact that we cannot assume that their theories would be at all adequate to cope with these problems. By adequate we mean that a meaningful research program, derived from a systematic theory, could be set up which would show promise of illuminating the kinds of problems we have been discussing. It should not be overlooked that the idiot and imbecile are human beings, and any theory which purports to be a theory of human behavior should be able, if not to give satisfactory answers to the problems which the behavior of these individuals present, *at least to indicate how to go about finding the answers.* The problem of theory is basic because we all operate, implicitly, or explicitly, on the basis of some theory of human behavior. It is only through the process of scientifically *testing* our theory that we can evaluate its adequacy as a basis for our practice. It is because psychological practice must be based on some theoretical conceptions that concern with psychological theory cannot be viewed as a luxury.

To our knowledge there has been but one attempt to view mental deficiency (particularly of the severe grades) from a systematic, theoretical position. We refer here to Clark's (42, 43, 44, 45) attempt to view the problem from the standpoint of psychoanalytic theory. There is much one can question and disagree with in Clark's ultra-orthodox psychoanalytic formulations. Aside from the fact that he was employing analytic theory of the 1925 variety, the major difficulty one encounters in reading Clark is his completely uncritical acceptance of the validity of the theory in all its aspects. The quotation which follows is less open to these weaknesses, and can serve to illustrate some of the points we have attempted to make (44, p. 36):

If we say that mental deficiency consists of some failure in the processes of acquiring, absorbing, and using knowledge for an adaptive mastery of reality, what are the specific defects which lie behind this failure? In many instances, brain lesions and organic injuries or defects have been indicated as the basis for a mental arrest. Other investigators have referred to "a pathologic variation in the germ cell," which makes complete mental growth impossible. Another plausible explanation for mental deficiency is advanced by those who hold that there is a defect or arrest in the development of the neurons. Each of these points of view would seem a reasonable attempt to determine the basic cause of mental arrest. Each consists of a formulation which the observed data frequently appear to warrant. Yet we feel that none of these theories can indicate just how the fundamental cause leads to the difficulties which the ament is seen to have. Nor do they contain possibilities for understanding the individual in such a way as to help him in his problem of getting along in the world.

Our belief is that even in cases where a definite organic injury is present, there are dynamic or psychological factors which play a prominent part. The ego, as we view it, is not only an organization of character-patterns and abstract capacities, but also is made up of the sum of the physical elements constituting the human body. The total "self" would consist of the individual's body, his mental impressions from it, and his co-ordination of the somatic, as well as the psychic elements referring to it. Any wound to the physical structure must be reflected in the ego's efficiency and in its sense of power to govern the total organism in its approach to reality. Especially must a handicap result, if the injury is to that portion of the machine which is most sensitive and most needed in the process of guiding or directing. A lesion in the brain, therefore, or an injury to the central nervous system would greatly impoverish the weapons by means of which the ego carries out its appointed tasks. Furthermore, a physical injury of this nature results in a severe psychic wounding of the ego. The sense of self-assurance and confidence is deeply hurt, for the ego misses some part of its feeling of completeness. In a sense it has been castrated, and it automatically seeks some emotional compensation. Case-studies have suggested that the ego's need for love is greatly emphasized in such instances; that there is an added impounding of libido within the personality, as a narcissistic agency for psychic healing and soothing. An injury coming early in life might thus serve to inbind a more solid formation of primary narcissism, and the extra narcissistic need might well inhibit the full ingestion and absorption of identifications. In other words, a lesion might cripple mental development, not directly but through its burden of handicap upon the ego and the libidinal processes necessary for mental growth and functioning. We must grant to organic factors, wherever present, a share in the causation of mental enfeeblement; but we hold that it is mainly through its effect upon the ego and upon the distribution of available energies that a physical defect exerts its mental crippling. If we regard the problem in this way, it seems to bridge the gap between an atypical organic "cause" and a "result'" in the realm of mental functioning. . . .

We should prefer to summarize these basic crippling factors and recognize them simply as constituting a fundamental ego-defect. Whether this be in the germ cell or in the development of the neurons, we may at least say that the total ego is without some degree of its usual endowment for meeting reality. In dealing with amentia, whatever more remote etiologic data may be held responsible for its inception, our major concern practically is with the imperfections noted in the ego's functioning. Here we must leave concrete, physical representations and turn towards capacities which have to do with definite mental processes. Our point of view is that the ego's defect lies within such capacities as perception, memory, ideation, judgment, and reasoning. These are specific phases of its endowment, necessary for mental grasp and adaptation or mastery of its surroundings. They may be originally handicapped from some physical lack in the elements which go to make up the ego (germ plasm, neurons, etc.) ; they may be crippled at some time as a result of organic injury (lesions, etc.) ; or they may be innately defective themselves as capacities forming part of the patterns which the ego inherits. Whatever the ultimate, basic cause, the important fact is that these capacities are the defective elements most typically observed; and these functions are the ones which need helpful understanding if development is to be brought up to the highest possible level of individual usefulness and happiness.

Our opposition, therefore, is not against the scientific investigators who indicate organic or constitutional defects as the basis of mental arrest. Rather, we take issue with those who infer from these findings that "therefore nothing can be done about it." Our opinion is that a recognition of certain unchangeable, irremediable factors in an individual is absolutely necessary, but that within the limits imposed by such physical or deeply ingrained handicaps there is much that can be better understood and more constructively dealt with.

It is for this reason that we emphasize the dynamic elements in the problems of amentia. They are the moving forces of energy which must be used in the actual functioning of whatever capacities the ego does possess. They are the vitalizing powers which are necessary for advancing mental development as far as inherently possible, and for directing this development into the channels of greatest individual efficiency. We refer specifically to instinctual energy, for it is from the libido and from the destructive impulses that the driving force for all contacts with reality seems to come.

Thus the main, immediate problem in mental arrest seems to concern the aspects of ego-development and the uses to which emotional energy is put. If we are to understand and help retarded individuals, we need to study the formation of primary narcissism and its effects upon the capacity for making identifications. It will be pertinent to investigate the manner in which oral-libido is used with the destructive impulses for an ingestion of knowledge from the outer world. We must get a clearer insight into the development of secondary narcissism, its advantages in supplying the urge towards grasping reality, and its disadvantages in obstructing the full absorption of what is taken in. Our understanding of the ament will be further advanced if we can observe the extent to which he has attained objectivity, by means of which he can re-project and use his acquirements for adaptive purposes. And finally, we may better appreciate his difficulties in attaining a social adaptability and in adhering consistently to moral codes when we see more deeply into the formation of the super-ego.

These are the factors we feel are all-important in any theory of mental arrest which strives to deal with backward individuals as living beings. They are the elements which seem to influence the ament's functioning in everyday life and his possibilities for a restricted but at least a further elaborated development.

The above quotation can serve as an example of how theory can direct our attention to problems ordinarily unnoticed. An important problem in analytic theory concerns the process whereby the dependent infant, whose behavior appears almost exclusively determined by *his* experience of pleasure and pain, becomes capable of directing attention and interest to another person and responding in a way so as to obtain "pleasure" from that person—the transition from a state of primary to secondary narcissism. It is assumed that this transition takes place by means of a process of identification with an external figure and that this process already reflects certain intact ego functions (e.g., perception, memory, increased control of motility). When these ego functions are defective in the very young children, it becomes much more difficult, if not impossible in some cases, to make the transition from a state of primary to secondary narcissism. What is important in Clark's formulation is that he raises the possibility that the defective ego functions may have the effect of reinforcing or fixating behavior on the primary narcissistic level, and that an *unusual* amount of attention and understanding would be necessary if the child were to begin to make the transition. From this theoretical formulation, therefore, research interest becomes focused on the psychological development of such children and the external conditions necessary for facilitating maximal development of potential.[29] Put in another way one could say that this formulation suggests that the behavior we observe in these cases, even in the severely defective ones, may not be representative of what they could do under other conditions of rearing and training. It is not surprising that Clark makes special reference to Itard's work and attributes the changes observed in Victor to the unusual amount of attention, love, and stimulation which Itard and the governess gave to him. It should also be noted that in the two severely defective boys whom Clark described, and with whom a therapeutic approach was attempted, support for the above formulation is found. In these two cases, however, the amount and quality of attention given does not begin to compare with that described by Itard.

There are several things which should be emphasized about Clark's theoretical formulations in order to illustrate the fruitfulness of viewing specific problems from the viewpoint of a general, systematic theory. First, it directs our attention to the earliest phases of development and emphasizes the importance of special handling *at those times*. It also makes us aware of how little interest has been shown in describing and understanding the ways in which the defective infant or very young child is reacted to and stimulated by parents.[30] Second, the theoretical formulation suggests a course of action. The process of testing the theoretical formulation involves attempts to change the behavior of the patient. In the work of Clark, as well as that of other analytic work (2, 41) with defectives, the course of action has basically in-

---

[29]Despite his formulations Clark, strangely enough, never gives what we would call a case history for any of the children he describes. Nothing is said about the parents or problems and methods in rearing the child—nothing about the earliest phases of development which are so crucial in his theory.

[30]This statement may not adequately convey the complexity of the problem. For example, there is probably great variation in when the diagnosis of severe mental deficiency is made or communicated to parents, so that these children differ in the amount of time they were responded to as normal children. We do not think one can assume, without further evidence, that to be handled and reacted to like a normal child can only be "good" for the severely defective child. In addition we do not know what changes take place in rearing practices after the parents know of the child's condition. We think it would be more than worth while if studies could be made of (a) the *specific* advice which parents are given in relation to ways of handling the infant or young child, (b) the justification which the physician can give for such advice, (c) and the adequacy of such advice when viewed in light of the everyday problems which such children present. It is our impression, which one of us (225) has elaborated on elsewhere, that the very nature of the diagnosis, the way in which it is frequently communicated to parents, and the vague or too general advice given to parents about details of rearing the child often produce marked psychological disruption in the parents. It would be doing violence to any psychological theory of child development to assume that the child, even the severely defective, was not in some way affected by such disruption.

volved the establishment of an interpersonal relationship and the subsequent use of this relationship to increase the range and adequacy of the individual's externally directed behavior. Even with the severely defective individual, as described by Clark and Itard, this type of relationship can frequently be established.

Following the completion of this section an article by Benoit (16) appeared which deserves mention because it is one of those rare efforts to discern the practical significances of a systematic theoretical position. In this instance, it was Hebb's (112) neurophysiological theory of brain function which was employed. The present writers are not competent to evaluate either Hebb's theory or the manner in which it is employed by Benoit. However, there is no doubt in our minds that the problems to which Benoit's attention has been drawn are important and one can only hope that they give rise to a formal research program.

1. Hebb's theory has been concerned (among other things) with the problem of the adverse effects of stimulational privation in early life.

> It seems appropriate to inquire into how the theory might illuminate and make possible a more effective control over the learning process in the mentally retarded. For one thing, there is a tendency for parental attention to shift to some extent from training in self-help and other activities to excessive care when reactions and general behavior are seen to deviate from normalcy; and there arises the question as to whether this inclination to overprotection might not have a destructive or stunting effect on the development of the child, over and above any neurological impairment that may occur. Furthermore, because the evidence gathered from animal studies seems to support the claim that stimulational privation in early life produces adverse effects even in late maturity, one is prone to wonder whether a conscious effort to lay more emphasis on training with reference to both amount and degree of adaptivity might not result in raising the achievement level in all the major spheres of performance (16, p. 500).

Benoit's focus on parental handling of the subnormal infant, and the possibility of understimulation in these instances, coincides with the speculations of the writers earlier in this section.

2. "The key element in the learning process is attention. In the Hebbian framework, the control of attention is assumed to be achieved through the delivery of facilitation from one organizational structure to another. Accordingly, in order to ensure attention, structures that may logically be presumed to be appropriate antecedents to any given response must be activated;

that is, a set must be established." Benoit points out that the establishment of appropriate sets in the defective organism may be made impossible or interfered with because of that organism's incapacity to handle or organize the variety of stimuli which impinge upon him. "One may infer that the successful production of new learning may require the elimination of irrelevant stimulation. When learning is very imperfect a complex situation may elicit mass activation, which obviously results in diffuse thinking. Accordingly, the theory suggests that the teaching situation be made more effective by simplifying contexts. By diminishing the volume of stimulation, there is less chance of disturbing a given organizational structure while it is in process of being reinforced with a repetitional series." This conclusion is very similar to that of Strauss and Kephart (267). Both Benoit, as well as Strauss and Kephart, discuss the problem of the control of irrelevant stimulation primarily in terms of the older, defective child. It would be our suggestion that equally (or more) important is the study of this problem in infancy and very early childhood, not only because they are the periods of initial learning but also because they are the times when the parents of the defective child receive the least guidance in training procedures. The significance of these early periods is central to Hebb's theory as the following statement by Benoit indicates:

> Finally, Hebb strongly urges that active concern with intellectual training begin early. On the face of it, a new organizational structure can be formed at any time in the life of the individual, provided the necessary maturational level has been achieved. Actually, however, the situation is not so simple. As a person ages without opportunity for new experiences, without acquiring new knowledge or new organizational structures, learning sets weaken or become relatively ineffectual, owing to the reversibility of the growth process that gives rise to the structures that mediate learning; in other words, behavior becomes permanently constrained within the limits of primitive habits. There is considerable evidence to the effect that providing the young with abundant suitable environmental stimulation greatly affects the course of their development right on into adulthood, whereas the same advantage later in life produces much less startling results.

In our opinion, Benoit's article not only underlines the importance of theory as a guide to problems and practice but also emphasizes the need for closer study of the experiences and training of the defective child in his earliest years.

E. Bourne's Protophrenia

In 1955 Bourne (22) reported a study of severely defective individuals which because of its implications requires special mention. His subjects, all with *IQ*'s below 50, were 154 young children admitted consecutively to an English hospital.

> Of the 154 cases, 138 had an evident organic cause and 16 had none. The distinction was based on clinical investigation and a medical history derived from several sources. The chief source was standard history forms completed by the hospital's social workers in each case, and in 74 by the outpatient consultants as well. Also there were 330 medical reports—an average of two per patient in the larger group and three in the smaller—specially requested from hospitals attended previously. Many of these were really plural reports, concerning more than one admission, or coming from independent departments, or referring to other members of the family too; in 100 of the cases, including 14 of the smaller group, the pregnancy and labour were described. In 34 cases I interviewed relatives—mostly at their wish, but in a few cases to get extra details.
>
> There were 36 deaths, all in the larger group, 31 coming to necropsy, and in all of these organic disease was found.
>
> . . . At the Fountain Hospital, with 600 beds for mentally defective children, almost all under 5 years old on admission, the processes causing severe mental defect are relatively recent and thus unusually accessible. It will be shown that clinically, as well as at necropsy, most of the severe cases can be explained by organic brain disease, and that heredity seems much less significant than is sometimes believed. There remains a small group of children, lacking any apparent organic or familial pathology, who appeared to me to display notably both a curious pattern of abnormal behaviour and a background of appalling misfortune. It was postulated that in such cases a faulty upbringing might cause failure of mental growth.
>
> . . . The information was gathered from the sources mentioned for the medical history, the standard forms ensuring certain items uniformly for all cases, and the reports from other hospitals supplying occasional psychiatric accounts of near relatives; in addition, there were 209 reports from outside social agencies, mainly local-authority workers.
>
> Where occasional discrepancies were met, an obviously less reliable report was discarded, or further inquiry was made. My judgment replaced that of others in a single instance:
>
> All accounts referred to a mother as mentally defective because she had been certified as such in prison and spent years in a colony. As her letters were far too fluent for this diagnosis, she was interviewed. She proved to be a psychopath, of at least average vocabulary and

literacy, from a criminal family, and now the prosperous young widow of an engineer who had died "suddenly." If she was defective, it was in morals and not intelligence.

For statistical treatment, the social histories compiled in this way were tabulated, the items extracted for this falling into some fifty categories. The two groups were then compared statistically, item for item, mainly by the X^2 test with Fisher-Yates correction, required because one group was numerically small.

Because the number of mongols in the organically affected group was large, it was necessary to prevent unknown factors that might be peculiar to them from influencing the comparisons, either by swamping real differences or by creating misleading ones. As a precaution, every calculation had to be repeated with mongols treated as an isolated group. In the event, this turned out to have been superfluous, uncovering nothing otherwise overlooked, and indicating only the differences to be expected between mongols and the rest of the organic cases.

We shall not go into the details of Bourne's findings. Suffice it to say that his data indicate that the small group with no organic pathology came from backgrounds which, both before and after their birth, could be described as psychologically unhealthy in the extreme.

The outlines of the condition isolated now emerge. The young child, though physically healthy, will present severe backwardness evident from about the second year, with curious behaviour disorder and a history of perverted mothering in infancy. In his first two years he will either have been reared by an extremely disordered person, commonly a psychopath, or else deprived for long and repeated periods of the mother or her substitute; usually he will have suffered both misfortunes. None here were simply reared in an institutional setting—of three so reared from the age of 18 months or less two first endured terrible neglect by unstable mothers, one passing later through five institutions, while the 3rd went from foster-mother to institution to institution.

Clinically these children's backwardness is uneven; despite an *IQ* about 40, their early milestones are not much delayed, and they lack the clumsiness and impoverished expression of other imbeciles—some, indeed, are very graceful and attractive. At times they appear extraordinarily remote and even deaf, tending to monotonous mannerisms, banging their heads, and tearing their hair out; many also have intolerable propensities for screaming and destructiveness.

Of those I have observed in hospital for a year or two beyond their 5th birthday, some become docile imbeciles, and others burnt out and dilapidated ones; yet others do not change.

The condition described here must be of great social interest since it cannot be rare, it is probably preventable, and it may initially be treatable.

At the Fountain Hospital about 10 per cent of severe aments seem to be in this category. Admissions are from a big area and without any selection, and this figure must be fairly representative of extreme defectives under hospital care. The condition may therefore be responsible for many thousands of people occupying hospital beds in this country. Moreover, this is a restricted estimate confined to psychogenic defect in apparently pure culture. This condition may be even commoner for the following reasons: (a) Milder emotional undernourishment or damage, or an equal degree in a more resistant victim, may account for some of the less extreme defectives in the community, and even more of those in institutions. (b) Some mental defectives of organic aetiology may have been reduced to the institutional level by such trauma, additionally. Possibly these children are less equipped to overcome indifferent rearing and very liable, by virtue of physical deformity, to elicit it.

The histories of these cases monotonously disclose how little realisation still exists among social agencies, doctors, and hospitals that a small infant is a social being who needs more than food alone to grow up. For example, the digestive difficulties, failure to thrive, and napkin rashes common in these infants, and a crying illustration of maternal incompetence, led to their spending weeks at a time in hospital, always to be discharged "recovered," and always to relapse with another complaint, but never led to serious probing of the mother. Even when backwardness was obvious, the exclusion, often recondite, of physical disease left inquiry exhausted; in all five cases in this series where the child was under one hospital while the mother was under another for psychological treatment no communication appears ever to have passed between the two.

. . . It will have become apparent that these children may superficially resemble adults with chronic schizophrenia. However, similar behaviour does not mean identical psychopathology, and merely to label these defectives as psychotic deprives the term of any precise meaning. Generally, psychosis designates disorders where ego functions disintegrate, where the person ceases to be himself. These children have no such disorder, and far from presenting disintegration, with two exceptions, they achieved integration at no time at all, their disruption being presumably of primitive infantile processes assembling towards an organized personality. The early distortion of those unintegrated processes that survive may account for the curious behavior which characterises these patients.

Protophrenia seems to me a suitable name for this condition, implying an aborted organization of the personality as distinct from disorganization, to which psychosis refers, and from undistorted retardation accompanying organic cerebral defect, which, by itself, seldom produces autistic behaviour disorder, to judge from the material here.

It is uncertain how protophrenia is related to the syndrome of "early infantile autism." There seem to be differences in that a proportion of the cases here are not autistic and in that only some of Kanner's cases were regarded as mentally defective and none are described as having behaviour disturbances apart from lack of emotional relationship to people and monotonous adherence to some daily routine. The background of his cases was different too, containing an excess of socially and intellectually superior forebears.

Protophrenia can be regarded as a psychogenic failure of ego formation. Its study must be relevant to that of pathological ego formation, generally, where early emotional trauma is at all important. This includes the fragility underlying adult schizophrenia and child psychoses, and the maldevelopment of psychopathic adults and problem children. The present arrangement whereby mental deficiency, child guidance, and adult psychiatry are practised in almost complete isolation from one another can only impede understanding of the common processes basic to each.

As Bourne recognized, the number of cases is small and the study requires replication by others. In such replications it would be recommended that the reliability of clinical judgment concerning organic pathology or no pathology be determined in order to evaluate unwitting bias due to knowledge of case history data. In his study Bourne did both the clinical examinations and analysis of background data. Bourne was aware of this source of contamination of judgment and seemed studiously to try to avoid its effects. But the methodological problem remains and should be squarely met in future studies. We would agree with Bourne that his findings are potentially of great significance and demand further study.

An important question raised by this study may be put as follows: Why is it that some children who have been subjected to the kinds of experiences and relationships which Bourne describes do *not* develop the picture of severe subnormality he calls protophrenia? It probably would not be difficult to find children who have been subjected to even worse experiences and relationships but who do not manifest such an extreme picture. We are here raising the possibility that there is a predisposing factor which selectively determines the degree to which a child will be affected by certain untoward experiences or relationships. We shall return to a consideration of this problem following a discussion of the idiot savant and infantile autism. At this point we wish merely to state that while it has been obvious that there are temperamental and behavioral differences among children from the earliest days of life, and it has been assumed that such variations are important in some way in atypical development, the problem has been little studied. As we hope to indicate later, however, certain clinical observations reported in the past decade or so allow one to think more specifically about the nature and varieties of predisposing factors.

F. The Idiot Savant and Infantile Autism

Although the idiot savant has been described and discussed many times over the years, it was not until 1945 that a really penetrating and comprehensive review and discussion of the problem appeared. In that year Scheerer, Rothmann, and Goldstein (235) published their monograph, a work which has not received the attention it merits. The reader is urged to read this monograph from which we give below the authors' summary statement:

L, an 11-year-old boy, with behavioral peculiarities has been studied over a period of 5 years and a reliable record of his previous development obtained. L showed distinct musical aptitude—he played melodies on the piano by ear—and was remarkable in verbal retentiveness. His skill in rapidly manipulating simple numbers was also unusual, and he performed so-called calendar calculations amazingly well. Numbers he remembered with the same ease as occurrences which to his mind had once become connected with them, so that he volunteered dates, names, places, and times of events at the slightest provocation.

In spite of all this, L's general information was surprisingly subnormal, and, with the exception of the just mentioned aspects of his surrounding, nothing aroused his interest. He never absorbed or learned in a normal fashion, nor could he attend a regular school. He was retarded in the mastery of many skills, commensurate to his age, and he was lacking in social awareness with a limited repertoire of social responses. L had an IQ of 50 which classifies him technically an "idiot-savant."

An investigation of L's personality structure was carried out with specially devised experiments, with standard tests and with careful exploration of his spontaneous behavior in everyday life. An analysis of all data and of the findings in multiform performance fields failed to disclose an individual segmental defect or several specific defects. Instead, his various deficiency symptoms pointed to a functionally common disturbance, a general impairment of abstract capacity (e.g., in the semantic use and ideational understanding of language, of social contents and relations; in reasoning, in the grasp of causation, of logical meaning, of symbols, of conceptual number relations; in the cognitive structuring of visual performances and visuo-motor tasks). This picture of general abstract impairment was corroborated by the experimental evidence that L succeeded in his own performance-specialties without having a genuine understanding of their meaning as to content and implication. Further exploration of his thinking, learning, and social behavior revealed an abnormal concretization. He could only grasp and learn what made situational or tangibly patterned sense to him. Otherwise, if he retained at all, it was in an automatic, associative manner by habituation.

A positive evaluation of his successful performances, abilities, and skills was attempted. After having experimentally ruled out other alternatives, it was found that *L* possesses an initial endowment in the acoustic and audio-motor sphere, probably supported by kindred imagery. This endowment expressed itself particularly in his sensory motor receptiveness for melodies, i.e., for acoustic "Gestalten" and for verbal patterns. On this basis his musical performances, his verbal and tonal memory (absolute pitch), and his aptitude for serial grouping became explicable (e.g., his rapid oral counting and spelling, forward and backward, his large digit span and his calendar performance).

Further analysis of his procedure in the utilization of this endowment revealed however, that it did not operate in a normal manner. It was bound to an abnormally rigid concreteness and functioned in a sterile, bizarre, and undiscerning form. Symptomatically, in music he could not develop his talent through study or practice. His performances were desultory, depending on specific circumstances and his interest ranged from obsession with a special phonograph record to appreciative enjoyment of opera arias or Handel's "Largo" on records and indifference to *any* radio music. Correspondingly anomalous function of his talent was manifest in his excessive tendency to count indiscriminately, and to resort to an enumerative verbalization and inane speech clichés whenever he was confronted with a task that overtaxed his power.

We find then that an individual who is handicapped in abstraction and endowed in a particular field of performance shows a *sub*normal intelligence and an *ab*normal canalization of his endowment. In interpreting this personality picture we concluded: owing to his impaired abstract attitude, *L* cannot realize his remaining potentialities in a normally integrated manner. He is therefore driven in an abnormal degree and direction to exercise those functions which nature permits him to develop, because these are the only performances through which he can actualize himself and come to terms with his surroundings. The least impaired function thus becomes a coping mechanism of adjustment, but, since it can only operate on the level of concrete reactions, it becomes canalized into atypical forms of expression. This result seems to point to an organizational interdependence of basic psychological functions. Certain pertinent implications with regard to normal personality structure and with regard to the problem of idiot savant are discussed and the following generalizations considered:

(1). How an endowment operates and develops, depends upon the organization of the person as a whole.

(2). There exists a functional interrelation between abstract capacity, intelligence, and special endowment.

(a). The abstract capacity is essential for the normal functioning of intelligence. The bearing of this on the association theory of intelligence is followed up.

(b). The abstract capacity is conditional for the normal functioning and development of an endowment, although the latter may be anchored in concrete processes, e.g., of Gestalt type.

(3). The term idiot savant is a misnomer. Idiot savants are talented aments who possess an amented talent.

In order to test these conclusions a comparative study of other reported cases of idiot savant was undertaken and various explanatory hypotheses of other authors were critically examined. The evaluation of this case material seems to confirm our interpretation, since no cases were found in which a talent functioned normally in an individual with abstract impairment. These led to the establishment of certain criteria for the psychological identification of a talented ament.

In studying the reported superior abilities in aments two phenomena invited particular attention because they posed an intriguing psychological problem. These were (a) the relative frequency of number manipulation and retention, and (b) unusual features of memory.

(a). The analysis of the psychological processes involved in these number performances laid bare their origin in concrete perceptual counting procedures with specific limitations. A comparison between this stage of primitive, concrete grouping and the initial procedures in arithmetical prodigies showed basically common characteristics. It became clear, however, that the arithmetical prodigy who developed further towards a cognitive understanding of mathematics outgrew this original stage of concrete dependency in his number operations, because he could increasingly adopt an abstract approach. In contrast the abstract impairment prevented the talented ament from passing beyond the initial stage of concrete grouping procedures.

(b). The striking retention of numbers or of outlandish and irrelevant data, as, e.g., railroad tables or an entire newspaper column, is all the more surprising as in most every instance the retained material is not understood by the ament in a normal way. A psychological appraisal of the changes in figure-ground organization as experienced during pathological concreteness led us to set forth a new explanation of these peculiar memory processes. The observations on the cases studied indicate that a defective organism will cling tenaciously to those aspects of a situation and those features of material which make concrete palpable sense to him, i.e., with which he can deal successfully. These aspects are thrust into the foreground of the phenomenal organization as the "figure." Such a difference in perceptive centering in the abnormal's coming to terms with the world of the "normal" leads to a different centering of performance. Therefore, these aments retain easily what may appear senseless or peripheral or irrelevant to the normal observer. To the aments in question, however, this is the only "sense" possible and pivotal in the experienced contents. This explanatory attempt is tested on diversified case material. Finally, comparing abnormal concreteness in aments with stages of concrete reaction in normal children the following question is raised: Does the atypical memory organization in a subnormal child represent a lawful modification of a normal development phase which has become pathologically "eccentric" and conditioned as a coping mechanism?

It has indeed been a rare event in psychology and psychiatry when clinical problems which have been considered rather different are brought in relation to each other. For this reason we give the following from Scheerer, Rothmann, and Goldstein (235, p. 57):

> Recently Kanner has discussed 11 cases of personality deviation in children in terms of "autistic disturbances of affective contact" which he considers a special syndrome. Pointing to the misplaced eagerness of parents to promote precociousness in their children he states: "Their excellent rôte memory, coupled with the inability to use language in any other way, often led the parents to stuff them with more and more verses, zoölogic and botanic names, titles and composers of Victrola record pieces and the like. Thus, from the start, language, which the children did not use for the purpose of communication—was deflected in a considerable measure to a self-sufficient, semantically and conversationally valueless or grossly distorted memory exercise. To a child 2 or 3 years old, all these words, numbers, and poems (questions and answers of the Presbyterian Catechism; Mendelssohn's violin concerto; the twenty-third Psalm, a French lullaby; an encyclopedia index page) could hardly have more meaning than sets of nonsense syllables to adults. It is difficult to know for certain whether the stuffing as such has contributed essentially to the course of the psychopathological condition. But it is also difficult to imagine that it did not cut deeply into the development of language as a tool for receiving and imparting meaningful messages."
>
> Kanner's behavioral observations in these children represent new valuable material for mental pathology. Since his case histories show many parallels to those here presented it may be in order to make some comparisons between his interpretation and our hypothesis on the rôle of concreteness in defective children and their retentivity.
>
> According to Kanner "the outstanding, 'pathognomic,' fundamental disorder is the children's *inability to relate themselves* in the ordinary way to people and situations from the beginning of life." He explains all behavioral abnormalities found in these children from their *affective*

disturbance, from their "desire for aloneness and sameness." To Kanner the inconsistent picture of intellectual ability, the obsessive repetitiousness, the shock reactions to loud noises and moving objects, and the "truly phenomenal memory" in these children is accounted for by their emotional resistance against change in the outer situation—the insistence upon "identical spatial or chronological order." In following Kanner's impressive observations in support of his view, it appears nevertheless as if Kanner has neglected the qualitative nature of the intellectual abnormalities in this picture. The case histories abound in instances of compulsive concreteness in thought and action. In our opinion this is only explicable on the basis of an impairment of abstract attitude which is intimately bound up with the affective disturbance. To mention only a few problems, it is hard to see how an affective disturbance alone can account for what Kanner calls the "literalness" in these children, their inability to use "yes" as a *general* symbol of affirmation, detached from the specific situation in which it had been acquired; their inability to understand prepositions in the abstract sense. (Asked to put something down, the child puts it on the floor—understanding the word only in the originally acquired situational sense.) It is hard to follow Kanner when he makes the affect-anomaly responsible for: "the absence of spontaneous sentence formation and the echolalia type of reproduction, which in every one of the eight speaking children has given rise to a peculiar grammatical phenomenon. *Personal pronouns are repeated just as heard.* The child once told by his mother 'now I will give you your milk' expresses the desire for milk in exactly the same words. Consequently he comes to speak of himself always as you and of the person addressed as I." We have encountered this reversal of pronouns in three cases here presented all of which showed pronounced impairment of abstraction.

This peculiar "grammatical" phenomenon appears to be more than a mere grammatical one or a purely mechanical echolalia. The child hears himself addressed as "you" and the other person speaking of himself as "I." Only on a concrete level of thinking is the literal application of the word "you" to the child himself and "I" to the other person explicable, because the child cannot detach the words from their experienced "belongingness" in the actual situation and reverse this belonging in terms of a relational symbol. (The corresponding phenomenon in normal children is their frequent use of their first name or the third person in referring to themselves.)

Is the child's inability to shift the word "you" from himself to the other person, and the word "I" from the other person, is this inability to grasp the relational meaning of "you" and "I" in the abstract, merely the result of the affective disturbance or is it not a symptom of impaired abstraction and limitation to the concrete as well?

In discussing their peculiar memory Kanner speaks of parrot-like

repetitions of heard word combinations, of "delayed echolalia."
As in the case of *L*, "the children had learned at an early age to repeat an inordinate number of nursery rhymes, prayers, lists of animals,
the roster of presidents, the alphabet forward and backward, foreign
(French) language lullabies . . . even long and unusual words were
retained with remarkable facility." Yet in contrast to these recitals,
their spontaneous language-development and understanding was retarded. In Kanner's concepts it is the need for "sameness and autistic
aloneness" that sufficiently accounts for both, this semantic retardation
and for the abnormal retention of verbal material, which latter he
characterizes as completely senseless for the children. This makes it
quite difficult to understand *why* they so eagerly and readily absorbed
and reproduced such material, and even liked to spell out words. Is
perhaps the fact that the children did not grasp the meaning of language in the normal way the motive for their heightened responsiveness to and their tenaciously obsessive reproduction of phonetic sound
patterns? In the light of our own case-material it seems highly probable that these children excelled precociously in verbal memory for the
same reasons as we outlined in our hypothesis. And the question
may arise, whether the disturbance in affective human contact they
suffered is not secondary to the defect in abstraction or parallel to it.
Perhaps this hindered a normal grasp of the semantic aspect of language and impelled these children to cling to that aspect of speech
which was concretely sensible and apprehensible for them in terms of
auditory motor patterns (235, p. 57).

The similarities between the autistic child and the idiot savant are indeed
striking. We feel, however, that there are several questions which seem to
pose difficulties for an explanation based primarily, if not exclusively, on an
impairment of abstraction.

How is such an explanation to explain (or to be integrated with) the impression, reported by Tredgold (276) and supported by our own review of
the literature, that the large majority of idiot savants are males? There also
seems to be a preponderance of males among the reported cases of infantile
autism.

There appear to be no grounds for doubting that there is an impairment
of abstraction in both the idiot savant and the autistic child. When Scheerer,
Rothmann, and Goldstein cautiously suggest that in these cases we may be
dealing with a lawful modification of a normal development phase which
has become pathologically "eccentric and conditioned as a coping mechanism," at least two questions arise. Is the coping mechanism always a response
to the impairment of abstraction—that is, is the impairment of abstraction

always the *etiological* factor "forcing" the child to develop atypically? Is development normal up until that phase when the organism should be able to respond abstractly? To answer either question in the positive would certainly conflict with the experience of those clinicians who report having discerned the characteristics of autism well before the period when abstraction as an intellectual characteristic normally becomes manifest (174, 213). In other words, factors other than intellectual seem, in some cases at least, to be primary.

To explain the idiot savant and the autistic child primarily in terms of an impairment in abstraction would be more plausible if these were cases with demonstrable central nervous system pathology. In the published literature many, if not the large majority, of these cases have no such discernible pathology. Because these conditions can and do appear in the presence of positive neurological evidence of brain injury does not allow one to assume that where such evidence is lacking it is because of the crudity of neurological procedures. This may be the case but the burden of proof would seem to be on those who make the assumption. Because schizophrenia can follow alterations in the central nervous system does not mean that all schizophrenia can be explained in this way.

Perhaps our most serious reservation to Scheerer, Rothmann, and Goldstein's discussion of the idiot savant and the autistic child concerns their failure to consider the possible ways in which familial personalities and organization either interact with or cause or exacerbate the impairment of abstraction. For example, Kanner, who has reported the largest series of cases of infantile autism, comes to the conclusion that the personality of the parents and their techniques of child rearing are not irrelevant factors in attempting to understand the autistic child. It may be that Kanner's sample is in some ways a biased one but until this is demonstrated one cannot dismiss the possibility that factors external to the autistic child are important in the development of the condition. In this connection it might be pointed out that in the case of the idiot savant which Scheerer, Rothmann, and Goldstein describe there is practically no discussion of the possible rôle of parental personality on the child. We point this out because of our impression that what little is contained in the monograph on parental personality and behavior suggests similarities to Kanner's descriptions of the parents of his cases. Unfortunately (but not unexpectedly) in the entire literature of the idiot savant there is not a single acceptable personality description of the parents. We are here not contending that parental personality and behavior is the etiological factor—for reasons to be discussed later we feel such a statement to be unjustified on theoretical grounds. However, for similar reasons, we are contending that any explanation of behavior which is based exclusively on factors "inside" the individual is likely to be a very incomplete one.[31]

If one were to assume that the kinds of cases we have been discussing were in some way primarily a function of non-environmental factors (e.g., brain-injury, genetic, constitutional, etc.) then one would expect that they would occur in any culture, e.g., the so-called primitive ones. There is no evidence that this is the case. However, since anthropologists have not been interested in these types of problems, and are not trained to pick them out, the absence of evidence in this instance means little or nothing. We would suggest that cross-cultural studies of infantile autism and idiot savants might be fruitful regardless of the direction of the evidence which would emerge.

In summary, Scheerer, Rothmann, and Goldstein have made an important contribution in pointing out and discussing the similarities between the autistic child and the idiot savant. There is little doubt that in both these conditions there is an impairment of abstraction. In raising questions about the adequacy of such an impairment for explaining these conditions, we have tried to suggest that such an explanation does not seem to cover what apparently are certain facts—particularly the sex difference in the incidence of the two conditions. In addition, we expressed the opinion that discovery of those factors which antedate and are related to the impairment of abstraction may be of vast importance for our understanding of the early development of intellectual functions—their nature, course, and relation to the external environment. The importance of these cases to the development of a science of psychology would seem to be vastly beyond what their relatively rare occurrence in the general population would suggest.

We hope it is clear from the previous discussion that we are dealing with conditions the etiology of which is very ambiguous. These cases are certainly not homogeneous in terms of presence and degree of organic pathology. It is also impossible to do other than grossly speculate about the possible rôle of environmental factors. It seems fair to say, then, that neither in the case

---

[31] In their discussion of very young autistic children, Ritvo and Provence (213) state: "We do not in our thinking neglect the part the mother's attitude plays in this condition. We believe that the child's disturbance sets in motion a circular process with child affecting mother and mother in turn affecting child. We would like to conclude with a remark made by the mother of one of these children when told of her child's need for continued stimulation from her: 'Why should I pick him up when he doesn't even smile at me?' "

of infantile autism nor in the idiot savant can one justifiably ascribe the condition to either environmental or organic pathological factors. It would indeed be surprising if the ultimate explanation required knowledge of but one of these factors—the conditions seem far too complex to hold out hope for such simple explanations.

There is one variable, however, which seems not to have been given the attention in theory and research which it seems to deserve. We might begin our discussion of this variable by posing a question we raised earlier in relation to Bourne's "protophrenia" (see page 205): Why is it that some children who have been subjected to the kinds of experiences and relationships which Bourne describes do *not* develop the picture of severe subnormality he calls protophrenia? It probably would not be difficult to find children who have been subjected to even worse experiences and relationships but who do not manifest such an extreme picture. Assuming that there is a relationship in Bourne's cases between certain environmental factors and extreme deficiency, we are unable to explain why more children do not develop this condition. We are faced with the same question of selectivity of occurrence with the idiot savant and infantile autism, regardless of whether one assigns primary importance to organic or environmental factors.

While we would agree that the organic and environmental factors have to be viewed in relation to each other, the variable we have in mind is perhaps independent of both, at least in the earliest months of life. We are here referring to something akin to what Bergman and Escalona (19) have called "unusual sensitivities in very young children":

> It was several years ago that the authors were first struck by the observations to be reported here. Some very young children possessed unusual sensitivities manifesting themselves in several, if not in all, sensory modalities (visual, auditory, tactile, etc.). Colors, bright lights, noises, unusual sounds, qualities of material, experiences of equilibrium, of taste, of smell, of temperature, seemed to have an extraordinarily intensive impact upon these children at a very early age. They were "sensitive" in both meanings of the word: easily hurt, and easily stimulated to enjoyment. Variations in sensory impression that made no difference to the average child made a great deal of difference to these children. They were also characterized by a certain precocity, though this was very unevenly distributed among the diverse functions of their personality. The first impression which some of their reactions and abilities gave was that of unusual giftedness such as might be observed in the budding of a genius. Further observation, however, suggested comparison with individuals suffering from a traumatic neurosis,

or a psychosis, and even with feebleminded children. Closer study and follow-up then made it appear that childhood psychosis was the fate of these children, though we are not sure yet that all children of the type to be described eventually develop a clear psychotic picture. . . .

If we examine more closely those facts that impressed us as bespeaking unusual sensitivity in the described children, we become aware that they differ from each other in several respects, and can be grouped accordingly. We find that we have observed facts pertaining to many parts of the sensorium, i.e., to visual, to auditive, to tactile, to olfactory, to gustatory, to equilibrium, and to temperature experiences. Some of the children reported on reacted very sensitively to light or colors, to noises and music, to materials that came in contact with their skin, to smells and perfumes, to foods, to rocking and swinging, to cold air or cool objects. Thus, one obvious principle of grouping our observations is furnished by the sensory modality.

Then we find that what impressed us in some observations was the reaction to the intensity or quantity of stimulation, while in other cases the observation is more easily understood as a reaction to quality. Thus if any kind of slight sound seems to awaken a sleeping infant, or arouses a reaction from the waking one, we will consider that he reacts to the intensity of the stimulation, in fact here to a very low intensity. But if certain sounds or combinations of sounds attract a child, while other sounds or combinations of sounds of equal loudness repel him, it seems plausible to consider this a reaction to quality. Other reactions to quantity that we find in our material are, e.g., reactions to light of a certain brightness, reactions to normally imperceptible (or at least not usually reacted to) amounts of odor, reactions to slight disturbances of the equilibrium, to slight impressions on the feeling of temperature. On the other hand, observations pertaining to certain colors, certain materials, specific odors, foods, we can group with reactions to quality. Whether a special fondness of rocking should be grouped with reactions to quality or to quantity may be debatable. With some sensory modalities this distinction does not seem to make much sense. We would not be able to say, e.g., what a reaction to quality would be like in the modality of the sense of temperature.

Bergman and Escalona go on to point out that unusual sensitivities in young children may result in premature defensive reactions which are inadequate in the face of later trauma. "The hypothesis will be offered that the infant who is not sufficiently protected from stimuli either because of a 'thin protective barrier,' or because of the failure of maternal protection, may have to resort for such protection to premature formation of an ego. When this premature ego breaks down, possibly as a consequence of a trauma, the psychotic manifestations are thought to set in."

Bergman and Escalona's clinical observations and conclusions allow one to raise several questions: (a) To what extent do autistic children have a history of unusual sensitivities?—a question which Bergman and Escalona raise but which existing studies cannot answer; (b) To what extent would the histories of idiot savants indicate unusual sensitivities preceding the appearance of unusual intellectual behavior?; (c) To what extent do the children described by Bourne have unusual sensitivities? *Perhaps of more significance than these questions is the assumption that the crucial factor in these types of atypical development is the interaction between unusual sensitivities, on the one hand, and environmental factors, on the other hand.* Whether the infant with unusual sensitivities develops atypically may be a function either of parental handling of these sensitivities or fortuitous organic conditions or some combination of both.[32]   In other words, not all children with unusual sensitivities would be expected to develop atypically. Similarly, objectively similar environments or organic pathologies would have differing effects on individuals who differed in terms of the unusual sensitivities described by Bergman and Escalona.   For example, the "protophrenics" described by Bourne may be those who had unusual sensitivities, while other children with similar or worse experiences and relationships but who did not show such extreme subnormality may not have had such sensitivities.

It is reasonable to assume that sensory hyperreactivity is but one of several ways in which the young child may be unusual.   Put in another way: the very young child can be viewed in terms of various behavioral continua, and extreme placement on any of these continua, as in the case of unusual sensitivities, may be the predisposing factor which when interacting with environmental or organic factors has untoward effects.   The work of Fries (74, 75, 76, 175) on "congenital activity types," as well as the recent intriguing investigations of Richmond and Lustman (212a), supports the contention that the study of temperamental and physiological variations in the very young

---

[32]The occurrence in the same child of an unusual sensitivity and an organic pathology does not, of course, mean that the two are causally related, although this may be the case in certain instances. The presence of an unrelated organic pathology may make it more difficult for the child (and parent) to cope with the sensitivity. For example, Frankl (72) described a case of severe autism in a child with tuberous sclerosis. Although most cases of tuberous sclerosis are severely defective, there are some whose intellectual functioning is less, or not at all, affected by the condition (277, p. 278). In any event, extreme autism is not a marked behavioral characteristic of these cases. The extreme picture of autism which Frankl describes need not be related, in its initial phases at least, to the central nervous system pathology. It is conceivable that their origins are independent but that the central nervous system pathology exacerbates the autistic tendencies.

child may provide at the least a partial answer to the question why different children are differentially affected by similar external events or similar organic conditions. This is clearly not a problem of peculiar significance to the area of atypical development but one which is truly basic to our understanding of normal development, the nature and range of the earliest individual differences in relation to rearing and educational techniques.

G. Lightner Witmer

If only for historical reasons we feel compelled to say something of Witmer's work. Psychologists, psychiatrists, and educators of today may know of Witmer's name in connection with the fact that he organized the first psychological clinic in this country in 1896 at the University of Pennsylvania. What has been forgotten, unfortunately, is that in the early years of this century he was concerned with and wrote most illuminatingly about the differential diagnosis between mental deficiency and childhood psychosis. Years before the autistic and schizophrenic young child was described and recognized by American psychiatrists, Witmer published his "orthogenic" case reports in which the major characteristics of this type of child were delineated. To be sure, Witmer's descriptions are not as sophisticated or complete as those of today, but the serious reader who studies Witmer's writing will probably agree that he must be considered one of the real pioneers of American child psychiatry.[33]

Aside from his awareness of the importance of differentiating between mental defect and childhood psychosis, the significance of Witmer's work lies in his therapeutic approach to and success with these instances of differential diagnosis. We give below excerpts from one of his reports (296):

> At the age of two years and seven months this boy responded to every test like a feebleminded child and he was diagnosed by competent experts as feebleminded. Today he is a normal boy, not quite seven years old, reading, writing, and doing the number work of the second school year. Either he was not feebleminded and the diagnosis was a mistake one, or feeblemindedness can be cured. What is feeblemindedness—a performance level or an irremediable mental defect? Don's response to treatment shows that he had grave but not irremediable de

---

[33]In 1907 Witmer started the journal called *Psychological Clinic*. It is no longer in existence. Some of his case reports (292, 293, 294, 295, 296, 297) are more concerned with subnormality than others. Throughout the journal will be found similar cases by his students. As would be expected, there is much in the journal which is now outmoded, but the serious student of the problem will gain much by scrutiny of all the volumes.

fects. His arrest of development was nearly complete, the results of disease and the psychosis which accompanied the disease.

When a normal adult becomes insane we observe a marked change of character. "He is no longer himself," we say, and a prominent symptom is a reduction of mental level called technically "dementia." Autointoxication, disease and shock may cause insanity. Let us suppose that one or all of these causes affect a child in his first or second year. We shall not be able to observe much change in the child's mentality except that his mental development will be arrested. I maintain that one type of feeblemindedness, better called arrested development, is due to the same causes which produce insanity in an adult, and that in some cases the psychosis or mental disorder can be cured and the child restored to completely normal condition, provided the case be taken in hand early enough.

Except to the very observant eye of an experienced expert, these cases look more like feeblemindedness than insanity. Nevertheless, they are a species of feeblemindedness or insanity, whichever name we choose to apply, very different from the congenital imbecile, one of the mongolian type, for example. The mental disorders of children which cause arrest of development and apparent feeblemindedness are as diverse as the mental disorders observed and classified by the alienists. A child may be either feebleminded or insane, or he may be both feebleminded and insane. Some of the Orthogenic Cases reported in the earlier numbers of the PSYCHOLOGICAL CLINIC, notably Orthogenic cases Nos. 4, 6, 12, and 13, are not primarily cases of congenital defect, but cases of mental disorder in which there is a greater presumption of possible cure than in the cases of the child who is both qualitatively and quantitatively feebleminded.

. . . He was five years old last July, and so I entered him the following autumn in a near-by school, where he is the youngest of a group of first-grade children. His teacher says that he reads better than any of them and, except that he is poor in handwork, she considers him as competent as the other children.

"Terence," said he to his pal, the gardener, who was taking him to school the first day, "don't call me Donnie when we get near the school; don't call me Donnie or Don; call me Donald, which is right."

I saw Donald for the first time when he was two years and seven months old. His father carried him into my office, and deposited him, a soulless image, absorbed in the inspection of a card which he held in his pudgy hands, as regardless of his father and mother as of the new objects about him. While his gaze moved over the card, he scratched the back of his teeth; and then again he made a crooning, humming sound with which it is his habit to lull himself to sleep.

He paid no attention to a rattle, to a bright-colored ball or to a picture book which I held before him, but every effort to remove the card from his hands he resisted. His face, already crimson, became empurpled. His physiognomy took on an expression of angry hostility; and I retreated before the approaching storm, leaving him again to his absorption in the card.

"He is fond of music," his mother said; but the liveliest strains of the talking machine were powerless to distract him from his chosen preoccupation. In the months to come I was to discover that by preference he would sit or lie in bed for hours, looking attentively at the object which he happened to be holding in his hands. It appeared to be persistent, concentrated attention, that most difficult and valuable of mental powers to cultivate.

From two to six years the child has the flitting attention of a monkey. "How do you select your monkeys for training?" a trainer of animals was once asked.

"I hold a lighted match before them," he replied, "and picking out as the easiest to train those that look longest at the burning match."

Donald would look at nothing but his card. One could not guess what lay behind those dull blue eyes. Was it interest, or only emptiness of mind—the dreamy listlessness with which the corner loafer looks at the passing world?

"What are those abrasions about the mouth and ears?" I asked.

"When he gets angry," his mother said, "he will scratch and tear at them."

"What else can he do?" I asked, not venturing to break in upon this obstinate immobility by trying to get him to perform the simple task which might, perchance, reveal some hidden mental ability.

"Can he walk?"

"A little, but he only began about two months ago," she replied. "Until he was over two years old he hadn't even crawled; and he only learned to crawl by his nurse taking hold of his knees and advancing them one after the other."

As the flower blooms, the fish swims or the bird flies, so the child crawls, walks and talks. It is the unfolding of his own instinctive impulses. But this child had to be taught to crawl and to walk, and even yet he could only toddle about uncertainly. If he fell upon his face he would lie helplessly crying with his nose to the floor. Either he did not have the strength to change his position, or he did not know how, or he was unwilling to make the effort.

He never uttered a word spontaneously, and he could repeat at command only a few words like "Kitty," "Mama"—eight words in all. His understanding of language seemed to be limited to pointing to his head, eyes, ears and nose when these words were spoken. Even a chimpanzee of the same age as this boy, if brought up in human surroundings, will give evidence of understanding more of spoken language than this boy did. He could not feed himself. A much younger child can hold a cup or a spoon, but this boy could not even close his lips upon a cup when it was offered to him. He was still in diapers, and weeks were to pass before he could be safely clothed like the normal boy of two years and a half.

At two years and seven months Donald was doing no more than many a child does at twelve months, no more than every child should do at fifteen months. No one who saw him needed to consult an expert before deciding that he was subnormal. You had only to look at the large head—"top-heavy Bill" one of his teachers called him—the fat red face, the expressionless eyes and the helpless body to arrive instantly at the conviction that "this child is feebleminded."

And feebleminded I thought him—of such low grade that I refused at first to accept him for educational treatment in my school. With reluctance I finally yielded to the parents' pleas. He was the youngest child I had ever accepted for psychological treatment, and apparently the most hopeless.

The expert, like the parent, bases his opinion on the child's appearance, behavior and history. But even more important than these is the *"attempt to teach."* In doubtful cases I do not like to express an opinion until after I have observed the results of attempting to teach the child something new. This can often be done at the first examination, but I could not even begin to teach Donald.

"I should like to see him walk," I said. But when he was lifted from the couch, put upon his feet and made to walk, he burst into a paroxysm of rage. His eyes became bloodshot; even his gums bled. When he was put back upon the couch he returned to his contemplative absorption in the card. Offered a block, he made no effort to take it. He even closed his eyes, as though the very sight of it and me were more than he could endure.

When I took the card away, so as to secure his undivided attention, he had another paroxysm of rage. From this, however, I derived a little hope, for passion and rage may be an expression of strength. The child at least had energy at his disposal. His violent resistance evidenced resolute determination. Obstinate children are better material for training than the overpliant sort. I looked at him, sitting impassive, but always bolt upright, and this too, I thought an encouraging sign.

"He is a very easy child to neglect," one of my teachers entered in her report soon after he came to the school. "If you let him alone he will sit or lie in bed for hours and give no trouble. It is only when you try to do something with him, to dress him, or bathe him, even at times to feed him, that the trouble begins."

It takes some time and care to adjust a child to new surroundings, so I considered it no great misfortune that Donnie promptly got the measles. For a couple of weeks it was necessary to isolate him in the care of a trained nurse. This probably helped to make him less resistant to strangers. Perhaps there also awoke within his soul some responsive feeling of gratification when the soothing hand of the nurse or the doctor brought him relief from his distress of body. One month after Donnie's arrival I began his education.

"What to do," and "How to do it" are two puzzling questions confronting teacher and parent at every turn. To answer the first question is to present the aims of education. In the early years of education the three R's are the chief objective. The answer to the second question, "How to do it," will determine our method of procedure.

Educational aims and practice are commonly the outcome of theory. For example, an interesting and important theory of recent origin is the Montessori method. It aims to develop a child's natural abilities. It also has a theory of educational practice. It emphasizes and, in the opinion of many, relies exclusively upon appealing to the child's natural inclinations and desires. Deprecating the use of constraint and force, it throws the reins over the neck of the horse. Several children have been brought to me for examination and educational treatment who were nearly ruined by too close adherence to this supposed Montessori method.

I hold that constraint and liberty have equal value. At one time constraint, at another liberty, will bring the best results. The wise employment of constraint and force calls for greater intelligence and judgment on the part of teacher and parent than the leaving of the child free to work out his own salvation and development.

I try to approach the problem of educating a child like Donald without any preferred theory. More than twenty years of experience has led me to see that there is some good in most theories. A few are fit only for the scrap heap. One guiding principle, however, has stood the test of time and use: "The first task of teacher and parent is to gain and hold the child's attention by giving him something he *can* do, and after that something he *can't* do"—this in general is my method.

My educational aim is to develop attention by choosing tasks which develop it. Whether a child be one year of age, or two years, or six, whether he be in high school or college, the guiding principle of the educator should be to gain and hold attention first, and then to cultivate concentration, alertness, persistence, and endurance, all of these being attributes of attention.

For the rest, I feel my way. I watch the child to discover what he does with interest and with ease, and from here I get him to take a step forward in the direction best calculated to bring him to what I am aiming at, "the next higher level of attention." Montessori provides the child with stimulating objects—her didactic material—and leaves it with the child to make the next step forward. This is doubtless an acceptable procedure; but suppose the child refuses to take a step in any direction. He must be shoved.

To shove a child in the direction you want him to go is easy if the child is pliant and submissive. If he is a fighter like Donnie, and if, like him, he has no desires except to be let alone, the development of attention and the enforcement of obedience must go hand in hand.

When you have a trout on a hook at the end of a thin line, the only way to land him is to play him. He is lively and vigorous. He has desires which conflict with yours. If you use too much force you will break the line. If you use skill, yielding and yet constraining, you will in time get him into your basket. In this way the skillful teacher "plays" the child. The hook of attention is attached to the line of obedience, and then she watches the child's every move to insure his advance in the required direction. Shall she coax or force him? On the lee short of this question many a gallant education craft lies shipwrecked.

You can coax most children, some of the time at least, by appealing to their interests and desires, even as the hunter entices the deer to come within gunshot by appealing to its curiosity. But some children can't be coaxed, any more than you can wheedle a trout into your basket.

For example, take Donald. He did not have a keen desire even for food. He would not eat prunes, apparently because he disliked their appearance, and so they had to be mixed with his cereal in order to get him to eat them. He would not drink milk or water from a transparent glass. It must be offered to him in a cup. In the early days, indeed, he declined to drink water at all, and got his only liquid in the shape of milk or soup.

He declined to accept a sugarplum offered as a reward of merit; and if you took away the object he so fondly clasped in his hands, and then yielded to his ragings and returned it to him, he would very likely throw it violently across the room. He disliked to be dressed. He disliked to be taken out of bed and put on the floor. He disliked to be taken for a walk.

All these things aroused angry resistance; and in his passion he went so far as to do himself bodily injury; but as long as Donald held something in his hand there was peace and quiet.

"What to do with him?" He could not be bathed and dressed in this happy state of calm contemplation. Take away what he held and his hands went up to his ears and mouth, tearing at them till they bled. Tell him to keep his hands down, they went up just the same; perhaps he only scratched himself a little more strenuously. Put mittens on him, as his former nurse did, and he still went through the motions.

Smack his hands, anger and passion intensified the violence of his resistance. The only thing to do was to hold his hands. Could he be compelled to keep them down after they were released? The historic battle lasted for an hour and a half. His hands were held while his teacher spoke to him from time to time: "If I let your hands go, will you keep them down?"

He raged, he stormed, he grew apoplectic, but the hands were firmly held. At every lull in the storm they were released, and up they went again. In the end he gave in. Ninety minutes showed remarkable endurance, determination and consistency of purpose, qualities which might be successfully employed in his educational development later. Never again did Donnie hold out for so long on this or any other issue. My records show that though he raged at intervals during the ensuing twelve months, the longest period of resistance lasted for ten minutes only. He had learned his lesson. There was an inevitable persistence that would outlast his own. He might as well give in first as last.

The subsequent development of this boy under Witmer's supervision was both dramatic and heartening. That Witmer was an astute observer who did not allow dramatic change in the patient to cause him to overlook problems and weaknesses may be gleaned from Witmer's concluding remarks:

If I began my work without a theory and without understanding Donnie's mental status, I am far from that position now. I have unraveled much of the mystery, and I find the understanding of this one child of important value in interpreting the behavior and progress of other normal children. I believe that Donnie was at the start dominated by fear, which plays still an important rôle in his behavior. His concentration on the card was in the nature of a defensive reaction. He disliked to get out of bed because he was afraid to get out of bed. He disliked to walk and talk because he was afraid—perhaps of failure.

It was noted on one occasion that when taken outdoors he would not stop screaming even after he had been put on the back of a pony. I know now that this was the worst thing that could have been done to him. Donnie is afraid of all animals. He takes kindly, however, to little creatures and has often alarmed his teachers by bringing them caterpillars and worms.

One day Donnie, while seated at a table playing with a train of cars, had his attention called to the fact that a little gray kitten was in the room. He was mortally afraid of it, so he would not turn his head to look, but kept moving the train back and forth, saying, "Ppff! Puff!" in the same absorbed concentration which was characteristic of him at the beginning. He was ignoring the kitten just as he used to ignore people he disliked by closing his eyes when they came into the room.

He was afraid to look down a well, he was afraid of a doll, of a soft rubber ball, of a balloon, a loaf of bread, a spinning top. He was afraid to go on a sailboat the first time, but the second time he went with joy. He took a fearful pleasure in trains, for he loved them as moving things, and yet they terrified him. He would say: "Let us go to town in the three trolleys"; but when you asked him why he would rather go in the trolleys than in a train he would never tell you.

He has never verbally admitted that he is afraid of anything. "Won't hurt you," he very early exclaimed whenever he was frightened by anything; and this was one of his first spontaneous reflections. "Don't have to pat the pony," he would reiterate during the many weeks required to get him to overcome his fear of the school pet. The effort to take him out driving in a little pony cart, which it was thought would entertain him, only succeeded after a period of two months. But then, as was usual with him, he couldn't get enough of driving behind the pony.

Even yet he is afraid. "I like dogs," he declared lately, as he started on his way to school. "Nice kind dogs which don't bite," he added thoughtfully. Nevertheless, he managed unobtrusively to place his companion between himself and every dog. "I like to pat dogs," he boasted; but when one appeared unexpectedly he excused himself tactfully: "I don't like them that color."

So, while Donnie is fearful, he is not a coward. He is doing his best to overcome his fears, and he has worked out his own method of doing this. He had no fear of dark or of the supernatural.

Fears and desires are the two greatest motive forces of mankind. No problem is more perplexing and none so absolutely fundamental as the proper treatment of fears and desires so that these motive forces may excite the actions desired. As I understand Donnie now, he had no desires, but many fears. We compelled him to do those things which he feared. As soon as he had done the fearful thing, the fear, in many instances, disappeared and desire took its place. Donnie is now afraid chiefly of what surprises him.

Donnie's obstinacy measured the intensity of his fear, but in part it measured also the intensity of his desires. Always, from the very beginning, Donnie has known just what he wanted. Never was there any wobbly uncertainty of choice. He either desired it or he didn't desire it. This, to my mind, is a strong and valuable trait of character if you can turn it to the right use.

The desire for possession gives rise perhaps to his keenest pleasure. He held on to his card, not only because it enabled him to ignore the fearful things of the world about him, but he held on to it because here was something "all his own." Not until recently has he been willing to share any of his possessions with others. For a long time he not only clung passionately to his own possessions, but appropriated the playthings of all the other children as well, so much so that his room was known as the "Robber's Den." He is now so far advanced on the road to generosity that he will give away his second-best toy.

He has always shown the same concentration of attention which he showed at the beginning. One day recently he wore to school a necktie which he had borrowed from the gardener, Terence. The teacher could do nothing with him that day because he persistently explored the attributes of his new possession. He met Terence, who came to take him home, with the matured fruit of his morning's work: "Terry, can you see the top of *your* necktie?"

His first craze was for automobiles, and then for sailboats, bicycles, trains and cars—anything that moved. As he learned to talk, he went through the magazines. "It's an automobile, see the automobile," he kept reiterating. When he grew fond of excursions abroad, "Are we going out, Agnes?" he would say, "Agnes, are we going out?" a thousand times until he threatened to drive his nurse to distraction. No child can have a better endowment for future accomplishment later than this power of persistent concentration.

Donnie's traits of character are therefore positive traits. He has a definite array of abilities, keen desires, self-dependence. Even from the first he preferred to walk alone, though in constant fear of falling, rather than hold someone's hand. He only sought the hand if a terrifying object came in view. With strong desires and fears, strong likes and dislikes, Donnie has an equal capacity for happiness and great unhappiness, for success and failure. He can be sweet-tempered or angry and resentful. His emotional balance is easily disturbed, and he still requires very careful handling.

Of the cause of Donnie's mental condition when he came to us, and which led several experts to diagnose him as feebleminded, I cannot be sure. He had an illness after birth, which I now believe left his brain so devitalized that it permitted fear to gain the upper hand over desire. Of one thing I am certain: If Donnie had not been given the painstaking and expert training to which we subjected him he would by now have fallen into a state of irremediable feeblemindedness.

Although today the term psychotherapy refers to a variety of techniques and interpersonal relationships, it is most likely that no "school of psychotherapy" would advocate Witmer's initial handling of this boy. It would be quite wrong, obviously, to view his initial approach as a punitive one (although from the standpoint of the boy this was the case) in the sense that it reflected Witmer's feelings and did not stem from any theoretical conceptions. By focussing on the boy's inability or unwillingness to respond to an external figure, Witmer was deliberately attacking in a direct and dramatic manner the most blatant symptom, i.e., the autistic-like way of relating to the external world. Equally important, we think, is that this child was placed in what was essentially a therapeutic-educational milieu in which all phases of his behavior were under scrutiny, supervision, and stimulation. One gets the impression of a total push situation which went far beyond what today takes place in individual psychotherapy with these kinds of cases (on those relatively rare occasions when such treatment is attempted). The fact that the above case is but one among many reported by Witmer and his students would seem to have implications for current attitudes toward the treatment (or, more frequently, the non-treatment) of the very young, withdrawn, autistic-like, and defective-like child.

There are two things which impress one in Witmer's work. First, Witmer seemed to employ therapeutic effort as a way of deciding between one or another diagnostic possibility—most frequently between normal or defective potential. Second, the fact that the child with whom he was working was subnormal, and in some cases apparently severely defective, did not seem to influence the intensity of Witmer's therapeutic efforts. One gets the impression from his writings that Witmer, like Itard, was not discouraged by outward appearances and was possessed by a fierce determination to demonstrate that in the most hopeless case there was unrealized potential which could be made manifest under proper guidance. Such an attitude may be a mixed blessing and result in failure and harm to others. But when in the case of people like Itard and Witmer such an attitude is combined with brilliance and creativity—and a remarkably painstaking attention to detail and method—one gets the kinds of results that shed real light on human potentialities. Research reports like the present one are far less needed in the area of subnormal functioning than people like Itard and Witmer. Freud did not need somebody else's research report to make his now recognized contributions to psychology and psychiatry and, in their own fields of interest, neither did Itard and Witmer.

X. THE HIGHER GRADES OF MENTAL DEFECT

Most psychological research in subnormal functioning has utilized the so-called high grade cases of mental defect. This research has tended to be of two kinds: (a) that which has been concerned with a particular type of mental defect (e.g., cerebral palsy, minimal brain injury), and (b) that which has been concerned with a particular procedure (e.g., psychotherapy) or personality characteristic (e.g., rigidity). In this chapter we shall be discussing both kinds of research; our choice being determined by the amount of previous research done on a problem as well as our opinion about the potential significance of the particular problem.

A. Cerebral Palsy[34]

In 1949 one of the writers (225, p. 186) stated:

> In reviewing the psychological work which has been done with the cerebral palsied, one is struck by the paucity of studies. Aside from the pioneer efforts of Lord and Doll, the psychological problems, practical and theoretical, presented by the cerebral palsied have not been attacked. What studies have been made indicate that while psychological procedures are an indispensable part of the diagnostic armamentarium, there are wide gaps in knowledge concerning the intellectual and emotional growth of the cerebral palsied child; especially with the very young child is there need for refined procedures which will make early diagnosis valid and reliable. There has not been a single study in which a sizable group of cerebral palsied children has been followed from infancy to maturity. If such a study should be done, the factors making for individual variations in rate of development would probably become clearer. In setting up such a study it would be necessary for the psychologist to focus some attention on parent-child relationships. In the past the presence of the severe motor defect has obscured the fact that the cerebral palsied child is being responded to and stimulated by people whose behavior in turn is affected by the severely handicapped child. Although many cerebral palsied children are severely limited in exploratory and locomotor activity, it seems reasonable to assume that parental behavior may either accentuate or lessen the deleterious effect of such restrictions. Case studies by Thorne and Gesell demonstrate that parental attitudes toward and the handling of the cerebral palsied child can be important factors in intellectual growth. It must

---

[34]Many cerebral palsied cases are characterized by a severe degree of mental deficiency. We have put our discussion at this point in the report because there has been some psychological interest in the high grade cerebral palsied child whereas little or none has been shown in the severe cases. The present discussion is relevant, we think, for most cases of cerebral palsy regardless of level.

be concluded that the nature of the growth of intellectual behavior in the presence of a severe motor handicap existing from birth remains a fertile area for research. Until the relation between capacity and functioning is better understood, the clinician must be cautious in interpreting the significance of test findings.

In 1955 Cruickshank (50) presented a survey of the literature on the psychological aspects of physically handicapped children and many of the studies he discussed concerned cerebral palsied children. It is our impression from his review that, while a little progress has been made in understanding some aspects of the functioning of these children, particularly in the perceptual area, there still has been little or nothing done along the lines of a *longitudinal* study of such children. There are several reasons for our emphasis on the longitudinal type of study:

1. It is our experience that when one groups cerebral palsied children on the basis of degree of physical or motor impairment, there is wide variation within any one group in personality organization and intellectual level and efficiency. Variation in these respects still obtains when one compares mildly with severely handicapped cerebral palsied children. It is by no means rare to see a quadraplegic whose functioning is discernibly better than many hemiplegics. It is our clinical impression that *one* source of such variation is parental reaction to and handling of such children. This is probably not a very revealing statement and by it we mean nothing more than that we have been impressed by how certain parents seem to have been able to respond to their child as if his physical handicaps were merely an obstacle which they had to help the child circumvent to whatever degree was possible. It is as if they were truly able to conceive of the child as a unique and developing individual. This is in marked contrast to many parents who seem fixated on the child's physical handicap and their own frustrations and disappointments. It goes without saying that parents *should* be expected to respond to the birth of such a child with feelings of frustration and disappointment, but many parents are unable to overcome these feelings to the point where they can gain satisfaction from their interaction with the child.

2. In the early study conducted at Vineland by Doll, Phelps, and Melcher (63), they noted a tendency in some of their subjects for test scores to increase over a longer period of time than is characteristic of an institutionalized, mentally defective population. In commenting on this finding one of the present writers stated (225, p. 176):

One of the most interesting findings in this study concerns the concept of delayed development. If the validity of this finding should be confirmed in studies with larger numbers of cases, it would mean that the clinician working with the younger cerebral palsied would have to exercise caution in predicting the course of a patient's intellectual development. From a theoretical standpoint it would be of significance to determine why some cases show this delayed development and others do not. The unpredictable relation between the focus of the brain lesion and the intellectual level indicates that anatomical factors may not be sufficient to explain the differences in the rate of intellectual growth. When one considers the possible effects of the presence of a cerebral palsied child on family structure and relationships, the influence of these factors cannot be disregarded. Not all parents react to the cerebral palsied child in an accepting, warm, consistently affectionate manner. The effects of such a child on the emotional stability of the parents are considerable, as Lord noted in her study. It seems reasonable to assume that parents of the cerebral palsied child react more realistically and less emotionally to his limitations and deformities when he is older than when he is younger. The number of parents who never "accept" their child is probably considerable. It is interesting to note that the children displaying delayed development in the Doll, Phelps, and Melcher study showed this growth after they had been admitted to the Vineland Training School. Although preadmission test data were not available, one might speculate about possible differences in the handling of the child at home and at Vineland and their differential effects on rate of development. The very high standard of care and individualized training for which Vineland is noted may well have been a factor in the delayed development of some of these children.

In light of the absence of longitudinal studies we do not feel justified in speculating further on the rôle of psychological factors on the intellectual development and personality organization of the cerebral palsied child. We are of the strong opinion that until these children are studied longitudinally— with the degree of attention to familial factors which psychological theory indicates—our understanding of these children will not be enhanced and our handling of them will not change in any fundamental respect. When it is remembered that we are dealing with individuals who vary markedly in degree of physical handicap, that these variations are psychologically effective or limiting at different phases in development, that methods of rearing and external stimulation must take such variations into account, and that the parents must understand the significance of all these factors and be able to respond to the psychological needs of the child—when the problem is stated in this way one soon becomes aware of how little we know, how inadequate our advice to parents must be, and the pressing need of research in this area.   In our opinion, the need for this type of research is further emphasized by recent studies (50, p. 319) which, in contrast to earlier ones, indicate that the bulk of cerebral palsied children are either mentally retarded or defective—at least insofar as test scores are concerned.   It is highly improbable that research confined only to the site of lesion and degree of motor involvement or physical handicap are sufficient to explain either such over-all findings or the individual differences in functioning which are always found.

Mention should be made here of some ongoing but unpublished research being carried out with cerebral palsied and other groups under the direction of Kirk at the University of Illinois.   Starting with Osgood's (199) theoretical analysis of the language process, Kirk and McCarthy (155) and Sievers (243) developed tests with the aim of determining as specifically as possible where in the complicated communication process an individual's difficulty could be pinpointed.   If this difficulty could be pinpointed there would then be the possibility of being able to develop more adequate training or remedial procedures than is now the case.   The following is an illustrative case:

> John was referred for a diagnosis because of delayed speech development.   He was diagnosed at several medical clinics with contradictory results.   Neurological and *EEG* examinations were essentially negative.   Due to poor motor coördination, delayed speech and behavior, it was suspected that he was brain-damaged.
>
> John did not speak in words and sentences until the age of four. Individual speech correction was tried at this time with little results. A teacher of the deaf worked with him at the age of five and obtained results in speech development.
>
> The language test was administered to him at the age of 6-8. . . . Although his language was quantitatively below that of the average child of his age (language age 3-11), his major deficits were in the association process at the grammatical or sequential level.   His association at the semantic level was relatively superior to his other processes and levels.
>
> To check his general development other tests were administered. On the Stanford-Binet he obtained a mental age of five years and five months with an *IQ* of 73.   On the WISC Scale he obtained an *IQ* of 76. An analysis of the subtests of the intelligence tests confirmed the profile on the language test.   For example, in repeating sentences, which utilizes association at the semantic level, he was superior.   In the repetition of numbers, which represents the association processes at the sequential (non-meaningful) level, he was inferior.   In a reading readiness test his lowest score was in rhyming, which represents association at the

grammatical or sequential level. In other words, when meaning was dominant he scored high; when the tasks involved putting together sequences or patterns with little or no semantic components he scored low. In a conference with the parents they informed us that this boy never went through the babbling stage. As a consequence, he did not imitate. It appears that language in this boy developed by a circuitous route. He did not babble (cause unknown), hence did not develop the decoding, association, or encoding processes at the integration level. This defect resulted in retarded imitation—which is decoding, associating, and encoding at the grammatical level. Speech was delayed. Meaning was established without the benefits of babbling and imitation. Instead, the language process had to await a decoding, association, and encoding process at the semantic level, a later stage of development. Even at the age of six and one-half he was still defective at the grammatical level. . . .

Because this case was of great interest to us, a tutor was hired and a special remedial program begun, aimed at training in sequential skills. Assessment after five months of training showed he had made 3.5 months gain at the grammatical level in the visual-manual and audio-vocal channels, respectively.

This case illustrates the ability of the test to differentially diagnose communication dysfunction in psycholinguistic terms for an individual child. It illustrates how the underlying language theory may be used to suggest a course of remediation.

Initial results with these language tests suggest that the underlying theoretical rationale has some validity. Kirk, et al., are well aware of the defects of the tests as now developed and work is under way to refine their procedures. What we feel at the present is most significant about this work is (a) the recognition of the utility of theory in focusing on and illuminating new aspects of an old problem (i.e., language and the communication process); and (b) the attempt to integrate meaningful psychological test results with remedial program planning—an attempt which, as we shall see below, is all too rare.

B. THE DIAGNOSIS OF MINIMAL BRAIN INJURY

The value of psychological tests as aids in the diagnosis of brain injury has been of much interest to psychologists and has given rise to some controversy (225). We would agree with Goldenberg's (267, p. 164) recent conclusion, based on his review of the literature, that even those tests which seem to have the most promise will have to be much more developed before they can provide a valid criterion of brain damage in the absence of positive neurological signs. When one considers that many high grade and border-line defective cases present thorny problems of differential diagnosis (e.g., between brain injury and emotional disturbance), it becomes apparent that the accurate determination of brain injury, especially minimal brain injury, is an important area of investigation.

There is an aspect to the problem of the diagnosis of minimal brain injury by psychological tests which deserves emphasis if only because it tends to be overlooked. We refer to the obvious fact that cases of minimal brain injury are undoubtedly not homogeneous in terms of site and extent of lesion. It would be expected, therefore, that different degrees and sites of lesion would interfere with or be manifested in behavior in differing ways, as a recent study by Morrell, Roberts, and Jasper suggests (188). Since the neurological criteria of minimal brain injury are far from perfect, the psychologist is comparing his test results and interpretation to a criterion of unknown validity. If in a particular case the neurological diagnosis is negative while the psychological examination is positive for brain injury, one can neither conclude that the psychologist is wrong nor right. If the neurological diagnosis is positive while the psychological examination is negative, it may be that the particular lesion does not show up in the behavior sampled by the tests; it may well be that the psychological examination is wrong. The point is that when one employs an imperfect criterion—and when in addition one assumes that different lesions probably have different effects—then unresolvable disagreements between the neurological diagnoses are inevitable in clinical practice or in research in which two diagnoses are compared.

The problem may become more clear in the following example which concerns two studies by S. B. Sarason and E. K. Sarason (227, 228) and which have been reported in detail elsewhere. In the first study high grade "familial," institutionalized individuals were studied. This group was divided in two according to certain psychometric criteria. One of the groups had a test pattern considered suggestive of minimal brain injury while the other group did not. All cases had been considered negative by neurological examination. When EEG's were then obtained there was a significantly greater incidence of abnormal records in the group with a test pattern considered suggestive of minimal brain injury. One thing that might be said about these findings is that the conventional neurological examination was far less sensitive in picking up brain disfunction than the EEG and that the latter is a far better criterion by which to judge psychological diagnosis than is the former. However, in a similar study of cerebral palsied children, all of whom obviously had brain damage which was reflected in the conventional neurological examination, 9 out of 17 cases had a normal *EEG* record. One might conclude from this that the *EEG* is not as good a criterion for the psychological results as is the neurological examination. These studies strongly indicate that one of the major research problems is the unreliability of a single diagnostic procedure for brain injury. It is undoubtedly true that no single procedure is adequate for detecting brain injuries which differ in site and degree. Until multiple neurological and neurophysiological measures are utilized—much in the same way as the psychologist uses multiple test criteria—the psychologist must proceed with caution when he attributes validity to his diagnoses of brain injury.

A characteristic of most studies in this area has been the use of more than one test each of which is administered once. There is certainly nothing inherently wrong in administering a test but once as long as one is aware that one has a relatively poor basis for discriminating at least two kinds of failures or poor performance: (*a*) those cases which as a result of practice or directed instruction could learn to respond more adequately to the particular kind of problem-solving task—failures, so to speak, with the potential of relative adequacy; (*b*) cases which as a result of practice and directed instruction show no potential for improved performance. What we are in effect suggesting is that the diagnostic process be viewed as a learning one in which stimulus and instruction variations are employed in order to ascertain the conditions under which a more adequate performance is possible. If the failure group could be discriminated in the manner indicated above, it would not be surprising if more of those who showed no improvement in the course of learning would be considered brain-injured by neurological criteria than would be true of those who showed potential for improvement.

An example may clarify our suggestion. According to the 1937 standardization of the Binet, the majority of seven-year-old children are able to reproduce a diamond from a model. With decreasing age there is a decreasing number of children who can do this. These findings are frequently interpreted as reflecting the maturation of certain intellectual processes. While this is undoubtedly in large part true, it does not follow that under certain conditions of learning and motivation the majority of six and even five-year-old children could not learn to perform adequately on the task. In short, one must not confuse what a child does with what he can learn to do under altered conditions of learning. It would seem that we are dealing with a similar situation when we conventionally administer tests for the purposes of discriminating between children with or without brain injury. We tend to assume that failure or poor performance on particular tests is indicative of brain injury without attempting to study further the conditions under which improved performance may be possible.

It is probably worthy of note that most investigators have been far more interested in the problem of diagnosis of brain injury than in the significance of such a diagnosis for the handling and treatment of the child. It is our impression that there is too often quite a gap between the diagnosis and its utilization in formulating a program which would minimize the adverse effects of injury or in some way compensate for it. Aside from the obvious benefits which could accrue to the child, we stress the aspect of program planning because it conceivably can provide data relevant to the validity or adequacy of diagnosis. If in a suspected or even clear-cut case of brain injury, no particular program is planned, it is extremely difficult, if not impossible, meaningfully to relate changes in the child's behavior to the diagnosis of brain injury. If, however, program planning is based explicitly on the nature and details of the diagnosis—if the program planning is akin to predictions about what should happen if this particular child were handled in certain ways—then one has a basis for evaluating the adequacy of the diagnosis. Even here one cannot arrive at unambiguous conclusions, but particularly in instances where expected changes do not occur, such an approach can serve as a spur to research not only on more refined diagnoses but on the nature and behavioral implications of different types of brain injury as well. In addition, such an approach cannot help but stimulate research on different kinds of treatment and training procedures.

The work of Strauss (267, 268) is perhaps the best example we have of the fruitfulness of an approach which is based on the integration of concepts in developmental neurology, diagnostic criteria of brain injury, and detailed program planning. Elsewhere one of us (225) has criticized the logic and validity of some of the diagnostic criteria employed by Strauss. Although Goldenberg (267, p. 145) felt that these criticisms were somewhat severe, it should be noted that they lead to a conclusion identical to his own stated at the beginning of this section.[35] Although the validity of some of

---

[35]Keller (150), in a recent but as yet unpublished study done at the Wayne County Training School, was unable to replicate earlier findings by Werner and Thuma (286, 287). In these earlier studies, stimulated by the conceptions of Strauss, significant differences were found between brain injured and non-brain injured in the perception of apparent motion and also flicker-frequency. Keller advances the hypothesis that unwitting examiner influence may have been responsible

the diagnoses of minimal brain injury based on Strauss' criteria can be questioned, it should not be overlooked that Strauss' conceptions have given rise to ingenious educational procedures and an environmental structuring which undoubtedly have had positive therapeutic effects. It is likely that there are cases where one would feel that a diagnosis of minimal brain injury by Strauss' criteria was unwarranted but where the child's response to the program planned for him, while it cannot "prove" the correctness of the diagnosis, certainly cannot be used as evidence against it. Unfortunately, we do not have the kind of detailed case reports which would allow one to gauge the frequency of this type of case. If we had such comprehensive case descriptions one could also get a better idea of the rôle of the "therapeutic milieu" in producing behavioral changes regardless of the presence or absence of brain injury. For example, we obviously have been impressed with the educational techniques and over-all therapeutic approach described by Strauss and Lehtinen (268). But one cannot avoid raising the following question: To what extent would children with no brain injury but with severely disabling learning difficulties and/or behavior problems benefit from the kinds of programs adapted to the presumably peculiar needs of brain-injured children? Inasmuch as the brain-injured child can be assumed to be one who also manifests personality disturbances, it is likely that some of the positive changes which occur are due to amelioration of these disturbances. This, of course, is a problem in cases where there is more than minimal brain injury, e.g., the cerebral palsied child.

Gallagher's (78) study of matched groups of brain-injured (*BI*) and familial (*F*) mentally retarded children has recently appeared. We shall quote in some detail from his concluding section for several reasons: (*a*) his results on lack of differences in perceptual behavior run counter to what has previously been found or believed, (*b*) he seems on the basis of his intensive studies to have arrived at conclusions and hypotheses similar to those discussed above, and (*c*) his suggestions about the direction of future research deserve emphasis:

> Matched groups of 24 brain-injured mentally retarded children and 24 familial mentally retarded children were compared on measures of

---

for the earlier significant findings, especially since the experimenters knew to which group each subject belonged and the nature of the experimental task was of a sufficiently ambiguous nature as to increase the subject's dependence on the examiner for guidance. This point, which may be or may not be correct insofar as the Werner and Thuma studies are concerned, has not been sufficiently stressed in the methodology of studies on this problem.

perception, learning aptitude, intellectual scatter, language development, quantitative ability and personality characteristics.

1. On tasks involving perceptual ability the results were as follows:

   a. There were no significant differences between groups on the Memory for Designs tests.

   b. There was some suggestion that the *F* group produces fewer reversals on the Copying Designs tests than the *BI* group although both have reversal difficulties on Memory for Designs tasks.

   c. A slight trend was found for a poorer performance by the *BI* group on producing designs on a marble board.

   d. Most of the *BI* group performed adequately on the perceptual tasks although a minority of the group displayed definite perceptual problems.

2. Contrary to predictions, no differences were found between groups on a test of direct and incidental learning aptitude, although a few of the *BI* group were much slower in completing the learning task, perhaps suggesting some distractibility in these children.

3. No differences were found between groups on measures of quantitative concepts.

4. On the measure of language development the results were as follows:

   a. Although no differences were found on general language development, there were distinct differences between groups on their patterns of language development.

   b. The *BI* group were superior to the *F* group on tasks requiring verbal imitative responses and good speech production.

   c. The *F* group were superior on ability to associate objects, trace mazes and supply correctly the missing words in a sentence. These results supplied some confirmation to the notion that many *BI* children have difficulty in making associations, correctly integrating verbal concepts, and using visual motor perceptual ability.

   d. Both institutionalized retarded groups revealed weaknesses in ability to produce adequate speech and verbal imitative responses.

5. Differences between groups were found on almost all personality variables in favor of the *F* group. On the rating scales the *BI* children as a group lived up to their reputation of being hyperactive, lacking attention, being fearful, less popular and generally more uninhibited children than their familial pairs.

6. An analysis of successes and failures on Binet items revealed essentially no differences between groups.

7. A factor analysis of all intellectual measures revealed:

   a. A high amount of variance in both groups accounted for by a factor of general mental development.

   b. The *BI* group produced a second factor related to poor perceptual ability.

c. General language development was found to be the second most important factor in the *F* group. The variance accounted for by both second factors was quite small.

Discussion

It makes sense to ask the question: Are the differences that can be seen between these two groups substantial enough to create recognizable differences in the total patterns of development of the children in these groups. The writer believes that this study and previous research direct an affirmative answer to this question. A second crucial question might be: Do these differences imply the need for drastically modified educational and training programs or merely slight modifications in existing programs? Here the answer is less clear and depends to a large degree on which brain-injured child you are talking about. The range of different problems and lack of problems within the brain-injured group is large enough to cast considerable doubt on the notion that plans can or should be made for brain-injured children as though they were a homogeneous group.

Practically all of the research which has attempted to describe the characteristics of brain-injured children has properly searched out areas of difference between them and groups of children without organic injury but of comparable mental status. One of the advantages of the present project is that it gave the writer a chance to observe the performance of two groups of children on a large variety of tests and ratings and thus to conclude that there are large areas of similarity between the two etiological groups as well as some differences.

Let us first examine those characteristics wherein the similarities between groups seemed to outweigh the differences.

No differences were found on quantitative ability between the groups and there seems to be little reason for making any special provision for teaching these concepts to groups of brain-injured children. Although perceptual problems were supposed to interfere with the development of quantitative conceptualization, this does not appear to have been the case. Some children in both groups did show a tendency to reverse numbers and geometric figures but this seemed to be an isolated difficulty which did not negatively influence the actual learning of grouping principles, number combinations, etc. Except in certain unique and individual cases, the rôle perceptual difficulties play in the development of quantitative concepts seems greatly overrated.

Essentially no differences between groups were obtained on the learning aptitude test which attempted to measure such important learning characteristics as memory, learning through experience, and response to the environment surrounding the learning situation. The fact that the brain-injured group seemed to learn almost as effectively as the familial children again suggests that perhaps too much emphasis has been placed on the differences between these diagnostic categories and not enough attention directed toward their similarities. Certainly it is as important for educators to realize that the *BI* group does not show inferior or unique approaches to standard learning tasks as it is to realize that *BI* children may have a tendency to turn the numeral "3" on its side.

There seemed to be general similarity in the patterns of successes and failures on the Stanford-Binet which suggested that this omnibus test (at these mental age levels) was unable to detect strong differences in intellectual approaches of the two groups. But the most surprising finding of the present study is the failure to obtain differences on a variety of measures of perceptual ability.

Although group differences were not obtained, examination of the individual cases did reveal that a minority of the children in the *BI* sample had definite perceptual problems. Conversely, it can be said that many of the *BI* children had adequate perceptual abilities in relation to their general mental development. The factor analysis on all measures, except personality ratings, did seem to suggest that perceptual difficulties play a secondary, but recognizable, part in the intellectual development of the brain-injured children but not in the familial children. However, the results of the factor analysis suggest, first of all, that general mental development is much more important in both groups than any unique and specific intellectual factors. The general mental ability factor accounted for approximately four times as much variance as did the perceptual factor in the brain-injured children. It would seem that the mental age score remains the best single piece of information an educator can have about a child although it can be made more meaningful by our knowledge of secondary patterns of factors in individual children.

Despite the rather impressive list of characteristics wherein there were no differences between the groups, there did seem to be two areas in which distinctive group differences existed. The most impressive area of difference was in the personality ratings where, as a group, the *BI* children seemed definitely inferior to the *F* group on desirable characteristics.

The fact of the difference was easier to oserve than was the underlying cause of it. One general explanation has been that the brain-injured child is not able to perceive social situations correctly or identify the correct social cues or distinguish between appropriate and non-appropriate behavior and thus becomes a behavior problem because of these deficiencies.

A second possible explanation was that the general lack of inhibition with its accompanying impulsivity and unpredictable behavior made the *BI* children socially unacceptable to peers and adults. This, in turn, produced secondary effects of fearful behavior and demands for complete attention and affection as a result of the distrust and rejection brought about by the original disinhibition.

Since this research project was not specifically designed to answer the above question, no definite conclusion can be made. Note, however, that these unfavorable personality characteristics still appeared clearly evident in the present *BI* group which did not seem to possess a large amount of perceptual difficulty. This suggested that disinhibition may have played a greater rôle in personality maladjustment than perceptual difficulties. At any rate, it presents an interesting hypothesis for further study.

The second large area of difference between the groups was their language development. It was only when the total language development scores were broken down into their component parts that these differences became noticeable. The relative inability of the *BI* group to associate objects in appropriate groupings confirmed to some extent the notion of the general difficulty they have, as a group, of developing concepts. More confidence could be displayed with this interpretation if the results on the Word Association test also had shown differences. The notion that the *BI* child has trouble placing concepts in proper association also gained some support from the poor *BI* results on the Vocal Cloze subtest which required the children to place an appropriate word in a sentence.

Strauss and Kephart have been concerned with the paradox that *BI* children can produce apparently adequate language performance even while their perceptual abilities are quite disturbed. They have considered three possible answers: The *BI* child uses language without really knowing the meaning of the words he used, he can make up for poor perception by learning about things through the perception of others conveyed to him through the medium of language, and he may learn language by listening and repeating parrot fashion. Our data supports the last of these three possibilities most strongly. The *BI* group was definitely superior on the mimicry items and also was only slightly deficient on those items which required adequate association and conceptualization.

An analysis of the language test data showed that there were tendencies for the brain-injured children to be superior to the familial children on items requiring the use of the auditory-vocal channel and inferior on items tapping the perceptual-motor channel. Although neither of these differences was statistically significant, this appears to remain a fruitful hypothesis if the measuring devices can be developed into sufficiently valid instruments.

Those brain-injured children who revealed these unique personality characteristics and language development patterns present a real challenge for educators who must develop unique teaching methods and methods of controlling environment to compensate for these differences.

It goes without saying that none of these results should be carelessly generalized to brain-injured children in the community until further investigations are made. Too many other factors such as family relationships or amount of control over behavior remain as potentially important variables in influencing personality development.

If one major difference can be pointed to in distinguishing the results of this study from previous research, it would be the lessened importance of perceptual disabilities and the increased importance of disinhibition and language development in the total developmental picture of the brain-injured child. As mentioned before, it is difficult to accept poor performance on many perceptual tasks as representing purely perceptual difficulties. Such poor performance may be due also to disturbing environmental or situational conditions which stimulate the child's disinhibitory characteristics as in the case of using confusing background patterns on a marble board test.

One important question seems to arise as a result of this study: How useful is it, from an educational point of view, to have the neurological information that a child is brain-injured? The distribution of cases, even where there were significant differences between groups, showed that many of the brain-injured children did not have the unfavorable characteristic that might be assigned to them as a group. Educational provisions made for brain-injured children on the basis of such over-all group differences would not be any more applicable to some brain-injured children than they would be to the familial children. Strauss has made the valid point that it is not necessary for everyone in a brain-injured group to be different from everyone in an organically sound group for a characteristic to be a good diagnostic indicator. The reader should not forget, however, that Strauss is referring to the use of these instruments as aids to medical diagnosis.

To ask the question another way: Does the educator not gain more information from the fact that the child is perceptually disturbed than from the fact that he is brain-injured? Brain injury is the proper province of the neurologist but the perceptual distortions, disinhibition, and problems of association that *sometimes* occur in *some* brain-injured children are the province of the educator and psychologist.

It would seem reasonable to expect the educator to make his own educational diagnosis of each child's perceptual development, personality skills or language development and make his plans accordingly whether or not a diagnosis of brain injury has been medically determined.

One thing that seems indicated is that greater attention be paid to the rôle that personality and behavior difficulties are playing in preventing many of these brain-injured children from attaining full efficiency. It is hoped that the individual training program now being tried with the

BI sample will give us some clues on the possible changes in behavior that can take place when a close personal teaching relationship is maintained with these children over a long period of time.

This leads to another question as to whether or not it is profitable to continue to do more studies designed in the same fashion as the present one. It would please the writer to believe that this study would represent the last of these attempts to obtain psychological and educational characteristics based on vague and oversimplified neurological classifications.

There would seem to be two general directions research might take from the present study. If one is interested in relating functioning behavior to the structure of the nervous system, then, test results can be compared in various groups who have injuries to demonstrably different areas of the brain. If one is interested in the educational implications of such psychological characteristics as disinhibition, perceptual abilities, or language development, then, these characteristics should be studied directly without being dependent upon medical diagnosis.

It is the function of science to attack one problem until it has been drained of its useful knowledge and then use that knowledge to move on to something else.

This may be the time to redirect our efforts to such complex problems as are suggested by the results of the present study and other similar research.

C. The Familial or Garden-Variety Defective

Throughout this report we have attempted to adhere to the practice of labelling as mentally defective those in whom there is some kind of central nervous system pathology. As was pointed out in Section II, there is tremendous variation within this group in degree and site of pathology and, of great practical importance, in the degree to which normal intellectual and social development are possible. For purposes of this report we have used the term mental deficiency to refer to those individuals who have demonstrable central nervous system pathology of a kind and to a degree which probably rules out normal social and intellectual functioning. These have been the individuals we have discussed in the earlier sections of this chapter, as well as in the previous one. In contrast, we have labelled as mentally retarded that large group of individuals whose retardation is not associated with organic pathology and who are able, or could become able, to maintain themselves in the community. The initial sections of this report were concerned primarily with the mentally retarded, particularly the large percentage of this group which never is institutionalized. We turn again at this point to the mentally retarded because the bulk of the "high grade" cases in our institutional population differs in no fundamental respect from those we have called mentally retarded. Parental neglect or abuse which comes to the attention of authorities, delinquent behavior, aggressive display in the school situation, lack of adequate community facilities (e.g., foster care, temporary shelters)—these are frequently the factors which determine whether or not a retarded child is likely to be institutionalized. We, therefore, think it misleading to group, as is traditionally done, the institutionalized mentally retarded with the mentally defective. Although labels frequently do not add to our knowledge, they can cause confusion. To classify the institutionalized mentally retarded child (variously called the familial, or garden-variety, or Kallikak type of defective) with the mentally defective can and has obscured in the minds of many that from the standpoint of organic pathology and cultural background the two groups are strikingly different.

In the first two sections we made suggestions about the kind of research which we felt had to be done if we were to gain an understanding of the rôle of psychological and cultural factors in the etiology of mental retardation. Sarason (225) has elsewhere reviewed the research literature and made suggestions about the direction of future research. It should come as no surprise that this research has yet to be developed. At this point we would like to indicate other areas of research which have not yet been attacked or adequately discussed.

1. From the standpoint of our society one of the most neglected research areas concerns the psychological changes which are associated with institutionalization.[36] When one realizes how many millions of dollars are spent in building and maintaining our institutions, it is surprising that very little research has been done to study the psychological changes which institutionalization brings about. Institutionalization involves a *drastic* change for the individual and there is every reason for assuming that it is experienced as a stressful one involving (*a*) separation from loved or familiar figures, (*b*) pressures to adjust to a completely new physical and interpersonal (peer and adult) environment, (*c*) confusion and resentment about their helplessness, (*d*) anxiety in relation to the future. In the case of the mentally retarded individual, who usually comes from an unfavorable family situation, we are usually struck by the material differences between home and in-

---

[36]This problem is also relevant for the various types and grades of mental deficiency. We raise the problem in connection with the institutionalized mentally retarded because they make up the large proportion of those whom the institutions consider placeable in the community.

stitution. But this is the way *we* view the change and one should not assume, therefore, that the child perceives it the way we do. What to us is a psychologically unfavorable family situation, and what may even be an unpleasant one to the child, may in the process of institutionalization be perceived by the child as his only source of security. As important as the immediate effects are those of prolonged institutionalization. It is our clinical impression that the major effects of prolonged institutionalization are four-fold: (*a*) overt conformity to the institutional culture at the expense of personal spontaneity and expression, (*b*) excessive phantasying, especially about the "outside world," (*c*) avoidance and fear of new problem-solving situations, and (*d*) excessive dependence on the institutional culture, which becomes most apparent when the possibility of leaving the institution arises. The effects of institutionalization undoubtedly vary with age at commitment. In stressing the possible deleterious effects of institutionalization we are not unmindful that we are dealing with a very complex problem. In this connection mention should be made of some interesting and unusually well-controlled studies by Clarke and Clarke (46) in England. They studied test score changes in mentally retarded individuals following institutionalization. In their published report the Clarkes present evidence for the conclusion that it was those who come to the institution from the very worst homes who showed the greatest test score changes. The ratings of home environment were made by someone with no knowledge of the test scores. In unpublished material which the Clarkes kindly sent to us further confirmation of these findings was found. In these unpublished studies "retesting was carried out by a colleague who knew neither the patients, nor their earlier test scores, nor their social ratings of early environment." Because length of time in the institution was not associated with size of test score increase, the Clarkes concluded that these changes "are more the effect of removal from a very adverse environment than of entry into a relatively better one"— a conclusion supported by their unpublished data. It is conceivable, therefore, that similar results could be obtained if this type of individual had been removed to an environment other than an institutional one. It is in no way to devalue the English studies to express the hope that research will be conducted on the personality as well as the intellectual changes which accompany institutionalization. In any event, we feel that this whole problem is a most crucial one because it bears not only on the problem of the effects of environmental change on performance and potential but on one of our society's major ways of handling the problem of mental retardation.

2. In an earlier paragraph we expressed the opinion that the bulk of the high grade cases in our institutions differed in no fundamental respect from those we have called mentally retarded but are not institutionalized. One could argue against such a conclusion on the grounds that the test scores of those institutionalized are probably significantly lower than the scores of those who are in the community and that such a difference may reflect a "basic" difference between the two groups. From all that we have said thus far in this report, it should be apparent that we do not think the grounds for such an argument are tenable. However, it should be noted that we do not have systematic studies on this problem. For example, we are not aware of any systematic study on factors associated with variations in intellectual performance *within* families of retarded children who have been institutionalized. The problems we are raising here seem very similar to that of why some children become delinquent while others in the same family or neighborhood do not. If studies of mental retardation similar to those of the Gluecks (91) on juvenile delinquency were carried out, our understanding of the problem would not only be increased but, as in the case of delinquency, we would have a more rational basis for picking out much earlier than we now can those mentally retarded children who are likely to require institutionalization.

3. In the previous chapter it was pointed out that the incidence of psychosis in the mentally defective population is apparently much higher than in the general population. The significance of this finding is obscured by the failure to break down the statistics according to etiological groups. Consequently, we do not know if the incidence rate is the same for the mentally defective and the mentally retarded. We also do not know whether the incidence rate for the institutional population is the same as for the non-institutional one. It is our clinical impression that the incidence of psychosis among the institutionalized mentally retarded is probably less than among the institutionalized, high grade defective and probably much lower than for the lower grades of mental defect. However, the recent findings by Hollingshead, Redlich, *et al.* (120, 121, 190, 210, 211, 215, 216, 234) that the prevalence of treated psychosis in lower class individuals—those to whom the mentally retarded are most similar in a cultural and intellectual sense—is much higher than for other social classes in our society suggests that the incidence rate for the non-institutionalized mentally retarded may be rather high—perhaps larger than for institutionalized mentally retarded who were not included in the survey by Hollingshead and

Redlich.[37] One might speculate that although the overprotective and infantilizing institutional environment may have deleterious effects on the personality of the mentally retarded individual, particularly if he is committed at an early age, it in some way makes the development of a psychosis less likely. These are speculations, however, which should not detract from recognition of the importance of the research problem of the relation between mental retardation and psychotic behavior.

D. PSYCHOTHERAPY

In 1955 Cowen (49) presented a comprehensive review of psychotherapeutic work with subnormal individuals, almost all of these studies being concerned with the mentally retarded and high grade defective. Cowen's excellent summary statement of the scientific status of the research on this problem follows:

> Any attempt to summarize the results of psychotherapeutic work with the defective child in a concise or confident manner must be regarded as hazardous. While there has undoubtedly been more work with defectives than with any other group of exceptional children, most authors have with good reason described their studies as exploratory. Firm generalizations would be difficult indeed to defend. It is, for example, not entirely clear why Neham, after a partial review of work in therapy with defectives concludes: "The experiments presented seem to indicate that the directive supportive method in which a warm, friendly, personal relationship is developed seems to be the best approach adapted to mental defectives." Certainly the evidence at this time is not sufficiently clear-cut to indicate that any one approach to therapy is best for mental defectives in general and even less for any specific group of defectives. There has not, in fact, been a single comparative study of the relative merits of various approaches to therapy with defectives. Similarly, one might question the basis of another of Neham's conclusions, namely that the ". . . weight of evidence indicates that high moron intelligence is necessary for therapeutic success." One must be careful to distinguish between what may appear logical and what is an interpretation of sound research. A generation ago the notion that

---

[37] In this survey a tremendous effort was made to determine the number of people in the Greater New Haven Area who were in psychiatric treatment (private, clinic, state hospital, etc.) on the arbitrarily chosen day. We think that it is a reflection of professional attitudes toward the psychological problems of subnormal functioning that individuals from the area who were in institutions for the mentally defective were excluded from the survey. To have included this large number of cases would have undoubtedly presented more than a few knotty problems for the survey but their omission does set limitations about generalizations concerning incidence of psychiatric disorders and their social class correlates.

therapy with defectives could not be successful may have seemed both logical and acceptable to most practitioners. Subsequent research has demonstrated otherwise. In the absence of comparative research in therapy with defectives at different intellectual levels, what Neham states as a conclusion should be regarded at best as a tentative hypothesis.

In a more positive vein this much can be said. Instances of successful therapeutic outcomes with defectives have peen reported from many settings by practitioners with diverse orientations. These include case reports, studies of interview therapy, reports of play therapy and expressive media, studies in group therapy, by psychoanalysts, directivists, non-directivists and eclectics with institutionalized and non-institutionalized defectives. Though many of these reports are open to serious criticism when considered alone, together they underscore the conclusion that therapy with at least some defectives can be successful. Further, the few comparative studies of therapy with the defective and intellectually normal child offer no support for the notion that the former has a poorer therapeutic prognosis.

Although there are some instances of increases in IQ following therapy with competently diagnosed defectives, there is no basis for concluding that such increases are either general or typical. Most subjective evaluations of personality and behavioral changes after therapy with these children suggest that significant changes have taken place. Regrettably, diagnostic test data before and after therapy are extremely rare and are not consistent enough either to support or to contradict generalizations derived from subjective reports.

One strong indication of a growing conviction that therapy with the defective is both feasible and potentially fruitful may be found in the ever increasing number of studies being reported in this area in recent years. Unfortunately there have been few systematic attempts to analyze research problems and formulate research needs. Notable exceptions to the preceding statement include Sarason's suggestions of some basic research problems in individual psychotherapy with defectives, Cotzin's proposals for a research program in group psychotherapy, and Mehlman's analysis of methodological problems in research on therapy with the defective.

There can be little question of the effectiveness of psychotherapy with some defectives. Much needed information in this area, however, is still lacking. It is not yet clear which children in this heterogeneous group can be helped by therapy and which ones cannot, nor do we know about the relative effectiveness of various types of therapies or different therapeutic media, either with the defective group as a whole or any of its sub-groups. These are some of the important future research problems that face us. Their solution should extend the usefulness of psychotherapy to many defective children heretofore regarded as essentially unapproachable.

We shall here not attempt to review the material covered by Cowen, or Sarason's (225) review and discussion. We will at this point present certain problems and considerations not previously discussed or emphasized.

One basis for evaluating therapeutic efforts with any individual is in terms of the goals which the therapist had hoped for or anticipated, i.e., what did *he* want to accomplish at the end of his therapeutic contacts with the patient? Since most therapeutic efforts with mentally retarded or defective individuals have been over relatively short periods of time involving few contacts, it can be assumed that the goals of the therapist did not involve attempts to achieve a generalized change in the patient—the goals were specific and modest (as indeed they are in most therapeutic relationships). The fact that the evidence suggests that these individuals can benefit from brief psychotherapy is, of course, important. But what are the factors which enter into the therapist's formulation of modest goals? Very frequently practical considerations (such as available time and money) dictate the restriction in therapeutic goals. It is our opinion, however, that as important as practical consideration are implicit assumptions about the amenability of these individuals to therapeutic efforts which have as their aim a more or less generalized personality change. Put in another way: far more frequently than not the retarded individual is considered to be incapable of utilizing a long lasting and intensive therapeutic relationship in a way so as to become able to change his perception of himself and others, to effect changes in his handling of his life problems, and to narrow the discrepancy between potential and performance. We are here *not* saying or implying that the aim of such a therapeutic approach is to make the subnormal individual "normal"— or the normal person an intellectual giant. What we are trying to say is that therapeutic efforts with the mentally retarded implicitly assume that such an individual is incapable of utilizing introspection and retrospection, of experiencing insight, of examining his motivations, phantasies, and anxieties, of being able to seriously want to change his characteristic pattern of overt and covert responding—of all of these things the retarded individual is implicitly considered incapable. As soon as one considers this statement either as an injustice or as a far too sweeping generalization then at least two questions arise. First, if these statements are too sweeping, then what are the limits of the retarded in these respects? Second, what accounts for the relative absence of research with such a therapeutic approach, despite the fact that case studies have been done which suggest that such an approach may be feasible? We refer particularly to the psychoanalytically treated

case reported by Chidester and Menninger (41), a case treated in an orthodox, intensive psychoanalytic way over a period of three years. We also
refer to some of the cases similarly treated and reported by Clark (44).
As important in these cases as the degree of change effected by treatment
are the indications that the functioning of the subnormal individual always
reflects in varying degrees extremely strong neurotic conflicts stemming
from earlier experiences and relationships.[38] To what extent a condition of subnormality predisposes the individual to an exacerbation of
neurotic symptoms, or to what extent the subnormality is an effect of these
conflicts, is impossible to say. What we feel could be said is that for any
individual whose functioning is considered subnormal, we can assume the
presence of long standing neurotic conflicts which, so to speak, have added
insult and injury to whatever handicaps he may originally have had. What
is also significant about these psychoanalytically treated cases is that they
were able to learn to think about themselves, others, and the past in a way
that is ordinarily not associated with subnormal functioning.

It is our opinion that the relative absence of intensive, psychoanalytic
studies of subnormal individuals is due to at least two factors. First, as a
group psychoanalytically trained therapists are simply not interested in the
problem, in which respect they are only somewhat more delinquent than
other psychiatrists and psychologists. From time to time there has appeared
in the psychoanalytic literature case studies of "pseudo-feeblemindedness"
but these are cases, unlike those described by Chidester and Menninger or
Clark, where an initial diagnosis of mental deficiency or mental retardation
was hardly warranted. It is also our impression that when the psycho-
analyst discusses or theorizes about the problem, his unfamiliarity with the
clinical material becomes too apparent. Second there has been an encouraging increase of interest in recent years in psychotherapy with subnormal indi-

---

[38]It should not be overlooked that *therapeutic* failure does not necessarily mean
that one's efforts have been totally unfruitful. The therapy may have produced
little or no effects but one may still have gained important hypotheses about the
causes of the failure, hypotheses which may result in changes in therapeutic procedure, or stimulate research with other than therapeutic techniques, or result in
changes in type of subject (e.g., age, etiology, life situation) utilized. To obtain
any of these benefits in the face of therapeutic failure at least two factors must
be present: (a) the therapist must be prepared to *test* his explanations for the failure and (b) the therapy (its technique and underlying rationale) should contain
the possibility of obtaining data and behavior from the patient which could
shed light on factors working against improvement in therapy. It would be our
opinion that not all therapeutic techniques have equal potentiality for benefiting
from therapeutic failure.

viduals on the part of the psychoanalytically oriented (as distinguished from psychoanalytically trained) therapists. As one might expect in the development of a new area of interest, these therapists seem primarily concerned with the effects of various procedures and the methodological problems involved. While such concerns are in no way to be derogated, it should be emphasized that such concerns are not likely to shed much light on personality dynamics and structure, on the one hand, and developmental variables and experiences, on the other hand. The most durable and fruitful consequences of the development of psychoanalytic therapy (or therapies) have been less the effects of such therapy than the way it has illuminated the rôle of certain variables and relationships in the development of personality. It is because intensive psychoanalytic therapy gives us the possibility of gaining a better understanding of the developmental interaction between intellectual and personality organization that we stress its importance as a research area. We would like to make it perfectly clear that in making such a recommendation we are not in any way prejudging the therapeutic merits of psychoanalytic as against other types of psychotherapy—itself an important research problem. What we are prejudging is the superiority of psychoanalytic therapy for achieving a better understanding of the personality structure and development of the subnormal individual—an understanding which may be of inestimable value for problems in rearing, training, and parent counselling.

The above recommendation will undoubtedly be reacted to with differing degrees of scepticism and rejection, by psychoanalysts and others. Aside from the practical problem of attracting people to the problem, and making appropriate training available to them, there will be many who on theoretical and other grounds will feel such a program to be unfeasible. It would be our guess that most, if not all, who would react in this way are those who have never had intimate, day-by-day, clinical contacts with the varieties of problems and personalities which are obscured by such labels as subnormal, mentally retarded, or mentally defective. We recognize this statement to be an *argumentum ad hominem* but there are too many examples where theorizing about a problem with which there has been little or no clinical experience can prevent the acquisition of further knowledge.

Intensive, psychoanalytic therapy is certainly not the only means whereby personality dynamics and their developmental course can be studied. In this connection a study done in Belgium by Bobon (20) is worthy of note. He reported a case of a 39-year-old woman who was mentally deficient, illiterate, and who exhibited delusions of persecution. From the case history material one might question the diagnosis of mental deficiency. In light of the family background—her mother, two maternal aunts, and a cousin were considered mentally defective—one might more cautiously consider her as mentally retarded, her retardation being evident from the beginning of school. Her schizoid character was also noted early in her life but it is impossible from the material to determine the relationship between the retardation and the schizoid characteristics (e.g., gentle, timid, shy, retiring). In his report Bobon reiterates that the woman was a mental defective who later developed a full blown psychosis. Bobon's interest in this woman, who was committed to the mental hospital when she was approximately 25 years of age, stemmed from changes in her speech and use of language. We need not go into the details of these changes except to say that Bobon considered them to reflect, in part, an "intentional" or motivational factor—apparently one of which the woman was not aware. Bobon then reasoned that if a motivational factor was at work its effects on the woman's linguistic behavior would be reduced "in states of least psycho-motor activity." Various experiments done with this woman while in a state of narcohypnosis clearly revealed that she could respond more accurately and less neologistically than in the waking state. In such a state "our subject expresses herself in a generally correct way in tests of object naming. The first verbal manifestations in awakening, spontaneous or provoked, show . . . neoformations of words of the aphasic type. In the spoken language of the waking state . . . the neoformations of words of the asphasic type seem non-existent, the naming of objects is usually faulty, as are the vocabulary deformations, giving to her speech its characteristic stamp. . . . We are the first, we believe, to try to use the experimental method for this type of problem, and we again conclude: a relatively important intentional component is found in the origin of this pseudo-glossolalia."

Bobon's contribution may have, we think, important research implications for research with subnormals. It has long been known that states of narcosis may not only be therapeutically advantageous but productive of important insights into an individual's personality structure, particularly when the individual has not been amenable to conventional psychotherapeutic procedures. For research which has as its focus an understanding of the personality dynamics of the subnormal individual, the procedures exemplified by Bobon's work seem deserving of further exploration.

E. Studies in Rigidity

The generalization has long been accepted that the subnormal individual is more rigid than the normal. This conclusion is based on anecdotal and observational data as well as on the results of some experimental studies (159, 160, 167, 285). Stevenson and Zigler (264) have succinctly summarized the basis for the generalization:

> Feebleminded individuals have been characterized as being "rigid" in numerous studies in which feebleminded children and adults and normal children have been compared. The tasks employed have been primarily of the "satiation" and "switching" types. In the former, Ss are instructed to perform a task and are allowed to repeat the task until they become satiated and no longer want to continue it. They are then instructed to perform a highly similar task and again are allowed to perform until satiated. Feebleminded Ss have been found to spend significantly more time on each task than normal Ss. This lack of influence of initial satiation on the performance of subsequent tasks has been interpreted as indicating a greater rigidity in the personality structure of the feebleminded S. In the "switching" tasks the S, after acquiring one response, is forced to switch from this response to a new response involving identical or highly similar stimuli. The smaller amount of transfer from the first to the second task shown by the feebleminded Ss has been interpreted as indicating greater rigidity.

A recent study by Plenderith (205) did not find any differences between normals and subnormals on a discrimination-learning and discrimination-reversal task. This unexpected finding has received confirmation from a series of systematic, experimental studies carried out recently by Stevenson and Zigler (264, 265) at the University of Texas. In these studies the subjects consisted of what is traditionally called the high grade, familial defective. These subjects were divided into two comparable mental age groups but differing in chronological age, i.e., a younger and an older group. In addition, a group of normal children of similar mental age as the subnormals was employed. Whereas in the earlier studies of rigidity the subject was required to perform a response *in compliance with instructions*, in the studies by Plenderith as well as those of Stevenson and Zigler, the subject was required to learn a response, i.e., the subject was required to initiate a course of action with minimal instructions and with minimal interaction with the experimenter. The following are the major findings and conclusions from these studies:

1. Neither in switching from a size-discrimination to another size-

discrimination problem nor in switching from a size-discrimination to a position-discrimination problem involving the same stimuli, were there any differences in rigidity among the three groups (normal, younger, and older high grade subjects) as measured by frequency of perseverative responses.

2. The frequency of rigid responsiveness was found to be a function of the difficulty of the problem presented. This was true for the three groups and no significant differences were found among them.

3. The discrepancy between the above and earlier findings are interpreted by Stevenson and Zigler as a function of differences in methodology employed. "In earlier studies involving tasks most comparable to the present one, S was not required to learn a response, but to perform a response in compliance with instructions. For example, in one of Kounin's studies, S was instructed to depress a lever in order to obtain marbles; following practice on this task, he was instructed to raise the lever to get the marbles. Studies such as Kounin's seem to introduce a variable which was minimized in the present study. With the present task, the correct response is acquired on the basis of the differential reinforcement S receives following each response, while in Kounin's task the response is made primarily on the basis of instructions. Differences in rigidity between normal and feebleminded Ss of the same MA in the instruction-initiated task may be related to differences in the Ss' motivation to comply with instructions, rather than to differences in a general personality characteristic of rigidity."

4. In a further study of rigidity in which the degree of supportive comments made by the examiner was varied, evidence was obtained that the subnormals who received support performed better than those who did not.

One of the major significances of the Stevenson and Zizler studies is that they illustrate that among the mentally retarded, as in the case of any other group, it is hazardous and may be very misleading to describe them as if they possess a particular characteristic (e.g., rigid) at all times in all situations. Those who have worked intensively with retarded children, as in a psychotherapeutic relationship, would probably agree that one cannot pin labels on these individuals without taking account of the stimulus conditions, the motivations engendered, and the nature of the interpersonal dynamics involved. It is probably fair to say that one of the reasons psychotherapy was for so long not attempted with subnormals was the assumption that they were too rigid to benefit from a therapeutic relationship.

The Stevenson and Zigler studies throw light on an apparent paradox involving the mentally retarded (which would include the institutionalized, high grade cases). On the one hand, it has long been the custom to regard the mentally retarded as operating best in simple, routine, monotonous situations which, so to speak, capitalized on their rigidity. This belief underlies the placement and training practices of most institutions. On the other hand, as we have discussed earlier in this report (Sections II, VI), many studies have demonstrated that the adult level of functioning of many individuals who in grade school were judged retarded is surprisingly good—the nature of their work and problem-solving is not compatible with the assumption that rigidity is a pervasive characteristic. The paradox resides in the fact that both conclusions (i.e., they operate well in simple situations and they also can operate well in more difficult situations) are probably true. From the standpoint of the Stevenson and Zigler studies the paradox could be resolved in the following way: if the retarded individual is put into a simple situation (e.g., vocational) in which he is instructed how to respond and in which a premium is put on compliance with instructions, the retarded individual (particularly the institutionalized one) will respond "efficiently" even though he may also impress one as rigid and perseverative. If, however, the vocational situation is one which requires a learning process, initiative in the sense of having to make judgments or choices, strong motivation, and meaningful rewards (aside from those accruing from compliance with the instructions of authority figures)—if the situation has these characteristics, then the retarded individual will perform significantly better than one would have expected from his *IQ* score. It seems reasonable to assume that in the latter instances the conditions of motivation and learning were far more similar to those of the Stevenson and Zigler studies than to the earlier studies of rigidity.

Perhaps the best observational or clinical evidence that can be cited in support of these conclusions as well as the Stevenson and Zigler studies is the work of Schaefer-Simmern (232) to which we have already alluded on page 43. It will be recalled that he was interested in the nature and development of artistic activity and in one of his studies utilized a group of high grade, familial, institutionalized cases. The artistic development and productions of these individuals were little short of dramatic, especially in light of the fact that initiative, decision-making, and criticism of one's own work was required of them. As we have said elsewhere (225, p. 320) about his work:

> Schaefer-Simmern's studies seem to have implications beyond the
> field of artistic activity. They corroborate a principle often neglected

in practice, namely, that the work an individual does must be of such a nature and at such a level as to engender a feeling of adequacy in relation to it and to allow him to observe his own growth process in it. Reward in the form of praise from others is important, but unless the individual receives satisfaction from his own realization of change the therapeutic effects will be temporary. Praise from others, like reassurance, is usually of small value when unaccompanied by insight. When Schaefer-Simmern's procedures are contrasted with those ordinarily employed in occupational therapy units in institutions for defectives, one wonders whether a reorientation in thinking is not indicated.

Our own experience with occupational or vocational units in institutions certainly supports the following eloquent statements by Schafer-Simmern (232, p. 47):

> [In these occupational units] the patient may attain control over his hands, he may even learn perfect manipulation of a tool, he may become so used to this occupation that he is able to execute it without personality participation in it, he may even feel at ease in doing it, but the compulsory attention and concentration repeated over and over will throw him into a mental and emotional rigidity worse than before. He may become more or less adept at making things, but his personal relationship to them remains external because the work does not have its origin within him; it does not reflect himself. The performance is not related to the nature of his organism as a whole, as a psychobiological unity. Merely manual execution employs only a very small fraction of the total organism, and the attention and concentration it demands are not a result of the patient's inner decision. Only when the innermost core of interest voluntarily determines the applying of one's energies, when one feels that the work being done is an indivisible part of oneself (a condition which requires, of course, that it be in full conformity with one's own stage of visual conception), and when one is aware that attention and concentration are indispensable in order to realize oneself—only then does work become constructive.

One can only hope that the Stevenson and Zigler studies give rise to interest in the nature and sources of individual differences in rigidity among the mentally retarded. Given any particular experimental situation, what is the range of individual differences and what are the kinds of experiential and personality factors to which the differences may be related? In asking these kinds of questions, we are in effect suggesting that the ultimate value, theoretically and practically, of studies of rigidity (or any other single behavioral characteristic) will depend on (*a*) the knowledge we gain about the function of these characteristics in personality organization and (*b*) the antecedent factors which give rise to such a characteristic. In other words, by more or less studying a characteristic in isolation we run the risk of over-looking both its functions and development within a complex personality organization. For too long our understanding of the subnormal individual has been blocked by focusing on his intelligence as if this "thing" operated in splendid isolation from the complexity we call personality. In recent years there has been an encouraging degree of interest in the personality of the subnormal individual and we are here expressing the hope that focusing on single personality characteristics will be followed by attempts to fathom their developmental sources and course as well as their functional relationships to other significant personality characteristics.

F. Intelligence and Family Size

There have been numerous studies (194, 270), particularly in England, demonstrating a negative correlation between the intelligence test score of a child and the size of the family of which he is a member. Thomson (270), who was for long concerned with the problem, concluded that the correlation was approximately —0.25. The following illustration by Thomson may be helpful to the reader:

> I have constructed the following artificial symmetrical grid of 2,050 cases, so as to give a correlation of —0.25. It does not represent any experiment and must not be taken as giving, say, the actual range or distribution of family size. It is merely illustrative. An experimental grid would show families up to 13 and more, and the distribution of family sizes would be skew.
>
> In this grid, in which we may suppose A, B, C, D, E, F to be grades of intelligence and 1, 2, 3, 4, 5, 6 to be family sizes, although the tendency is unmistakable, and is expressed by the quantitative statement $r = -0.25$, there are nevertheless eighteen (14 + 3 + 1) "only" children who are below average intelligence, and eighteen members of the largest families (here families of six) who are above average intelligence.
>
> Casual observers, moreover, and even people like teachers, or journalists, or clergymen, do not see the whole population but only a selected part of it. They know secondary schoolchildren or slum children. Their acquaintances tend to belong to a class with large (or with small) families, to a certain occupational or social stratum, and so on. That is to say, they are unacquainted with the whole of the data shown in a grid [like the one below] and though, of course, they do not actually make a grid, they draw conclusions *as though* from a grid which is only *part* of the . . . [one below]. . . . Suppose we take such a part, say the top

AN ARTIFICIAL CORRELATION GRID OF 2,050 CASES REPRE-
SENTING A NEGATIVE CORRELATION OF 0.25

	1	2	3	4	5	6
A	5	18	24	14	3	1
B	18	73	114	84	28	3
C	24	114	212	192	84	14
D	14	84	192	212	114	24
E	3	28	84	114	73	18
F	1	3	14	24	18	5

left hand quadrant only, where all the families are below average in
size and above average in intelligence. That is the part of the data,
for example, which will represent the relations, friends, and acquaint-
ances of most of the readers of this memorandum. This truncated grid is

5	18	24
18	73	114
24	114	212

and gives on calculation a correlation of —0.07 only, so small as entirely to escape casual notice. Yet in the whole group of 2,050 the correlation is —0.25, and this is what matters.

In the bibliographic references given above, the reader will find discussions of the major explanations which have advanced for understanding the
negative correlation. The interested reader will also wish to refer to Anastasi's (5) recent and excellent discussion of the methodological and interpretive problems involved. For the purposes of the present report, we shall
focus on Nisbet's (194) study of the effect of "environmental influence of
the size of family on verbal ability and through it on general mental development." We choose this study because its findings and implications
seem to be very relevant for the mentally retarded individual who frequently
comes from a family the size of which is larger than that of the non-retarded
person. Our own experience with an institutional population suggests that
the incidence of large families among the high grade portion of such a population might even be higher than in the case of the non-institutionalized retarded population.

The following is Nisbet's summary of his hypotheses and findings:

> The slight but definitely established tendency for intelligent children
> to be found in small families and dull children in large families has
> been attributed to the inheritance by intelligent children of an intelli-

gence which in their parents is associated with a smaller size of family. However, the observed tendency may be due at least in part to the fact that being a member of a large family under present circumstances depresses the environmental component of a child's test score. Predictions of the future level of national intelligence depend on how far one or the other of these causes is operating to produce the observed tendency.

The former cause is suggested by the results of previous investigations in which attempts to hold constant such factors as parental occupation or overcrowding in the home have failed to dispel the negative correlation; but such methods are not adequate if the actual family size is itself an environmental factor—if the lack of adult contact and consequent retardation in verbal development suffered by a child from a large family depresses the environmental component of his test score. Such is the hypothesis which is put forward on the basis of previous work, both on the negative association of family size and intelligence test score, and in other fields, for example, in the comparison of orphanage children and only children, in studies of bilinguals, deaf children and twins. It is not suggested that this cause alone operates to produce the negative correlation of family size and intelligence test score, but only that it contributes to the correlation to an extent sufficient with other influences to mask any possible downward trend in national intelligence and to prevent the possibility of using the testing of age-groups of children for predicting the amount of any possible decline in national intelligence level.

The hypothesis was tested by three methods: by partial correlation of family size and verbal ability with intelligence held constant; by correlation of family size and several tests with different verbal loadings; and by correlation of family size and intelligence test score at different ages.

In two groups each of some 2,500 children aged eleven plus, the partial correlation between family size and score in a test of English attainment (with intelligence test score held constant) was negative (about —.10) and significant in both groups at the .05 level. In a random sample of 200 children aged eleven, the correlation between family size and score in a verbal Moray House Test was —.30, the difference being significant at the .05 level. These results support the hypothesis that the environment of the large family constitutes a handicap to verbal development, and that this verbal retardation affects general mental development. If this were so, one would expect the negative correlation between family size and intelligence test score to be more marked at later ages when the cumulative effect of environment begins to show itself; and this prediction was confirmed with tests applied at different ages. The correlation between family size and intelligence test score in an age-group of 1,236 children aged seven was —.26; in a similar age-group of 1,270 children aged nine was —.29; and in four such age-groups aged eleven plus was —.33. The difference between the correlation at age seven and at age eleven was significant at the .01 level, and was not attributable to the effect of incomplete families. In a group of 178 children who were tested at ages seven, nine and eleven, confirmatory results were obtained, though the difference between the correlations in this group was not significant because of the small numbers.

The results suggest that part (but not all) of the negative correlation of family size and intelligence test score such as was found in the Scottish Mental Survey among children aged eleven, may be attributed to the environmental influence of the size of family on verbal ability and through it on general mental development. At the same time, in each experiment it seemed clear that the whole of the negative correlation could not be explained in terms of this environmental influence. Others who have worked on this problem on a nation-wide scale do not deny a certain amount of environmental influence, and would probably wish attention to be drawn to the substantial negative correlation which remains even when the environmental influence is allowed for.

One of the more obvious implications of Nisbet's study is the further evidence it provides that test scores cannot be interpreted as measures of innate ability. Less obvious, perhaps, is the implication or possibility that language attainment is but one of many factors affected by the influence of family size on intellectual functioning and personality organization, and that the over-all correlation between family size and intelligence would be reduced even further if other possible effects could be isolated. For example, Nisbet states that "words are more than mere instruments of expression but are the very material of thought and afford a system of symbols which greatly increases the efficiency of abstract thought." In light of this statement, one can justifiably maintain that a test of language attainment may by no means reflect the possibly pervasive effects of adverse factors on the development of verbal behavior. In fact, some of Nisbet's findings may be interpreted in this way. He found, "The correlation between family size and score in the non-verbal Matrices test was —.20 while the correlation between family size and score in a Moray House Test was —.30, the difference being significant at the .05 level. These results support the hypothesis that the environment of the large family constitutes a handicap to verbal development, and that this verbal retardation affects general mental development." To arrive at this conclusion one must assume that the non-verbal Matrices Test does not require verbalization and the manipulation of symbols. The test does not require articulation *but it does require sustained self-verbalization and symbolization.* Consequently, the correlation of —.20 between family size and the "non-verbal" test may also be a reflection of the pervasive effect of handicapped verbal development. We can put the point in this way: There is probably such an intimate reciprocal relationship between the development of language and thought processes, that whatever impoverishes the former would likely have a generalized rather than an isolated effect on the latter.

Among the mentally retarded, the effect of family size on language and mental development is further complicated by the fact that they also differ culturally or in social-class terms from most of the non-retarded population. It is far more likely that these differences operate, as does family size, in a negative rather than positive fashion, especially when we are perceiving and evaluating the mentally retarded in a situation (e.g., a test or school situation) the values and language of which derive from other social class groups.

The basic question arising from this important study concerns the psychological significances of a variable like family size. Nisbet's study indicates that size of family influences language development but it does not tell us how this comes about. Is it simply that when there is a large family each child is exposed to a great deal of verbal stimulation but receives less training from adults? Is it possible that the effect of family size on language development is less a quantitative one (i.e., amount of stimulation and training) than a qualitative one in the sense of the content and style of the stimulation? These questions cannot be answered at the present time but they do suggest that a variable such as family size has implications for some of the most important developmental problems. It is easy to determine the size of a family but it is another thing to study and determine how this variable is experienced by children and affects their development. It is both sobering and instructive to note that beginning with the oft found correlation between size of family and *IQ* score, and then indicating, as Nisbet did, that the variable of language had to be considered, one soon finds oneself faced with the central problems of human development—an instance of where the more you know the more you need to know.

XI. RECOMMENDATIONS

In various places in this report we have made suggestions about specific research problems which if pursued would, in our opinion, provide important information having both practical and theoretical significance for the field of subnormal functioning. At this point we would like to summarize briefly only those recommendations which seem to be of major import.

A. Cultural Factors

Most of this report has been concerned with what we have termed·the mentally retarded individual. Such individuals, of somewhat staggering numbers in our population, come largely from the lowest social classes, or from culturally distinct minority groups, or from regions with conspicuously poor educational facilities or standards. Because the condition is so highly correlated with social class and cultural factors we have insisted on distinguishing it from mental deficiency, where such relationships do not obtain and where, in contrast to mental retardation, there is demonstrable central nervous system pathology which effectively precludes an independent social existence. Regardless of theoretical bent, no responsible investigator has denied that the level and quality of the functioning of the mentally retarded reflects social and cultural factors. *What has not been systematically studied is how these kinds of factors operate so as to have an interfering effect on development.* The question of the degree of influnce of these factors can not be answered until we understand how and when they exert their influence. There would probably be general agreement that one of the more significant impacts on the behavior sciences in the last 50 years has been made by the study of cultural variations as they affect personality development. It is because the field of subnormal functioning in general, and the mentally retarded group in particular, have in contrast been neglected or bypassed by social scientists—despite the obvious importance of such areas for these workers—that we have emphasized the importance of studying the problems of subnormal functioning in terms of social science theory and methodology. Our approach to and understanding of such areas as delinquency, alcoholism, neurosis, psychosis, and child-rearing have changed and increased in part because of the application to them of modern social science thinking and research procedures.

The field of subnormal functioning is unfortunately distinctive in its isolation from such developments, yet it is in several ways able to derive maximum profit from similar research orientations. Many non-European cultures provide learning situations for children which, while quite appropriate for living within those societies, render their members almost totally unfit for meeting the intellectual problems of our culture. Just as in the case of research in culture and personality, knowledge derived from such non-European cultures can give us the perspective to isolate more clearly the relevant positive and negative factors operative in intellectual development in our own culture, and will permit us to test hypotheses in this field in a wide variety of settings. Furthermore, within our own society there exist many subcultural groups many of whose currently young children we can safely predict will be rejected by the larger society as retarded during later childhood or early adolescence. We can therefore study them at an early developmental level when they are actually in the process of acquiring those intellectual attributes which will later become handicaps, and thus determine the early dynamics of some kinds of retarded intellectual development.

Culture also determines the degree and kind of intellectual ability required for adequate—including minimally adequate—performance in any society. The fact that many retarded adolescents in our society pass school age and proceed to function adequately as adults in the larger society, but some do not, points to the importance of research which will identify the necessary intellectual abilities. Virtually nothing is available in systematic form on this subject, although many persons in social work and special education are capable of making notably effective intuitive judgments as to the deficits and remedial needs of individual children.

B. Cross-Cultural Research in Pathology

Our culture has maximized control of the physical environment in all its aspects to such a degree that it often becomes very difficult to determine what dietary and other factors have impinged on a given individual even in the recent past. In contrast the usually smaller and more stable non-European societies, most of whose members live more exposed to the physical environment, prepare similar foods in similar ways, and so on, can provide populations far superior for the testing of hypotheses regarding genetic, dietary, metabolic, or other factors in the etiology of pathological conditions. These populations have received some attention from researchers in a variety of fields of pathology but not nearly to the degree that would result from a wider awareness of the opportunities available.

C. Longitudinal Studies

When it is merely noted that there has not been a single comprehensive longitudinal study of subnormal individuals, mentally retarded or mentally deficient, it will probably be understandable why throughout this report we have discussed the need for such studies. It is as if there have been two implicit assumptions about the importance of longitudinal studies: (a) the subnormal child is relatively unaffected by his environment and the longitudinal study, therefore, would not be very revealing; (b) all behavior of the subnormal individual is explainable by his intellectual deficit—he is what he is because of his deficit and all other factors are secondary. There is no evidence for either assumption. From the standpoint of any psychological theory one would assume that the subnormal individual, even the severely defective one, *is influenced by and in turn influences* the familial and social milieu into which he is born and in which he develops. In terms of this assumption the study of the early development of the subnormal individual as a scientific problem needs no justification. Furthermore, from a practical standpoint such studies would provide empirical data which could serve as a basis for parental guidance. In the case of the defective child, for example, there simply is no available scientific basis for the guidance of parents in the rearing of the child. It is only in recent years, and largely in the case of the severely defective child, that we have begun to see how the defective infant and child affects and changes the familial environment. We have not yet gotten to the point of studying the impact on the child of the environment which he blamelessly but markedly has disrupted.

D. Intellectual Factors

In the past several decades there have been a few, but very important, developments in the theory and measurement of intellectual functions. These developments suggest that the variety of intellectual factors or functions is greater than had previously been thought and that our conventional tests are most inadequate for the evaluation of these factors. Despite the fact that the clinical psychologist has long been aware of the limitations of conventional tests, clinical practice in general, and in the field of subnormal functioning in particular, has been relatively uninfluenced by these newer developments. In the case of the mentally retarded, most of whom maintain themselves in the community, there is strong evidence that our conventional tests leave much to be desired both as evaluators or predictors. In part this is undoubtedly a function of the narrow range of functions which these tests presumably measure. It should be pointed out that there are surprisingly few psychologists who have been concerned with the problem of the nature and development of intellectual functions. With the exception of Jastak, we know of no psychologist who has attempted to apply such theorizing to the problems of subnormal functioning. Our recommendation (it would be better to say hope) is that as a first step an attempt be made to bring together those few workers who are primarily concerned with the theory and development of intellectual functions in order that the status of this problem area can be described in terms of varieties of theoretical approach, conflicts between theories, existing research, and the direction of future research. We would also recommend that an attempt be made at such a meeting to present to these workers, most if not all of whom have thus far not been interested in subnormal functioning, aspects of this subject which seem relevant to the development of a theory of intelligence. The publication of such proceedings would not only be a contribution to the field of psychology but could serve as an important source of research stimulation to those working in subnormal functioning. It could also serve the purpose of demonstrating to those not now in the field (or uninterested in it) the kind of productive research, theoretical and applied, which can be done.

E. Problem Solving in Non-Test Situations

This next recommendation concerns what may be termed a bottleneck in the constructive use of intelligence tests. We are here referring to the practice of evaluating performance on a test either by performance on another test or with behavior and achievement in the school situation—a situation, for the mentally retarded in particular, which involves values and motivations which are different from or clash with those in their social milieu. In addition, it is probably true that the range of problem-solving situations which confronts the child in school is not representative, for the mentally retarded at least, of the problem-solving situations which confront him in non-school situations. *Many people tend to assume without the justification of research, that the level of problem-solving in a test situation is the same as that in the non-test situation. There is evidence that this assumption is least valid for the mentally retarded and the mentally deficient. We strongly recommend the encouragement and support of research which has as its aim the observation and calibration of problem-solving behavior in non-test and non-school situations.*

F. PSYCHOSIS AND SUBNORMALITY

The relation between psychosis and subnormal functioning involves two of the most frequent problems in our society. Although there have been a number of studies, we are far from secure in our estimate of the frequency with which this relationship occurs. Aside from the long-standing problem of establishing explicit criteria and reliable diagnoses of psychosis, the *samples* of subnormal individuals which have been studied have not been representative either of the mentally retarded or of mentally deficient populations. More important—because it reflects professional attitudes toward and handling of the subnormal individual—is that the clinical evaluation of such an individual rarely focusses on those questions which allow one to determine the presence or absence of psychotic thinking and behavior. The focus is customarily so entirely on intellectual functions and considerations of level of functioning, and only a narrow sector of these, that the concept of the "total personality" receives not even lip service. From the standpoint of management, treatment, and program planning it should make a difference whether one is dealing with consequences of an intellectual deficit or with a more complicated and pathological set of relationships. From the scientific standpoint the question is one of elucidating the *mutual* effects of intellectual and personality disfunction. Far more often than not the deviant behavior of a subnormal child is "explained" by his low *IQ*. Rarely is his level of intellectual functioning viewed as possibly being influenced, in part at least, by personality factors. In addition to recommending in a general way the systematic study of the relation between psychosis and subnormality, we would suggest that for certain aspects of the problem there might be special value in focussing on an institutional population. For one thing, within relatively few years in such a setting one can expect to find more than a few cases where the aberrant behavior has become manifest only after a period of institutionalization. Rarely does one have the opportunity to observe the development in any individual of a psychosis (or other aberrant behavior) in a setting in which events and interpersonal relationships can be directly recorded and observed. It is our hunch that this approach to the appearance of psychotic-like behavior in severely defective individuals may give us data on the rôle of external factors in pathological behavior which would have significance beyond the field of subnormal functioning. This setting also may provide an opportunity for the testing of any predictive hypotheses which may be developed with respect to metabolic or biochemical factors in psychosis. Nowhere else is available a population of presumably non-psychotic individuals among whom one can expect the emergence of a sufficient number of psychotics to justify clinical studies of the total population with the aim of obtaining valid pre-psychotic data.

G. EARLY VARIATIONS IN TEMPERAMENT

There is a problem of great significance for normal as well as atypical development which has not yet received systematic research attention. We refer here to the study in the infancy period of variations in sensory reactivity and temperament and their interactions with different types of parental personality, family setting, and social class. The study by Bergman and Escalona discussed in Section IX clearly indicates the significance of the problem for atypical development. It has been suggested that infantile autism, the idiot savant, and Bourne's "protophrenia" may be instances of early and unusual reaction tendencies which have interacted with environmental factors in an adverse way. The point we wish to emphasize, however, is that the study of the early interaction between constitutional and environmental factors would seem to be of central importance (*a*) for our understanding of the relation between intellectual potential and functioning, (*b*) for the development of more discerning and comprehensive diagnostic procedures of early development, and (*c*) for the establishment of a base for parental guidance which would really take account of individual differences in temperament. Our recommendation that research in this problem be encouraged and supported is but one way in which we can call attention to a question the importance of which has long been recognized but which has not been the focus of very much research: how do we account for the fact that any environmental factor, or constellation of factors, has very different effects on different children?

We now turn to a series of recommendations which concern what are undoubtedly the most immediate, pressing, and crucial problems: the recruitment and training of research personnel and the establishment of appropriate settings in which they may work. The suggestions we shall make are based on certain facts and assumptions: (*a*) at the present time the behavior sciences (and we would include here psychiatry) are little interested in developing subnormal functioning as a recognized research area requiring special training, although it is clear from all seven of the preceding recommendations that research initially oriented toward the problems of mental subnormality will, if broadly conceived, have almost immediate importance for a wide range of pressing research areas in other fields and can thus be expected to retain the interest of those behavior scientists whom it attracts; (*b*) there is, to our knowledge, no research and training center where all the behavior sciences are represented and which is of such professional status so as to attract to it the best students in these fields; (*c*) the development in a university of a truly coördinated training program involving independent academic departments is beset with so many problems that it would be a mistake to look *primarily* to such centers for the kinds of programs which are necessary; and (*d*) both because of the desperate need for research personnel and the importance of insuring (to the extent which one can) that those who are attracted to the field have strong motivation for research, it would appear that the post-doctoral programs would have advantages over pre-doctoral ones.

H. RESEARCH CENTER

Our first suggestion is that an appropriate setting be found in one of the major research centers of the United States for the establishment of a fully staffed research unit to investigate the problems of mental subnormality through the full range of its medical, biochemical, psychological, social, and other aspects. Such a center can provide the leadership and focus essential to the proper development of a research program which is starting almost from fundamentals, and can at the same time attract the high quality trainees which will assure its continuation.

I. CHILD-DEVELOPMENT RESEARCH CENTERS

There are more than a few research centers in this country with a primary focus on child development. Some of these have in addition to a research program, well-developed training programs. Because of our belief that longitudinal studies in subnormal functioning are necessary if certain problems are to be better understood, an attempt should be made to set up research and training programs in a selected few of these child development centers. Such centers already have some of the necessary personnel, in some instances there is an awareness of the general significance of developmental studies in subnormal functioning, and in most cases they have available to them excellent clinical facilities. We, like many others, are of the opinion that one cannot engender interest in a research area in mature researchers by dangling large sums of money before them. However, in the case of some child research centers there is interest in subnormal functioning and their ongoing research projects are of a nature which could benefit greatly

from the inclusion of different types of subnormal individuals. There would therefore seem to be a real possibility that the knowledge of *stable* financial support over a period of years would encourage them to expand their research and training programs. In our opinion these centers will have to be stimulated to such expansion by those agencies (public and private) which are ready to support program development on a long term basis—it is doubtful if such developments will come spontaneously from within. It may be profitable as a first step for a meeting to be arranged with the research and training representatives of the leading child research centers in order to determine: (*a*) the strength of their interest in expanding such programs, (*b*) the problems which each of the centers would face, (*c*) the ways in which training in atypical development could be related to current training in normal child development, and (*d*) the extent and duration of the financial support which would be necessary to initiate and maintain expanded programs.

J. Additional Training for Workers in the Field

It is disappointing but true that the quality of research being done in our institutions is poor. The psychological personnel are for the most part geographically, financially, and socially apart from their professional brethren. The disinterest of behavior science departments (psychology, anthropology, sociology, psychiatry) in the area of subnormal functioning makes the solution of the problem most difficult. We must frankly state that we do not have any bright ideas of how to begin to go about remedying this situation. On the assumption that this particular problem will not change markedly in the foreseeable future it might be profitable to consider a program which would allow the institutional worker to go for extended periods to certain centers where there is an active research and training program—a center where he can possibly learn new skills and content which he could apply to research in his own setting. *This suggestion, however, presupposes that there will be several research centers which can offer this kind of opportunity.* An increment in skill and knowledge sufficient to justify this kind of effort can probably not be attained in a one- or two-week workshop, but should rather be viewed as requiring at least a half-year or year training course.

K. Future Reports

Our final recommendation concerns what to us is a limitation of this kind of report—that is, this report was prepared by two individuals who,

like the rest of the human race, have prejudices, intellectual blind spots, and limitations in knowledge and wisdom. It may turn out, therefore, that some of our suggestions and critical evaluations will be found to be in error. It may also be that some important problems have not even been raised by us. We would suggest, therefore, that after a period of time another stock-taking report be prepared by other workers. Wrong conceptions and the conclusions of faulty research have remarkably prolonged lives and the field of subnormal functioning has already suffered under more than its share of fallacious assumptions and outmoded ideas. In addition, because of its present status the field must be kept alert to new ideas and developments and their dissemination in systematic form assured.

BIBLIOGRAPHY

1. ABRAHAMSON, S. School rewards and social-class status. *Educ. Res. Bull.,* 1952, **31,** 8-15.

2. ACKERMAN, N. W., & MENNINGER, C. F. Treatment techniques for mental retardation in a school for personality disorders of children. *Amer. J. Orthopsychiat.,* 1936, **6,** 294-312.

3. ALDRICH, C. G. Experimental studies of idiot behavior. *Proceedings and Addresses of the American Association for the Study of the Feebleminded,* 1931, **36,** 282-291.

4. ALTUS, G. T. Some correlates of the Davis-Eells Tests. *J. Consult. Psychol.,* 1956, **20,** 227-232.

5. ANASTASI, A. Intelligence and family size. *Psychol. Bull.,* 1956, **53,** 187-209.

6. ANASTASI, A., & CORDOVA, F. A. Some effects of bilingualism upon the intelligence test performance of Puerto Rican children in New York City. *J. Educ. Psychol.,* 1953, **44,** 1-19.

7. ANASTASI, A., & FOLEY, J. Differential Psychology. New York: Macmillan, 1949.

8. ANDERSON, V. V., & FEARING, F. M. A Study of the Careers of 322 Feebleminded Persons. New York: National Committee of Mental Hygiene, 1923.

9. ANGELINO, H., & SHEDD, C. L. An initial report of a validation study of the Davis-Eells tests of general intelligence or problem-solving ability. *J. of Psychol.,* 1955, **40,** 35-38.

10. ARMSTRONG, C. P. A study of the intelligence of rural and urban children. *J. Educ. Sociol.,* 1931, **4,** 301-315.

11. ARSENIAN, S. Bilingualism and mental development. *Teach. Coll. Contrib. Educ.,* 1937, No. 712.

12. ————. Bilingualism in the post-war world. *Psychol. Bull.,* 1945, **42,** 65-86.

13. ARTLITT, A. H. On the need for caution in establishing race norms. *J. Appl. Psychol.,* 1921, **5,** 179-183.

14. BALLER, W. R. A study of the present social status of a group of adults, who, when they were in elementary school, were classified as mentally deficient. *Genet. Psychol. Monog.,* 1936, **18,** 165-244.

15. BECKHAM, A. S. A study of the intelligence of colored adolescents of different social-economic status in typical metropolitan areas. *J. Soc. Psychol.,* 1933, **4,** 70-91.

16. BENOIT, E. P. Relevance of Hebb's theory of the organization of behavior to educational research on the mentally retarded. *Amer. J. Ment. Def.,* 1957, **61,** 497-507.

17. BERE, M. A comparative study of the mental capacity of children of foreign parentage. *Teach. Coll. Contrib. Educ.,* 1924, No. 154.

18. BERGMAN, M., WALLER, H., & MARCHAND, J. Schizophrenic reactions during childhood in mental defectives. *Psychiat. Quart.,* 1951, **25,** 294-333.

19. BERGMAN, P., & ESCALONA, S. B. Unusual sensitivities in very young children. *The Psychoanalytic Study of the Child,* Volume 3-4. New York: International Univ. Press, 1949.

20. BOBON, J. Contribution a l'etude des phenomenes regressifs en psychopathologic. Les pseudoglossolalies ludiques et magiques. (A contribution to the study of regressive phenomena in psychopathology. Ludical and magical pseudo-glossalalias.) *J. Belge de Neurol. et de Psychiat.* (Brussels) 1947, **47,** 219-238.

21. BOGARAS, W. The Chukchee. Memoirs of the American Museum of Natural History, 1904, 11.

22. BOURNE, H. Protophrenia, a study of perverted rearing and mental dwarfism. Lancet, 1955, Part 2, 1156-1163.

23. BOVET, P. Les problèmes scolaires posés par le bilinguisme. Pour l'Ere Nouvelle, 1935, No. 105.

24. BOWMAN, P. H., DEHAAN, R. F., KOUGH, J. K., & LIDDLE, G. P. Mobilizing community resources for youth: Identification and treatment of maladjusted, delinquent, and gifted children. Youth Development Series, No. 3. Suppl. Educ. Monog., 1956, No. 85.

25. BOYD, G. F. The levels of aspiration of white and Negro children in a non-segregated elementary school. J. Soc. Psychol., 1952, 36, 191-196.

26. BRAY, D. W. Issues in the Study of Talent. New York: King's Crown Press, 1954.

27. BRITTON, J. H. Influence of social class upon performance on the Draw-A-Man test. J. Educ. Psychol., 1954, 45, 44-51.

28. BROMBERG, W. Schizophrenic-like psychoses in defective children. Proc. Amer. Assoc. Ment. Def., 1934, 39, 226-257.

29. BROWN, F. A comparative study of the intelligence of Jewish and Scandinavian kindergarten children. J. Genet. Psychol., 1944, 64, 67-92.

30. ————. An experimental and critical study of the intelligence of Negro and white kindergarten children. J. Genet. Psychol., 1944, 65, 161-175.

31. BRUGGER, C. Die Landflucht der Begabten. (The emigration of the gifted from rural areas.) All. Z. Psychiat., 1939, 112, 337-348.

32. BUDD, W. C. Educators and culture-fair intelligence tests. J. Educ. Sociol., 1954, 27, 333-334.

33. BURLINGHAM, D. Twins, a Study of Three Pairs of Identical Twins. New York: International Univ. Press, 1952.

34. BURT, C. The Causes and Treatment of Backwardness. New York: Philosophical Library, 1953.

35. BUTLER, F. O. Psychosis in the mentally defective. California & Western Med., 1937, 46, 84-89.

36. CANADY, H. G. The intelligence of Negro college students and parental occupation. Amer. J. Sociol., 1936, 42, 388-389.

37. CARLSON, H. B., & HENDERSON, N. The intelligence of American children of Mexican parentage. J. Abn. & Soc. Psychol., 1950, 45, 544-551.

38. CASSEL, R. H. A rigorous criterion of feeblemindedness: A critique. J. Abn. & Soc. Psychol., 1951, 46, 116-117.

39. CATTELL, R. B. A culture-free intelligence test. J. Educ. Psychol., 1940, 31, 161-179.

40. CHARLES, D. C. Ability and accomplishment of persons earlier judged mentally deficient. Genet. Psychol. Monog., 1953, 47, 3-71.

41. CHIDESTER, L., & MENNINGER, K. A. The application of psychoanalytic methods to the study of mental retardation. Amer. J. Orthopsychiat., 1936, 6, 616-625.

42. CLARK, L. P. The psychology of idiocy. Psychoanal. Rev., 1932, 19, 257-269.

43. ————. Psychoanalysis and mental arrest. Proceedings and Addresses of the American Association for the Study of the Feebleminded, 1932, 37, 316-325.

44. ————. The Nature and Treatment of Amentia. Baltimore: Wood, 1933.

45. ————. The present and the future outlook in the treatment of amentia. *Psychiat. Quart.*, 1933, **7**, 50-71.

46. CLARKE, A. D. B., & CLARKE, A. M. Cognitive changes in the feebleminded. *Brit. J. Psychol.*, 1954, **45**, 173-179.

47. CLARKE, A. D. B., & HERMELIN, B. F. Adult imbeciles, their abilities and trainability. *Lancet*, 1955, Part 1, 337-339.

48. CLEMENTS, F. Notes on the construction of mental tests for American Indians. *J. Soc. Psychol.*, 1930, **1**, 542-548.

49. COWEN, E. L. Psychotherapy and play techniques with the exceptional child and youth: In *Psychology of Exceptional Children and Youth.* Cruickshank, W. M. (*Ed.*). Englewood Cliffs, N. J.: Prentice-Hall, 1955.

50. CRUICKSHANK, W. M. (*Ed.*). Psychology of Exceptional Children and Youth. Englewood Cliffs, New Jersey: Prentice-Hall, 1955.

51. DANIEL, R. P. Basic considerations for valid interpretations of experimental studies pertaining to racial differences. *J. Educ. Psychol.*, 1932, **23**, 15-27.

52. DARCY, N. T. A review of the literature on the effects of bilingualism upon the measurement of intelligence. *J. Genet. Psychol.*, 1953, **82**, 21-57.

53. DAVENPORT, K. S., & REMMERS, H. H. Factors in state characteristics related to average A-12, V-12 test scores. *J. Educ. Psychol.*, 1950, **41**, 110-115.

54. DAVIS, A. American status systems and the socialization of the child. *Amer. Sociol. Rev.*, 1941, **6**, 345-354.

55. ————. Social-Class Influences Upon Learning. (The Inglis Lecture, Harvard University, 1948.) Cambridge, Mass.: Harvard Univ. Press, 1948.

56. DAVIS, A., & EELLS, K. Davis-Eells Test of General Intelligence or Problem-Solving Ability. New York: World Book, 1953.

57. DAVIS, A., & HAVIGHURST, R. J. Social class and color differences in child-rearing. *Amer. Sociol. Rev.*, 1946, **11**, 698-710.

58. ————. Father of the Man: How Your Child Gets His Personality. Boston: Houghton-Mifflin, 1947.

59. ————. The measurement of mental systems. (Can intelligence be measured?) *Sci. Mo.*, 1948, **66**, 301-316.

60. DAVIS, R. A., JR. Some relations between amount of school training and intelligence among Negroes. *J. Educ. Psychol.*, 1928, **19**, 127-130.

61. DEGROOT, A. D. The effects of war upon the intelligence of youth. *J. Abn. & Soc. Psychol.*, 1948, **43**, 311-317.

62. ————. War and the intelligence of youth. *J. Abn. & Soc. Psychol.*, 1951, **46**, 596-597.

63. DOLL, E. A., PHELPS, W. M., & MELCHER, R. T. Mental Deficiency Due to Birth Injuries. New York: Macmillan, 1932.

64. EARL, C. J. C. The primitive catatonic psychosis of idiocy. *Brit. J. Med. Psychol.*, 1934, **14**, 230-253.

65. EATON, J. W., & WEIL, R. J. Culture and Mental Disorders: A Comparative Study of the Hutterites and Other Populations. Glencoe: Free Press, 1955.

66. EDMISTON, R. W., & McBAIN, L. C. Social and economic background affects school achievement. *Sch. & Soc.*, 1945, **61**, 190-191.

67. EELLS, K. W. Some implications for school practice of the Chicago studies of cultural bias in intelligence tests. *Harvard Educ. Rev.*, 1953, **23**, 284-297.

68. EELLS, K. W., DAVIS, A., HAVIGHURST, R. J., HERRICK, V. E., & TYLER, R. W. Intelligence and Cultural Differences: A Study of Cultural Learning and Problem-Solving. Chicago: Univ. Chicago Press, 1951.

69. ESTES, B. W. Influence of socioeconomic status on Wechsler Intelligence Scale for Children: An exploratory study. *J. Consult. Psychol.*, 1953, **17**, 58-62.

70. FAIRBANK, R. The subnormal child; seventeen years after. *Ment. Hyg.*, 1933, **17**, 177-208.

71. FORBES, J. K. The distribution of intelligence among elementary children in Northern Ireland. *Brit. J. Educ. Psychol.*, 1945, **15**, 139-145.

72. FRANKL, G. Language and affective contact. *Nerv. Child,* 1942-43, **2**, 251-262.

73. FRANZBLAU, R. N. Race differences in mental and physical traits studied in different environments. *Arch. of Psychol.,* 1935, No. 177.

74. FRIES, M. E. Psychosomatic relationships between mother and infant. *Psychosomat. Med.,* 1944, **6**, 159-162.

75. ————. The child's ego development and the training of adults in his environment. In *The Psychoanalytic Study of the Child,* Volume 2. New York: International Univ. Press, 1946. .

76. FRIES, M. E., & LEWI, B. Interrelated factors in development: A study of pregnancy, labor, delivery, lying-in period and childhood. *Amer. J. Orthopsychiat.,* 1938, **8**, 726-752.

77. FROMM, E. Escape From Freedom. New York: Rinehart, 1941.

78. GALLAGHER, J. J. A comparison of brain-injured and non-brain injured mentally retarded children on several psychological variables. *Monog. Soc. Res. Child Devel.,* 1957, **22**, No. 2.

79. GARDNER, L. P. Responses of idiots and imbeciles in a conditioning experiment. *Amer. J. Ment. Def.,* 1945, **50**, 59-80.

80. GARRETT, H. E. Negro-white differences in mental ability in the United States. *Sci. Mo.,* 1947, **65**, 329-333.

81. GARTH, T. R. The intelligence and achievement of mixed-blood Indians. *J. Soc. Psychol.,* 1933, **4**, 134-137.

82. GARTH, T. R., & JOHNSON, H. D. The intelligence and achievement of Mexican children in the United States. *J. Abn. & Soc. Psychol.,* 1934, **29**, 222-229.

83. GARTH, T. R., LOVELADY, B. E., & SMITH, H. W. The intelligence and achievement of southern Negro children. *Sch. & Soc.,* 1930, **32**, 431-435.

84. GEIST, H. Evaluation of culture-free intelligence. *California J. Educ. Res.,* 1954, **5**, 209-214.

85. GIBSON, D., & BUTLER, A. J. Culture as a possible contributor to feeblemindedness. *Amer. J. Ment. Def.,* 1954, **58**, 490-495.

86. GINSBERG, A. M. Comparação entre os resultados de um teste de nível mental aplicado em diferentes grupos étnicos e socais. (Comparison of the results of a test of mental level administered in different ethnic and social groups.) *Arch. Brasileiros de Psicotec.,* 1951, **3**, 27-44.

87. GINZBERG, E., & BRAY, D. W. The Uneducated. New York: Columbia Univ. Press, 1953.

88. GIRARD, A. L'orientation et la sélection des enfants d'âge scolaire dans le départment de la Seine. *Population,* 1953, **8**, 649-672.

89. GIST, N. P., & CLARK, C. D. Intelligence as a selective factor in rural-urban migrations. *Amer. J. Sociol.,* 1938, **44**, 36-58.

90. GLADWIN, T., & SARASON, S. B. Truk: Man in Paradise. New York: Viking Fund Publications in Anthropology, No. 2, 1953.

91. GLUECK, S., & GLUECK, E. Unraveling Juvenile Delinquency. New York: Commonwealth Fund, 1950.

92. GODDARD, H. H. The Kallikak Family. A Study in the Heredity of Feeblemindedness. New York: Macmillan, 1912.

93. GORDON, S., O'CONNOR, N., & TIZARD, J. Some effects of incentives on the performance of imbeciles. *Brit. J. Psychol.,* 1954, **45**, 277-287.

94. ————. Some effects of incentives on the performance of imbeciles on a repetitive task. *Amer. J. Ment. Def.,* 1955, **60**, 371-377.

95. GOULD, R. Some sociological determinants of goal strivings. *J. Soc. Psychol.,* 1941, **13**, 461-473.

96. GRAHAM, V. T. Health studies of Negro children: I. Intelligence studies of Negro children in Atlanta, Georgia. *Public Health Reports,* 1926.

97. GREENE, R. A. Psychoses and mental deficiencies, comparisons and relationship. *Proceedings and Addresses of the American Association for the Study of the Feebleminded,* 1930, **35**, 128-147.

98. ————. Conflicts in diagnosis between mental deficiency and certain psychoses. *Proceedings and Addresses of the American Association on Mental Deficiency,* 1933, **38**, 127-143.

99. GUILFORD, J. P. The structure of intellect. *Psychol. Bull.,* 1956, **53**, 267-293.

100. GUNNARSON, S. Dementia infantilis Heller. *Acta Paediat.,* Stockholm, 1949, **38**, 209-214.

101. HAGGARD, E. A. Social-status and intelligence: An experimental study of certain cultural determinants of measured intelligence. *Genet. Psychol. Monog.,* 1954, **49**, 141-186.

102. HAGGARD, E. A., DAVIS, A., & HAVIGHURST, R. J. Some factors which influence performance of children on intelligence tests. *Amer. Psychol.,* 1948, **3**, 265-266.

103. HALPERIN, S. L. A clinico-genetic study of mental defect. *Amer. J. Ment. Def.,* 1945, **50**, 8-26.

104. HAUCH, E. Zur differentiellen Psychologie des Industrie und Landkindes. (A contribution to the differential psychology of children from industrial and rural environments.) *Jenaer. Beitr. Z. Jugend., U. Entwicklungspsychol.,* 1929, **10**, 1-65.

105. HAUGHT, B. F. Mental growth of the southwestern Indian. *J. Appl. Psychol.,* 1934, **18**, 137-142.

106. HAVIGHURST, R. J., & BREESE, F. H. Relation between ability and social status in a midwestern community: III. Primary mental abilities. *J. Educ. Psychol.,* 1947, **38**, 241-247.

107. HAVIGHURST, R. J., & DAVIS, A. Comparison of the Chicago and Harvard studies of social class differences in child rearing. *Amer. Sociol. Rev.,* 1955, **20**, 439-442.

108. HAVIGHURST, R. J., & HILKEVITCH, R. R. The intelligence of Indian children as measured by a performance scale. *J. Abn. & Soc. Psychol.,* 1944, **39**, 419-433.

109. HAVIGHURST, R. J., & JANKE, L. L. Relations between ability and social status in a midwestern community: I. Ten-year-old children. *J. Educ. Psychol.,* 1944, **35**, 357-368.

110. HAWES, C. H. In the Uttermost East. New York: Harper, 1903.

111. HAYMAN, M. The interrelations of mental defect and mental disorder. *J. Ment. Sci.,* 1939, **85**, 1183-1193.

112. HEBB, D. O. The Organization of Behavior. New York: Wiley, 1949.

113. HEGGE, T. G. The occupational status of higher-grade mental defectives in the present emergency: A study of parolees from the Wayne County Training School at Northville, Michigan. *Amer. J. Ment. Def.,* 1944, **49**, 86-98.

114. HERNDON, C. N. Intelligence in family groups in the Blue Ridge Mountains. *Eugen. Quart.*, 1954, **1**, 53-57.

115. HERSKOVITZ, H. H., & PLESSET, M. R. Psychosis in adult mental defectives. *Psychiat. Quart.*, 1941, **15**, 574-588.

116. HEUYER, G., PIÉRON, H., PIÉRON, MME. H., & SAUVY, A. Le niveau intellectuel des enfants d'âge scolaire, une enquête nationale dans l'enseignment primaire. (A national survey of primary schools—the intellectual level of school-age children.) Paris: Institut National D'études Démographiques, 1954.

117. HIMMELWEIT, H. T., & WHITFIELD, J. W. Mean intelligence scores of a random sample of occupations. *Brit. J. Indust. Med.*, 1944, **1**, 224-226.

118. HOGBIN, H. I. A New Guinea childhood: From weaning till the eighth year in Wogeo. *Oceania*, 1946, **16**, 275-296.

119. HOLLINGSHEAD, A. B. Elmtown's Youth. New York: Wiley, 1949.

120. HOLLINGSHEAD, A. B., & REDLICH, F. C. Schizophrenia and social structure. *Amer. J. Psychiat.*, 1954, **110**, 695-701.

121. ———. Social mobility and mental illness. *Amer. J. Psychiat.*, 1955, **112**, 179-185.

122. HONZIK, M. P. Age changes in the relationship between certain environmental variables and children's intelligence. *Yearbook Nat. Soc. Stud. Educ.*, 1940, **39**, pt. 2.

123. HULSE, W. C. Dementia infantilis. *J. Nerv. & Ment. Dis.*, 1954, **119**, 471-477.

124. HUSÉN, T. Till frågan om den selektiva migrationen ur intellektuell synpunkt. (Concerning the problem of selective migration on the basis of intellectual differences.) *Studia Psychol. Paedagog. (Lund)* 1948, **2**, 30-63.

125. ———. The influence of schooling upon *IQ*. *Theoria*, 1951, **17**, 61-88.

126. HYDE, R. W., & KINGSLEY, L. V. Studies in medical sociology: II. The relation of mental disorders to population density. *New England J. Med.*, 1944, **231**, 571-577.

127. ITARD, J. M. G. The Wild Boy of Aveyron. (Trans. by G. and M. Humphrey.) New York: Appleton-Century, 1932.

128. JAMES, S. G. The relationship of dementia praecox to mental deficiency. *J. Ment. Sci.*, 1939, **85**, 1194-1211.

129. JANKE, L. L., & HAVIGHURST, R. J. Relations between ability and social status in a mid-western community: II. Sixteen-year-old boys and girls. *J. Educ. Psychol.*, 1945, **36**, 499-509.

130. JASTAK, J. A rigorous criterion of feeblemindedness. *J. Abn. & Soc. Psychol.*, 1949, **44**, 367-378.

131. ———. The endogenous slow learner. *Amer. J. Ment. Def.*, 1950-51, **55**, 269-274.

132. ———. On Robert H. Cassel's critique of "A rigorous criterion of feeblemindedness." *J. Abn. & Soc. Psychol.*, 1951, **46**, 118-119.

133. JASTAK, J., & WHITEMAN, M. The prevalence of mental retardation in Delaware. Preliminary report on a state-wide survey. In *The Nature and Transmission of the Genetic and Cultural Characteristics of Human Populations*. New York: Millbank Memorial Fund, 1957.

134. JENKINS, M. D. A socio-psychological study of Negro children of superior intelligence. *J. Negro Educ.*, 1936, **5**, 175-190.

135. ———. Case studies of Negro children of Binet *IQ* 160 and above. *J. Negro Educ.*, 1943, **12**, 159-166.

136. ————. The upper limit of ability among American Negroes. *Sci. Mo.,* 1948, **66**, 399-401.

137. JENKINS, M. D., & RANDALL, C. M. Differential characteristics of superior and unselected Negro college students. *J. Soc. Psychol.,* 1948, **27**, 187-202.

138. JONES, H. E., CONRAD, H. S., & BLANCHARD, M. D. Environmental handicaps in mental test performance. *Univ. California Publ. Psychol.,* 1932, **5**, 63-99.

139. JOSEPH, A., & MURRAY, V. F. Chamorros and Carolinians of Saipan. Cambridge: Harvard Univ. Press, 1951.

140. KALLMANN, F. J. The genetic theory of schizophrenia. *Amer. J. Psychiat.,* 1946, **103**, 309-322.

141. KALLMANN, F. J., BARRERA, S. E., HOCH, P. H., & KELLEY, D. M. The rôle of mental deficiency in the incidence of schizophrenia. *Amer. J. Ment., Def.,* 1940-1941, **45**, 514-539.

142. KANNER, L. Autistic disturbances of affective contact. *Nerv. Child,* 1943, **2**, 217-250.

143. ————. Early infantile autism. *J. Pediat.,* 1944, **25**, 211-217.

144. ————. Irrelevant and metaphorical language in early infantile autism. *Amer. J. Psychiat.,* 1946, **103**, 242-246.

145. ————. Child Psychiatry. Springfield, Ill.: Thomas, 1948.

146. ————. A miniature textbook of feeblemindedness. *Child Care Monographs, No. 1.* New York: Child Care Publications, 1949.

147. ————. Problems of nosology and psychodynamics of early infantile autism. *Amer. J. Orthopsychiat.,* 1949, **19**, 416-426.

148. ————. The conception of wholes and parts in early infantile autism. *Amer. J. Psychiat.,* 1951, **108**, 23-26.

149. ————. A discussion of early infantile autism. *Digest Neurol. & Psychiat.,* 1951, **19**, 158.

150. KELLER, J. E. The use of certain perceptual measures of brain injury with mentally retarded children. Unpublished manuscript (Wayne County Training School).

151. KENNEDY, R. J. R. The Social Adjustment of Morons in a Connecticut City. Hartford: Mansfield-Southbury Training Schools (Social Service Department, State Office Building), 1948.

152. KESTON, M. J., & JIMINEZ, C. A study of the performance on English and Spanish editions of the Stanford-Binet intelligence test by Spanish-American children. *J. Genet. Psychol.,* 1954, **85**, 263-269.

153. KIRAHARA, H. Development of intelligence and social factors. *Rôdô Kagaku* (Study in the science of labor), **1**, No. 2.

154. KIRK, S. A. Experiments in the early training of the mentally retarded. *Amer. J. Ment. Def.,* 1952, **56**, 692-700.

155. KIRK, S. A., & MCCARTHY, J. J. A study of the language process of preschool cerebral palsied children. *Progress Report to the United Cerebral Palsy Foundation,* 1950.

156. KLINEBERG, O. An experimental study of speed and other factors in "racial" differences. *Arch. of Psychol.,* 1928, **15**, No. 93.

157. ————. Negro Intelligence and Selective Migration. New York: Columbia Univ. Press, 1935.

158. ————. Mental testing of racial and national groups. In *Scientific Aspects of the Race Problem.* New York: Longmans, Green, 1941.

159. KOUNIN, J. S. Experimental studies of rigidity: I. The measurement of rigidity in normal and feebleminded persons. *Charac. & Personal.*, 1941, **9**, 251-273.

160. ————. The meaning of rigidity: A reply to Heinz Werner. *Psychol. Rev.*, 1948, **55**, 157-166.

161. KUIPER, T. Maatschappelik milieu, algemene intelligentie, en de selectie voor het middelbar onderwijs. (Social environment, general intelligence and selection for secondary instruction.) *Mensch en Maatschappij*, 1930, **6**, 418-424.

162. League of Nations, Health Organization (Conference on rural hygiene). *Report of French Indo-China.* Geneva: 1937.

163. LEE, E. S. Negro intelligence and selective migration: A Philadelphia test of the Klineberg hypothesis. *Amer. Sociol. Rev.*, 1951, **16**, 227-233.

164. LEIGHTON, D., & KLUCKHOHN, C. Children of the People; the Navaho Individual and His Development. Cambridge: Harvard Univ. Press, 1947.

165. LEMKAU, P. V. Epidemiological aspects. In *The Evaluation and Treatment of the Mentally Retarded Child in Clinics.* New York: National Association for Retarded Children, 1956.

166. LEMKAU, P. V., TIETZE, C., & COOPER, M. Mental health problems in an urban district. *Ment. Hyg.*, 1942, **26**, 275-288.

167. LEWIN, K. A Dynamic Theory of Personality. New York: McGraw-Hill, 1936.

168. LEWIS, C. Children of the Cumberland. New York: Columbia Univ. Press, 1946.

169. LOEVINGER, J. Intelligence as related to socio-economic factors. *Yearbook of of the National Society for the Study of Education*, 1940, **39**, 159-160.

170. LONG, H. H. The intelligence of colored elementary pupils in Washington, D. C. *J. Negro Educ.*, 1934, **3**, 205-222.

171. LOOS, F. M., & TIZARD, J. The employment of adult imbeciles in a hospital workshop. *Amer. J. Ment. Def.*, 1954-55, **59**, 395-403.

172. LORGE, I. Schooling makes a difference. *Teach. Coll. Rec.*, 1945, **46**, 483-492.

173. LURIE, L. A., SCHLAN, L., & FREIBERG, M. A critical analysis of the progress of fifty-five feebleminded children over a period of eight years. *Amer. J. Orthopsychiat.*, 1932, **2**, 58-69.

174. MAHLER, M. S. On child psychosis and schizophrenia: Autistic and symbiotic infantile psychoses. In *The Psychoanalytic Study of the Child*, Volume 7. New York: International Univ. Press, 1952.

175. MALCOVE, L. E. Margaret E. Fries' research in problems of infancy and childhood. In *The Psychoanalytic Study of the Child*, Volume 1. New York: International Univ. Press, 1945.

176. MCALPIN, A. S. Changes in the intelligence quotients of Negro children. *J. Negro Educ.*, 1932, **1**, 44-48.

177. MCCANDLESS, B. Environment and intelligence. *Amer. J. Ment. Def.*, 1952, **56**, 674-691.

178. MCCARTHY, D. A. The Language Development of the Preschool Child. Minneapolis: Univ. Minnesota Press, 1930.

179. MCCLELLAND, D. C., ATKINSON, J. W., CLARK, R. A., & LOWELL, E. L. The Achievement Motive. New York: Appleton-Century, 1953.

180. MCCLELLAND, D. C., RINDLISBACHER, A., & DECHARMS, R. Religious and other sources of parental attitudes toward independence training. In *Studies in Motivation* (D. C. McClelland, *Ed.*). New York: Appleton-Century, 1955.

181. McGURK, F. C. J. "Psychological tests"—a scientist's report on race differences. *U. S. News & World Report,* Sept. 21, 1956, 92-96.

182. McPHERSON, M. W. A survey of experimental studies of learning in individuals who achieve subnormal ratings on standardized psychometric measures. *Amer. J. Ment. Def.,* 1948, **52**, 232-254.

183. MARGOLIN, J. B., ROMAN, M., & HARARI, C. Reading disability in the delinquent child: A microcosm of psychosocial pathology. *Amer. J. Orthopsychiat.,* 1955, **25**, 25-35.

184. MEAD, M. Group intelligence tests and linguistic disability among Italian children. *Sch. & Soc.,* 1927, **25**, 465-468.

185. (anon). Report of the Mental Deficiency Committee. London: H. M. Stationery Office, 1929.

186. MONTAGU, M. F. A. Intelligence of northern Negroes and southern whites in the first World War. *Amer. J. Psychol.,* 1945, **58**, 161-188.

187. MOORE, E. Our national burden: A survey of the report on mental deficiency. *Eugen. Rev.,* 1929, **21**, 117-126.

188. MORRELL, F., ROBERTS, L., & JASPER, H. H. Effects of focal epileptogenic lesions and their ablation upon conditioned electrical responses of the brain in the monkey. *J. Electroencephalog. & Clin. Neurophysiol.,* 1956, **8**, 217-236.

189. MUENCH, G. A. A follow-up of mental defectives after 18 years. *J. Abn. & Soc. Psychol.,* 1944, **39**, 407-418.

190. MYERS, J. K., & SCHAFFER, L. Social stratification and psychiatric practice: A study of an out-patient clinic. *Amer. Sociol. Rev.,* 1954, **19**, 307-310.

191. NEFF, W. S. Socio-economic status and intelligence: A critical survey. *Psychol. Bull.,* 1938, **35**, 727-757.

192. NELSON, C. W. Testing the influence of rural and urban environment on *ACE* intelligence test scores. *Amer. Sociol. Rev.,* 1942, **7**, 751-793.

193. New York State Department of Mental Hygiene, Mental Health Research Unit. Technical Report. Syracuse, N. Y.: 1955.

194. NISBET, J. D. Family environment: A direct effect of family size on intelligence. Occasional paper (No. 8) on Eugenics. London, England: Eugenics Society, 1953.

195. NISSEN, H. W., MACHOVER, S., & KINDER, E. F. A study of performance tests given to a group of native African Negro children. *Brit. J. Psychol.,* 1935, **25**, 308-355.

196. O'CONNOR, N. The occupational success of feebleminded adolescents. *Occupat. Psychol.,* 1953, **27**, 157-163.

197. O'CONNOR, N., & TIZARD, J. The Social Problem of Mental Deficiency. London: Pergamon Press, 1956.

198. O'GORMAN, G. Psychosis as a cause of mental defect. *J. Ment. Sci.,* 1954, **100**, 934-943.

199. OSGOOD, C. E., & SEBEOCK, T. A. (*Eds.*). Psycholinguistics. *J. Abn. & Soc. Psychol.,* 1954, **49**, No. 4, Part 2 (Supplemental Issue).

200. PASAMANICK, B. A. A comparative study of the behavioral development of Negro infants. *J. Genet. Psychol.,* 1946, **69**, 3-44.

201. ————. The intelligence of American children of Mexican parentage: A discussion of uncontrolled variables. *J. Abn. & Soc. Psychol.,* 1951, **46**, 598-602.

202. ————. The contribution of some organic factors to school retardation in Negro children. Paper read before the American Psychological Association, Chicago, September 1, 1956.

203. PASTORE, N. A comment on "psychological differences as among races." *Sch. & Soc.*, 1946, **63**, 136-137.

204. PEARSON, G. B. The psychoses with mental deficiency as viewed in a mental hospital: Clinical syndromes. *Proceedings of the American Association on Mental Deficiency*, 1938, **43**, 166-172.

205. PLENDERITH, M. Discrimination learning and discrimination reversal learning in normal and feebleminded children. *J. Genet. Psychol.*, 1956, **88**, 107-112.

206. POLLOCK, H. M. Mental disease among mental defectives. *Amer. J. Psychiat.*, 1944, **101**, 361-363.

207. ———. Mental disease among mental defectives. *Amer. J. Ment. Def.*, 1945, **49**, 477-480.

208. PORTEUS, S. D. Primitive Intelligence and Environment. New York: Macmillan, 1937.

209. POTTER, H. W. Mental deficiency and the psychiatrist. *Amer. J. Psychiat.*, 1927, **6**, 691-700.

210. REDLICH, F. C., HOLLINGSHEAD, A. B., & BELLIS, E. Social class differences in attitudes toward psychiatry. *Amer. J. Orthopsychiat.*, 1955, **25**, 60-70.

211. REDLICH, F. C., HOLLINGSHEAD, A. B., ROBERTS, B. H., ROBINSON, H. A., FREEDMAN, L. Z., & MYERS, J. K. Social structure and psychiatric disorders. *Amer. J. Psychiat.*, 1953, **109**, 729-734.

212. REED, S. C., REED, E. W., & PALM, J. D. Fertility and intelligence among families of the mentally deficient. *Eugen. Quart.*, 1954, **1**, 44-52.

212a. RICHMOND, J. B., & LUSTMAN, S. Autonomic function in the neonate. *Psychosomatic Medicine*, 1955, **17**, 269-274.

213. RITVO, S., & PROVENCE, S. Form perception and imitation in some autistic children: Diagnostic findings and their contextual interpretation. In *Psychoanalytic Study of the Child*, 1953, **8**, 155-161.

214. ROBBINS, J. E. The home and family background of Ottawa public school children in relation to their *IQ*'s. *Can. J. Psychol.*, 1948, **2**, 35-41.

215. ROBERTS, B. H., & MYERS, J. K. Religion, national origin, immigration, and mental illness. *Amer. J. Psychiat.*, 1954, **110**, 759-764.

216. ROBINSON, H. A., REDLICH, F. C., & MYERS, J. K. Social structure and psychiatric treatment. *Amer. J. Orthopsychiat.*, 1954, **24**, 307-316.

217. ROBINSON, M. L., & MEENES, M. The relationship between test intelligence of third grade Negro children and the occupations of their parents. *J. Negro Educ.*, 1947, **16**, 136-141.

218. ROBSON, G. M. Social factors in mental retardation. *Brit. J. Psychol.*, 1931, **22**, 118-135.

219. ROHRER, J. H. The test intelligence of Osage Indians. *J. Sac. Psychol.*, 1942, **16**, 99-105.

220. RONJAT, J. Le développement du language observé chez un enfant bilingue. Paris: Champion, 1913.

221. ROSEN, B. C. The achievement motive and value systems of selected ethnic groups. Paper read before the American Sociological Society, Washington, D. C., Aug. 27, 1957.

222. ROSENBLUM, S., KELLER, J., & PAPANIA, N. Davis-Eells ("Culture-Fair") test performance of lower-class retarded children. *J. Consult. Psychol.*, 1955, **19**, 51-54.

223. SANDELS, S. Om intelligensmätningar av barn i forskolealdern enligt Terman-Merrill skala, L-formen. (The use of the Terman-Merrill scale for measuring intelligence of preschool children, Form L). *Tidskr. Psychol. Pedag.*, 1942, **1**, 65-72.

224. SARASON, S. B. Projective techniques in mental deficiency. *J. Personal.*, 1944, **13**, 237-245.

225. ————. Psychological Problems in Mental Deficiency. 2nd ed. New York: Harper, 1953.

226. SARASON, S. B., DAVIDSON, K., LIGHTHALL, F., & WAITE, R. A test anxiety scale for children. *Child Devel.*, (in press).

227. SARASON, S. B., & SARASON, E. K. The discriminatory value of a test pattern in the high grade familial defective. *J. Clin. Psychol.*, 1946, **2**, 38-49.

228. ————. The discriminatory value of a test pattern with cerebral palsied defective children. *J. Clin. Psychol.*, 1947, **3**, 141-147.

229. SATTER, G. Retarded adults who have developed beyond expectation—Part III: Further analysis and summary. *Train. Sch. Bull.*, 1955, **51**, 237-243.

230. SATTER, G., & McGEE, E. Retarded adults who have developed beyond expectation—Part I: Intellectual functions. *Train. Sch. Bull.*, 1954, **51**, 43-55.

231. ————. Retarded adults who have developed beyond expectation—Part II: Non-intellectual functions. *Train. Sch. Bull.*, 1951, **51**, 67-81.

232. SCHAEFER-SIMMERN, H. The Unfolding of Artistic Activity. Berkeley: Univ. California Press, 1948.

233. SCHAEFER-SIMMERN, H., & SARASON, S. B. Therapeutic implications of artistic activity—a case study. *Amer. J. Ment. Def.*, 1944, **49**, 185-196.

234. SCHAFFER, L., & MYERS, J. K. Psychotherapy and social stratification. *Psychiatry*, 1954, **17**, 83-93.

235. SCHEERER, M., ROTHMANN, E., & GOLDSTEIN, K. A case of "Idiot Savant": An experimental study of personality organization. *Psychol. Monog.*, 1945, **58**, No. 4.

236. SCHMIDT, J. Uber Beziehungen zwischen Landflucht und Intelligenz. (The relation between urban migration and intelligence.) *Arch. Rass. U. Gesbiol.*, 1938, **32**, 358-370.

237. SCHULMAN, M. J., & HAVIGHURST, R. J. Relations between ability and social status in a mid-western community: IV. Size of vocabulary. *J. Educ. Psychol.*, 1947, **38**, 437-442.

238. SEARS, R. R., MACCOBY, E. E., & LEVIN, H. Patterns of Child Rearing. Evanston, Ill.: Row, Peterson, 1957.

239. SHEPARD, E. L. Measurements of certain nonverbal abilities of urban and rural children. *J. Educ. Psychol.*, 1942, **33**, 458-462.

240. SHERMAN, M., & KEY, C. B. The intelligence of isolated mountain children. *Child Devel.*, 1932, **3**, 279-290.

241. SHERWIN, A. C. Reactions to music of autistic children. *Amer. J. Psychiat.*, 1953, **109**, 823-831.

242. SHOTWELL, A. M. Arthur performance ratings of Mexican and American high-grade mental defectives. *Amer. J. Ment. Def.*, 1945, **49**, 445-449.

243. SIEVERS, D. J. The development and standardization of a test of psycholinguistic growth in preschool children. Ph.D. Thesis, Univ. Illinois, 1955.

244. SKEELS, H. M., & DYE, H. B. A study of the effects of differential stimulation on mentally retarded children. *Proceedings and Addresses of the American Association on Mental Deficiency*, 1939, **44**, 114-136.

245. SKEELS, H. M., & FILLMORE, E. M. The mental development of children from underprivileged homes. *J. Genet. Psychol.*, 1937, **50**, 427-439.

246. SKEELS, H. M., & HARMS, I. Children with inferior social histories: Their mental development in adoptive homes. *J. Genet. Psychol.*, 1948, **72**, 283-294.

247. SKEELS, H. M., UPDEGRAFF, R., WELLMAN, B. L., & WILLIAMS, H. M. A study of environmental stimulation, an orphanage preschool project. *Univ. Iowa Stud. Child Wel.*, 1938, **15**, No. 4.

248. SKODAK, M., & SKEELS, H. M. A final follow-up study of one hundred adopted children. *J. Genet. Psychol.*, 1949, **75**, 85-125.

249. SMITH, M. Intelligence of university students by size of community of residence. *Sch. & Soc.*, 1942, **55**, 565-567.

250. ————. An urban-rural intellectual gradient. *Sociol. & Soc. Res.*, 1943, **27**, 307-315.

251. SMITH, M. E. Some light on the problem of bilingualism as found from a study of the progress in mastery of English among preschool children of non-American ancestry in Hawaii. *Genet. Psychol. Monog.*, 1939, **21**, 121-284.

252. ————. Measurement of vocabularies of young bilingual children in both of the languages used. *J. Genet. Psychol.*, 1949, **74**, 305-310.

253. SMITH, S. Language and non-verbal test performance of racial groups in Honolulu before and after a fourteen-year interval. *J. Genet. Psychol.*, 1943, **26**, 51-93.

254. SNYDER, L. H. Human heredity and its modern applications. *Amer. Sci.*, 1955, **43**, 391-419.

255. SNYGG, D. The relation between the intelligence of mothers and of their children living in foster homes. *J. Genet. Psychol.*, 1938, **52**, 401-406.

256. SPARLING, M. E. Intelligence of Indian children; the relationship between Binet and Porteus scores. *Amer. J. Ment. Def.*, 1941, **46**, 60-62.

257. SPEER, G. S. The intelligence of foster children. *J. Genet. Psychol.*, 1940, **57**, 49-55.

258. SPOERL, D. T. The adjustment at college age of students who were bilingual in childhood. Abstract of dissertation, Clark Univ., Worcester, Mass., 1942.

259. ————. Bilinguality and emotional adjustment. *J. Abn. & Soc. Psychol.*, 1943, **38**, 35-57.

260. ————. The academic and verbal adjustment of college age bilingual students. *J. Genet. Psychol.*, 1944, **64**, 139-157.

261. STEGGERDA, M. Racial psychometry. *Eugen. News,* 1934, **19**, 132-133.

262. STENDLER, C. B. Social class differences in parental attitudes toward school at Grade I level. *Child Devel.*, 1951, **22**, 36-46.

263. STENQUIST, J. L., & LORGE, I. Implications of intelligence and cultural differences; as seen by a test-user; as seen by a test-maker. *Teach. Coll. Rec.,* 1953, **54**, 184-193.

264. STEVENSON, H. W., & ZIGLER, E. F. Discrimination learning and discrimination reversal in normal and feebleminded individuals. Abstract of paper delivered at 1957 meeting of the American Psychological Association (New York). To be published in *J. Personal.*

265. STEVENSON, H. W., ZIGLER, E. F., & HODDEN, L. Performance of normal and feebleminded children in repetitive tasks as a function of motivating conditions. (Abstract and data supplied by authors, Univ. Texas).

266. STOKE, S. M. Occupational groups and child development. *Harvard Monog. Educ.*, 1927, No. 8.

267. STRAUSS, A. A., & KEPHART, N. C. Psychopathology and Education of the Brain-Injured Child. Vol. II, Progress in Theory and Clinic. New York: Grune & Stratton, 1955.

268. STRAUSS, A. A., & LEHTINEN, L. E. Psychopathology and Education of the Brain-Injured Child. New York: Grune and Stratton, 1947.

269. THOMPSON, C. H. The educational achievements of Negro children. *Ann. Amer. Acad. Polit. & Soc. Sci.*, 1928, **140**, 193-208.

270. THOMSON, G. H. The relations between intelligence and fertility. A memorandum in *Papers of the Royal Commission on Population,* Volume 5. London: Her Majesty's Stationery Office, 1950.

271. THORNDIKE, R. L. Community variables as predictors of intelligence and academic achievement. *J. Educ. Psychol.,* 1951, **42**, 321-338.

272. TIZARD, J., & LOOS, F. M. The learning of a spatial relations test by adult imbeciles. *Amer. J. Ment. Def.,* 1954-55, **59**, 85-90.

273. TOMLINSON, H. Differences between preschool Negro children and their older siblings on the Stanford-Binet scales. *J. Negro Educ.,* 1944, **13**, 474-479.

274. TOUSSAINT, N. Bilinguisme et éducation. (Bilingualism and education). Brussels: Lamertin, 1935.

275. TOWN, C. H. Familial Feeblemindedness, a Study of One Hundred and Forty-one Families. Buffalo: Foster & Stewart, 1939.

276. TREDGOLD, A. F. Mental Deficiency. New York: Wood, 1922.

277. TREDGOLD, R. F., & SODDY, K. A Text-Book of Mental Deficiency. London: Baillière, Tindall & Cox, 1956.

278. VANUXEM, M. The prevalence of mental disease among mental defectives. *Proc. Amer. Assoc. Ment. Def.,* 1935, **40**, 242-249.

279. VITELES, M. S. The mental status of the Negro. *Ann. Amer. Acad. Polit. & Soc. Sci.,* 1928, **140**, 166-177.

280. WARNER, W. L. American Life, Dream and Reality. Chicago: Univ. Chicago Press, 1953.

281. WASHBURN, S. L. The strategy of physical anthropology. In *Anthropology Today* (A. L. Kroeber, *Ed.*). Chicago: Univ. Chicago Press, 1953.

282. WELLMAN, B. The meaning of environment. *Yearbook Nat. Soc. Stud. Educ.,* 1940, **39**, 21-40.

283. WELLMAN, B., & McCANDLESS, B. R. Factors associated with Binet *IQ* changes of preschool children. *Psychol. Monog.,* 1946, **60**, No. 278.

284. WELLS, J., & ARTHUR, G. Effect of foster-home placement on the intelligence ratings of children of feebleminded parents. *Ment. Hyg.,* 1939, **23**, 277-285.

285. WERNER, H. The concept of rigidity: A critical evaluation. *Psychol. Rev.,* 1948, **53**, 43-53.

286. WERNER, H., & THUMA, B. D. A deficiency in the perception of apparent motion in children with brain injury. *Amer. J. Psychol.,* 1942, **55**, 58-67.

287. ———. Critical flicker-frequency in children with brain injury. *Amer. J. Psychol.,* 1942, **55**, 394-399.

288. WERTHEIMER, M. Productive Thinking. New York: Harper, 1945.

289. WHEELER, L. R. The intelligence of East Tennessee mountain children. *J. Educ. Psychol.,* 1932, **23**, 351-370.

290. ———. A comparative study of the intelligence of East Tennessee mountain children. *J. Educ. Psychol.,* 1942, **33**, 321-334.

291. WHITTEN, B. O. Psychotic manifestations of mental defectives. *Proc. Amer. Assoc. Ment. Def.,* 1938, **43**, 72-79.

292. WITMER, E. R., & WITMER, L. Orthogenic cases, XVI George: Mentally restored to normal but intellectually deficient. *Psychol. Clin.,* 1928, **17**, 153-169.

293. WITMER, L. The fifteen months' training of a feebleminded child. *Psychol. Clin.,* 1907-08, 69-80.

294. ————. The treatment and cure of a case of mental and moral deficiency. *Psychol. Clin.,* 1908-09, **2**, 153-179.

295. ————. A fettered mind. *Psychol. Clin.,* 2, 1916-17, **10**, 241-249.

296. ————. (Orthogenic Cases)-XIV. Don: A curable case of arrested development due to a fear psychosis the result of shock in a three-year-old infant. *Psychol. Clin.,* 1919-22, **13**, 97-111.

297. WITMER, L., & AMBLER, M. Orthogenic cases, XVII-Jack: Feebleminded or normal. *Psychol. Clin.,* 1928-29, **17**, 217-225.

298. WITTY, P. A., & JENKINS, M. D. The educational achievement of a group of gifted Negro children. *J. Educ. Psychol.,* 1934, **25**, 585-597.

299. ————. Intra-race testing and Negro intelligence. *J. of Psychol.,* 1936, **1**, 179-192.

300. WOODWORTH, R. S. Heredity and environment—a critical survey of recently published material on twins and foster children. (A report prepared for the Committee on Social Adjustment.) New York: Social Science Research Council, 1941.

301. WORLD HEALTH ORGANIZATION. The mentally subnormal child. World Health Organization Technical Report Series, 1954, No. 75.

302. ZWEIBELSON, I. Relationship of pupil worries to performance on tests of mental ability. Unpublished doctor's dissertation, Teachers College, Columbia University, 1955.

303. ————. Test anxiety and intelligence test performance. *J. Consult. Psychol.,* 1956, **20**, 470-481.

INDEX OF NAMES

667

INDEX OF SUBJECTS